W9-BWZ-519

THE BEAUTIFUL AND DAMNED

BY F. SCOTT FITZGERALD

Novels

THE LAST TYCOON (Unfinished), with a Foreword by Edmund Wilson and Notes by the Author

TENDER IS THE NIGHT

THE GREAT GATSBY

THE BEAUTIFUL AND DAMNED

THIS SIDE OF PARADISE

Stories

THE STORIES OF F. SCOTT FITZGERALD
A Selection of 28 Stories, with an Introduction by Malcolm Cowley

Previously Uncollected

AFTERNOON OF AN AUTHOR, with an Introduction and Notes by Arthur Mizener

THE BEAUTIFUL AND DAMNED

BY F. SCOTT FITZGERALD

The victor belongs to the spoils.

—ANTHONY PATCH

CHARLES SCRIBNER'S SONS

NEW YORK

TO

SHANE LESLIE, GEORGE JEAN NATHAN
AND MAXWELL PERKINS

IN APPRECIATION OF MUCH LITERARY HELP
AND ENCOURAGEMENT

D-3.63 [MH]

CONTENTS

BOOK ONE

BOOK TWO

BOOK THREE

BOOK ONE

CHAPTER I

ANTHONY PATCH

IN 1913, when Anthony Patch was twenty-five, two years were already gone since irony, the Holy Ghost of this later day, had, theoretically at least, descended upon him. Irony was the final polish of the shoe, the ultimate dab of the clothes-brush, a sort of intellectual "There!"—yet at the brink of this story he has as yet gone no further than the conscious stage. As you first see him he wonders frequently whether he is not without honor and slightly mad, a shameful and obscene thinness glistening on the surface of the world like oil on a clean pond, these occasions being varied, of course, with those in which he thinks himself rather an exceptional young man, thoroughly sophisticated, well adjusted to his environment, and somewhat more significant than any one else he knows.

This was his healthy state and it made him cheerful, pleasant, and very attractive to intelligent men and to all women. In this state he considered that he would one day accomplish some quiet subtle thing that the elect would deem worthy and, passing on, would join the dimmer stars in a nebulous, indeterminate heaven half-way between death and immortality. Until the time came for this effort he would be Anthony Patch—not a portrait of a man but a distinct and dynamic personality, opinionated, contemptuous, functioning from within outward—a man who was aware that there could be no honor and yet had honor, who knew the sophistry of courage and yet was brave.

A Worthy Man and His Gifted Son

Anthony drew as much consciousness of social security from being the grandson of Adam J. Patch as he would have had from tracing his line over the sea to the crusaders. This is inevitable; Virginians and Bostonians to the contrary notwithstanding, an aristocracy founded sheerly on money postulates wealth in the particular.

Now Adam J. Patch, more familiarly known as "Cross Patch," left his father's farm in Tarrytown early in sixty-one to join a New York cavalry regiment. He came home from the war a major, charged into Wall Street, and amid much fuss, fume, applause, and ill will he gathered to himself some seventy-five million dollars.

This occupied his energies until he was fifty-seven years old. It was then that he determined, after a severe attack of sclerosis, to consecrate the remainder of his life to the moral regeneration of the world. He became a reformer among reformers. Emulating the magnificent efforts of Anthony Comstock, after whom his grandson was named, he levelled a varied assortment of uppercuts and body-blows at liquor, literature, vice, art, patent medicines, and Sunday theatres. His mind, under the influence of that insidious mildew which eventually forms on all but the few, gave itself up furiously to every indignation of the age. From an armchair in the office of his Tarrytown estate he directed against the enormous hypothetical enemy, unrighteousness, a campaign which went on through fifteen years, during which he displayed himself a rabid monomaniac, an unqualified nuisance, and an intolerable bore. The year in which this story opens found him wearying; his campaign had grown desultory; 1861 was creeping up slowly on 1895; his thoughts ran a great deal on the Civil War, somewhat on his dead wife and son, almost infinitesimally on his grandson Anthony.

Early in his career Adam Patch had married an anæmic lady of thirty, Alicia Withers, who brought him one hundred thousand dollars and an impeccable entré into the banking circles of New York. Immediately and rather spunkily she had borne him a son and, as if completely devitalized by the magnificence of this performance, she had thenceforth effaced herself within the shadowy dimensions of the nursery. The boy, Adam Ulysses Patch, became an inveterate joiner of clubs, connoisseur of good form, and driver of tandems—at the astonishing age of twenty-six he began his memoirs under the title "New York Society as I Have Seen It." On the rumor of its conception this work was eagerly bid for among publishers, but as it proved after his death to be immoderately verbose and overpoweringly dull, it never obtained even a private printing.

This Fifth Avenue Chesterfield married at twenty-two. His wife was Henrietta Lebrune, the Boston "Society Contralto," and the single child of the union was, at the request of his grandfather, christened Anthony Comstock Patch. When he went to Harvard, the Comstock dropped out of his name to a nether hell of oblivion and was never heard of thereafter.

Young Anthony had one picture of his father and mother together—so often had it faced his eyes in childhood that it had acquired the impersonality of furniture, but every one who came into his bedroom regarded it with interest. It showed a dandy of the nineties, spare and handsome, standing beside a tall dark lady with a muff and the suggestion of a bustle. Between them was a little boy with long brown curls, dressed in a velvet Lord Fauntleroy suit. This was Anthony at five, the year of his mother's death.

His memories of the Boston Society Contralto were nebulous and musical. She was a lady who sang, sang, sang, in the music room of their house on Washington Square—sometimes with guests scattered all about her, the men with their arms folded, balanced breathlessly on the edges of sofas, the women with their hands in their laps, occasionally making little whispers to the men and always clapping very briskly and uttering cooing cries after each song—and often she sang to Anthony alone, in Italian or French or in a strange and terrible dialect which she imagined to be the speech of the Southern negro.

His recollections of the gallant Ulysses, the first man in America to roll the lapels of his coat, were much more vivid. After Henrietta Lebrune Patch had "joined another choir," as her widower huskily remarked from time to time, father and son lived up at grampa's in Tarrytown, and Ulysses came daily to Anthony's nursery and expelled pleasant, thick-smelling words for sometimes as much as an hour. He was continually promising Anthony hunting trips and fishing trips and excursions to Atlantic City, "oh, some time soon now"; but none of them ever materialized. One trip they did take; when Anthony was eleven they went abroad, to England and Switzerland, and there in the best hotel in Lucerne his father died with much sweating and grunting and crying aloud for air. In a panic of despair and terror Anthony was brought back to America, wedded to a vague melancholy that was to stay beside him through the rest of his life.

Past and Person of the Hero

At eleven he had a horror of death. Within six impressionable years his parents had died and his grandmother had faded off almost imperceptibly, until, for the first time since her marriage, her person held for one day an unquestioned supremacy over her own drawing room. So to Anthony life was a struggle against death, that waited at every corner. It was as a concession to his hypochondriacal imagination that he formed the habit of reading in bed—it soothed him. He read until he was tired and often fell asleep with the lights still on.

His favorite diversion until he was fourteen was his stamp collection; enormous, as nearly exhaustive as a boy's could be—his grandfather considered fatuously that it was teaching him geography. So Anthony kept up a correspondence with a half dozen "Stamp and Coin" companies and it was rare that the mail failed to bring him new stamp-books or packages of glittering approval sheets—there was a mysterious fascination in transferring his acquisitions interminably from one book to another. His stamps were his greatest happiness and he bestowed impatient frowns on any one who interrupted him at play with them; they devoured his allowance every month, and he lay awake at night musing untiringly on their variety and many-colored splendor.

At sixteen he had lived almost entirely within himself, an inarticulate boy, thoroughly un-American, and politely bewildered by his contemporaries. The two preceding years had been spent in Europe with a private tutor, who persuaded him that Harvard was the thing; it would "open doors," it would be a tremendous tonic, it would give him innumerable self-sacrificing and devoted friends. So he went to Harvard—there was no other logical thing to be done with him.

Oblivious to the social system, he lived for a while alone and unsought in a high room in Beck Hall—a slim dark boy of medium height with a shy sensitive mouth. His allowance was more than liberal. He laid the foundations for a library by purchasing from a wandering bibliophile first editions of Swinburne, Meredith, and Hardy, and a yellowed illegible autograph letter of Keats's, finding later that he had been amazingly overcharged. He became an exquisite dandy, amassed a rather pathetic collection of silk pajamas, brocaded dressing-gowns, and neckties too flamboyant to wear; in this secret finery he would parade before a mirror in his room or lie stretched in satin along his window-seat looking down on the yard and realizing dimly this clamor, breathless and immediate, in which it seemed he was never to have a part.

Curiously enough he found in senior year that he had acquired a position in his class. He learned that he was looked upon as a rather romantic figure, a scholar, a recluse, a tower of erudition. This amused him but secretly pleased him—he began going out, at first a little and then a great deal. He made the Pudding. He drank—quietly and in the proper tradition. It was said of him that had he not come to college so young he might have "done extremely well." In 1909, when he graduated, he was only twenty years old.

Then abroad again—to Rome this time, where he dallied with architecture and painting in turn, took up the violin, and wrote some ghastly Italian sonnets, supposedly the ruminations of a thirteenth-century monk on the joys of the contemplative life. It became established among his Harvard intimates that he was in Rome, and those of them who were abroad that year looked him up and discovered with him, on many moonlight excursions, much in the city that was older than the Renaissance or indeed than the republic. Maury Noble, from Philadelphia, for instance, remained two months, and together they realized the peculiar charm of Latin women and had a delightful sense of being very young and free in a civilization that was very old and free. Not a few acquaintances of his grandfather's called on him, and had he so desired he might have been *persona grata* with the diplomatic set—indeed, he found that his inclinations tended more and more toward conviviality, but that long adolescent aloofness and consequent shyness still dictated to his conduct.

He returned to America in 1912 because of one of his grandfather's sudden illnesses, and after an excessively tiresome talk with the perpetually convalescent old man he decided to put off until his grandfather's death the idea of living permanently abroad. After a prolonged search he took an apartment on Fifty-second Street and to all appearances settled down.

In 1913 Anthony Patch's adjustment of himself to the universe was in process of consummation. Physically, he had improved since his undergraduate days—he was still too thin but his shoulders had widened and his brunette face had lost the frightened look of his freshman year. He was secretly orderly and in person spick and span—his friends declared that they had never seen his hair rumpled. His nose was too sharp; his mouth was one of those unfortunate mirrors of mood inclined to droop perceptibly in moments of unhappiness, but his blue eyes were charming, whether alert with intelligence or half closed in an expression of melancholy humor.

One of those men devoid of the symmetry of feature essential to the Aryan ideal, he was yet, here and there, considered handsome—moreover, he was very clean, in appearance and in reality, with that especial cleanness borrowed from beauty.

The Reproachless Apartment

Fifth and Sixth Avenues, it seemed to Anthony, were the uprights of a gigantic ladder stretching from Washington Square to Central Park. Coming up-town on top of a bus toward Fifty-second Street invariably gave him the sensation of hoisting himself hand by hand on a series of treacherous rungs, and when the bus jolted to a stop at his own rung he found something akin to relief as he descended the reckless metal steps to the sidewalk.

After that, he had but to walk down Fifty-second Street half a block, pass a stodgy family of brownstone houses—and then in a jiffy he was under the high ceilings of his great front room. This was entirely satisfactory. Here, after all, life began. Here he slept, breakfasted, read, and entertained.

The house itself was of murky material, built in the late nineties; in response to the steadily growing need of small apartments each floor had been thoroughly remodelled and rented individually. Of the four apartments Anthony's, on the second floor, was the most desirable.

The front room had fine high ceilings and three large windows that loomed down pleasantly upon Fifty-second Street. In its appointments it escaped by a safe margin being of any particular period; it escaped stiffness, stuffiness, bareness, and decadence. It smelt neither of smoke nor of incense—it was tall and faintly blue. There was a deep lounge of the softest brown leather with somnolence drifting about it like a haze. There was a high screen of Chinese lacquer chiefly concerned with geometrical fishermen and huntsmen in black and gold; this made a corner alcove for a voluminous chair guarded by an orange-colored standing lamp.

Deep in the fireplace a quartered shield was burned to a murky black.

Passing through the dining-room, which, as Anthony took only breakfast at home, was merely a magnificent potentiality, and down a comparatively long hall, one came to the heart and core of the apartment—Anthony's bedroom and bath.

Both of them were immense. Under the ceilings of the former even the great canopied bed seemed of only average size. On the floor an exotic rug of crimson velvet was soft as fleece on his bare feet. His bathroom, in contrast to the rather portentous character of his bedroom, was gay, bright, extremely habitable and even faintly facetious. Framed around the walls were photographs of four celebrated thespian beauties of the day: Julia Sanderson as "The Sunshine Girl," Ina Claire as "The Quaker Girl," Billie Burke as "The Mind-the-Paint Girl," and Hazel Dawn as "The Pink Lady." Between Billie Burke and Hazel Dawn hung a print representing a great stretch of snow presided over by a cold and formidable sun—this, claimed Anthony, symbolized the cold shower.

The bathtub, equipped with an ingenious book-holder, was low and large. Beside it a wall wardrobe bulged with sufficient linen for three men and with a generation of neckties. There was no skimpy glorified towel of a carpet—instead, a rich rug, like the one in his bedroom a miracle of softness, that seemed almost to massage the wet foot emerging from the tub. . . .

All in all a room to conjure with—it was easy to see that Anthony dressed there, arranged his immaculate hair there, in fact did everything but sleep and eat there. It was his pride, this bathroom. He felt that if he had a love he would have hung her picture just facing the tub so that, lost in the soothing steamings of the hot water, he might lie and look up at her and muse warmly and sensuously on her beauty.

Nor Does He Spin

The apartment was kept clean by an English servant with the singularly, almost theatrically, appropriate name of Bounds, whose technic was marred only by the fact that he wore a soft collar. Had he been entirely Anthony's Bounds this defect would have been summarily remedied, but he was also the Bounds of two other gentlemen in the neighborhood. From eight until eleven in the morning he was entirely Anthony's. He arrived with the mail and cooked breakfast. At nine-thirty he pulled the edge of Anthony's blanket and spoke a few terse words—Anthony never remembered clearly what they were and rather suspected they were deprecative; then he served breakfast on a card-table in the front room, made the bed and, after asking with some hostility if there was anything else, withdrew.

In the mornings, at least once a week, Anthony went to see his broker. His income was slightly under seven thousand a year, the interest on money inherited from his mother. His grandfather, who had never allowed his own son to graduate from a very liberal allowance, judged that this sum was sufficient for young Anthony's needs. Every Christmas he sent him a five-hundred-dollar bond, which Anthony usually sold, if possible, as he was always a little, not very, hard up.

The visits to his broker varied from semi-social chats to discussions of the safety of eight per cent investments, and Anthony always enjoyed them. The big trust company building seemed to link him definitely to the great fortunes whose solidarity he respected and to assure him that he was adequately chaperoned by the hierarchy of finance. From these hurried men he derived the same sense of safety that he had in contemplating his grandfather's money—even more, for the latter appeared, vaguely, a demand loan made by the world to Adam Patch's own moral righteousness, while this money down-town seemed rather to have been grasped and held by sheer indomitable strengths and tremendous feats of will; in addition, it seemed more definitely and explicitly—money.

Closely as Anthony trod on the heels of his income, he considered it to be enough. Some golden day, of course, he would have many millions; meanwhile he possessed a *raison d'être* in the theoretical creation of essays on the popes of the Renaissance. This flashes back to the conversation with his grandfather immediately upon his return from Rome.

He had hoped to find his grandfather dead, but had learned by telephoning from the pier that Adam Patch was comparatively well again—the next day he had concealed his disappointment and gone out to Tarrytown. Five miles from the station his taxicab entered an elaborately groomed drive that threaded a veritable maze of walls and wire fences guarding the estate—this, said the public, was because it was definitely known that if the Socialists had their way, one of the first men they'd assassinate would be old Cross Patch.

Anthony was late and the venerable philanthropist was awaiting him in a glass-walled sun parlor, where he was glancing through the morning papers for the second time. His secretary, Edward Shuttleworth—who before his regeneration had been gambler, saloon-keeper, and general reprobate—ushered Anthony into the room, exhibiting his redeemer and benefactor as though he were displaying a treasure of immense value.

They shook hands gravely. "I'm awfully glad to hear you're better," Anthony said.

The senior Patch, with an air of having seen his grandson only last week, pulled out his watch.

"Train late?" he asked mildly.

It had irritated him to wait for Anthony. He was under the delusion not only that in his youth he had handled his practical affairs with the utmost scrupulousness, even to keeping every engagement on the dot, but also that this was the direct and primary cause of his success.

"It's been late a good deal this month," he remarked with a shade of meek accusation in his voice—and then after a long sigh, "Sit down."

Anthony surveyed his grandfather with that tacit amazement which always attended the sight. That this feeble, unintelligent old man was possessed of such power that, yellow journals to the contrary, the men in the republic whose souls he could not have bought directly or indirectly would scarcely have populated White Plains, seemed as impossible to believe as that he had once been a pink-and-white baby.

The span of his seventy-five years had acted as a magic bellows—the first quarter-century had blown him full with life, and the last had sucked it all back. It had sucked in the cheeks and the chest and the girth of arm and leg. It had tyrannously demanded his teeth, one by one, suspended his small eyes in dark-bluish sacks, tweeked out his hairs, changed him from gray to white in some places, from pink to yellow in others—callously transposing his colors like a child trying over a paint-box. Then through his body and his soul it had attacked his brain. It had sent him night-sweats and tears and unfounded dreads. It had split his intense normality into credulity and suspicion. Out of the coarse material of his enthusiasm it had cut dozens of meek but petulant obsessions; his energy was shrunk to the bad temper of a spoiled child, and for his will to power was substituted a fatuous puerile desire for a land of harps and canticles on earth.

The amenities having been gingerly touched upon, Anthony felt that he was expected to outline his intentions —and simultaneously a glimmer in the old man's eye warned him against broaching, for the present, his desire to live abroad. He wished that Shuttleworth would have tact enough to leave the room—he detested Shuttleworth —but the secretary had settled blandly in a rocker and was dividing between the two Patches the glances of his faded eyes.

"Now that you're here you ought to *do* something," said his grandfather softly, "accomplish something."

Anthony waited for him to speak of "leaving something done when you pass on." Then he made a suggestion:

"I thought—it seemed to me that perhaps I'm best qualified to write——"

Adam Patch winced, visualizing a family poet with long hair and three mistresses.

"—history," finished Anthony.

"History? History of what? The Civil War? The Revolution?"

"Why—no, sir. A history of the Middle Ages." Simultaneously an idea was born for a history of the Renaissance popes, written from some novel angle. Still, he was glad he had said "Middle Ages."

"Middle Ages? Why not your own country? Something you know about?"

"Well, you see I've lived so much abroad——"

"Why you should write about the Middle Ages, I don't know. Dark Ages, we used to call 'em. Nobody knows what happened, and nobody cares, except that they're over now." He continued for some minutes on the uselessness of such information, touching, naturally, on the Spanish Inquisition and the "corruption of the monasteries." Then:

"Do you think you'll be able to do any work in New York—or do you really intend to work at all?" This last with soft, almost imperceptible, cynicism.

"Why, yes, I do, sir."

"When'll you be done?"

"Well, there'll be an outline, you see—and a lot of preliminary reading."

"I should think you'd have done enough of that already."

The conversation worked itself jerkily toward a rather abrupt conclusion, when Anthony rose, looked at his watch, and remarked that he had an engagement with his broker that afternoon. He had intended to stay a few days with his grandfather, but he was tired and irritated from a rough crossing, and quite unwilling to stand a subtle and sanctimonious browbeating. He would come out again in a few days, he said.

Nevertheless, it was due to this encounter that work had come into his life as a permanent idea. During the year that had passed since then, he had made several lists of authorities, he had even experimented with chapter titles and the division of his work into periods, but not one line of actual writing existed at present, or seemed likely ever to exist. He did nothing—and contrary to the most accredited copy-book logic, he managed to divert himself with more than average content.

Afternoon

It was October in 1913, midway in a week of pleasant days, with the sunshine loitering in the cross-streets and the atmosphere so languid as to seem weighted with ghostly falling leaves. It was pleasant to sit lazily by the open window finishing a chapter of "Erewhon." It was pleasant to yawn about five, toss the book on a table, and saunter humming along the hall to his bath.

"To . . . you . . . beaut-if-ul lady,"

he was singing as he turned on the tap.

"I raise . . . my . . . eyes;
To . . . you . . . beaut-if-ul la-a-dy
My . . . heart . . . cries——"

He raised his voice to compete with the flood of water pouring into the tub, and as he looked at the picture of Hazel Dawn upon the wall he put an imaginary violin to his shoulder and softly caressed it with a phantom bow. Through his closed lips he made a humming noise, which he vaguely imagined resembled the sound of a violin. After a moment his hands ceased their gyrations and wandered to his shirt, which he began to unfasten. Stripped, and adopting an athletic posture like the tiger-skin man in the advertisement, he regarded himself with some satisfaction in the mirror, breaking off to dabble a tentative foot in the tub. Readjusting a faucet and indulging in a few preliminary grunts, he slid in.

Once accustomed to the temperature of the water he relaxed into a state of drowsy content. When he finished his bath he would dress leisurely and walk down Fifth Avenue to the Ritz, where he had an appointment for dinner with his two most frequent companions, Dick Caramel and Maury Noble. Afterward he and Maury were going to the theatre—Caramel would probably trot home and work on his book, which ought to be finished pretty soon.

Anthony was glad *he* wasn't going to work on *his*

book. The notion of sitting down and conjuring up, not only words in which to clothe thoughts but thoughts worthy of being clothed—the whole thing was absurdly beyond his desires.

Emerging from his bath he polished himself with the meticulous attention of a bootblack. Then he wandered into the bedroom, and whistling the while a weird, uncertain melody, strolled here and there buttoning, adjusting, and enjoying the warmth of the thick carpet on his feet.

He lit a cigarette, tossed the match out the open top of the window, then paused in his tracks with the cigarette two inches from his mouth—which fell faintly ajar. His eyes were focussed upon a spot of brilliant color on the roof of a house farther down the alley.

It was a girl in a red negligé, silk surely, drying her hair by the still hot sun of late afternoon. His whistle died upon the stiff air of the room; he walked cautiously another step nearer the window with a sudden impression that she was beautiful. Sitting on the stone parapet beside her was a cushion the same color as her garment and she was leaning both arms upon it as she looked down into the sunny areaway, where Anthony could hear children playing.

He watched her for several minutes. Something was stirred in him, something not accounted for by the warm smell of the afternoon or the triumphant vividness of red. He felt persistently that the girl was beautiful—then of a sudden he understood: it was her distance, not a rare and precious distance of soul but still distance, if only in terrestrial yards. The autumn air was between them, and the roofs and the blurred voices. Yet for a not altogether explained second, posing perversely in time, his emotion had been nearer to adoration than in the deepest kiss he had ever known.

He finished his dressing, found a black bow tie and adjusted it carefully by the three-sided mirror in the bathroom. Then yielding to an impulse he walked quickly into the bedroom and again looked out the window. The woman was standing up now; she had tossed her hair back and he had a full view of her. She was fat, full thirty-five, utterly undistinguished. Making a clicking noise with his mouth he returned to the bathroom and reparted his hair.

"To . . . you . . . beaut-if-ul lady,"

he sang lightly,

"I raise . . . my . . . eyes——"

Then with a last soothing brush that left an iridescent surface of sheer gloss he left his bathroom and his apartment and walked down Fifth Avenue to the Ritz-Carlton.

Three Men

At seven Anthony and his friend Maury Noble are sitting at a corner table on the cool roof. Maury Noble is like nothing so much as a large slender and imposing cat. His eyes are narrow and full of incessant, protracted blinks. His hair is smooth and flat, as though it has been licked by a possible—and, if so, Herculean—mother-cat. During Anthony's time at Harvard he had been considered the most unique figure in his class, the most brilliant, the most original—smart, quiet and among the saved.

This is the man whom Anthony considers his best friend. This is the only man of all his acquaintance whom he admires and, to a bigger extent than he likes to admit to himself, envies.

They are glad to see each other now—their eyes are full of kindness as each feels the full effect of novelty after a short separation. They are drawing a relaxation from each other's presence, a new serenity; Maury Noble behind that fine and absurdly catlike face is all but purring. And Anthony, nervous as a will-o'-the-wisp, restless—he is at rest now.

They are engaged in one of those easy short-speech conversations that only men under thirty or men under great stress indulge in.

ANTHONY: Seven o'clock. Where's the Caramel? (*Impatiently.*) I wish he'd finish that interminable novel. I've spent more time hungry——

MAURY: He's got a new name for it. "The Demon Lover"—not bad, eh?

ANTHONY: (*Interested*) "The Demon Lover"? Oh "woman wailing"— No—not a bit bad! Not bad at all—d'you think?

MAURY: Rather good. What time did you say?

ANTHONY: Seven.

MAURY: (*His eyes narrowing—not unpleasantly, but to express a faint disapproval*) Drove me crazy the other day.

ANTHONY: How?

MAURY: That habit of taking notes.

ANTHONY: Me, too. Seems I'd said something night before that he considered material but he'd forgotten it—so he had at me. He'd say "Can't you try to concentrate?" And I'd say "You bore me to tears. How do I remember?"

(MAURY *laughs noiselessly, by a sort of bland and appreciative widening of his features.*)

MAURY: Dick doesn't necessarily see more than any one else. He merely can put down a larger proportion of what he sees.

ANTHONY: That rather impressive talent——

MAURY: Oh, yes. Impressive!

ANTHONY: And energy—ambitious, well-directed energy. He's so entertaining—he's so tremendously stimulating and exciting. Often there's something breathless in being with him.

MAURY: Oh, yes.

(*Silence, and then:*)

ANTHONY: (*With his thin, somewhat uncertain face at its most convinced*) But not indomitable energy. Some day, bit by bit, it'll blow away, and his rather impressive talent with it, and leave only a wisp of a man, fretful and egotistic and garrulous.

MAURY: (*With laughter*) Here we sit vowing to each other that little Dick sees less deeply into things than we do. And I'll bet he feels a measure of superiority on his side—creative mind over merely critical mind and all that.

ANTHONY: Oh, yes. But he's wrong. He's inclined to fall for a million silly enthusiasms. If it wasn't that he's absorbed in realism and therefore has to adopt the garments of the cynic he'd be—he'd be credulous as a college religious leader. He's an idealist. Oh, yes. He thinks he's not, because he's rejected Christianity. Remember him in college? Just swallow every writer whole, one after another, ideas, technic, and characters, Chesterton. Shaw, Wells, each one as easily as the last.

MAURY: (*Still considering his own last observation*) I remember.

ANTHONY: It's true. Natural born fetich-worshipper. Take art——

MAURY: Let's order. He'll be——

ANTHONY: Sure. Let's order. I told him——

MAURY: Here he comes. Look—he's going to bump that waiter. (*He lifts his finger as a signal—lifts it as though it were a soft and friendly claw.*) Here y'are, Caramel.

A NEW VOICE: (*Fiercely*) Hello, Maury. Hello, Anthony Comstock Patch. How is old Adam's grandson? Débutantes still after you, eh?

In person RICHARD CARAMEL *is short and fair—he is to be bald at thirty-five. He has yellowish eyes—one of them startlingly clear, the other opaque as a muddy pool—and a bulging brow like a funny-paper baby. He bulges in other places—his paunch bulges, prophetically, his words have an air of bulging from his mouth, even his dinner coat pockets bulge, as though from contamination, with a dog-eared collection of time-tables, programmes, and miscellaneous scraps—on these he takes his notes with great screwings up of his unmatched yellow eyes and motions of silence with his disengaged left hand.*

When he reaches the table he shakes hands with ANTHONY *and* MAURY. *He is one of those men who invariably shake hands, even with people whom they have seen an hour before.*

ANTHONY: Hello, Caramel. Glad you're here. We needed a comic relief.

MAURY: You're late. Been racing the postman down the block? We've been clawing over your character.

DICK: (*Fixing* ANTHONY *eagerly with the bright eye*) What'd you say? Tell me and I'll write it down. Cut three thousand words out of Part One this afternoon.

MAURY: Noble æsthete. And I poured alcohol into my stomach.

DICK: I don't doubt it. I bet you two have been sitting here for an hour talking about liquor.

ANTHONY: We never pass out, my beardless boy.

MAURY: We never go home with ladies we meet when we're lit.

ANTHONY: All in all our parties are characterized by a certain haughty distinction.

DICK: The particularly silly sort who boast about being "tanks"! Trouble is you're both in the eighteenth century. School of the Old English Squire. Drink quietly until you roll under the table. Never have a good time. Oh, no, that isn't done at all.

ANTHONY: This from Chapter Six, I'll bet.

DICK: Going to the theatre?

MAURY: Yes. We intend to spend the evening doing some deep thinking over of life's problems. The thing is tersely called "The Woman." I presume that she will "pay."

ANTHONY: My God! Is that what it is? Let's go to the Follies again.

MAURY: I'm tired of it. I've seen it three times. (*To* DICK.) The first time, we went out after Act One and found a most amazing bar. When we came back we entered the wrong theatre.

ANTHONY: Had a protracted dispute with a scared young couple we thought were in our seat.

DICK: (*As though talking to himself*) I think—that when I've done another novel and a play, and maybe a book of short stories, I'll do a musical comedy.

MAURY: I know—with intellectual lyrics that no one will listen to. And all the critics will groan and grunt about "Dear old Pinafore." And I shall go on shining as a brilliantly meaningless figure in a meaningless world.

DICK: (*Pompously*) Art isn't meaningless.

MAURY: It is in itself. It isn't in that it tries to make life less so.

ANTHONY: In other words, Dick, you're playing before a grand stand peopled with ghosts.

MAURY: Give a good show anyhow.

ANTHONY: (*To* MAURY) On the contrary, I'd feel that it being a meaningless world, why write? The very attempt to give it purpose is purposeless.

DICK: Well, even admitting all that, be a decent pragmatist and grant a poor man the instinct to live. Would you want every one to accept that sophistic rot?

ANTHONY: Yeah, I suppose so.

MAURY: No, sir! I believe that every one in America but a selected thousand should be compelled to accept a very rigid system of morals—Roman Catholicism, for instance. I don't complain of conventional morality. I complain rather of the mediocre heretics who seize upon the findings of sophistication and adopt the pose of a moral freedom to which they are by no means entitled by their intelligences.

(*Here the soup arrives and what* MAURY *might have gone on to say is lost for all time.*)

NIGHT

Afterward they visited a ticket speculator and, at a price, obtained seats for a new musical comedy called "High Jinks." In the foyer of the theatre they waited a few moments to see the first-night crowd come in. There were opera cloaks stitched of myriad, many-colored silks and furs; there were jewels dripping from arms and throats and ear-tips of white and rose; there were innumerable broad shimmers down the middles of innumerable silk hats; there were shoes of gold and bronze and red and shining black; there were the high-piled, tight-packed coiffures of many women and the slick, watered hair of well-kept men—most of all there was the ebbing, flowing, chattering, chuckling, foaming, slow-rolling wave effect of this cheerful sea of people as to-night it poured its glittering torrent into the artificial lake of laughter. . . .

After the play they parted—Maury was going to a dance at Sherry's, Anthony homeward and to bed.

He found his way slowly over the jostled evening mass of Times Square, which the chariot race and its thousand satellites made rarely beautiful and bright and intimate with carnival. Faces swirled about him, a kaleidoscope of girls, ugly, ugly as sin—too fat, too lean, yet floating upon this autumn air as upon their own warm and passionate breaths poured out into the night. Here, for all their vulgarity, he thought, they were faintly and subtly mysterious. He inhaled carefully, swallowing into his lungs perfume and the not unpleasant scent of many cigarettes. He caught the glance of a dark young beauty sitting alone in a closed taxicab. Her eyes in the half-light suggested night and violets, and for a moment he stirred again to that half-forgotten remoteness of the afternoon.

Two young Jewish men passed him, talking in loud voices and craning their necks here and there in fatuous supercilious glances. They were dressed in suits of the exaggerated tightness then semi-fashionable; their turnover collars were notched at the Adam's apple; they wore gray spats and carried gray gloves on their cane handles.

Passed a bewildered old lady borne along like a basket of eggs between two men who exclaimed to her of the wonders of Times Square—explained them so quickly that the old lady, trying to be impartially interested, waved her head here and there like a piece of wind-worried old orange-peel. Anthony heard a snatch of their conversation:

"There's the Astor, mama!"

"Look! See the chariot race sign——"

"There's where we were to-day. No, *there!*"

"Good gracious! . . ."

"You should worry and grow thin like a dime." He

recognized the current witticism of the year as it issued stridently from one of the pairs at his elbow.

"And I says to him, I says——"

The soft rush of taxis by him, and laughter, laughter hoarse as a crow's, incessant and loud, with the rumble of the subways underneath—and over all, the revolutions of light, the growings and recedings of light—light dividing like pearls—forming and reforming in glittering bars and circles and monstrous grotesque figures cut amazingly on the sky.

He turned thankfully down the hush that blew like a dark wind out of a cross-street, passed a bakery-restaurant in whose windows a dozen roast chickens turned over and over on an automatic spit. From the door came a smell that was hot, doughy, and pink. A drugstore next, exhaling medicines, spilt soda water and a pleasant undertone from the cosmetic counter; then a Chinese laundry, still open, steamy and stifling, smelling folded and vaguely yellow. All these depressed him; reaching Sixth Avenue he stopped at a corner cigar store and emerged feeling better—the cigar store was cheerful, humanity in a navy blue mist, buying a luxury. . . .

Once in his apartment he smoked a last cigarette, sitting in the dark by his open front window. For the first time in over a year he found himself thoroughly enjoying New York. There was a rare pungency in it certainly, a quality almost Southern. A lonesome town, though. He who had grown up alone had lately learned to avoid solitude. During the past several months he had been careful, when he had no engagement for the evening, to hurry to one of his clubs and find some one. Oh, there was a loneliness here——

His cigarette, its smoke bordering the thin folds of curtain with rims of faint white spray, glowed on until the clock in St. Anne's down the street struck one with a querulous fashionable beauty. The elevated, half a quiet block away, sounded a rumble of drums—and should he lean from his window he would see the train, like an angry eagle, breasting the dark curve at the corner. He was reminded of a fantastic romance he had lately read in which cities had been bombed from aerial trains, and for a moment he fancied that Washington Square had declared war on Central Park and that this was a north-bound menace loaded with battle and sudden death. But as it passed the illusion faded; it diminished to the faintest of drums—then to a far-away droning eagle.

There were the bells and the continued low blur of auto horns from Fifth Avenue, but his own street was silent and he was safe in here from all the threat of life, for there was his door and the long hall and his guardian bedroom—safe, safe! The arc-light shining into his window seemed for this hour like the moon, only brighter and more beautiful than the moon.

A Flash-Back in Paradise

Beauty, who was born anew every hundred years, sat in a sort of outdoor waiting room through which blew gusts of white wind and occasionally a breathless hurried star. The stars winked at her intimately as they went by and the winds made a soft incessant flurry in her hair. She was incomprehensible, for, in her, soul and spirit were one—the beauty of her body was the essence of her soul. She was that unity sought for by philosophers through many centuries. In this outdoor waiting room of winds and stars she had been sitting for a hundred years, at peace in the contemplation of herself.

It became known to her, at length, that she was to be born again. Sighing, she began a long conversation with a voice that was in the white wind, a conversation that took many hours and of which I can give only a fragment here.

BEAUTY: (*Her lips scarcely stirring, her eyes turned, as always, inward upon herself*) Whither shall I journey now?

THE VOICE: To a new country—a land you have never seen before.

BEAUTY: (*Petulantly*) I loathe breaking into these new civilizations. How long a stay this time?

THE VOICE: Fifteen years.

BEAUTY: And what's the name of the place?

THE VOICE: It is the most opulent, most gorgeous land on earth—a land whose wisest are but little wiser than its dullest; a land where the rulers have minds like little children and the law-givers believe in Santa Claus; where ugly women control strong men——

BEAUTY: (*In astonishment*) What?

THE VOICE: (*Very much depressed*) Yes, it is truly a melancholy spectacle. Women with receding chins and shapeless noses go about in broad daylight saying "Do this!" and "Do that!" and all the men, even those of great wealth, obey implicitly their women to whom they refer sonorously either as "Mrs. So-and-so" or as "the wife."

BEAUTY: But this can't be true! I can understand, of course, their obedience to women of charm—but to fat women? to bony women? to women with scrawny cheeks?

THE VOICE: Even so.

BEAUTY: What of me? What chance shall I have?

THE VOICE: It will be "harder going," if I may borrow a phrase.

BEAUTY: (*After a dissatisfied pause*) Why not the old lands, the land of grapes and soft-tongued men or the land of ships and seas?

THE VOICE: It's expected that they'll be very busy shortly.

BEAUTY: Oh!

THE VOICE: Your life on earth will be, as always, the interval between two significant glances in a mundane mirror.

BEAUTY: What will I be? Tell me?

THE VOICE: At first it was thought that you would go this time as an actress in the motion pictures but, after all, it's not advisable. You will be disguised during your fifteen years as what is called a "susciety gurl."

BEAUTY: What's that?

(*There is a new sound in the wind which must for our purposes be interpreted as* THE VOICE *scratching its head.*)

THE VOICE: (*At length*) It's a sort of bogus aristocrat.

BEAUTY: Bogus? What is bogus?

THE VOICE: That, too, you will discover in this land. You will find much that is bogus. Also, you will do much that is bogus.

BEAUTY: (*Placidly*) It all sounds so vulgar.

THE VOICE: Not half as vulgar as it is. You will be known during your fifteen years as a ragtime kid, a flapper, a jazz-baby, and a baby vamp. You will dance new dances neither more nor less gracefully than you danced the old ones.

BEAUTY: (*In a whisper*) Will I be paid?

THE VOICE: Yes, as usual—in love.

BEAUTY: (*With a faint laugh which disturbs only momentarily the immobility of her lips*) And will I like being called a jazz-baby?

THE VOICE: (*Soberly*) You will love it. . . .

(*The dialogue ends here, with* BEAUTY *still sitting quietly, the stars pausing in an ecstasy of appre-*

ciation, the wind, white and gusty, blowing through her hair.

All this took place seven years before ANTHONY *sat by the front windows of his apartment and listened to the chimes of St. Anne's.)*

CHAPTER II

PORTRAIT OF A SIREN

CRISPNESS folded down upon New York a month later, bringing November and the three big football games and a great fluttering of furs along Fifth Avenue. It brought, also, a sense of tension to the city, and suppressed excitement. Every morning now there were invitations in Anthony's mail. Three dozen virtuous females of the first layer were proclaiming their fitness, if not their specific willingness, to bear children unto three dozen millionaires. Five dozen virtuous females of the second layer were proclaiming not only this fitness, but in addition a tremendous undaunted ambition toward the first three dozen young men, who were of course invited to each of the ninety-six parties—as were the young lady's group of family friends, acquaintances, college boys, and eager young outsiders. To continue, there was a third layer from the skirts of the city, from Newark and the Jersey suburbs up to bitter Connecticut and the ineligible sections of Long Island—and doubtless contiguous layers down to the city's shoes: Jewesses were coming out into a society of Jewish men and women, from Riverside to the Bronx, and looking forward to a rising young broker or jeweller and a kosher wedding; Irish girls were casting their eyes, with license at last to do so, upon a society of young Tammany politicians, pious undertakers, and grown-up choirboys.

And, naturally, the city caught the contagious air of entré—the working girls, poor ugly souls, wrapping soap in the factories and showing finery in the big stores, dreamed that perhaps in the spectacular excitement of this winter they might obtain for themselves the coveted male—as in a muddled carnival crowd an inefficient pickpocket may consider his chances increased. And the chimneys commenced to smoke and the subway's foulness was freshened. And the actresses came out in new plays and the publishers came out with new books and the Castles came out with new dances. And the railroads came out with new schedules containing new mistakes instead of the old ones that the commuters had grown used to. . . .

The City was coming out!

Anthony, walking along Forty-second Street one afternoon under a steel-gray sky, ran unexpectedly into Richard Caramel emerging from the Manhattan Hotel barber shop. It was a cold day, the first definitely cold day, and Caramel had on one of those knee-length, sheep-lined coats long worn by the working men of the Middle West, that were just coming into fashionable approval. His soft hat was of a discreet dark brown, and from under it his clear eye flamed like a topaz. He stopped Anthony enthusiastically, slapping him on the arms more from a desire to keep himself warm than from playfulness, and, after his inevitable hand shake, exploded into sound.

"Cold as the devil— Good Lord, I've been working like the deuce all day till my room got so cold I thought I'd get pneumonia. Darn landlady economizing on coal came up when I yelled over the stairs for her for half an hour. Began explaining why and all. God! First she drove me crazy, then I began to think she was sort of a character, and took notes while she talked—so she couldn't see me, you know, just as though I were writing casually——"

He had seized Anthony's arm and was walking him briskly up Madison Avenue.

"Where to?"

"Nowhere in particular."

"Well, then what's the use?" demanded Anthony.

They stopped and stared at each other, and Anthony wondered if the cold made his own face as repellent as Dick Caramel's, whose nose was crimson, whose bulging brow was blue, whose yellow unmatched eyes were red and watery at the rims. After a moment they began walking again.

"Done some good work on my novel." Dick was looking and talking emphatically at the sidewalk. "But I have to get out once in a while." He glanced at Anthony apologetically, as though craving encouragement. "I have to talk. I guess very few people ever really *think*, I mean sit down and ponder and have ideas in sequence. I do my thinking in writing or conversation. You've got to have a start, sort of—something to defend or contradict—don't you think?"

Anthony grunted and withdrew his arm gently.

"I don't mind carrying you, Dick, but with that coat——"

"I mean," continued Richard Caramel gravely, "that on paper your first paragraph contains the idea you're going to damn or enlarge on. In conversation you've got your vis-à-vis's last statement—but when you simply *ponder*, why, your ideas just succeed each other like magic-lantern pictures and each one forces out the last."

They passed Forty-fifth Street and slowed down slightly. Both of them lit cigarettes and blew tremendous clouds of smoke and frosted breath into the air.

"Let's walk up to the Plaza and have an egg-nog," suggested Anthony. "Do you good. Air'll get the rotten nicotine out of your lungs. Come on—I'll let you talk about your book all the way."

"I don't want to if it bores you. I mean you needn't do it as a favor." The words tumbled out in haste, and though he tried to keep his face casual it screwed up uncertainly. Anthony was compelled to protest: "Bore me? I should say not!"

"Got a cousin—" began Dick, but Anthony interrupted by stretching out his arms and breathing forth a low cry of exultation.

"Good weather!" he exclaimed, "isn't it? Makes me feel about ten. I mean it makes me feel as I should have felt when I was ten. Murderous! Oh, God! one minute it's my world, and the next I'm the world's fool. To-day it's my world and everything's easy, easy. Even Nothing is easy!"

"Got a cousin up at the Plaza. Famous girl. We can go up and meet her. She lives there in the winter—has lately anyway—with her mother and father."

"Didn't know you had cousins in New York."

"Her name's Gloria. She's from home—Kansas City. Her mother's a practising Bilphist, and her father's quite dull but a perfect gentleman."

"What are they? Literary material?"

"They try to be. All the old man does is tell me he just met the most wonderful character for a novel. Then he tells me about some idiotic friend of his and then he says: '*There's* a character for you! Why don't you write him up? Everybody'd be interested in *him*.' Or else he tells me about Japan or Paris, or some other very obvious place, and says: 'Why don't you write a story about that place? That'd be a wonderful setting for a story!'"

"How about the girl?" inquired Anthony casually, "Gloria—Gloria what?"

"Gilbert. Oh, you've heard of her—Gloria Gilbert. Goes to dances at colleges—all that sort of thing."

"I've heard her name."

"Good-looking—in fact damned attractive."

They reached Fiftieth Street and turned over toward the Avenue.

"I don't care for young girls as a rule," said Anthony, frowning.

This was not strictly true. While it seemed to him that the average débutante spent every hour of her day thinking and talking about what the great world had mapped out for her to do during the next hour, any girl who made a living directly on her prettiness interested him enormously.

"Gloria's darn nice—not a brain in her head."

Anthony laughed in a one-syllabled snort.

"By that you mean that she hasn't a line of literary patter."

"No, I don't."

"Dick, you know what passes as brains in a girl for you. Earnest young women who sit with you in a corner and talk earnestly about life. The kind who when they were sixteen argued with grave faces as to whether kissing was right or wrong—and whether it was immoral for freshmen to drink beer."

Richard Caramel was offended. His scowl crinkled like crushed paper.

"No—" he began, but Anthony interrupted ruthlessly.

"Oh, yes; kind who just at present sit in corners and confer on the latest Scandinavian Dante available in English translation."

Dick turned to him, a curious falling in his whole countenance. His question was almost an appeal.

"What's the matter with you and Maury? You talk sometimes as though I were a sort of inferior."

Anthony was confused, but he was also cold and a little uncomfortable, so he took refuge in attack.

"I don't think your brains matter, Dick."

"Of course they matter!" exclaimed Dick angrily. "What do you mean? Why don't they matter?"

"You might know too much for your pen."

"I couldn't possibly."

"I can imagine," insisted Anthony, "a man knowing too much for his talent to express. Like me. Suppose, for instance, I have more wisdom than you, and less talent. It would tend to make me inarticulate. You, on the contrary, have enough water to fill the pail and a big enough pail to hold the water."

"I don't follow you at all," complained Dick in a crestfallen tone. Infinitely dismayed, he seemed to bulge in protest. He was staring intently at Anthony and caroming off a succession of passers-by, who reproached him with fierce, resentful glances.

"I simply mean that a talent like Wells's could carry the intelligence of a Spencer. But an inferior talent can only be graceful when it's carrying inferior ideas. And the more narrowly you can look at a thing the more entertaining you can be about it."

Dick considered, unable to decide the exact degree of criticism intended by Anthony's remarks. But Anthony, with that facility which seemed so frequently to flow from him, continued, his dark eyes gleaming in his thin face, his chin raised, his voice raised, his whole physical being raised:

"Say I am proud and sane and wise—an Athenian among Greeks. Well, I might fail where a lesser man would succeed. He could imitate, he could adorn, he could be enthusiastic, he could be hopefully constructive. But this hypothetical me would be too proud to imitate, too sane to be enthusiastic, too sophisticated to be Utopian, too Grecian to adorn."

"Then you don't think the artist works from his intelligence?"

"No. He goes on improving, if he can, what he imitates in the way of style, and choosing from his own interpretation of the things around him what constitutes material. But after all every writer writes because it's his mode of living. Don't tell me you like this 'Divine Function of the Artist' business?"

"I'm not accustomed even to refer to myself as an artist."

"Dick," said Anthony, changing his tone, "I want to beg your pardon."

"Why?"

"For that outburst. I'm honestly sorry. I was talking for effect."

Somewhat mollified, Dick rejoined:

"I've often said you were a Philistine at heart."

It was a crackling dusk when they turned in under the white façade of the Plaza and tasted slowly the foam and yellow thickness of an egg-nog. Anthony looked at his companion. Richard Caramel's nose and brow were slowly approaching a like pigmentation; the red was leaving the one, the blue deserting the other. Glancing in a mirror, Anthony was glad to find that his own skin had not discolored. On the contrary, a faint glow had kindled in his cheeks—he fancied that he had never looked so well.

"Enough for me," said Dick, his tone that of an athlete in training. "I want to go up and see the Gilberts. Won't you come?"

"Why—yes. If you don't dedicate me to the parents and dash off in the corner with Dora."

"Not Dora—Gloria."

A clerk announced them over the phone, and ascending to the tenth floor they followed a winding corridor and knocked at 1088. The door was answered by a middle-aged lady—Mrs. Gilbert herself.

"How do you do?" She spoke in the conventional American lady-lady language. "Well, I'm *aw*fully glad to see you——"

Hasty interjections by Dick, and then:

"Mr. Pats? Well, do come in, and leave your coat there." She pointed to a chair and changed her inflection to a deprecatory laugh full of minute gasps. "This is really lovely—lovely. Why, Richard, you haven't been here for *so* long—no!—no!" The latter monosyllables served half as responses, half as periods, to some vague starts from Dick. "Well, do sit down and tell me what you've been doing."

One crossed and recrossed; one stood and bowed ever so gently; one smiled again and again with helpless stupidity; one wondered if she would ever sit down—at length one slid thankfully into a chair and settled for a pleasant call.

"I suppose it's because you've been busy—as much as anything else," smiled Mrs. Gilbert somewhat ambiguously. The "as much as anything else" she used to balance all her more rickety sentences. She had two other ones: "at least that's the way I look at it" and "pure and simple"—these three, alternated, gave each of her remarks an air of being a general reflection on life, as though she had calculated all causes and, at length, put her finger on the ultimate one.

Richard Caramel's face, Anthony saw, was now quite normal. The brow and cheeks were of a flesh color, the nose politely inconspicuous. He had fixed his aunt with the bright-yellow eye, giving her that acute and exaggerated attention that young males are accustomed to render to all females who are of no further value.

"Are you a writer too, Mr. Pats? . . . Well, perhaps we can all bask in Richard's fame."—Gentle laughter led by Mrs. Gilbert.

"Gloria's out," she said, with an air of laying down an axiom from which she would proceed to derive results. "She's dancing somewhere. Gloria goes, goes, goes. I tell her I don't see how she stands it. She dances all afternoon and all night, until I think she's going to wear herself to a shadow. Her father is very worried about her."

She smiled from one to the other. They both smiled.

She was composed, Anthony perceived, of a succession of semicircles and parabolas, like those figures that gifted folk make on the typewriter: head, arms, bust, hips, thighs, and ankles were in a bewildering tier of roundnesses. Well ordered and clean she was, with hair of an artificially rich gray; her large face sheltered weather-beaten blue eyes and was adorned with just the faintest white mustache.

"I always say," she remarked to Anthony, "that Richard is an ancient soul."

In the tense pause that followed, Anthony considered a pun—something about Dick having been much walked upon.

"We all have souls of different ages," continued Mrs. Gilbert radiantly; "at least that's what I say."

"Perhaps so," agreed Anthony with an air of quickening to a hopeful idea. The voice bubbled on:

"Gloria has a very young soul—irresponsible, as much as anything else. She has no sense of responsibility."

"She's sparkling, Aunt Catherine," said Richard pleasantly. "A sense of responsibility would spoil her. She's too pretty."

"Well," confessed Mrs. Gilbert, "all I know is that she goes and goes and goes——"

The number of goings to Gloria's discredit was lost

in the rattle of the door-knob as it turned to admit Mr. Gilbert.

He was a short man with a mustache resting like a small white cloud beneath his undistinguished nose. He had reached the stage where his value as a social creature was a black and imponderable negative. His ideas were the popular delusions of twenty years before; his mind steered a wabbly and anæmic course in the wake of the daily newspaper editorials. After graduating from a small but terrifying Western university, he had entered the celluloid business, and as this required only the minute measure of intelligence he brought to it, he did well for several years—in fact until about 1911, when he began exchanging contracts for vague agreements with the moving picture industry. The moving-picture industry had decided about 1912 to gobble him up, and at this time he was, so to speak, delicately balanced on its tongue. Meanwhile he was supervising manager of the Associated Mid-western Film Materials Company, spending six months of each year in New York and the remainder in Kansas City and St. Louis. He felt credulously that there was a good thing coming to him—and his wife thought so, and his daughter thought so too.

He disapproved of Gloria: she stayed out late, she never ate her meals, she was always in a mix-up—he had irritated her once and she had used toward him words that he had not thought were part of her vocabulary. His wife was easier. After fifteen years of incessant guerilla warfare he had conquered her—it was a war of muddled optimism against organized dulness, and something in the number of "yes's" with which he could poison a conversation had won him the victory.

"Yes-yes-yes-yes," he would say, "yes-yes-yes-yes. Let me see. That was the summer of—let me see—ninety-one or ninety-two— Yes-yes-yes-yes——"

Fifteen years of yes's had beaten Mrs. Gilbert. Fifteen further years of that incessant unaffirmative affirmative, accompanied by the perpetual flicking of ash-mushrooms from thirty-two thousand cigars, had broken her. To this husband of hers she made the last concession of married life, which is more complete, more irrevocable, than the first—she listened to him. She told herself that the years had brought her tolerance—actually they had slain what measure she had ever possessed of moral courage.

She introduced him to Anthony.

"This is Mr. Pats," she said.

The young man and the old touched flesh; Mr. Gilbert's hand was soft, worn away to the pulpy semblance of a squeezed grapefruit. Then husband and wife exchanged greetings—he told her it had grown colder out; he said he had walked down to a news-stand on Forty-fourth Street for a Kansas City paper. He had intended to ride back in the bus but he had found it too cold, yes, yes, yes, yes, too cold.

Mrs. Gilbert added flavor to his adventure by being impressed with his courage in braving the harsh air.

"Well, you *are* spunky!" she exclaimed admiringly. "You *are* spunky. I wouldn't have gone out for anything."

Mr. Gilbert with true masculine impassivity disregarded the awe he had excited in his wife. He turned to the two young men and triumphantly routed them on the subject of the weather. Richard Caramel was called on to remember the month of November in Kansas. No sooner had the theme been pushed toward him, however, than it was violently fished back to be lingered over, pawed over, elongated, and generally devitalized by its sponsor.

The immemorial thesis that the days somewhere were warm but the nights very pleasant was successfully propounded and they decided the exact distance on an obscure railroad between two points that Dick had inadvertently mentioned. Anthony fixed Mr. Gilbert with a steady stare and went into a trance through which, after a moment, Mrs. Gilbert's smiling voice penetrated:

"It seems as though the cold were damper here—it seems to eat into my bones."

As this remark, adequately yessed, had been on the tip of Mr. Gilbert's tongue, he could not be blamed for rather abruptly changing the subject.

"Where's Gloria?"

"She ought to be here any minute."

"Have you met my daughter, Mr.——?"

"Haven't had the pleasure. I've heard Dick speak of her often."

"She and Richard are cousins."

"Yes?" Anthony smiled with some effort. He was not used to the society of his seniors, and his mouth was stiff from superfluous cheerfulness. It was such a pleasant thought about Gloria and Dick being cousins. He managed within the next minute to throw an agonized glance at his friend.

Richard Caramel was afraid they'd have to toddle off.

Mrs. Gilbert was tremendously sorry.

Mr. Gilbert thought it was too bad.

Mrs. Gilbert had a further idea—something about being glad they'd come, anyhow, even if they'd only seen an old lady 'way too old to flirt with them. Anthony and Dick evidently considered this a sly sally, for they laughed one bar in three-four time.

Would they come again soon?

"Oh, yes."

Gloria would be *aw*fully sorry!

"Good-by——"

"Good-by——"

Smiles!

Smiles!

Bang!

Two disconsolate young men walking down the tenth-floor corridor of the Plaza in the direction of the elevator.

A Lady's Legs

Behind Maury Noble's attractive indolence, his irrelevance and his easy mockery, lay a surprising and relentless maturity of purpose. His intention, as he stated it in college, had been to use three years in travel, three years in utter leisure—and then to become immensely rich as quickly as possible.

His three years of travel were over. He had accomplished the globe with an intensity and curiosity that in any one else would have seemed pedantic, without redeeming spontaneity, almost the self-editing of a human Baedeker; but, in this case, it assumed an air of mysterious purpose and significant design—as though Maury Noble were some predestined anti-Christ, urged by a preordination to go everywhere there was to go along the earth and to see all the billions of humans who bred and wept and slew each other here and there upon it.

Back in America, he was sallying into the search for amusement with the same consistent absorption. He who had never taken more than a few cocktails or a pint of wine at a sitting, taught himself to drink as he would have taught himself Greek—like Greek it would be the gateway to a wealth of new sensations, new psychic states, new reactions in joy or misery.

His habits were a matter for esoteric speculation. He had three rooms in a bachelor apartment on Forty-fourth Street, but he was seldom to be found there. The telephone girl had received the most positive instructions that no one should even have his ear without first giving a name to be passed upon. She had a list of half a dozen people to whom he was never at home, and of the same number to whom he was always at home. Foremost on the latter list were Anthony Patch and Richard Caramel.

Maury's mother lived with her married son in Philadelphia, and there Maury went usually for the week-ends, so one Saturday night when Anthony, prowling the chilly streets in a fit of utter boredom, dropped in at the Molton Arms he was overjoyed to find that Mr. Noble was at home.

His spirits soared faster than the flying elevator. This was so good, so extremely good, to be about to talk to Maury—who would be equally happy at seeing him. They would look at each other with a deep affection just behind their eyes which both would conceal beneath some attenuated raillery. Had it been summer they would have gone out together and indolently sipped two long Tom Collinses, as they wilted their collars and watched the faintly diverting round of some lazy August cabaret. But it was cold outside, with wind around the edges of the tall buildings and December just up the street, so better far an evening together under the soft lamplight and a drink or two of Bushmill's, or a thimbleful of Maury's Grand Marnier, with the books gleaming like ornaments against the walls, and Maury radiating a divine inertia as he rested, large and catlike, in his favorite chair.

There he was! The room closed about Anthony, warmed him. The glow of that strong persuasive mind, that temperament almost Oriental in its outward impassivity, warmed Anthony's restless soul and brought him a peace that could be likened only to the peace a stupid woman gives. One must understand all—else one must take all for granted. Maury filled the room, tigerlike, godlike. The winds outside were stilled; the brass candlesticks on the mantel glowed like tapers before an altar.

"What keeps you here to-day?" Anthony spread himself over a yielding sofa and made an elbow-rest among the pillows.

"Just been here an hour. Tea dance—and I stayed so late I missed my train to Philadelphia."

"Strange to stay so long," commented Anthony curiously.

"Rather. What'd you do?"

"Geraldine. Little usher at Keith's. I told you about her."

"Oh!"

"Paid me a call about three and stayed till five. Peculiar little soul—she gets me. She's so utterly stupid."

Maury was silent.

"Strange as it may seem," continued Anthony, "so far as I'm concerned, and even so far as I know, Geraldine is a paragon of virtue."

He had known her a month, a girl of nondescript and nomadic habits. Some one had casually passed her on to Anthony, who considered her amusing and rather liked the chaste and fairylike kisses she had given him on the third night of their acquaintance, when they had driven in a taxi through the Park. She had a vague family—a shadowy aunt and uncle who shared with her an apartment in the labyrinthine hundreds. She was company, familiar and faintly intimate and restful. Further than that he did not care to experiment—not from any moral compunction, but from a dread of allowing any entanglement to disturb what he felt was the growing serenity of his life.

"She has two stunts," he informed Maury; "one of them is to get her hair over her eyes some way and then blow it out, and the other is to say 'You cra-a-azy!' when some one makes a remark that's over her head. It fascinates me. I sit there hour after hour, completely intrigued by the maniacal symptoms she finds in my imagination."

Maury stirred in his chair and spoke.

"Remarkable that a person can comprehend so little and yet live in such a complex civilization. A woman like that actually takes the whole universe in the most matter-of-fact way. From the influence of Rousseau to the bearing of the tariff rates on her dinner, the whole phenomenon is utterly strange to her. She's just been carried along from an age of spearheads and plunked down here with the equipment of an archer for going into a pistol duel. You could sweep away the entire crust of history and she'd never know the difference."

"I wish our Richard would write about her."

"Anthony, surely you don't think she's worth writing about."

"As much as anybody," he answered, yawning. "You know I was thinking to-day that I have a great confidence in Dick. So long as he sticks to people and not to ideas, and as long as his inspirations come from life and not from art, and always granting a normal growth, I believe he'll be a big man."

"I should think the appearance of the black note-book would prove that he's going to life."

Anthony raised himself on his elbow and answered eagerly:

"He tries to go to life. So does every author except the very worst, but after all most of them live on predigested food. The incident or character may be from life, but the writer usually interprets it in terms of the last book he read. For instance, suppose he meets a sea captain and thinks he's an original character. The truth is that he sees the resemblance between the sea-captain and the last sea captain Dana created, or whoever creates sea captains, and therefore he knows how to set this sea captain on paper. Dick, of course, can set down any consciously picturesque, character-like character, but could he accurately transcribe his own sister?"

Then they were off for half an hour on literature.

"A classic," suggested Anthony, "is a successful book that has survived the reaction of the next period or generation. Then it's safe, like a style in architecture or furniture. It's acquired a picturesque dignity to take the place of its fashion. . . ."

After a time the subject temporarily lost its tang. The interest of the two young men was not particularly technical. They were in love with generalities. Anthony had recently discovered Samuel Butler and the brisk aphorisms in the note-book seemed to him the quintessence of criticism. Maury, his whole mind so thoroughly mellowed by the very hardness of his scheme of life, seemed inevitably the wiser of the two, yet in the actual stuff of their intelligences they were not, it seemed, fundamentally different.

They drifted from letters to the curiosities of each other's day.

"Whose tea was it?"

"People named Abercrombie."

"Why'd you stay late? Meet a luscious débutante?"

"Yes."

"Did you really?" Anthony's voice lifted in surprise.

"Not a débutante exactly. Said she came out two winters ago in Kansas City."

"Sort of left-over?"

"No," answered Maury with some amusement, "I think that's the last thing I'd say about her. She seemed—well, somehow the youngest person there."

"Not too young to make you miss a train."

"Young enough. Beautiful child."

Anthony chuckled in his one-syllable snort.

"Oh, Maury, you're in your second childhood. What do you mean by beautiful?"

Maury gazed helplessly into space.

"Well, I can't describe her exactly—except to say that she was beautiful. She was—tremendously alive. She was eating gum-drops."

"What!"

"It was a sort of attenuated vice. She's a nervous kind—said she always ate gum-drops at teas because she had to stand around so long in one place."

"What'd you talk about—Bergson? Bilphism? Whether the one-step is immoral?"

Maury was unruffled; his fur seemed to run all ways.

"As a matter of fact we did talk on Bilphism. Seems her mother's a Bilphist. Mostly, though, we talked about legs."

Anthony rocked in glee.

"My God! Whose legs?"

"Hers. She talked a lot about hers. As though they were a sort of choice bric-à-brac. She aroused a great desire to see them."

"What is she—a dancer?"

"No, I found she was a cousin of Dick's."

Anthony sat upright so suddenly that the pillow he released stood on end like a live thing and dove to the floor.

"Name's Gloria Gilbert?" he cried.

"Yes. Isn't she remarkable?"

"I'm sure I don't know—but for sheer dulness her father——"

"Well," interrupted Maury with implacable conviction, "her family may be as sad as professional mourners but I'm inclined to think that she's a quite authentic and original character. The outer signs of the cut-and-dried Yale prom girl and all that—but different, very emphatically different."

"Go on, go on!" urged Anthony. "Soon as Dick told me she didn't have a brain in her head I knew she must be pretty good."

"Did he say that?"

"Swore to it," said Anthony with another snorting laugh.

"Well, what he means by brains in a woman is——"

"I know," interrupted Anthony eagerly, "he means a smattering of literary misinformation."

"That's it. The kind who believes that the annual moral let-down of the country is a very good thing or the kind who believes it's a very ominous thing. Either pince-nez or postures. Well, this girl talked about legs. She talked about skin too—her own skin. Always her own. She told me the sort of tan she'd like to get in the summer and how closely she usually approximated it."

"You sat enraptured by her low alto?"

"By her low alto! No, by tan! I began thinking about tan. I began to think what color I turned when I made my last exposure about two years ago. I did use to get a pretty good tan. I used to get a sort of bronze, if I remember rightly."

Anthony retired into the cushions, shaken with laughter.

"She's got you going—oh, Maury! Maury the Connecticut life-saver. The human nutmeg. Extra! Heiress elopes with coast-guard because of his luscious pigmentation! Afterward found to be Tasmanian strain in his family!"

Maury sighed; rising he walked to the window and raised the shade.

"Snowing hard."

Anthony, still laughing quietly to himself, made no answer.

"Another winter." Maury's voice from the window was almost a whisper. "We're growing old, Anthony. I'm twenty-seven, by God! Three years to thirty, and then I'm what an undergraduate calls a middle-aged man."

Anthony was silent for a moment.

"You *are* old, Maury," he agreed at length. "The first signs of a very dissolute and wabbly senescence—you have spent the afternoon talking about tan and a lady's legs."

Maury pulled down the shade with a sudden harsh snap.

"Idiot!" he cried, "that from you! Here I sit, young Anthony, as I'll sit for a generation or more and watch such gay souls as you and Dick and Gloria Gilbert go past me, dancing and singing and loving and hating one another and being moved, being eternally moved. And I am moved only by my lack of emotion. I shall sit and the snow will come—oh, for a Caramel to take notes—and another winter and I shall be thirty and you and Dick and Gloria will go on being eternally moved and dancing by me and singing. But after you've all gone I'll be saying things for new Dicks to write down, and listening to the disillusions and cynicisms and emotions of new Anthonys—yes, and talking to new Glorias about the tans of summers yet to come."

The firelight flurried up on the hearth. Maury left the window, stirred the blaze with a poker, and dropped a log upon the andirons. Then he sat back in his chair and the remnants of his voice faded in the new fire that spit red and yellow along the bark.

"After all, Anthony, it's you who are very romantic and young. It's you who are infinitely more susceptible and afraid of your calm being broken. It's me who tries again and again to be moved—let myself go a thousand times and I'm always me. Nothing—quite—stirs me.

"Yet," he murmured after another long pause, "there was something about that little girl with her absurd tan that was eternally old—like me."

Turbulence

Anthony turned over sleepily in his bed, greeting a patch of cold sun on his counterpane, crisscrossed with the shadows of the leaded window. The room was full of morning. The carved chest in the corner, the ancient and inscrutable wardrobe, stood about the room like dark symbols of the obliviousness of matter; only the rug was beckoning and perishable to his perishable feet, and Bounds, horribly inappropriate in his soft collar, was of stuff as fading as the gauze of frozen breath he uttered. He was close to the bed, his hand still lowered where he had been jerking at the upper blanket, his dark-brown eyes fixed imperturbably upon his master.

"Bows!" muttered the drowsy god. "Thachew, Bows?"

"It's I, sir."

Anthony moved his head, forced his eyes wide, and blinked triumphantly.

"Bounds."

"Yes, sir?"

"Can you get off—yeow-ow-oh-oh-oh God!—" Anthony yawned insufferably and the contents of his brain seemed to fall together in a dense hash. He made a fresh start.

"Can you come around about four and serve some tea and sandwiches or something?"

"Yes, sir."

Anthony considered with chilling lack of inspiration.

"Some sandwiches," he repeated helplessly, "oh, some cheese sandwiches and jelly ones and chicken and olive, I guess. Never mind breakfast."

The strain of invention was too much. He shut his eyes wearily, let his head roll to rest inertly, and quickly relaxed what he had regained of muscular control. Out of a crevice of his mind crept the vague but inevitable spectre of the night before—but it proved in this case to be nothing but a seemingly interminable conversation with Richard Caramel, who had called on him at midnight; they had drunk four bottles of beer and munched dry crusts of bread while Anthony listened to a reading of the first part of "The Demon Lover."

—Came a voice now after many hours. Anthony disregarded it, as sleep closed over him, folded down upon him, crept up into the byways of his mind.

Suddenly he was awake, saying: "What?"

"For how many, sir?" It was still Bounds, standing patient and motionless at the foot of the bed—Bounds who divided his manner among three gentlemen.

"How many what?"

"I think, sir, I'd better know how many are coming. I'll have to plan for the sandwiches, sir."

"Two," muttered Anthony huskily; "lady and a gentleman."

Bounds said, "Thank you, sir," and moved away, bearing with him his humiliating reproachful soft collar, reproachful to each of the three gentlemen, who only demanded of him a third.

After a long time Anthony arose and drew an opalescent dressing grown of brown and blue over his slim pleasant figure. With a last yawn he went into the bathroom, and turning on the dresser light (the bathroom had no outside exposure) he contemplated himself in the mirror with some interest. A wretched apparition, he thought; he usually thought so in the morning—sleep made his face unnaturally pale. He lit a cigarette and glanced through several letters and the morning Tribune.

An hour later, shaven and dressed, he was sitting at his desk looking at a small piece of paper he had taken out of his wallet. It was scrawled with semi-legible memoranda: "See Mr. Howland at five. Get hair-cut. See about Rivers' bill. Go book-store."

—And under the last: "Cash in bank, $690 (crossed out), $612 (crossed out), $607."

Finally, down at the bottom and in a hurried scrawl: "Dick and Gloria Gilbert for tea."

This last item brought him obvious satisfaction. His day, usually a jelly-like creature, a shapeless, spineless thing, had attained Mesozoic structure. It was marching along surely, even jauntily, toward a climax, as a play should, as a day should. He dreaded the moment when the backbone of the day should be broken, when he should have met the girl at last, talked to her, and then bowed her laughter out the door, returning only to the melancholy dregs in the teacups and the gathering staleness of the uneaten sandwiches.

There was a growing lack of color in Anthony's days. He felt it constantly and sometimes traced it to a talk he had had with Maury Noble a month before. That anything so ingenuous, so priggish, as a sense of waste should oppress him was absurd, but there was no denying the fact that some unwelcome survival of a fetish had drawn him three weeks before down to the public library, where, by the token of Richard Caramel's card, he had drawn out half a dozen books on the Italian Renaissance. That these books were still piled on his desk in the original order of carriage, that they were daily increasing his liabilities by twelve cents, was no mitigation of their testimony. They were cloth and morocco witnesses to the fact of his defection. Anthony had had several hours of acute and startling panic.

In justification of his manner of living there was first, of course, The Meaninglessness of Life. As aides and ministers, pages and squires, butlers and lackeys to this great Khan there were a thousand books glowing on his shelves, there was his apartment and all the money that was to be his when the old man up the river should choke on his last morality. From a world fraught with the menace of débutantes and the stupidity of many Geraldines he was thankfully delivered—rather should he emulate the feline immobility of Maury and wear proudly the culminative wisdom of the numbered generations.

Over and against these things was something which his brain persistently analyzed and dealt with as a tiresome complex but which, though logically disposed of and bravely trampled under foot, had sent him out through the soft slush of late November to a library which had none of the books he most wanted. It is fair to analyze Anthony as far as he could analyze himself; further than that it is, of course, presumption. He found in himself a growing horror and loneliness. The idea of eating alone frightened him; in preference he dined often with men he detested. Travel, which had once charmed him, seemed, at length, unendurable, a business of color without substance, a phantom chase after his own dream's shadow.

—If I am essentially weak, he thought, I need work to do, work to do. It worried him to think that he was, after all, a facile mediocrity, with neither the poise of Maury nor the enthusiasm of Dick. It seemed a tragedy to want nothing—and yet he wanted something, something. He knew in flashes what it was—some path of hope to lead him toward what he thought was an imminent and ominous old age.

After cocktails and luncheon at the University Club Anthony felt better. He had run into two men from his class at Harvard, and in contrast to the gray heaviness of their conversation his life assumed color. Both of them were married: one spent his coffee time in sketching an extra-nuptial adventure to the bland and appreciative smiles of the other. Both of them, he thought, were Mr. Gilberts in embryo; the number of their "yes's" would have to be quadrupled, their natures crabbed by twenty years—then they would be no more than obsolete and broken machines, pseudo-wise and valueless, nursed to an utter senility by the women they had broken.

Ah, he was more than that, as he paced the long carpet in the lounge after dinner, pausing at the window to look into the harried street. He was Anthony Patch, brilliant, magnetic, the heir of many years and many men. This was his world now—and that last strong irony he craved lay in the offing.

With a stray boyishness he saw himself a power upon the earth; with his grandfather's money he might build his own pedestal and be a Talleyrand, a Lord Verulam. The clarity of his mind, its sophistication, its versatile intelligence, all at their maturity and dominated by some purpose yet to be born would find him work to do. On this minor his dream faded—work to do: he tried to imagine himself in Congress rooting around in the litter of that incredible pigsty with the narrow and porcine brows he saw pictured sometimes in the rotogravure sections of the Sunday newspapers, those glorified proletarians babbling blandly to the nation the ideas of high school seniors! Little men with copy-book ambitions who by mediocrity had thought to emerge from mediocrity into the lustreless and unromantic heaven of a government by the people—and the best, the dozen shrewd men at the top, egotistic and cynical, were content to lead this choir of white ties and wire collar-buttons in a discordant and amazing hymn, compounded of a vague confusion between wealth as a reward of virtue and wealth as a proof of vice, and continued cheers for God, the Constitution, and the Rocky Mountains!

Lord Verulam! Talleyrand!

Back in his apartment the grayness returned. His cocktails had died, making him sleepy, somewhat befogged and inclined to be surly. Lord Verulam—he? The very thought was bitter. Anthony Patch with no record of achievement, without courage, without strength to be satisfied with truth when it was given him. Oh, he was a pretentious fool, making careers out of cocktails and meanwhile regretting, weakly and secretly, the collapse of an insufficient and wretched idealism. He had garnished his soul in the subtlest taste and now he longed for the old rubbish. He was empty, it seemed, empty as an old bottle——

The buzzer rang at the door. Anthony sprang up and lifted the tube to his ear. It was Richard Caramel's voice, stilted and facetious:

"Announcing Miss Gloria Gilbert."

The Beautiful Lady

"How do you do?" he said, smiling and holding the door ajar.

Dick bowed.

"Gloria, this is Anthony."

"Well!" she cried, holding out a little gloved hand.

Under her fur coat her dress was Alice-blue, with white lace crinkled stiffly about her throat.

"Let me take your things."

Anthony stretched out his arms and the brown mass of fur tumbled into them.

"Thanks."

"What do you think of her, Anthony?" Richard Caramel demanded barbarously. "Isn't she beautiful?"

"Well!" cried the girl defiantly—withal unmoved.

She was dazzling—alight; it was agony to comprehend her beauty in a glance. Her hair, full of a heavenly glamour, was gay against the winter color of the room.

Anthony moved about, magician-like, turning the mushroom lamp into an orange glory. The stirred fire burnished the copper andirons on the hearth——

"I'm a solid block of ice," murmured Gloria casually, glancing around with eyes whose irises were of the most delicate and transparent bluish white. "What a slick fire! We found a place where you could stand on an iron-bar grating, sort of, and it blew warm air up at you—but Dick wouldn't wait there with me. I told him to go on alone and let me be happy."

Conventional enough this. She seemed talking for her own pleasure, without effort. Anthony, sitting at one end of the sofa, examined her profile against the foreground of the lamp: the exquisite regularity of nose and upper lip, the chin, faintly decided, balanced beautifully on a rather short neck. On a photograph she must have been completely classical, almost cold—but the glow of her hair and cheeks, at once flushed and fragile, made her the most living person he had ever seen.

"... Think you've got the best name I've heard," she was saying, still apparently to herself; her glance rested on him a moment and then flitted past him—to the Italian bracket-lamps clinging like luminous yellow turtles at intervals along the walls, to the books row upon row, then to her cousin on the other side. "Anthony Patch. Only you ought to look sort of like a horse, with a long narrow face—and you ought to be in tatters."

"That's all the Patch part, though. How should Anthony look?"

"You look like Anthony," she assured him seriously—he thought she had scarcely seen him—"rather majestic," she continued, "and solemn."

Anthony indulged in a disconcerted smile.

"Only I like alliterative names," she went on, "all except mine. Mine's too flamboyant. I used to know two girls named Jinks, though, and just think if they'd been named anything except what they were named—Judy Jinks and Jerry Jinks. Cute, what? Don't you think?" Her childish mouth was parted, awaiting a rejoinder.

"Everybody in the next generation," suggested Dick, "will be named Peter or Barbara—because at present all the piquant literary characters are named Peter or Barbara."

Anthony continued the prophecy:

"Of course Gladys and Eleanor, having graced the last generation of heroines and being at present in their social prime, will be passed on to the next generation of shop-girls——"

"Displacing Ella and Stella," interrupted Dick.

"And Pearl and Jewel," Gloria added cordially, "and Earl and Elmer and Minnie."

"And then I'll come along," remarked Dick, "and picking up the obsolete name, Jewel, I'll attach it to some quaint and attractive character and it'll start its career all over again."

Her voice took up the thread of subject and wove along with faintly upturning, half-humorous intonations for sentence ends—as though defying interruption—and intervals of shadowy laughter. Dick had told her that Anthony's man was named Bounds—she thought that was wonderful! Dick had made some sad pun about Bounds doing patchwork, but if there was one thing worse than a pun, she said, it was a person who, as the inevitable come-back to a pun, gave the perpetrator a mock-reproachful look.

"Where are you from?" inquired Anthony. He knew, but beauty had rendered him thoughtless.

"Kansas City, Missouri."

"They put her out the same time they barred cigarettes."

"Did they bar cigarettes? I see the hand of my holy grandfather."

"He's a reformer or something, isn't he?"

"I blush for him."

"So do I," she confessed. "I detest reformers, especially the sort who try to reform me."

"Are there many of those?"

"Dozens. It's 'Oh, Gloria, if you smoke so many cigarettes you'll lose your pretty complexion!' and 'Oh, Gloria, why don't you marry and settle down?'"

Anthony agreed emphatically while he wondered who had had the temerity to speak thus to such a personage.

"And then," she continued, "there are all the subtle reformers who tell you the wild stories they've heard about you and how they've been sticking up for you."

He saw, at length, that her eyes were gray, very level and cool, and when they rested on him he understood what Maury had meant by saying she was very young and very old. She talked always about herself as a very charming child might talk, and her comments on her tastes and distastes were unaffected and spontaneous.

"I must confess," said Anthony gravely, "that even *I*'ve heard one thing about you."

Alert at once, she sat up straight. Those eyes, with the grayness and eternity of a cliff of soft granite, caught his.

"Tell me. I'll believe it. I always believe anything any one tells me about myself—don't you?"

"Invariably!" agreed the two men in unison.

"Well, tell me."

"I'm not sure that I ought to," teased Anthony, smiling unwillingly. She was so obviously interested, in a state of almost laughable self-absorption.

"He means your nickname," said her cousin.

"What name?" inquired Anthony, politely puzzled.

Instantly she was shy—then she laughed, rolled back against the cushions, and turned her eyes up as she spoke:

"Coast-to-Coast Gloria." Her voice was full of laughter, laughter undefined as the varying shadows playing between fire and lamp upon her hair. "O Lord!"

Still Anthony was puzzled.

"What do you mean?"

"*Me*, I mean. That's what some silly boys coined for *me*."

"Don't you see, Anthony," explained Dick, "traveller of nation-wide notoriety and all that. Isn't that what you've heard? She's been called that for years—since she was seventeen."

Anthony's eyes became sad and humorous.

"Who's this female Methuselah you've brought in here, Caramel?"

She disregarded this, possibly rather resented it, for she switched back to the main topic.

"What *have* you heard of me?"

"Something about your physique."

"Oh," she said, coolly disappointed, "that all?"

"Your tan."

"My tan?" She was puzzled. Her hand rose to her throat, rested there an instant as though the fingers were feeling variants of color.

"Do you remember Maury Noble? Man you met about a month ago. You made a great impression."

She thought a moment.

"I remember—but he didn't call me up."

"He was afraid to, I don't doubt."

It was black dark without now and Anthony wondered that his apartment had ever seemed gray—so warm and friendly were the books and pictures on the walls and the good Bounds offering tea from a respectful shadow and the three nice people giving out waves of interest and laughter back and forth across the happy fire.

Dissatisfaction

On Thursday afternoon Gloria and Anthony had tea together in the grill room at the Plaza. Her fur-trimmed suit was gray—"because with gray you *have* to wear a lot of paint," she explained—and a small toque sat rakishly on her head, allowing yellow ripples of hair to wave out in jaunty glory. In the higher light it seemed to Anthony that her personality was infinitely softer—she seemed so young, scarcely eighteen; her form under the tight sheath, known then as a hobble-skirt, was amazingly supple and slender, and her hands, neither "artistic" nor stubby, were small as a child's hands should be.

As they entered, the orchestra were sounding the preliminary whimpers to a maxixe, a tune full of castanets and facile faintly languorous violin harmonies, appropriate to the crowded winter grill teeming with an excited college crowd, high-spirited at the approach of the holidays. Carefully, Gloria considered several locations, and rather to Anthony's annoyance paraded him circuitously to a table for two at the far side of the room. Reaching it she again considered. Would she sit on the right or on the left? Her beautiful eyes and lips were very grave as she made her choice, and Anthony thought again how naïve was her every gesture; she took all the things of life for hers to choose from and apportion, as though she were continually picking out presents for herself from an inexhaustible counter.

Abstractedly she watched the dancers for a few moments, commenting murmurously as a couple eddied near.

"There's a pretty girl in blue"—and as Anthony looked obediently—"there! No. behind you—there!"

"Yes," he agreed helplessly.

"You didn't see her."

"I'd rather look at you."

"I know, but she was pretty. Except that she had big ankles."

"Was she?—I mean, did she?" he said indifferently.

A girl's salutation came from a couple dancing close to them.

"Hello, Gloria! O Gloria!"

"Hello there."

"Who's that?" he demanded.

"I don't know. Somebody." She caught sight of another face. "Hello, Muriel!" Then to Anthony: "There's Muriel Kane. Now I think she's attractive, 'cept not very."

Anthony chuckled appreciatively.

"Attractive, 'cept not very," he repeated.

She smiled—was interested immediately.

"Why is that funny?" Her tone was pathetically intent.

"It just was."

"Do you want to dance?"

"Do you?"

"Sort of. But let's sit," she decided.

"And talk about you? You love to talk about you, don't you?"

"Yes." Caught in a vanity, she laughed.

"I imagine your autobiography would be a classic."

"Dick says I haven't got one."

"Dick!" he exclaimed. "What does he know about you?"

"Nothing. But he says the biography of every woman begins with the first kiss that counts, and ends when her last child is laid in her arms."

"He's talking from his book."

"He says unloved women have no biographies—they have histories."

Anthony laughed again.

"Surely you don't claim to be unloved!"

"Well, I suppose not."

"Then why haven't you a biography? Haven't you ever had a kiss that counted?" As the words left his lips he drew in his breath sharply as though to suck them back. This *baby!*

"I don't know what you mean 'counts,'" she objected.

"I wish you'd tell me how old you are."

"Twenty-two," she said, meeting his eyes gravely. "How old did you think?"

"About eighteen."

"I'm going to start being that. I don't like being twenty-two. I hate it more than anything in the world."

"Being twenty-two?"

"No. Getting old and everything. Getting married."

"Don't you ever want to marry?"

"I don't want to have responsibility and a lot of children to take care of."

Evidently she did not doubt that on her lips all things were good. He waited rather breathlessly for her next remark, expecting it to follow up her last. She was smiling, without amusement but pleasantly, and after an interval half a dozen words fell into the space between them:

"I wish I had some gum-drops."

"You shall!" He beckoned to a waiter and sent him to the cigar counter.

"D'you mind? I love gum-drops. Everybody kids me about it because I'm always whacking away at one—whenever my daddy's not around."

"Not at all.—Who are all these children?" he asked suddenly. "Do you know them all?"

"Why—no, but they're from—oh, from everywhere, I suppose. Don't you ever come here?"

"Very seldom. I don't care particularly for 'nice girls.'"

Immediately he had her attention. She turned a definite shoulder to the dancers, relaxed in her chair, and demanded:

"What *do* you do with yourself?"

Thanks to a cocktail Anthony welcomed the question. In a mood to talk, he wanted, moreover, to impress this girl whose interest seemed so tantalizingly elusive—she stopped to browse in unexpected pastures, hurried quickly over the inobviously obvious. He wanted to pose. He wanted to appear suddenly to her in novel and heroic colors. He wanted to stir her from that casualness she showed toward everything except herself.

"I do nothing," he began, realizing simultaneously that his words were to lack the debonair grace he craved for them. "I do nothing, for there's nothing I can do that's worth doing."

"Well?" He had neither surprised her nor even held her, yet she had certainly understood him, if indeed he had said aught worth understanding.

"Don't you approve of lazy men?"

She nodded.

"I suppose so, if they're gracefully lazy. Is that possible for an American?"

"Why not?" he demanded, discomfited.

But her mind had left the subject and wandered up ten floors.

"My daddy's mad at me," she observed dispassionately.

"Why? But I want to know just why it's impossible for an American to be gracefully idle"—his words gathered conviction—"it astonishes me. It—it—I don't understand why people think that every young man ought to go down-town and work ten hours a day for the best twenty years of his life at dull, unimaginative work, certainly not altruistic work."

He broke off. She watched him inscrutably. He waited for her to agree or disagree, but she did neither.

"Don't you ever form judgments on things?" he asked with some exasperation.

She shook her head and her eyes wandered back to the dancers as she answered:

"I don't know. I don't know anything about—what you should do, or what anybody should do."

She confused him and hindered the flow of his ideas. Self-expression had never seemed at once so desirable and so impossible.

"Well," he admitted apologetically, "neither do I, of course, but——"

"I just think of people," she continued, "whether they seem right where they are and fit into the picture. I don't mind if they don't do anything. I don't see why they should; in fact it always astonishes me when anybody does anything."

"You don't want to do anything?"

"I want to sleep."

For a second he was startled, almost as though she had meant this literally.

"Sleep?"

"Sort of. I want to just be lazy and I want some of the people around me to be doing things, because that makes me feel comfortable and safe—and I want some of them to be doing nothing at all, because they can be graceful and companionable for me. But I never want to change people or get excited over them."

"You're a quaint little determinist," laughed Anthony. "It's your world, isn't it?"

"Well—" she said with a quick upward glance, "isn't it? As long as I'm—young."

She had paused slightly before the last word and Anthony suspected that she had started to say "beautiful." It was undeniably what she had intended.

Her eyes brightened and he waited for her to enlarge on the theme. He had drawn her out, at any rate—he bent forward slightly to catch the words.

But "Let's dance!" was all she said.

Admiration

That winter afternoon at the Plaza was the first of a succession of "dates" Anthony made with her in the blurred and stimulating days before Christmas. Invariably she was busy. What particular strata of the city's social life claimed her he was a long time finding out. It seemed to matter very little. She attended the semi-public charity dances at the big hotels; he saw her several times at dinner parties in Sherry's, and once as he waited for her to dress, Mrs. Gilbert, apropos of her daughter's habit of "going," rattled off an amazing holiday programme that included half a dozen dances to which Anthony had received cards.

He made engagements with her several times for lunch and tea—the former were hurried and, to him at least, rather unsatisfactory occasions, for she was sleepy-eyed and casual, incapable of concentrating upon anything or of giving consecutive attention to his remarks. When after two of these sallow meals he accused her of tendering him the skin and bones of the day she laughed and gave him a tea-time three days off. This was infinitely more satisfactory.

One Sunday afternoon just before Christmas he called up and found her in the lull directly after some important but mysterious quarrel: she informed him in a tone of mingled wrath and amusement that she had sent a man out of her apartment—here Anthony speculated violently—and that the man had been giving a little dinner for her that very night and that of course she wasn't going. So Anthony took her to supper.

"Let's go to something!" she proposed as they went down in the elevator. "I want to see a show, don't you?"

Inquiry at the hotel ticket desk disclosed only two Sunday night "concerts."

"They're always the same," she complained unhappily, "same old Yiddish comedians. Oh, let's go somewhere!"

To conceal a guilty suspicion that he should have arranged a performance of some kind for her approval Anthony affected a knowing cheerfulness.

"We'll go to a good cabaret."

"I've seen every one in town."

"Well, we'll find a new one."

She was in wretched humor; that was evident. Her gray eyes were granite now indeed. When she wasn't speaking she stared straight in front of her as if at some distasteful abstraction in the lobby.

"Well, come on, then."

He followed her, a graceful girl even in her enveloping fur, out to a taxicab, and, with an air of having a definite place in mind, instructed the driver to go over to Broadway and then turn south. He made several casual attempts at conversation but as she adopted an impenetrable armor of silence and answered him in sentences as morose as the cold darkness of the taxicab he gave up, and assuming a like mood fell into a dim gloom.

A dozen blocks down Broadway Anthony's eyes were caught by a large and unfamiliar electric sign spelling "Marathon" in glorious yellow script, adorned with electrical leaves and flowers that alternately vanished and beamed upon the wet and glistening street. He leaned and rapped on the taxi-window and in a moment was receiving information from a colored doorman: Yes, this was a cabaret. Fine cabaret. Bes' showina city!

"Shall we try it?"

With a sigh Gloria tossed her cigarette out the open door and prepared to follow it; then they had passed under the screaming sign, under the wide portal, and up by a stuffy elevator into this unsung palace of pleasure.

The gay habitats of the very rich and the very poor, the very dashing and the very criminal, not to mention the lately exploited very Bohemian, are made known to the awed high school girls of Augusta, Georgia, and Redwing, Minnesota, not only through the bepictured and entrancing spreads of the Sunday theatrical supplements but through the shocked and alarmful eyes of Mr. Rupert Hughes and other chroniclers of the mad pace of America. But the excursions of Harlem onto Broadway, the deviltries of the dull and the revelries of the respectable are a matter of esoteric knowledge only to the participants themselves.

A tip circulates—and in the place knowingly mentioned, gather the lower moral-classes on Saturday and Sunday nights—the little troubled men who are pictured in the comics as "the Consumer" or "the Public." They have made sure that the place has three qualifications: it is cheap; it imitates with a sort of shoddy and mechanical wistfulness the glittering antics of the great cafés in the theatre district; and—this, above all, important—it is a place where they can "take a nice girl," which means, of course, that every one has become equally harmless, timid, and uninteresting through lack of money and imagination.

There on Sunday nights gather the credulous, sentimental, underpaid, overworked people with hyphenated occupations: book-keepers, ticket-sellers, office-managers, salesmen, and, most of all, clerks—clerks of the express, of the mail, of the grocery, of the brokerage, of the bank. With them are their giggling, over-gestured, pathetically pretentious women, who grow fat with them, bear them too many babies, and float helpless and uncontent in a colorless sea of drudgery and broken hopes.

They name these brummagem cabarets after Pullman cars. The "Marathon"! Not for them the salacious similes borrowed from the cafés of Paris! This is where their docile patrons bring their "nice women," whose starved fancies are only too willing to believe that the scene is comparatively gay and joyous, and even faintly immoral. This is life! Who cares for the morrow?

Abandoned people!

Anthony and Gloria, seated, looked about them. At the next table a party of four were in process of being joined by a party of three, two men and a girl, who were evidently late—and the manner of the girl was a study in national sociology. She was meeting some new men—and she was pretending desperately. By gesture she was pretending and by words and by the scarcely perceptible motionings of her eyelids that she belonged to a class a little superior to the class with which she now had to do, that a while ago she had been, and presently would again be, in a higher, rarer air. She was almost painfully refined—she wore a last year's hat covered with violets no more yearningly pretentious and palpably artificial than herself.

Fascinated, Anthony and Gloria watched the girl sit down and radiate the impression that she was only condescendingly present. For *me*, her eyes said, this is practically a slumming expedition, to be cloaked with belittling laughter and semi-apologetics.

—And the other women passionately poured out the impression that though they were in the crowd they were not of it. This was not the sort of place to which they were accustomed; they had dropped in because it was near by and convenient—every party in the restaurant poured out that impression . . . who knew? They were forever changing class, all of them—the women often marrying above their opportunities, the men striking suddenly a magnificent opulence: a sufficiently preposterous advertising scheme, a celestialized ice cream cone. Meanwhile, they met here to eat, closing their eyes to the economy displayed in infrequent changings of table-cloths, in the casualness of the cabaret performers, most of all in the colloquial carelessness and familiarity of the waiters. One was sure that these waiters were not impressed by their patrons. One expected that presently they would sit at the tables. . . .

"Do you object to this?" inquired Anthony.

Gloria's face warmed and for the first time that evening she smiled.

"I love it," she said frankly. It was impossible to doubt her. Her gray eyes roved here and there, drowsing, idle or alert, on each group, passing to the next with unconcealed enjoyment, and to Anthony were made plain the different values of her profile, the wonderfully alive expressions of her mouth, and the authentic distinction of face and form and manner that made her like a single flower amidst a collection of cheap bric-à-brac. At her happiness, a gorgeous sentiment welled into his eyes, choked him up, set his nerves a-tingle, and filled his throat with husky and vibrant emotion. There was a hush upon the room. The careless violins and saxophones, the shrill rasping complaint of a child near by, the voice of the violet-hatted girl at the next table, all moved slowly out, receded, and fell away like shadowy reflections on the shining floor—and they two, it seemed to him, were alone and infinitely remote, quiet. Surely the freshness of her cheeks was a gossamer projection from a land of delicate and undiscovered shades; her hand gleaming on the stained table-cloth was a shell from some far and wildly virginal sea. . . .

Then the illusion snapped like a nest of threads; the room grouped itself around him, voices, faces, movement; the garish shimmer of the lights overhead became real, became portentous; breath began, the slow respiration that she and he took in time with this docile hundred, the rise and fall of bosoms, the eternal meaningless play and interplay and tossing and reiterating of word and phrase—all these wrenched his senses open to the suffocating pressure of life—and then her voice came at him, cool as the suspended dream he had left behind.

"I belong here," she murmured, "I'm like these people."

For an instant this seemed a sardonic and unnecessary paradox hurled at him across the impassable distances she created about herself. Her entrancement had increased—her eyes rested upon a Semitic violinist who swayed his shoulders to the rhythm of the year's mellowest fox-trot:

"Something—goes
Ring-a-ting-a-ling-a-ling
Right in-your ear——"

Again she spoke, from the centre of this pervasive illusion of her own. It amazed him. It was like blasphemy from the mouth of a child.

"I'm like they are—like Japanese lanterns and crape paper, and the music of that orchestra."

"You're a young idiot!" he insisted wildly.

She shook her blond head.

"No, I'm not. I *am* like them. . . . You ought to see. . . . You don't know me." She hesitated and her eyes came back to him, rested abruptly on his, as though surprised at the last to see him there. "I've got a streak of what you'd call cheapness. I don't know where I get it but it's—oh, things like this and bright colors and gaudy vulgarity. I seem to belong here. These people could appreciate me and take me for granted, and these men would fall in love with me and admire me, whereas the clever men I meet would just analyze me and tell me I'm this because of this or that because of that."

—Anthony for the moment wanted fiercely to paint her, to set her down *now*, as she was, as, as with each relentless second she could never be again.

"What were you thinking?" she asked.

"Just that I'm not a realist," he said, and then: "No, only the romanticist preserves the things worth preserving."

Out of the deep sophistication of Anthony an understanding formed, nothing atavistic or obscure, indeed scarcely physical at all, an understanding remembered from the romancings of many generations of minds that as she talked and caught his eyes and turned her lovely head, she moved him as he had never been moved before. The sheath that held her soul had assumed significance—that was all. She was a sun, radiant, growing, gathering light and storing it—then after an eternity pouring it forth in a glance, the fragment of a sentence, to that part of him that cherished all beauty and all illusion.

CHAPTER III

THE CONNOISSEUR OF KISSES

FROM his undergraduate days as editor of The Harvard Crimson Richard Caramel had desired to write. But as a senior he had picked up the glorified illusion that certain men were set aside for "service" and, going into the world, were to accomplish a vague yearnful something which would react either in eternal reward or, at the least, in the personal satisfaction of having striven for the greatest good of the greatest number.

This spirit has long rocked the colleges in America. It begins, as a rule, during the immaturities and facile impressions of freshman year—sometimes back in preparatory school. Prosperous apostles known for their emotional acting go the rounds of the universities and, by frightening the amiable sheep and dulling the quickening of interest and intellectual curiosity which is the purpose of all education, distil a mysterious conviction of sin, harking back to childhood crimes and to the ever-present menace of "women." To these lectures go the wicked youths to cheer and joke and the timid to swallow the tasty pills, which would be harmless if administered to farmers' wives and pious drug-clerks but are rather dangerous medicine for these "future leaders of men."

This octopus was strong enough to wind a sinuous tentacle about Richard Caramel. The year after his graduation it called him into the slums of New York to muck about with bewildered Italians as secretary to an "Alien Young Men's Rescue Association." He labored at it over a year before the monotony began to weary him. The aliens kept coming inexhaustibly—Italians, Poles, Scandinavians, Czechs, Armenians—with the same wrongs, the same exceptionally ugly faces and very much the same smells, though he fancied that these grew more profuse and diverse as the months passed. His eventual conclusions about the expediency of service were vague, but concerning his own relation to it they were abrupt and decisive. Any amiable young man, his head ringing with the latest crusade, could accomplish as much as he could with the débris of Europe—and it was time for him to write.

He had been living in a down-town Y. M. C. A., but when he quit the task of making sow-ear purses out of sows' ears, he moved up-town and went to work immediately as a reporter for The Sun. He kept at this for a year, doing desultory writing on the side, with little success, and then one day an infelicitous incident peremptorily closed his newspaper career. On a February afternoon he was assigned to report a parade of Squadron A. Snow threatening, he went to sleep instead before a hot fire, and when he woke up did a smooth column about the muffled beats of the horses' hoofs in the snow. . . . This he handed in. Next morning a marked copy of the paper was sent down to the City Editor with a scrawled note: "Fire the man who wrote this." It seemed that Squadron A had also seen the snow threatening—and had postponed the parade until another day.

A week later he had begun "The Demon Lover." . . .

In January, the Monday of the months, Richard Caramel's nose was blue constantly, a sardonic blue, vaguely suggestive of the flames licking around a sinner. His book was nearly ready, and as it grew in completeness it seemed to grow also in its demands, sapping him, overpowering him, until he walked haggard and conquered in its shadow. Not only to Anthony and Maury did he pour out his hopes and boasts and indecisions, but to any one who could be prevailed upon to listen. He called on polite but bewildered publishers, he discussed it with his casual vis-à-vis at the Harvard Club; it was even claimed by Anthony that he had been discovered, one Sunday night, debating the transposition of Chapter Two with a literary ticket-collector in the chill and dismal recesses of a Harlem subway station. And latest among his confidantes was Mrs. Gilbert, who sat with him by the hour and alternated between Bilphism and literature in an intense cross-fire.

"Shakespeare was a Bilphist," she assured him through a fixed smile. "Oh, yes! He was a Bilphist. It's been proved."

At this Dick would look a bit blank.

"If you've read 'Hamlet' you can't help but see."

"Well, he—he lived in a more credulous age—a more religious age."

But she demanded the whole loaf:

"Oh, yes, but you see Bilphism isn't a religion. It's the science of all religions." She smiled defiantly at him. This was the *bon mot* of her belief. There was something in the arrangement of words which grasped her mind so definitely that the statement became superior to any obligation to define itself. It is not unlikely that she would have accepted any idea encased in this radiant formula—which was perhaps not a formula; it was the *reductio ad absurdum* of all formulas.

Then eventually, but gorgeously, would come Dick's turn.

"You've heard of the new poetry movement. You haven't? Well, it's a lot of young poets that are breaking away from the old forms and doing a lot of good. Well, what I was going to say was that my book is going to start a new prose movement, a sort of renaissance."

"I'm sure it will," beamed Mrs. Gilbert. "I'm *sure* it will. I went to Jenny Martin last Tuesday, the palmist, you know, that every one's *mad* about. I told her my nephew was engaged upon a work and she said she knew I'd be glad to hear that his success would be *extraordinary*. But she'd never seen you or known anything about you—not even your *name*."

Having made the proper noises to express his amazement at this astounding phenomenon, Dick waved her theme by him as though he were an arbitrary traffic policeman, and, so to speak, beckoned forward his own traffic.

"I'm absorbed, Aunt Catherine," he assured her, "I really am. All my friends are joshing me—oh, I see the humor in it and I don't care. I think a person ought to be able to take joshing. But I've got a sort of conviction," he concluded gloomily.

"You're an ancient soul, I always say."

"Maybe I am." Dick had reached the stage where he no longer fought, but submitted. He *must* be an ancient soul, he fancied grotesquely; so old as to be absolutely rotten. However, the reiteration of the phrase still somewhat embarrassed him and sent uncomfortable shivers up his back. He changed the subject.

"Where is my distinguished cousin Gloria?"

"She's on the go somewhere, with some one."

Dick paused, considered, and then, screwing up his face into what was evidently begun as a smile but ended as a terrifying frown, delivered a comment.

"I think my friend Anthony Patch is in love with her."

Mrs. Gilbert started, beamed half a second too late, and breathed her "Really?" in the tone of a detective play-whisper.

"I *think* so," corrected Dick gravely. "She's the first girl I've ever seen him with, so much."

"Well, of course," said Mrs. Gilbert with meticulous carelessness, "Gloria never makes me her confidante. She's very secretive. Between you and me"—she bent forward cautiously, obviously determined that only Heaven and her nephew should share her confession—"between you and me, I'd like to see her settle down."

Dick arose and paced the floor earnestly, a small, active, already rotund young man, his hands thrust unnaturally into his bulging pockets.

"I'm not claiming I'm right, mind you," he assured the infinitely-of-the-hotel steel-engraving which smirked respectably back at him. "I'm saying nothing that I'd want Gloria to know. But I think Mad Anthony is interested—tremendously so. He talks about her constantly. In any one else that'd be a bad sign."

"Gloria is a very young soul—" began Mrs. Gilbert eagerly, but her nephew interrupted with a hurried sentence:

"Gloria'd be a very young nut not to marry him." He stopped and faced her, his expression a battle map of lines and dimples, squeezed and strained to its ultimate show of intensity—this as if to make up by his sincerity for any indiscretion in his words. "Gloria's a wild one, Aunt Catherine. She's uncontrollable. How she's done it I don't know, but lately she's picked up a lot of the funniest friends. She doesn't seem to care. And the men she used to go with around New York were—" He paused for breath.

"Yes-yes-yes," interjected Mrs. Gilbert, with an

anæmic attempt to hide the immense interest with which she listened.

"Well," continued Richard Caramel gravely, "there it is. I mean that the men she went with and the people she went with used to be first rate. Now they aren't."

Mrs. Gilbert blinked very fast—her bosom trembled, inflated, remained so for an instant, and with the exhalation her words flowed out in a torrent.

She knew, she cried in a whisper; oh, yes, mothers see these things. But what could she do? He knew Gloria. He'd seen enough of Gloria to know how hopeless it was to try to deal with her. Gloria had been so spoiled—in a rather complete and unusual way. She had been suckled until she was three, for instance, when she could probably have chewed sticks. Perhaps—one never knew—it was this that had given that health and *hardiness* to her whole personality. And then ever since she was twelve years old she'd had boys about her so thick—oh, so thick one couldn't *move*. At sixteen she began going to dances at preparatory schools, and then came the colleges; and everywhere she went, boys, boys, boys. At first, oh, until she was eighteen there had been so many that it never seemed one any more than the others, but then she began to single them out.

She knew there had been a string of affairs spread over about three years, perhaps a dozen of them altogether. Sometimes the men were undergraduates, sometimes just out of college—they lasted on an average of several months each, with short attractions in between. Once or twice they had endured longer and her mother had hoped she would be engaged, but always a new one came—a new one——

The men? Oh, she made them miserable, literally! There was only one who had kept any sort of dignity, and he had been a mere child, young Carter Kirby, of Kansas City, who was so conceited anyway that he just sailed out on his vanity one afternoon and left for Europe next day with his father. The others had been—wretched. They never seemed to know when she was tired of them, and Gloria had seldom been deliberately unkind. They would keep phoning, writing letters to he trying to see her, making long trips after her around the country. Some of them had confided in Mrs. Gilbert, told her with tears in their eyes that they would never get over Gloria . . . at least two of them had since married, though. . . . But Gloria, it seemed, struck to kill—to this day Mr. Carstairs called up once a week, and sent her flowers which she no longer bothered to refuse.

Several times, twice, at least, Mrs. Gilbert knew it had gone as far as a private engagement—with Tudor Baird and that Holcome boy at Pasadena. She was sure it had, because—this must go no further—she had come in unexpectedly and found Gloria acting, well, very much engaged indeed. She had not spoken to her daughter, of course. She had had a certain sense of delicacy and, besides, each time she had expected an announcement in a few weeks. But the announcement never came; instead, a new man came.

Scenes! Young men walking up and down the library like caged tigers! Young men glaring at each other in the hall as one came and the other left! Young men calling up on the telephone and being hung up upon in desperation! Young men threatening South America! . . . Young men writing the most pathetic letters! (She said nothing to this effect, but Dick fancied that Mrs. Gilbert's eyes had seen some of these letters.)

. . . And Gloria, between tears and laughter, sorry, glad, out of love and in love, miserable, nervous, cool, amidst a great returning of presents, substitution of pictures in immemorial frames, and taking of hot baths and beginning again—with the next.

That state of things continued, assumed an air of permanency. Nothing harmed Gloria or changed her or moved her. And then out of a clear sky one day she informed her mother that undergraduates wearied her. She was absolutely going to no more college dances.

This had begun the change—not so much in her actual habits, for she danced, and had as many "dates" as ever—but they were dates in a different spirit. Previously it had been a sort of pride, a matter of her own vainglory. She had been, probably, the most celebrated and sought-after young beauty in the country. Gloria Gilbert of Kansas City! She had fed on it ruthlessly—enjoying the crowds around her, the manner in which the most desirable men singled her out; enjoying the fierce jealousy of other girls; enjoying the fabulous, not to say scandalous, and, her mother was glad to say, entirely unfounded rumors about her—for instance, that she had gone in the Yale swimming-pool one night in a chiffon evening dress.

And from loving it with a vanity that was almost masculine—it had been in the nature of a triumphant and dazzling career—she became suddenly anæsthetic to it. She retired. She who had dominated countless parties, who had blown fragrantly through many ballrooms to the tender tribute of many eyes, seemed to care no longer. He who fell in love with her now was dismissed utterly, almost angrily. She went listlessly with the most indifferent men. She continually broke engagements, not as in the past from a cool assurance that she was irreproachable, that the man she insulted would return like a domestic animal—but indifferently, without contempt or pride. She rarely stormed at men any more—she yawned at them. She seemed—and it was so strange—she seemed to her mother to be growing cold.

Richard Caramel listened. At first he had remained standing, but as his aunt's discourse waxed in content —it stands here pruned by half, of all side references to the youth of Gloria's soul and to Mrs. Gilbert's own mental distresses—he drew a chair up and attended rigorously as she floated, between tears and plaintive helplessness, down the long story of Gloria's life. When she came to the tale of this last year, a tale of the ends of cigarettes left all over New York in little trays marked "Midnight Frolic" and "Justine Johnson's Little Club," he began nodding his head slowly, then faster and faster, until, as she finished on a staccato note, it was bobbing briskly up and down, absurdly like a doll's wired head, expressing—almost anything.

In a sense Gloria's past was an old story to him. He had followed it with the eyes of a journalist, for he was going to write a book about her some day. But his interests, just at present, were family interests. He wanted to know, in particular, who was this Joseph Bloeckman that he had seen her with several times; and those two girls she was with constantly, "this" Rachael Jerryl and "this" Miss Kane—surely Miss Kane wasn't exactly the sort one would associate with Gloria!

But the moment had passed. Mrs. Gilbert having climbed the hill of exposition was about to glide swiftly down the ski-jump of collapse. Her eyes were like a blue sky seen through two round, red window-casements. The flesh about her mouth was trembling.

And at the moment the door opened, admitting into the room Gloria and the two young ladies lately mentioned.

Two Young Women

"Well!"

"How do you do, Mrs. Gilbert!"

Miss Kane and Miss Jerryl are presented to Mr. Richard Caramel. "This is Dick" (laughter).

"I've heard so much about you," says Miss Kane between a giggle and a shout.

"How do you do," says Miss Jerryl shyly.

Richard Caramel tries to move about as if his figure were better. He is torn between his innate cordiality and the fact that he considers these girls rather common —not at all the Farmover type.

Gloria has disappeared into the bedroom.

"Do sit down," beams Mrs. Gilbert, who is by now quite herself. "Take off your things." Dick is afraid she will make some remark about the age of his soul, but he forgets his qualms in completing a conscientious, novelist's examination of the two young women.

Muriel Kane had originated in a rising family of East Orange. She was short rather than small, and hovered audaciously between plumpness and width. Her hair was black and elaborately arranged. This, in conjunction with her handsome, rather bovine eyes, and her over-red lips, combined to make her resemble Theda Bara, the prominent motion picture actress. People told her constantly that she was a "vampire," and she believed them. She suspected hopefully that they were afraid of her, and she did her utmost under all circumstances to give the impression of danger. An imaginative man could see the red flag that she constantly carried, waving it wildly, beseechingly—and, alas, to little spectacular avail. She was also tremendously timely: she knew the latest songs, all the latest songs—when one of them was played on the phonograph she would rise to her feet and rock her shoulders back and forth and snap her fingers, and if there was no music she would accompany herself by humming.

Her conversation was also timely: "I don't care," she would say, "I should worry and lose my figure"—and again: "I can't make my feet behave when I hear that tune. Oh, baby!"

Her finger-nails were too long and ornate, polished to a pink and unnatural fever. Her clothes were too tight, too stylish, too vivid, her eyes too roguish, her smile too coy. She was almost pitifully overemphasized from head to foot.

The other girl was obviously a more subtle personality. She was an exquisitely dressed Jewess with dark hair and a lovely milky pallor. She seemed shy and vague, and these two qualities accentuated a rather delicate charm that floated about her. Her family were "Episcopalians," owned three smart women's shops along Fifth Avenue, and lived in a magnificent apartment on Riverside Drive. It seemed to Dick, after a few moments, that she was attempting to imitate Gloria—he wondered that people invariably chose inimitable people to imitate.

"We had the most *hectic* time!" Muriel was exclaiming enthusiastically. "There was a crazy woman behind us on the bus. She was absitively, posolutely *nutty!* She kept talking to herself about something she'd like to do to somebody or something. I was *pet*rified, but Gloria simply *wouldn't* get off."

Mrs. Gilbert opened her mouth, properly awed.

"Really?"

"Oh, she was crazy. But we should worry, she didn't hurt us. Ugly! Gracious! The man across from us said her face ought to be on a night-nurse in a home for the blind, and we all *howled*, naturally, so the man tried to pick us up."

Presently Gloria emerged from her bedroom and in unison every eye turned on her. The two girls receded into a shadowy background, unperceived, unmissed.

"We've been talking about you," said Dick quickly, "—your mother and I."

"Well," said Gloria.

A pause—Muriel turned to Dick.

"You're a great writer, aren't you?"

"I'm a writer," he confessed sheepishly.

"I always say," said Muriel earnestly, "that if I ever had time to write down all my experiences it'd make a wonderful book."

Rachael giggled sympathetically; Richard Caramel's bow was almost stately. Muriel continued:

"But I don't see how you can sit down and do it. And poetry! Lordy, I can't make two lines rhyme. Well, I should worry!"

Richard Caramel with difficulty restrained a shout of laughter. Gloria was chewing an amazing gum-drop and staring moodily out the window. Mrs. Gilbert cleared her throat and beamed.

"But you see," she said in a sort of universal exposition, "you're not an ancient soul—like Richard."

The Ancient Soul breathed a gasp of relief—it was out at last.

Then as if she had been considering it for five minutes, Gloria made a sudden announcement:

"I'm going to give a party."

"Oh, can I come?" cried Muriel with facetious daring.

"A dinner. Seven people: Muriel and Rachael and I, and you, Dick, and Anthony, and that man named Noble—I liked him—and Bloeckman."

Muriel and Rachael went into soft and purring ecstasies of enthusiasm. Mrs. Gilbert blinked and beamed. With an air of casualness Dick broke in with a question:

"Who is this fellow Bloeckman, Gloria?"

Scenting a faint hostility, Gloria turned to him.

"Joseph Bloeckman? He's the moving picture man. Vice-president of 'Films Par Excellence.' He and father do a lot of business."

"Oh!"

"Well, will you all come?"

They would all come. A date was arranged within the week. Dick rose, adjusted hat, coat, and muffler, and gave out a general smile.

"By-by," said Muriel, waving her hand gaily, "call me up some time."

Richard Caramel blushed for her.

Deplorable End of the Chevalier O'Keefe

It was Monday and Anthony took Geraldine Burke to luncheon at the Beaux Arts—afterward they went up to his apartment and he wheeled out the little rolling-table that held his supply of liquor, selecting vermouth, gin, and absinthe for a proper stimulant.

Geraldine Burke, usher at Keith's, had been an amusement of several months. She demanded so little that he liked her, for since a lamentable affair with a débutante the preceding summer, when he had discovered that after half a dozen kisses a proposal was expected, he had been wary of girls of his own class. It was only too easy to turn a critical eye on their imperfections: some physical harshness or a general lack of personal delicacy—but a girl who was usher at Keith's was approached with a different attitude. One could tolerate qualities in an intimate valet that would be unforgivable in a mere acquaintance on one's social level.

Geraldine, curled up at the foot of the lounge, considered him with narrow slanting eyes.

"You drink all the time, don't you?" she said suddenly.

"Why, I suppose so," replied Anthony in some surprise. "Don't you?"

"Nope. I go on parties sometimes—you know, about once a week, but I only take two or three drinks. You and your friends keep on drinking all the time. I should think you'd ruin your health."

Anthony was somewhat touched.

"Why, aren't you sweet to worry about me!"

"Well, I do."

"I don't drink so very much," he declared. "Last month I didn't touch a drop for three weeks. And I only get really tight about once a week."

"But you have something to drink every day and you're only twenty-five. Haven't you any ambition? Think what you'll be at forty?"

"I sincerely trust that I won't live that long."

She clicked her tongue with her teeth.

"You cra-azy!" she said as he mixed another cocktail—and then: "Are you any relation to Adam Patch?"

"Yes, he's my grandfather."

"Really?" She was obviously thrilled.

"Absolutely."

"That's funny. My daddy used to work for him."

"He's a queer old man."

"Is he nice?" she demanded.

"Well, in private life he's seldom unnecessarily disagreeable."

"Tell us about him."

"Why," Anthony considered "—he's all shrunken up and he's got the remains of some gray hair that always looks as though the wind were in it. He's very moral."

"He's done a lot of good," said Geraldine with intense gravity.

"Rot!" scoffed Anthony. "He's a pious ass—a chickenbrain."

Her mind left the subject and flitted on.

"Why don't you live with him?"

"Why don't I board in a Methodist parsonage?"

"You cra-azy!"

Again she made a little clicking sound to express disapproval. Anthony thought how moral was this little waif at heart—how completely moral she would still be after the inevitable wave came that would wash her off the sands of respectability.

"Do you hate him?"

"I wonder. I never liked him. You never like people who do things for you."

"Does he hate you?"

"My dear Geraldine," protested Anthony, frowning humorously, "do have another cocktail. I annoy him. If I smoke a cigarette he comes into the room sniffing. He's a prig, a bore, and something of a hypocrite. I probably wouldn't be telling you this if I hadn't had a few drinks, but I don't suppose it matters."

Geraldine was persistently interested. She held her glass, untasted, between finger and thumb and regarded him with eyes in which there was a touch of awe.

"How do you mean a hypocrite?"

"Well," said Anthony impatiently, "maybe he's not. But he doesn't like the things that I like, and so, as far as I'm concerned, he's uninteresting."

"Hm." Her curiosity seemed, at length, satisfied. She sank back into the sofa and sipped her cocktail.

"You're a funny one," she commented thoughtfully. "Does everybody want to marry you because your grandfather is rich?"

"They don't—but I shouldn't blame them if they did. Still, you see, I never intend to marry."

She scorned this.

"You'll fall in love some day. Oh, you will—I know." She nodded wisely.

"It'd be idiotic to be overconfident. That's what ruined the Chevalier O'Keefe."

"Who was he?"

"A creature of my splendid mind. He's my one creation, the Chevalier."

"Cra-a-azy!" she murmured pleasantly, using the clumsy rope-ladder with which she bridged all gaps and climbed after her mental superiors. Subconsciously she felt that it eliminated distances and brought the person whose imagination had eluded her back within range.

"Oh, no!" objected Anthony, "oh, no, Geraldine. You mustn't play the alienist upon the Chevalier. If you feel yourself unable to understand him I won't bring him in. Besides, I should feel a certain uneasiness because of his regrettable reputation."

"I guess I can understand anything that's got any sense to it," answered Geraldine a bit testily.

"In that case there are various episodes in the life of the Chevalier which might prove diverting."

"Well?"

"It was his untimely end that caused me to think of him and made him apropos in the conversation. I hate to introduce him end foremost, but it seems inevitable that the Chevalier must back into your life."

"Well, what about him? Did he die?"

"He did! In this manner. He was an Irishman, Geraldine, a semi-fictional Irishman—the wild sort with a genteel brogue and 'reddish hair.' He was exiled from Erin in the late days of chivalry and, of course, crossed over to France. Now the Chevalier O'Keefe, Geraldine, had, like me, one weakness. He was enormously susceptible to all sorts and conditions of women. Besides being a sentimentalist he was a romantic, a vain fellow, a man of wild passions, a little blind in one eye and almost stone-blind in the other. Now a male roaming the world in this condition is as helpless as a lion without teeth, and in consequence the Chevalier was made utterly miserable for twenty years by a series of women who hated him, used him, bored him, aggravated him, sickened him, spent his money, made a fool of him—in brief, as the world has it, loved him.

"This was bad, Geraldine, and as the Chevalier, save for this one weakness, this exceeding susceptibility, was a man of penetration, he decided that he would rescue himself once and for all from these drains upon him. With this purpose he went to a very famous monastery in Champagne called—well, anachronistically known as St. Voltaire's. It was the rule at St. Voltaire's that no monk could descend to the ground story of the monastery so long as he lived, but should exist engaged in prayer and contemplation in one of the four towers, which were called after the four commandments of the monastery rule: Poverty, Chastity, Obedience, and Silence.

"When the day came that was to witness the Chevalier's farewell to the world he was utterly happy. He gave all his Greek books to his landlady, and his sword he sent in a golden sheath to the King of France, and all his mementos of Ireland he gave to the young Huguenot who sold fish in the street where he lived.

"Then he rode out to St. Voltaire's, slew his horse at the door, and presented the carcass to the monastery cook.

"At five o'clock that night he felt, for the first time, free—forever free from sex. No woman could enter the monastery; no monk could descend below the second story. So as he climbed the winding stair that led to his cell at the very top of the Tower of Chastity he paused for a moment by an open window which looked down fifty feet on to a road below. It was all so beautiful, he thought, this world that he was leaving, the golden shower of sun beating down upon the long fields, the spray of trees in the distance, the vineyards, quiet and green, freshening wide miles before him. He leaned his elbows on the window casement and gazed at the winding road.

"Now, as it happened, Thérèse, a peasant girl of sixteen from a neighboring village, was at that moment passing along this same road that ran in front of the monastery. Five minutes before, the little piece of ribbon which held up the stocking on her pretty left leg had worn through and broken. Being a girl of rare modesty she had thought to wait until she arrived home before repairing it, but it had bothered her to such an extent that she felt she could endure it no longer. So, as she passed the Tower of Chastity, she stopped and with a pretty gesture lifted her skirt—as little as possible, be it said to her credit—to adjust her garter.

"Up in the tower the newest arrival in the ancient monastery of St. Voltaire, as though pulled forward by a gigantic and irresistible hand, leaned from the window. Further he leaned and further until suddenly one of the stones loosened under his weight, broke from its cement with a soft powdery sound—and, first headlong, then head over heels, finally in a vast and impressive revolution tumbled the Chevalier O'Keefe, bound for the hard earth and eternal damnation.

"Thérèse was so much upset by the occurrence that she ran all the way home and for ten years spent an hour a day in secret prayer for the soul of the monk whose neck and vows were simultaneously broken on that unfortunate Sunday afternoon.

"And the Chevalier O'Keefe, being suspected of suicide, was not buried in consecrated ground, but tumbled into a field near by, where he doubtless improved the quality of the soil for many years afterward. Such was the untimely end of a very brave and gallant gentleman. What do you think, Geraldine?"

But Geraldine, lost long before, could only smile roguishly, wave her first finger at him, and repeat her bridge-all, her explain-all:

"Crazy!" she said, "you cra-a-azy!"

His thin face was kindly, she thought, and his eyes quite gentle. She liked him because he was arrogant without being conceited, and because, unlike the men she met about the theatre, he had a horror of being conspicuous. What an odd, pointless story! But she had enjoyed the part about the stocking!

After the fifth cocktail he kissed her, and between laughter and bantering caresses and a half-stifled flare of passion they passed an hour. At four-thirty she claimed an engagement, and going into the bathroom she rearranged her hair. Refusing to let him order her a taxi she stood for a moment in the doorway.

"You *will* get married," she was insisting, "you wait and see."

Anthony was playing with an ancient tennis ball, and he bounced it carefully on the floor several times before he answered with a soupçon of acidity:

"You're a little idiot, Geraldine."

She smiled provokingly.

"Oh, I am, am I? Want to bet?"

"That'd be silly too."

"Oh, it would, would it? Well, I'll just bet you'll marry somebody inside of a year."

Anthony bounced the tennis ball very hard. This was one of his handsome days, she thought; a sort of intensity had displaced the melancholy in his dark eyes.

"Geraldine," he said, at length, "in the first place I have no one I want to marry; in the second place I haven't enough money to support two people; in the third place I am entirely opposed to marriage for people of my type; in the fourth place I have a strong distaste for even the abstract consideration of it."

But Geraldine only narrowed her eyes knowingly, made her clicking sound, and said she must be going. It was late.

"Call me up soon," she reminded him as he kissed her good-by, "you haven't for three weeks, you know."

"I will," he promised fervently.

He shut the door and coming back into the room stood for a moment lost in thought with the tennis-ball still clasped in his hand. There was one of his lonelinesses coming, one of those times when he walked the streets or sat, aimless and depressed, biting a pencil at his desk. It was a self-absorption with no comfort, a demand for expression with no outlet, a sense of time rushing by, ceaselessly and wastefully—assuaged only by that conviction that there was nothing to waste, because all efforts and attainments were equally valueless.

He thought with emotion—aloud, ejaculative, for he was hurt and confused.

"No *idea* of getting married, by *God!*"

Of a sudden he hurled the tennis ball violently across the room, where it barely missed the lamp, and, rebounding here and there for a moment, lay still upon the floor.

Signlight and Moonlight

For her dinner Gloria had taken a table in the Cascades at the Biltmore, and when the men met in the hall outside a little after eight, "that person Bloeckman" was the target of six masculine eyes. He was a stoutening, ruddy Jew of about thirty-five, with an expressive face under smooth sandy hair—and, no doubt, in most business gatherings his personality would have been considered ingratiating. He sauntered up to the three younger men, who stood in a group smoking as they waited for their hostess, and introduced himself with a little too evident assurance—nevertheless it is to be doubted whether he received the intended impression of faint and ironic chill: there was no hint of understanding in his manner.

"You related to Adam J. Patch?" he inquired of Anthony, emitting two slender strings of smoke from nostrils overwide.

Anthony admitted it with the ghost of a smile.

"He's a fine man," pronounced Bloeckman profoundly. "He's a fine example of an American."

"Yes," agreed Anthony, "he certainly is."

—I detest these underdone men, he thought coldly. Boiled looking! Ought to be shoved back in the oven; just one more minute would do it.

Bloeckman squinted at his watch.

"Time these girls were showing up . . ."

—Anthony waited breathlessly; it came——

". . . but then," with a widening smile, "you know how women are."

The three young men nodded; Bloeckman looked casually about him, his eyes resting critically on the ceiling and then passing lower. His expression combined that of a Middle Western farmer appraising his wheat crop and that of an actor wondering whether he is observed—the public manner of all good Americans. As he finished his survey he turned back quickly to the reticent trio, determined to strike to their very heart and core.

"You college men? . . . Harvard, eh. I see the Princeton boys beat you fellows in hockey."

Unfortunate man. He had drawn another blank. They had been three years out and heeded only the big football games. Whether, after the failure of this sally, Mr. Bloeckman would have perceived himself to be in a cynical atmosphere is problematical, for——

Gloria arrived. Muriel arrived. Rachael arrived. After a hurried "Hello, people!" uttered by Gloria and echoed by the other two, the three swept by into the dressing room.

A moment later Muriel appeared in a state of elaborate undress and *crept* toward them. She was in her element: her ebony hair was slicked straight back on her head; her eyes were artificially darkened; she reeked of insistent perfume. She was got up to the best of her ability as a siren, more popularly a "vamp"—a picker up and thrower away of men, an unscrupulous and fundamentally unmoved toyer with affections. Something in the exhaustiveness of her attempt fascinated Maury at first sight—a woman with wide hips affecting a pantherlike litheness! As they waited the extra three minutes for Gloria, and, by polite assumption, for Rachael, he was unable to take his eyes from her. She would turn her head away, lowering her eyelashes and biting her nether lip in an amazing exhibition of coyness. She would rest her hands on her hips and sway from side to side in tune to the music, saying:

"Did you ever hear such perfect ragtime? I just can't make my shoulders behave when I hear that."

Mr. Bloeckman clapped his hands gallantly.

"You ought to be on the stage."

"I'd like to be!" cried Muriel; "will you back me?"

"I sure will."

With becoming modesty Muriel ceased her motions and turned to Maury, asking what he had "seen" this year. He interpreted this as referring to the dramatic world, and they had a gay and exhilarating exchange of titles, after this manner:

MURIEL: Have you seen "Peg o' My Heart"?

MAURY: No, I haven't.

MURIEL: (*Eagerly*) It's wonderful! You want to see it.

MAURY: Have you seen "Omar, the Tentmaker"?

MURIEL: No, but I hear it's wonderful. I'm very anxious to see it. Have you seen "Fair and Warmer"?

MAURY: (*Hopefully*) Yes.

MURIEL: I don't think it's very good. It's trashy.

MAURY: (*Faintly*) Yes, that's true.

MURIEL: But I went to "Within the Law" last night and I thought it was fine. Have you seen "The Little Café"? . . .

This continued until they ran out of plays. Dick, meanwhile, turned to Mr. Bloeckman, determined to extract what gold he could from this unpromising load.

"I hear all the new novels are sold to the moving pictures as soon as they come out."

"That's true. Of course the main thing in a moving picture is a strong story."

"Yes, I suppose so."

"So many novels are all full of talk and psychology. Of course those aren't as valuable to us. It's impossible to make much of that interesting on the screen."

"You want plots first," said Richard brilliantly.

"Of course. Plots first—" He paused, shifted his gaze. His pause spread, included the others with all the authority of a warning finger. Gloria followed by Rachael was coming out of the dressing room.

Among other things it developed during dinner that Joseph Bloeckman never danced, but spent the music time watching the others with the bored tolerance of an elder among children. He was a dignified man and a proud one. Born in Munich he had begun his American career as a peanut vender with a travelling circus. At eighteen he was a side show ballyhoo; later, the manager of the side show, and, soon after, the proprietor of a second-class vaudeville house. Just when the moving picture had passed out of the stage of a curiosity and become a promising industry he was an ambitious young man of twenty-six with some money to invest, nagging financial ambitions and a good working knowledge of the popular show business. That had been nine years before. The moving picture industry had borne him up with it where it threw off dozens of men with more financial ability, more imagination, and more practical ideas . . . and now he sat here and contemplated the immortal Gloria for whom young Stuart Holcome had gone from New York to Pasadena—watched her, and knew that presently she would cease dancing and come back to sit on his left hand.

He hoped she would hurry. The oysters had been standing some minutes.

Meanwhile Anthony, who had been placed on Gloria's left hand, was dancing with her, always in a certain fourth of the floor. This, had there been stags, would have been a delicate tribute to the girl, meaning "Damn you, don't cut in!" It was very consciously intimate.

"Well," he began, looking down at her, "you look mighty sweet to-night."

She met his eyes over the horizontal half foot that separated them.

"Thank you—Anthony."

"In fact you're uncomfortably beautiful," he added. There was no smile this time.

"And you're very charming."

"Isn't this nice?" he laughed. "We actually approve of each other."

"Don't you, usually?" She had caught quickly at his remark, as she always did at any unexplained allusion to herself, however faint.

He lowered his voice, and when he spoke there was in it no more than a wisp of badinage.

"Does a priest approve the Pope?"

"I don't know—but that's probably the vaguest compliment I ever received."

"Perhaps I can muster a few bromides."

"Well, I wouldn't have you strain yourself. Look at Muriel! Right here next to us."

He glanced over his shoulder. Muriel was resting her brilliant cheek against the lapel of Maury Noble's dinner coat and her powdered left arm was apparently twisted around his head. One was impelled to wonder why she failed to seize the nape of his neck with her hand. Her eyes, turned ceiling-ward, rolled largely back and forth; her hips swayed, and as she danced she kept up a constant low singing. This at first seemed to be a translation of the song into some foreign tongue but became eventually apparent as an attempt to fill out the metre of the song with the only words she knew—the words of the title—

"He's a rag-picker,
A rag-picker,
A rag-time picking man,
Rag-picking, picking, pick, pick,
Rag-pick, pick, pick."

—and so on, into phrases still more strange and barbaric. When she caught the amused glances of Anthony and Gloria she acknowledged them only with a faint smile and a half-closing of her eyes, to indicate that the music entering into her soul had put her into an ecstatic and exceedingly seductive trance.

The music ended and they returned to their table, whose solitary but dignified occupant arose and tendered each of them a smile so ingratiating that it was as if he were shaking their hands and congratulating them on a brilliant performance.

"Blockhead never will dance! I think he has a wooden leg," remarked Gloria to the table at large. The three young men started and the gentleman referred to winced perceptibly.

This was the one rough spot in the course of Bloeckman's acquaintance with Gloria. She relentlessly punned on his name. First it had been "Block-house," lately, the more invidious "Blockhead." He had requested with a strong undertone of irony that she use his first name, and this she had done obediently several times—then slipping, helpless, repentant but dissolved in laughter, back into "Blockhead."

It was a very sad and thoughtless thing.

"I'm afraid Mr. Bloeckman thinks we're a frivolous crowd," sighed Muriel, waving a balanced oyster in his direction.

"He has that air," murmured Rachael. Anthony tried to remember whether she had said anything before. He thought not. It was her initial remark.

Mr. Bloeckman suddenly cleared his throat and said in a loud, distinct voice:

"On the contrary. When a man speaks he's merely tradition. He has at best a few thousand years back of him. But woman, why, she is the miraculous mouthpiece of posterity."

In the stunned pause that followed this astounding remark, Anthony choked suddenly on an oyster and hurried his napkin to his face. Rachael and Muriel raised a mild if somewhat surprised laugh, in which Dick and Maury joined, both of them red in the face and restraining uproariousness with the most apparent difficulty.

"—My God!" thought Anthony. "It's a subtitle from one of his movies. The man's memorized it!"

Gloria alone made no sound. She fixed Mr. Bloeckman with a glance of silent reproach.

"Well, for the love of Heaven! Where on earth did you dig that up?"

Bloeckman looked at her uncertainly, not sure of her intention. But in a moment he recovered his poise and assumed the bland and consciously tolerant smile of an intellectual among spoiled and callow youth.

The soup came up from the kitchen—but simultaneously the orchestra leader came up from the bar, where he had absorbed the tone color inherent in a seidel of beer. So the soup was left to cool during the delivery of a ballad entitled "Everything's at Home Except Your Wife."

Then the champagne—and the party assumed more amusing proportions. The men, except Richard Caramel, drank freely; Gloria and Muriel sipped a glass apiece; Rachael Jerryl took none. They sat out the waltzes but danced to everything else—all except Gloria, who seemed to tire after a while and preferred to sit smoking at the table, her eyes now lazy, now eager, according to whether she listened to Bloeckman or watched a pretty woman among the dancers. Several times Anthony wondered what Bloeckman was telling her. He was chewing a cigar back and forth in his mouth, and had expanded after dinner to the extent of violent gestures.

Ten o'clock found Gloria and Anthony beginning a dance. Just as they were out of ear-shot of the table she said in a low voice:

"Dance over by the door. I want to go down to the drug-store."

Obediently Anthony guided her through the crowd in the designated direction; in the hall she left him for a moment, to reappear with a cloak over her arm.

"I want some gum-drops," she said, humorously apologetic; "you can't guess what for this time. It's just that I want to bite my finger-nails, and I will if I don't get some gum-drops." She sighed, and resumed as they stepped into the empty elevator: "I've been biting 'em all day. A bit nervous, you see. Excuse the pun. It was unintentional—the words just arranged themselves. Gloria Gilbert, the female wag."

Reaching the ground floor they naïvely avoided the hotel candy counter, descended the wide front staircase, and walking through several corridors found a drug-store in the Grand Central Station. After an intense examination of the perfume counter she made her purchase. Then on some mutual unmentioned impulse they strolled, arm in arm, not in the direction from which they had come, but out into Forty-third Street.

The night was alive with thaw; it was so nearly warm that a breeze drifting low along the sidewalk brought to Anthony a vision of an unhoped-for hyacinthine spring. Above in the blue oblong of sky, around them in the caress of the drifting air, the illusion of a new season carried relief from the stiff and breathed-over atmosphere they had left, and for a hushed moment the traffic sounds and the murmur of water flowing in the gutters seemed an illusive and rarefied prolongation of that music to which they had lately danced. When Anthony spoke it was with surety that his words came from something breathless and desirous that the night had conceived in their two hearts.

"Let's take a taxi and ride around a bit!" he suggested, without looking at her.

Oh, Gloria, Gloria!

A cab yawned at the curb. As it moved off like a boat on a labyrinthine ocean and lost itself among the inchoate night masses of the great buildings, among the now stilled, now strident, cries and clangings, Anthony put his arm around the girl, drew her over to him and kissed her damp, childish mouth.

She was silent. She turned her face up to him, pale under the wisps and patches of light that trailed in like moonshine through a foliage. Her eyes were gleaming ripples in the white lake of her face; the shadows of her hair bordered the brow with a persuasive unintimate dusk. No love was there, surely; nor the imprint of any love. Her beauty was cool as this damp breeze, as the moist softness of her own lips.

"You're such a swan in this light," he whispered after a moment. There were silences as murmurous as sound. There were pauses that seemed about to shatter and were only to be snatched back to oblivion by the tightening of his arms about her and the sense that she was resting there as a caught, gossamer feather, drifted in out of the dark. Anthony laughed, noiselessly and exultantly, turning his face up and away from her, half in an overpowering rush of triumph, half lest her sight of him should spoil the splendid immobility of her expression. Such a kiss—it was a flower held against the face, never to be described, scarcely to be remembered; as though her beauty were giving off emanations of itself which settled transiently and already dissolving upon his heart.

. . . The buildings fell away in melted shadows; this was the Park now, and after a long while the great white ghost of the Metropolitan Museum moved majestically past, echoing sonorously to the rush of the cab.

"Why, Gloria! Why, Gloria!"

Her eyes appeared to regard him out of many thousand years: all emotion she might have felt, all words she might have uttered, would have seemed inadequate beside the adequacy of her silence, ineloquent against the eloquence of her beauty—and of her body, close to him, slender and cool.

"Tell him to turn around," she murmured, "and drive pretty fast going back. . . ."

Up in the supper room the air was hot. The table, littered with napkins and ash-trays, was old and stale. It was between dances as they entered, and Muriel Kane looked up with roguishness extraordinary.

"Well, where have *you* been?"

"To call up mother," answered Gloria coolly. "I promised her I would. Did we miss a dance?"

Then followed an incident that though slight in itself Anthony had cause to reflect on many years afterward. Joseph Bloeckman, leaning well back in his chair, fixed him with a peculiar glance, in which several emotions were curiously and inextricably mingled. He did not greet Gloria except by rising, and he immediately resumed a conversation with Richard Caramel about the influence of literature on the moving pictures.

Magic

The stark and unexpected miracle of a night fades out with the lingering death of the last stars and the premature birth of the first newsboys. The flame retreats to some remote and platonic fire; the white heat has gone from the iron and the glow from the coal.

Along the shelves of Anthony's library, filling a wall amply, crept a chill and insolent pencil of sunlight touching with frigid disapproval Thérèse of France and Ann the Superwoman, Jenny of the Orient Ballet and Zuleika the Conjurer—and Hoosier Cora—then down a shelf and into the years, resting pityingly on the over-invoked shades of Helen, Thaïs, Salome, and Cleopatra.

Anthony, shaved and bathed, sat in his most deeply

cushioned chair and watched it until at the steady rising of the sun it lay glinting for a moment on the silk ends of the rug—and went out.

It was ten o'clock. The Sunday Times, scattered about his feet, proclaimed by rotogravure and editorial, by social revelation and sporting sheet, that the world had been tremendously engrossed during the past week in the business of moving toward some splendid if somewhat indeterminate goal. For his part Anthony had been once to his grandfather's, twice to his broker's, and three times to his tailor's—and in the last hour of the week's last day he had kissed a very beautiful and charming girl.

When he reached home his imagination had been teeming with high-pitched, unfamiliar dreams. There was suddenly no question on his mind, no eternal problem for a solution and re-solution. He had experienced an emotion that was neither mental nor physical, nor merely a mixture of the two, and the love of life absorbed him for the present to the exclusion of all else. He was content to let the experiment remain isolated and unique.

Almost impersonally he was convinced that no woman he had ever met compared in any way with Gloria. She was deeply herself; she was immeasurably sincere—of these things he was certain. Beside her the two dozen schoolgirls and débutantes, young married women and waifs and strays whom he had known were so many *females*, in the word's most contemptuous sense, breeders and bearers, exuding still that faintly odorous atmosphere of the cave and the nursery.

So far as he could see, she had neither submitted to any will of his nor caressed his vanity—except as her pleasure in his company was a caress. Indeed he had no reason for thinking she had given him aught that she did not give to others. This was as it should be. The idea of an entanglement growing out of the evening was as remote as it would have been repugnant. And she had disclaimed and buried the incident with a decisive untruth. Here were two young people with fancy enough to distinguish a game from its reality—who by the very casualness with which they met and passed on would proclaim themselves unharmed.

Having decided this he went to the phone and called up the Plaza Hotel.

Gloria was out. Her mother knew neither where she had gone nor when she would return.

It was somehow at this point that the first wrongness in the case asserted itself. There was an element of callousness, almost of indecency, in Gloria's absence from home. He suspected that by going out she had intrigued him into a disadvantage. Returning she would find his name, and smile. Most discreetly! He should have waited a few hours in order to drive home the utter inconsequence with which he regarded the incident. What an asinine blunder! She would think he considered himself particularly favored. She would think he was reacting with the most inept intimacy to a quite trivial episode.

He remembered that during the previous month his janitor, to whom he had delivered a rather muddled lecture on the "brother-hoove man," had come up next day and, on the basis of what had happened the night before, seated himself in the window seat for a cordial and chatty half-hour. Anthony wondered in horror if Gloria would regard him as he had regarded that man. Him—Anthony Patch! Horror!

It never occurred to him that he was a passive thing, acted upon by an influence above and beyond Gloria, that he was merely the sensitive plate on which the photograph was made. Some gargantuan photographer had focussed the camera on Gloria and *snap!*—the poor plate could but develop, confined like all things to its nature.

But Anthony, lying upon his couch and staring at the orange lamp, passed his thin fingers incessantly through his dark hair and made new symbols for the hours. She was in a shop now, it seemed, moving lithely among the velvets and the furs, her own dress making, as she walked, a debonair rustle in that world of silken rustles and cool soprano laughter and scents of many slain but living flowers. The Minnies and Pearls and Jewels and Jennies would gather round her like courtiers, bearing wispy frailties of Georgette crepe, delicate chiffon to echo her cheeks in faint pastel, milky lace to rest in pale disarray against her neck—damask was used but to cover priests and divans in these days, and cloth of Samarand was remembered only by the romantic poets.

She would go elsewhere after a while, tilting her head a hundred ways under a hundred bonnets, seeking in vain for mock cherries to match her lips or plumes that were graceful as her own supple body.

Noon would come—she would hurry along Fifth Avenue, a Nordic Ganymede, her fur coat swinging fashionably with her steps, her cheeks redder by a stroke of the wind's brush, her breath a delightful mist upon the bracing air—and the doors of the Ritz would revolve, the crowd would divide, fifty masculine eyes would start, stare, as she gave back forgotten dreams to the husbands of many obese and comic women.

One o'clock. With her fork she would tantalize the heart of an adoring artichoke, while her escort served himself up in the thick, dripping sentences of an enraptured man.

Four o'clock: her little feet moving to melody, her face distinct in the crowd, her partner happy as a petted puppy and mad as the immemorial hatter. . . . Then—then night would come drifting down and perhaps another damp. The signs would spill their light into the street. Who knew? No wiser than he, they haply sought to recapture that picture done in cream and shadow they had seen on the hushed Avenue the night before. And they might, ah, they might! A thousand taxis would yawn at a thousand corners, and only to him was that kiss forever lost and done. In a thousand guises Thaïs would hail a cab and turn up her face for loving. And her pallor would be virginal and lovely, and her kiss chaste as the moon. . . .

He sprang excitedly to his feet. How inappropriate that she should be out! He had realized at last what he wanted—to kiss her again, to find rest in her great immobility. She was the end of all restlessness, all malcontent.

Anthony dressed and went out, as he should have done long before, and down to Richard Caramel's room to hear the last revision of the last chapter of "The Demon Lover." He did not call Gloria again until six. He did not find her in until eight and—oh, climax of anticlimaxes!—she could give him no engagement until Tuesday afternoon. A broken piece of gutta-percha clattered to the floor as he banged up the phone.

Black Magic

Tuesday was freezing cold. He called at a bleak two o'clock and as they shook hands he wondered confusedly whether he had ever kissed her; it was almost unbelievable—he seriously doubted if she remembered it.

"I called you four times on Sunday," he told her.

"Did you?"

There was surprise in her voice and interest in her expression. Silently he cursed himself for having told her. He might have known her pride did not deal in such petty triumphs. Even then he had not guessed at the truth—that never having had to worry about men she had seldom used the wary subterfuges, the playings out and haulings in, that were the stock in trade of her sisterhood. When she liked a man, that was trick enough. Did she think she loved him—there was an ultimate and fatal thrust. Her charm endlessly preserved itself.

"I was anxious to see you," he said simply. "I want to talk to you—I mean really talk, somewhere where we can be alone. May I?"

"What do you mean?"

He swallowed a sudden lump of panic. He felt that she knew what he wanted.

"I mean, not at a tea table," he said.

"Well, all right, but not to-day. I want to get some exercise. Let's walk!"

It was bitter and raw. All the evil hate in the mad heart of February was wrought into the forlorn and icy wind that cut its way cruelly across Central Park and down along Fifth Avenue. It was almost impossible to talk, and discomfort made him distracted, so much so that he turned at Sixty-first Street to find that she was no longer beside him. He looked around. She was forty feet in the rear standing motionless, her face half hidden in her fur coat collar, moved either by anger or laughter—he could not determine which. He started back.

"Don't let me interrupt your walk!" she called.

"I'm mighty sorry," he answered in confusion. "Did I go too fast?"

"I'm cold," she announced. "I want to go home. And you walk too fast."

"I'm very sorry."

Side by side they started for the Plaza. He wished he could see her face.

"Men don't usually get so absorbed in themselves when they're with me."

"I'm sorry."

"That's very interesting."

"It *is* rather too cold to walk," he said, briskly, to hide his annoyance.

She made no answer and he wondered if she would dismiss him at the hotel entrance. She walked in without speaking, however, and to the elevator, throwing him a single remark as she entered it:

"You'd better come up."

He hesitated for the fraction of a moment.

"Perhaps I'd better call some other time."

"Just as you say." Her words were murmured as an aside. The main concern of life was the adjusting of some stray wisps of hair in the elevator mirror. Her cheeks were brilliant, her eyes sparkled—she had never seemed so lovely, so exquisitely to be desired.

Despising himself, he found that he was walking down the tenth-floor corridor a subservient foot behind her; was in the sitting room while she disappeared to shed her furs. Something had gone wrong—in his own eyes he had lost a shred of dignity; in an unpremeditated yet significant encounter he had been completely defeated.

However, by the time she reappeared in the sitting-room he had explained himself to himself with sophistic satisfaction. After all he had done the strongest thing, he thought. He had wanted to come up, he had come. Yet what happened later on that afternoon must be traced to the indignity he had experienced in the elevator; the girl was worrying him intolerably, so much so that when she came out he involuntarily drifted into criticism.

"Who's this Bloeckman, Gloria?"

"A business friend of father's."

"Odd sort of fellow!"

"He doesn't like you either," she said with a sudden smile.

Anthony laughed.

"I'm flattered at his notice. He evidently considers me a—" He broke off with "Is he in love with you?"

"I don't know."

"The deuce you don't," he insisted. "Of course he is. I remember the look he gave me when we got back to the table. He'd probably have had me quietly assaulted by a delegation of movie supes if you hadn't invented that phone call."

"He didn't mind. I told him afterward what really happened."

"You told him!"

"He asked me."

"I don't like that very well," he remonstrated.

She laughed again.

"Oh, you don't?"

"What business is it of his?"

"None. That's why I told him."

Anthony in a turmoil bit savagely at his mouth.

"Why should I lie?" she demanded directly. "I'm not ashamed of anything I do. It happened to interest him to know that I kissed you, and I happened to be in a good humor, so I satisfied his curiosity by a simple and precise 'yes.' Being rather a sensible man, after his fashion, he dropped the subject."

"Except to say that he hated me."

"Oh, it worries you? Well, if you must probe this stupendous matter to its depths he didn't say he hated you. I simply know he does."

"It doesn't wor——"

"Oh, let's drop it!" she cried spiritedly. "It's a most uninteresting matter to me."

With a tremendous effort Anthony made his acquiescence a twist of subject, and they drifted into an ancient question-and-answer game concerned with each other's pasts, gradually warming as they discovered the age-old, immemorial resemblances in tastes and ideas. They said things that were more revealing than they intended—but each pretended to accept the other at face, or rather word, value.

The growth of intimacy is like that. First one gives off his best picture, the bright and finished product mended with bluff and falsehood and humor. Then more details are required and one paints a second portrait, and a third—before long the best lines cancel out—and the secret is exposed at last; the planes of the pictures have intermingled and given us away, and though we paint and paint we can no longer sell a picture. We must be satisfied with hoping that such fatuous accounts of ourselves as we make to our wives and children and business associates are accepted as true.

"It seems to me," Anthony was saying earnestly, "that the position of a man with neither necessity nor ambition is unfortunate. Heaven knows it'd be pathetic of me to be sorry for myself—yet, sometimes I envy Dick."

Her silence was encouragement. It was as near as she ever came to an intentional lure.

"—And there used to be dignified occupations for a gentleman who had leisure, things a little more constructive than filling up the landscape with smoke or juggling some one else's money. There's science, of course: sometimes I wish I'd taken a good foundation, say at Boston Tech. But now, by golly, I'd have to sit down for two years and struggle through the fundamentals of physics and chemistry."

She yawned.

"I've told you I don't know what anybody ought to do," she said ungraciously, and at her indifference his rancor was born again.

"Aren't you interested in anything except yourself?"

"Not much."

He glared; his growing enjoyment in the conversation was ripped to shreds. She had been irritable and vindictive all day, and it seemed to him that for this moment he hated her hard selfishness. He stared morosely at the fire.

Then a strange thing happened. She turned to him and smiled, and as he saw her smile every rag of anger and hurt vanity dropped from him—as though his very moods were but the outer ripples of her own, as though emotion rose no longer in his breast unless she saw fit to pull an omnipotent controlling thread.

He moved closer and taking her hand pulled her ever so gently toward him until she half lay against his shoulder. She smiled up at him as he kissed her.

"Gloria," he whispered very softly. Again she had made a magic, subtle and pervading as a spilt perfume, irresistible and sweet.

Afterward, neither the next day nor after many years, could he remember the important things of that afternoon. Had she been moved? In his arms had she spoken a little—or at all? What measure of enjoyment had she taken in his kisses? And had she at any time lost herself ever so little?

Oh, for him there was no doubt. He had risen and paced the floor in sheer ecstasy. That such a girl should be; should poise curled in a corner of the couch like a swallow newly landed from a clean swift flight, watching him with inscrutable eyes. He would stop his pacing and, half shy each time at first, drop his arm around her and find her kiss.

She was fascinating, he told her. He had never met any one like her before. He besought her jauntily but earnestly to send him away; he didn't want to fall in love. He wasn't coming to see her any more—already she had haunted too many of his ways.

What delicious romance! His true reaction was neither fear nor sorrow—only this deep delight in being with her that colored the banality of his words and made the mawkish seem sad and the posturing seem wise. He *would* come back—eternally. He should have known!

"This is all. It's been very rare to have known you, very strange and wonderful. But this wouldn't do—and wouldn't last." As he spoke there was in his heart that tremulousness that we take for sincerity in ourselves.

Afterward he remembered one reply of hers to something he had asked her. He remembered it in this form—perhaps he had unconsciously arranged and polished it:

"A woman should be able to kiss a man beautifully and romantically without any desire to be either his wife or his mistress."

As always when he was with her she seemed to grow gradually older until at the end ruminations too deep for words would be wintering in her eyes.

An hour passed, and the fire leaped up in little ecstasies as though its fading life was sweet. It was five now, and the clock over the mantel became articulate in sound. Then as if a brutish sensibility in him was reminded by those thin, tinny beats that the petals were falling from the flowered afternoon, Anthony pulled her quickly to her feet and held her helpless, without breath, in a kiss that was neither a game nor a tribute.

Her arms fell to her side. In an instant she was free.

"Don't!" she said quietly. "I don't want that."

She sat down on the far side of the lounge and gazed straight before her. A frown had gathered between her eyes. Anthony sank down beside her and closed his hand over hers. It was lifeless and unresponsive.

"Why, Gloria!" He made a motion as if to put his arm about her but she drew away.

"I don't want that," she repeated.

"I'm very sorry," he said, a little impatiently. "I—I didn't know you made such fine distinctions."

She did not answer.

"Won't you kiss me, Gloria?"

"I don't want to." It seemed to him she had not moved for hours.

"A sudden change, isn't it?" Annoyance was growing in his voice.

"Is it?" She appeared uninterested. It was almost as though she were looking at some one else.

"Perhaps I'd better go."

No reply. He rose and regarded her angrily, uncertainly. Again he sat down.

"Gloria, Gloria, won't you kiss me?"

"No." Her lips, parting for the word, had just faintly stirred.

Again he got to his feet, this time with less decision, less confidence.

"Then I'll go."

Silence.

"All right—I'll go."

He was aware of a certain irremediable lack of originality in his remarks. Indeed he felt that the whole atmosphere had grown oppressive. He wished she would speak, rail at him, cry out upon him, anything but this pervasive and chilling silence. He cursed himself for a weak fool; his clearest desire was to move her, to hurt her, to see her wince. Helplessly, involuntarily, he erred again.

"If you're tired of kissing me I'd better go."

He saw her lips curl slightly and his last dignity left him. She spoke, at length:

"I believe you've made that remark several times before."

He looked about him immediately, saw his hat and coat on a chair—blundered into them, during an intolerable moment. Looking again at the couch he perceived that she had not turned, not even moved. With a shaken, immediately regretted "good-by" he went quickly but without dignity from the room.

For over a moment Gloria made no sound. Her lips were still curled; her glance was straight, proud, remote. Then her eyes blurred a little, and she murmured three words half aloud to the death-bound fire:

"Good-by, you ass!" she said.

Panic

The man had had the hardest blow of his life. He knew at last what he wanted, but in finding it out it seemed that he had put it forever beyond his grasp. He reached home in misery, dropped into an armchair without even removing his overcoat, and sat there for over an hour, his mind racing the paths of fruitless and wretched self-absorption. She had sent him away! That was the reiterated burden of his despair. Instead of seizing the girl and holding her by sheer strength until she became passive to his desire, instead of beating down her will by the force of his own, he had walked, defeated and powerless, from her door, with the corners of his mouth drooping and what force there might have been in his grief and rage hidden behind the manner of a whipped schoolboy. At one minute she had liked him tremendously—ah, she had nearly loved him. In the next he had become a thing of indifference to her, an insolent and efficiently humiliated man.

He had no great self-reproach—some, of course, but there were other things dominant in him now, far more urgent. He was not so much in love with Gloria as mad for her. Unless he could have her near him again, kiss her, hold her close and acquiescent, he wanted nothing more from life. By her three minutes of utter unwavering indifference the girl had lifted herself from a high but somehow casual position in his mind, to be instead his complete preoccupation. However much his wild thoughts varied between a passionate desire for her kisses and an equally passionate craving to hurt and mar her, the residue of his mind craved in finer fashion to possess the triumphant soul that had shone through those three minutes. She was beautiful—but especially she was without mercy. He must own that strength that could send him away.

At present no such analysis was possible to Anthony. His clarity of mind, all those endless resources which he thought his irony had brought him were swept aside. Not only for that night but for the days and weeks that followed his books were to be but furniture and his friends only people who lived and walked in a nebulous outer world from which he was trying to escape—that world was cold and full of bleak wind, and for a little while he had seen into a warm house where fires shone.

About midnight he began to realize that he was hungry. He went down into Fifty-second Street, where it was so cold that he could scarcely see; the moisture froze on his lashes and in the corners of his lips. Everywhere dreariness had come down from the north, settling upon the thin and cheerless street, where black bundled figures blacker still against the night, moved stumbling along the sidewalk through the shrieking wind, sliding their feet cautiously ahead as though they were on skis. Anthony turned over toward Sixth Avenue, so absorbed in his thoughts as not to notice that several passers-by had stared at him. His overcoat was wide open, and the wind was biting in, hard and full of merciless death.

. . . After a while a waitress spoke to him, a fat waitress with black-rimmed eye-glasses from which dangled a long black cord.

"Order, please!"

Her voice, he considered, was unnecessarily loud. He looked up resentfully.

"You wanna order or doncha?"

"Of course," he protested.

"Well, I ast you three times. This ain't no restroom."

He glanced at the big clock and discovered with a start that it was after two. He was down around Thirtieth Street somewhere, and after a moment he found and translated the

CHILD'S

in a white semicircle of letters upon the glass front. The place was inhabited sparsely by three or four bleak and half-frozen night-hawks.

"Give me some bacon and eggs and coffee, please."

The waitress bent upon him a last disgusted glance and, looking ludicrously intellectual in her corded glasses, hurried away.

God! Gloria's kisses had been such flowers. He remembered as though it had been years ago the low freshness of her voice, the beautiful lines of her body shining through her clothes, her face lily-colored under the lamps of the street—under the lamps.

Misery struck at him again, piling a sort of terror upon the ache and yearning. He had lost her. It was true—no denying it, no softening it. But a new idea had seared his sky—what of Bloeckman! What would happen now? There was a wealthy man, middle-aged enough to be tolerant with a beautiful wife, to baby her whims and indulge her unreason, to wear her as she perhaps wished to be worn—a bright flower in his buttonhole, safe and secure from the things she feared. He felt that she had been playing with the idea of marrying Bloeckman, and it was well possible that this disappointment in Anthony might throw her on sudden impulse into Bloeckman's arms.

The idea drove him childishly frantic. He wanted to kill Bloeckman and make him suffer for his hideous presumption. He was saying this over and over to himself with his teeth tight shut, and a perfect orgy of hate and fright in his eyes.

But, behind this obscene jealousy, Anthony was in love at last, profoundly and truly in love, as the word goes between man and woman.

His coffee appeared at his elbow and gave off for a certain time a gradually diminishing wisp of steam. The night manager, seated at his desk, glanced at the motionless figure alone at the last table, and then with a sigh moved down upon him just as the hour hand crossed the figure three on the big clock.

Wisdom

After another day the turmoil subsided and Anthony began to exercise a measure of reason. He was in love—he cried it passionately to himself. The things that a week before would have seemed insuperable obstacles, his limited income, his desire to be irresponsible and independent, had in this forty hours become the merest chaff before the wind of his infatuation. If he did not marry her his life would be a feeble parody on his own adolescence. To be able to face people and to endure the constant reminder of Gloria that all existence had become, it was necessary for him to have hope. So he built hope desperately and tenaciously out of the stuff of his dream, a hope flimsy enough, to be sure, a hope that was cracked and dissipated a dozen times a day, a hope mothered by mockery, but, nevertheless, a hope that would be brawn and sinew to his self-respect.

Out of this developed a spark of wisdom, a true perception of his own from out the effortless past.

"Memory is short," he thought.

So very short. At the crucial point the Trust President is on the stand, a potential criminal needing but one push to be a jailbird, scorned by the upright for leagues around. Let him be acquitted—and in a year all is forgotten. "Yes, he did have some trouble once, just a technicality, I believe." Oh, memory is very short!

Anthony had seen Gloria altogether about a dozen times, say two dozen hours. Supposing he left her alone for a month, made no attempt to see her or speak to her, and avoided every place where she might possibly be. Wasn't it possible, the more possible because she had never loved him, that at the end of that time the rush of events would efface his personality from her conscious mind, and with his personality his offense and humiliation? She would forget, for there would be other men. He winced. The implication struck out at him—other men. Two months—God! Better three weeks, two weeks——

He thought this the second evening after the catastrophe when he was undressing, and at this point he threw himself down on the bed and lay there, trembling very slightly and looking at the top of the canopy.

Two weeks—that was worse than no time at all. In two weeks he would approach her much as he would have to now, without personality or confidence—remaining still the man who had gone too far and then for a period that in time was but a moment but in fact an eternity, whined. No, two weeks was too short a time. Whatever poignancy there had been for her in that afternoon must have time to dull. He must give her a period when the incident should fade, and then a new period when she should gradually begin to think of him, no matter how dimly, with a true perspective that would remember his pleasantness as well as his humiliation.

He fixed, finally, on six weeks as approximately the interval best suited to his purpose, and on a desk calendar he marked the days off, finding that it would fall on the ninth of April. Very well, on that day he would phone and ask her if he might call. Until then—silence.

After his decision a gradual improvement was manifest. He had taken at least a step in the direction to which hope pointed, and he realized that the less he brooded upon her the better he would be able to give the desired impression when they met.

In another hour he fell into a deep sleep.

The Interval

Nevertheless, though, as the days passed, the glory of her hair dimmed perceptibly for him and in a year of separation might have departed completely, the six weeks held many abominable days. He dreaded the sight of Dick and Maury, imagining wildly that they knew all—but when the three met it was Richard

Caramel and not Anthony who was the centre of attention; "The Demon Lover" had been accepted for immediate publication. Anthony felt that from now on he moved apart. He no longer craved the warmth and security of Maury's society which had cheered him no further back than November. Only Gloria could give that now and no one else ever again. So Dick's success rejoiced him only casually and worried him not a little. It meant that the world was going ahead—writing and reading and publishing—and living. And he wanted the world to wait motionless and breathless for six weeks—while Gloria forgot.

Two Encounters

His greatest satisfaction was in Geraldine's company. He took her once to dinner and the theatre and entertained her several times in his apartment. When he was with her she absorbed him, not as Gloria had, but quieting those erotic sensibilities in him that worried over Gloria. It didn't matter how he kissed Geraldine. A kiss was a kiss—to be enjoyed to the utmost for its short moment. To Geraldine things belonged in definite pigeonholes: a kiss was one thing, anything further was quite another; a kiss was all right; the other things were "bad."

When half the interval was up two incidents occurred on successive days that upset his increasing calm and caused a temporary relapse.

The first was—he saw Gloria. It was a short meeting. Both bowed. Both spoke, yet neither heard the other. But when it was over Anthony read down a column of The Sun three times in succession without understanding a single sentence.

One would have thought Sixth Avenue a safe street! Having forsworn his barber at the Plaza he went around the corner one morning to be shaved, and while waiting his turn he took off coat and vest, and with his soft collar open at the neck stood near the front of the shop. The day was an oasis in the cold desert of March and the sidewalk was cheerful with a population of strolling sun-worshippers. A stout woman upholstered in velvet, her flabby cheeks too much massaged, swirled by with her poodle straining at its leash—the effect being given of a tug bringing in an ocean liner. Just behind them a man in a striped blue suit, walking slue-footed in white-spatted feet, grinned at the sight and catching Anthony's eye, winked through the glass. Anthony laughed, thrown immediately into that humor in which men and women were graceless and absurd phantasms, grotesquely curved and rounded in a rectangular world of their own building. They inspired the same sensations in him as did those strange and monstrous fish who inhabit the esoteric world of green in the aquarium.

Two more strollers caught his eye casually, a man and a girl—then in a horrified instant the girl resolved herself into Gloria. He stood here powerless; they came nearer and Gloria, glancing in, saw him. Her eyes widened and she smiled politely. Her lips moved. She was less than five feet away.

"How do you do?" he muttered inanely.

Gloria, happy, beautiful, and young—with a man he had never seen before!

It was then that the barber's chair was vacated and he read down the newspaper column three times in succession.

The second incident took place the next day. Going into the Manhattan bar about seven he was confronted with Bloeckman. As it happened, the room was nearly deserted, and before the mutual recognition he had stationed himself within a foot of the older man and ordered his drink, so it was inevitable that they should converse.

"Hello, Mr. Patch," said Bloeckman amiably enough.

Anthony took the proffered hand and exchanged a few aphorisms on the fluctuations of the mercury.

"Do you come in here much?" inquired Bloeckman.

"No, very seldom." He omitted to add that the Plaza bar had, until lately, been his favorite.

"Nice bar. One of the best bars in town."

Anthony nodded. Bloeckman emptied his glass and picked up his cane. He was in evening dress.

"Well, I'll be hurrying on. I'm going to dinner with Miss Gilbert."

Death looked suddenly out at him from two blue eyes. Had he announced himself as his vis-à-vis's prospective murderer he could not have struck a more vital blow at Anthony. The younger man must have reddened visibly, for his every nerve was in instant clamor. With tremendous effort he mustered a rigid—oh, so rigid—smile, and said a conventional good-by. But that night he lay awake until after four, half wild with grief and fear and abominable imaginings.

Weakness

And one day in the fifth week he called her up. He had been sitting in his apartment trying to read "L'Éducation Sentimental," and something in the book had sent his thoughts racing in the direction that, set free, they always took, like horses racing for a home stable. With suddenly quickened breath he walked to the telephone. When he gave the number it seemed to him that his voice faltered and broke like a schoolboy's. The Central must have heard the pounding of his heart. The sound of the receiver being taken up at the other end was a crack of doom, and Mrs. Gilbert's voice, soft as maple syrup running into a glass container, had for him a quality of horror in its single "Hello-o-ah?"

"Miss Gloria's not feeling well. She's lying down, asleep. Who shall I say called?"

"Nobody!" he shouted.

In a wild panic he slammed down the receiver; collapsed into his armchair in the cold sweat of breathless relief.

Serenade

The first thing he said to her was: "Why, you've bobbed your hair!" and she answered: "Yes, isn't it gorgeous?"

It was not fashionable then. It was to be fashionable in five or six years. At that time it was considered extremely daring.

"It's all sunshine outdoors," he said gravely. "Don't you want to take a walk?"

She put on a light coat and a quaintly piquant Napoleon hat of Alice Blue, and they walked along the Avenue and into the Zoo, where they properly admired the grandeur of the elephant and the collar-height of the giraffe, but did not visit the monkey house because Gloria said that monkeys smelt so bad.

Then they returned toward the Plaza, talking about nothing, but glad for the spring singing in the air and for the warm balm that lay upon the suddenly golden city. To their right was the Park, while at the left a great bulk of granite and marble muttered dully a millionaire's chaotic message to whosoever would listen: something about "I worked and I saved and I was sharper than all Adam and here I sit, by golly, by golly!"

All the newest and most beautiful designs in automobiles were out on Fifth Avenue, and ahead of them the

Plaza loomed up rather unusually white and attractive. The supple, indolent Gloria walked a short shadow's length ahead of him, pouring out lazy casual comments that floated a moment on the dazzling air before they reached his ear.

"Oh!" she cried, "I want to go south to Hot Springs! I want to get out in the air and just roll around on the new grass and forget there's ever been any winter."

"Don't you, though!"

"I want to hear a million robins making a frightful racket. I sort of like birds."

"All women *are* birds," he ventured.

"What kind am I?"—quick and eager.

"A swallow, I think, and sometimes a bird of paradise. Most girls are sparrows, of course—see that row of nurse-maids over there? They're sparrows—or are they magpies? And of course you've met canary girls—and robin girls."

"And swan girls and parrot girls. All grown women are hawks, I think, or owls."

"What am I—a buzzard?"

She laughed and shook her head.

"Oh, no, you're not a bird at all, do you think? You're a Russian wolfhound."

Anthony remembered that they were white and always looked unnaturally hungry. But then they were usually photographed with dukes and princesses, so he was properly flattered.

"Dick's a fox terrier, a trick fox terrier," she continued.

"And Maury's a cat." Simultaneously it occurred to him how like Bloeckman was to a robust and offensive hog. But he preserved a discreet silence.

Later, as they parted, Anthony asked when he might see her again.

'Don't you ever make long engagements?" he pleaded, "even if it's a week ahead, I think it'd be fun to spend a whole day together, morning and afternoon both."

"It would be, wouldn't it?" She thought for a moment. "Let's do it next Sunday."

"All right. I'll map out a programme that'll take up every minute."

He did. He even figured to a nicety what would happen in the two hours when she would come to his apartment for tea: how the good Bounds would have the windows wide to let in the fresh breeze—but a fire going also lest there be chill in the air—and how there would be clusters of flowers about in big cool bowls that he would buy for the occasion. They would sit on the lounge.

And when the day came they did sit upon the lounge. After a while Anthony kissed her because it came about quite naturally; he found sweetness sleeping still upon her lips, and felt that he had never been away. The fire was bright and the breeze sighing in through the curtains brought a mellow damp, promising May and world of summer. His soul thrilled to remote harmonies; he heard the strum of far guitars and waters lapping on a warm Mediterranean shore—for he was young now as he would never be again, and more triumphant than death.

Six o'clock stole down too soon and rang the querulous melody of St. Anne's chimes on the corner. Through the gathering dusk they strolled to the Avenue, where the crowds, like prisoners released, were walking with elastic step at last after the long winter, and the tops of the busses were thronged with congenial kings and the shops full of fine soft things for the summer, the rare summer, the gay promising summer that seemed for love what the winter was for money. Life was singing for his supper on the corner! Life was handing round cocktails in the street! Old women there were in that crowd who felt that they could have run and won a hundred-yard dash!

In bed that night with the lights out and the cool room swimming with moonlight, Anthony lay awake and played with every minute of the day like a child playing in turn with each one of a pile of long-wanted Christmas toys. He had told her gently, almost in the middle of a kiss, that he loved her, and she had smiled and held him closer and murmured, "I'm glad," looking into his eyes. There had been a new quality in her attitude, a new growth of sheer physical attraction toward him and a strange emotional tenseness, that was enough to make him clinch his hands and draw in his breath at the recollection. He had felt nearer to her than ever before. In a rare delight he cried aloud to the room that he loved her.

He phoned next morning—no hesitation now, no uncertainty—instead a delirious excitement that doubled and trebled when he heard her voice:

"Good morning—Gloria."

"Good morning."

"That's all I called you up to say—dear."

"I'm glad you did."

"I wish I could see you."

"You will, to-morrow night."

"That's a long time, isn't it?"

"Yes—" Her voice was reluctant. His hand tightened on the receiver.

"Couldn't I come to-night?" He dared anything in the glory and revelation of that almost whispered "yes."

"I have a date."

"Oh——"

"But I might—I might be able to break it."

"Oh!"—a sheer cry, a rhapsody. "Gloria?"

"What?"

" I love you."

Another pause and then:

"I—I'm glad."

Happiness, remarked Maury Noble one day, is only the first hour after the alleviation of some especially intense misery. But oh, Anthony's face as he walked down the tenth-floor corridor of the Plaza that night! His dark eyes were gleaming—around his mouth were lines it was a kindness to see. He was handsome then if never before, bound for one of those immortal moments which come so radiantly that their remembered light is enough to see by for years.

He knocked and, at a word, entered. Gloria, dressed in simple pink, starched and fresh as a flower, was across the room, standing very still, and looking at him wide-eyed.

As he closed the door behind him she gave a little cry and moved swiftly over the intervening space, her arms rising in a premature caress as she came near. Together they crushed out the stiff folds of her dress in one triumphant and enduring embrace.

BOOK TWO

CHAPTER I

THE RADIANT HOUR

AFTER a fortnight Anthony and Gloria began to indulge in "practical discussions," as they called those sessions when under the guise of severe realism they walked in an eternal moonlight.

"Not as much as I do you," the critic of belles-lettres would insist. "If you really loved me you'd want every one to know it."

"I do," she protested; "I want to stand on the street corner like a sandwich man, informing all the passers-by."

"Then tell me all the reasons why you're going to marry me in June."

"Well, because you're so clean. You're sort of blowy clean, like I am. There's two sorts, you know. One's like Dick: he's clean like polished pans. You and I are clean like streams and winds. I can tell whenever I see a person whether he is clean, and if so, which kind of clean he is."

"We're twins."

Ecstatic thought!

"Mother says"—she hesitated uncertainly—"mother says that two souls are sometimes created together and —and in love before they're born."

Bilphism gained its easiest convert. . . . After a while he lifted up his head and laughed soundlessly toward the ceiling. When his eyes came back to her he saw that she was angry.

"Why did you laugh?" she cried, "you've done that

twice before. There's nothing funny about our relation to each other. I don't mind playing the fool, and I don't mind having you do it, but I can't stand it when we're together."

"I'm sorry."

"Oh, don't say you're sorry! If you can't think of anything better than that, just keep quiet!"

"I love you."

"I don't care."

There was a pause. Anthony was depressed. . . . At length Gloria murmured:

"I'm sorry I was mean."

"You weren't. I was the one."

Peace was restored—the ensuing moments were so much more sweet and sharp and poignant. They were stars on this stage, each playing to an audience of two: the passion of their pretense created the actuality. Here, finally, was the quintessence of self-expression—yet it was probable that for the most part their love expressed Gloria rather than Anthony. He felt often like a scarcely tolerated guest at a party she was giving.

Telling Mrs. Gilbert had been an embarrassed matter. She sat stuffed into a small chair and listened with an intense and very blinky sort of concentration. She must have known it—for three weeks Gloria had seen no one else—and she must have noticed that this time there was an authentic difference in her daughter's attitude. She had been given special deliveries to post; she had heeded, as all mothers seem to heed, the hither end of telephone conversations, disguised but still rather warm——

—Yet she had delicately professed surprise and declared herself immensely pleased; she doubtless was; so were the geranium plants blossoming in the window-boxes, and so were the cabbies when the lovers sought the romantic privacy of hansom cabs—quaint device—and the staid bill of fares on which they scribbled "you know I do," pushing it over for the other to see.

But between kisses Anthony and this golden girl quarrelled incessantly.

"Now, Gloria," he would cry, "please let me explain!"

"Don't explain. Kiss me."

"I don't think that's right. If I hurt your feelings we ought to discuss it. I don't like this kiss-and-forget."

"But I don't want to argue. I think it's wonderful that we *can* kiss and forget, and when we can't it'll be time to argue."

At one time some gossamer difference attained such bulk that Anthony arose and punched himself into his overcoat—for a moment it appeared that the scene of the preceding February was to be repeated, but knowing how deeply she was moved he retained his dignity with his pride, and in a moment Gloria was sobbing in his arms, her lovely face miserable as a frightened little girl's.

Meanwhile they kept unfolding to each other, unwillingly, by curious reactions and evasions, by distastes and prejudices and unintended hints of the past. The girl was proudly incapable of jealousy and, because he was extremely jealous, this virtue piqued him. He told her recondite incidents of his own life on purpose to arouse some spark of it, but to no avail. She possessed him now—nor did she desire the dead years.

"Oh, Anthony," she would say, "always when I'm mean to you I'm sorry afterward. I'd give my right hand to save you one little moment's pain."

And in that instant her eyes were brimming and she was not aware that she was voicing an illusion. Yet Anthony knew that there were days when they hurt each other purposely—taking almost a delight in the thrust. Incessantly she puzzled him: one hour so intimate and charming, striving desperately toward an unguessed, transcendent union; the next, silent and cold, apparently unmoved by any consideration of their love or anything he could say. Often he would eventually trace these portentous reticences to some physical discomfort—of these she never complained until they were over—or to some carelessness or presumption in him, or to an unsatisfactory dish at dinner, but even then the means by which she created the infinite distances she spread about herself were a mystery, buried somewhere back in those twenty-two years of unwavering pride.

"Why do you like Muriel?" he demanded one day.

"I don't—very much."

"Then why do you go with her?"

"Just for some one to go with. They're no exertion, those girls. They sort of believe everything I tell 'em—but I rather like Rachael. I think she's cute—and so clean and slick, don't you? I used to have other friends—in Kansas City and at school—casual, all of them, girls who just flitted into my range and out of it for no more reason than that boys took us places together. They didn't interest me after environment stopped throwing us together. Now they're mostly married. What does it matter—they were all just people."

"You like men better, don't you?"

"Oh, much better. I've got a man's mind."

"You've got a mind like mine. Not strongly gendered either way."

Later she told him about the beginnings of her friendship with Bloeckman. One day in Delmonico's, Gloria and Rachael had come upon Bloeckman and Mr. Gilbert having luncheon and curiosity had impelled her to make it a party of four. She had liked him—rather.

He was a relief from younger men, satisfied as he was with so little. He humored her and he laughed, whether he understood her or not. She met him several times, despite the open disapproval of her parents, and within a month he had asked her to marry him, tendering her everything from a villa in Italy to a brilliant career on the screen. She had laughed in his face—and he had laughed too.

But he had not given up. To the time of Anthony's arrival in the arena he had been making steady progress. She treated him rather well—except that she had called him always by an invidious nickname—perceiving, meanwhile, that he was figuratively following along beside her as she walked the fence, ready to catch her if she should fall.

The night before the engagement was announced she told Bloeckman. It was a heavy blow. She did not enlighten Anthony as to the details, but she implied that he had not hesitated to argue with her. Anthony gathered that the interview had terminated on a stormy note, with Gloria very cool and unmoved lying in her corner of the sofa and Joseph Bloeckman of "Films Par Excellence" pacing the carpet with eyes narrowed and head bowed. Gloria had been sorry for him but she had judged it best not to show it. In a final burst of kindness she had tried to make him hate her, there at the last. But Anthony, understanding that Gloria's indifference was her strongest appeal, judged how futile this must have been. He wondered, often but quite casually, about Bloeckman—finally he forgot him entirely.

Heyday

One afternoon they found front seats on the sunny roof of a bus and rode for hours from the fading Square up along the sullied river, and then, as the stray beams fled the westward streets, sailed down the turgid Avenue, darkening with ominous bees from the department stores. The traffic was clotted and gripped in a patternless jam; the busses were packed four deep like platforms above the crowd as they waited for the moan of the traffic whistle.

"Isn't it good!" cried Gloria. "Look!"

A miller's wagon, stark white with flour, driven by a powdery clown, passed in front of them behind a white horse and his black team-mate.

"What a pity!" she complained; "they'd look so beautiful in the dusk, if only both horses were white. I'm mighty happy just this minute, in this city."

Anthony shook his head in disagreement.

"I think the city's a mountebank. Always struggling to approach the tremendous and impressive urbanity ascribed to it. Trying to be romantically metropolitan."

"I don't. I think it is impressive."

"Momentarily. But it's really a transparent, artificial sort of spectacle. It's got its press-agented stars and its flimsy, unenduring stage settings and, I'll admit, the greatest army of supers ever assembled—" He paused, laughed shortly, and added: "Technically excellent, perhaps, but not convincing."

"I'll bet policemen think people are fools," said Gloria thoughtfully, as she watched a large but cowardly lady being helped across the street. "He always sees them frightened and inefficient and old—they are," she added. And then: "We'd better get off. I told mother I'd have an early supper and go to bed. She says I look tired, damn it."

"I wish we were married," he muttered soberly; "there'll be no good night then and we can do just as we want."

"Won't it be good! I think we ought to travel a lot. I want to go to the Mediterranean and Italy. And I'd like to go on the stage some time—say for about a year."

"You bet. I'll write a play for you."

"Won't that be good! And I'll act in it. And then some time when we have more money"—old Adam's death was always thus tactfully alluded to—"we'll build a magnificent estate, won't we?"

"Oh, yes, with private swimming pools."

"Dozens of them. And private rivers. Oh, I wish it were now."

Odd coincidence—he had just been wishing that very thing. They plunged like divers into the dark eddying crowd and emerging in the cool fifties sauntered indolently homeward, infinitely romantic to each other . . . both were walking alone in a dispassionate garden with a ghost found in a dream.

Halcyon days like boats drifting along slow-moving rivers; spring evenings full of a plaintive melancholy that made the past beautiful and bitter, bidding them look back and see that the loves of other summers long gone were dead with the forgotten waltzes of their years. Always the most poignant moments were when some artificial barrier kept them apart: in the theatre their hands would steal together, join, give and return gentle pressures through the long dark; in crowded rooms they would form words with their lips for each other's eyes—not knowing that they were but following in the footsteps of dusty generations but comprehending dimly that if truth is the end of life happiness is a mode of it, to be cherished in its brief and tremulous moment. And then, one fairy night, May became June. Sixteen days now—fifteen—fourteen——

Three Disgressions

Just before the engagement was announced Anthony had gone up to Tarrytown to see his grandfather, who, a little more wizened and grizzly as time played its ultimate chuckling tricks, greeted the news with profound cynicism.

"Oh, you're going to get married, are you?" He said this with such a dubious mildness and shook his head up and down so many times that Anthony was not a little depressed. While he was unaware of his grandfather's intentions he presumed that a large part of the money would come to him. A good deal would go in charities, of course; a good deal to carry on the business of reform.

"Are you going to work?"

"Why—" temporized Anthony, somewhat disconcerted. "I *am* working. You know——"

"Ah, I mean work," said Adam Patch dispassionately.

"I'm not quite sure yet what I'll do. I'm not exactly a beggar, grampa," he asserted with some spirit.

The old man considered this with eyes half closed. Then almost apologetically he asked:

"How much do you save a year?"

"Nothing so far——"

"And so after just managing to get along on your money you've decided that by some miracle two of you can get along on it."

"Gloria has some money of her own. Enough to buy clothes."

"How much?"

Without considering this question impertinent, Anthony answered it.

"About a hundred a month."

"That's altogether about seventy-five hundred a

year." Then he added softly: "It ought to be plenty. If you have any sense it ought to be plenty. But the question is whether you have any or not."

"I suppose it is." It was shameful to be compelled to endure this pious browbeating from the old man, and his next words were stiffened with vanity. "I can manage very well. You seem convinced that I'm utterly worthless. At any rate I came up here simply to tell you that I'm getting married in June. Good-by, sir." With this he turned away and headed for the door, unaware that in that instant his grandfather, for the first time, rather liked him.

"Wait!" called Adam Patch, "I want to talk to you."

Anthony faced about.

"Well, sir?"

"Sit down. Stay all night."

Somewhat mollified, Anthony resumed his seat.

"I'm sorry, sir, but I'm going to see Gloria to-night."

"What's her name?"

"Gloria Gilbert."

"New York girl? Some one you know?"

"She's from the Middle West."

"What business her father in?"

"In a celluloid corporation or trust or something. They're from Kansas City."

"You going to be married out there?"

"Why, no, sir. We thought we'd be married in New York—rather quietly."

"Like to have the wedding out here?"

Anthony hesitated. The suggestion made no appeal to him, but it was certainly the part of wisdom to give the old man, if possible, a proprietary interest in his married life. In addition Anthony was a little touched.

"That's very kind of you, grampa, but wouldn't it be a lot of trouble?"

"Everything's a lot of trouble. Your father was married here—but in the old house."

"Why—I thought he was married in Boston."

Adam Patch considered.

"That's true. He *was* married in Boston."

Anthony felt a moment's embarrassment at having made the correction, and he covered it up with words.

"Well, I'll speak to Gloria about it. Personally I'd like to, but of course it's up to the Gilberts, you see."

His grandfather drew a long sigh, half closed his eyes, and sank back in his chair.

"In a hurry?" he asked in a different tone.

"Not especially."

"I wonder," began Adam Patch, looking out with a mild, kindly glance at the lilac bushes that rustled against the windows, "I wonder if you ever think about the after-life."

"Why—sometimes."

"I think a great deal about the after-life." His eyes were dim but his voice was confident and clear. "I was sitting here to-day thinking about what's lying in wait for us, and somehow I began to remember an afternoon nearly sixty-five years ago, when I was playing with my little sister Annie, down where that summer-house is now." He pointed out into the long flower-garden, his eyes trembling of tears, his voice shaking.

"I began thinking—and it seemed to me that *you* ought to think a little more about the after-life. You ought to be—steadier"—he paused and seemed to grope about for the right word—"more industrious—why——"

Then his expression altered, his entire personality seemed to snap together like a trap, and when he continued the softness had gone from his voice.

"—Why, when I was just two years older than you,"

he rasped with a cunning chuckle, "I sent three members of the firm of Wrenn and Hunt to the poorhouse."

Anthony started with embarrassment.

"Well, good-by," added his grandfather suddenly, "you'll miss your train."

Anthony left the house unusually elated, and strangely sorry for the old man; not because his wealth could buy him "neither youth nor digestion" but because he had asked Anthony to be married there, and because he had forgotten something about his son's wedding that he should have remembered.

Richard Caramel, who was one of the ushers, caused Anthony and Gloria much distress in the last few weeks by continually stealing the rays of their spot-light. "The Demon Lover" had been published in April, and it interrupted the love affair as it may be said to have interrupted everything its author came in contact with. It was a highly original, rather overwritten piece of sustained description concerned with a Don Juan of the New York slums. As Maury and Anthony had said before, as the more hospitable critics were saying then, there was no writer in America with such power to describe the atavistic and unsubtle reactions of that section of society.

The book hesitated and then suddenly "went." Editions, small at first, then larger, crowded each other week by week. A spokesman of the Salvation Army denounced it as a cynical misrepresentation of all the uplift taking place in the underworld. Clever press-agenting spread the unfounded rumor that "Gypsy" Smith was beginning a libel suit because one of the principal characters was a burlesque of himself. It was barred from the public library of Burlington, Iowa, and a Mid-Western columnist announced by innuendo that

Richard Caramel was in a sanitarium with delirium tremens.

The author, indeed, spent his days in a state of pleasant madness. The book was in his conversation three-fourths of the time—he wanted to know if one had heard "the latest"; he would go into a store and in a loud voice order books to be charged to him, in order to catch a chance morsel of recognition from clerk or customer. He knew to a town in what sections of the country it was selling best; he knew exactly what he cleared on each edition, and when he met any one who had not read it, or, as it happened only too often, had not heard of it, he succumbed to moody depression.

So it was natural for Anthony and Gloria to decide, in their jealousy, that he was so swollen with conceit as to be a bore. To Dick's great annoyance Gloria publicly boasted that she had never read "The Demon Lover," and didn't intend to until every one stopped talking about it. As a matter of fact, she had no time to read now, for the presents were pouring in—first a scattering, then an avalanche, varying from the bric-à-brac of forgotten family friends to the photographs of forgotten poor relations.

Maury gave them an elaborate "drinking set," which included silver goblets, cocktail shaker, and bottle-openers. The extortion from Dick was more conventional—a tea set from Tiffany's. From Joseph Bloeckman came a simple and exquisite travelling clock, with his card. There was even a cigarette-holder from Bounds; this touched Anthony and made him want to weep—indeed, any emotion short of hysteria seemed natural in the half-dozen people who were swept up by this tremendous sacrifice to convention. The room set aside in the Plaza bulged with offerings sent by Harvard friends and by associates of his grandfather, with remembrances of Gloria's Farmover days, and with rather pathetic trophies from her former beaux, which last arrived with esoteric, melancholy messages, written on cards tucked carefully inside, beginning "I little thought when—" or "I'm sure I wish you all the happiness—" or even "When you get this I shall be on my way to——"

The most munificent gift was simultaneously the most disappointing. It was a concession of Adam Patch's—a check for five thousand dollars.

To most of the presents Anthony was cold. It seemed to him that they would necessitate keeping a chart of the marital status of all their acquaintances during the next half-century. But Gloria exulted in each one, tearing at the tissue-paper and excelsior with the rapaciousness of a dog digging for a bone, breathlessly seizing a ribbon or an edge of metal and finally bringing to light the whole article and holding it up critically, no emotion except rapt interest in her unsmiling face.

"Look, Anthony!"

"Darn nice, isn't it!"

No answer until an hour later when she would give him a careful account of her precise reaction to the gift, whether it would have been improved by being smaller or larger, whether she was surprised at getting it, and, if so, just how much surprised.

Mrs. Gilbert arranged and rearranged a hypothetical house, distributing the gifts among the different rooms, tabulating articles as "second-best clock" or "silver to use *every* day," and embarrassing Anthony and Gloria by semi-facetious references to a room she called the nursery. She was pleased by old Adam's gift and thereafter had it that he was a very ancient soul, "as much as anything else." As Adam Patch never quite decided whether she referred to the advancing senility of his mind or to some private and psychic schema of her own, it cannot be said to have pleased him. Indeed he always spoke of her to Anthony as "that old woman, the mother," as though she were a character in a comedy he had seen staged many times before. Concerning Gloria he was unable to make up his mind. She attracted him but, as she herself told Anthony, he had decided that she was frivolous and was afraid to approve of her.

Five days!—A dancing platform was being erected on the lawn at Tarrytown. Four days!—A special train was chartered to convey the guests to and from New York. Three days!——

THE DIARY

She was dressed in blue silk pajamas and standing by her bed with her hand on the light to put the room in darkness, when she changed her mind and opening a table drawer brought out a little black book—a "Line-a-day" diary. This she had kept for seven years. Many of the pencil entries were almost illegible and there were notes and references to nights and afternoons long since forgotten, for it was not an intimate diary, even though it began with the immemorial "I am going to keep a diary for my children." Yet as she thumbed over the pages the eyes of many men seemed to look out at her from their half-obliterated names. With one she had gone to New Haven for the first time—in 1908, when she was sixteen and padded shoulders were fashionable at Yale—she had been flattered because "Touch down" Michaud had "rushed" her all evening. She sighed, remembering the grown-up satin dress she had been so proud of and the orchestra playing "Yama-yama, My Yama Man" and "Jungle-Town." So long ago!—the names: Eltynge Reardon, Jim Parsons, "Curly"

McGregor, Kenneth Cowan, "Fish-eye" Fry (whom she had liked for being so ugly), Carter Kirby—he had sent her a present; so had Tudor Baird;—Marty Reffer, the first man she had been in love with for more than a day, and Stuart Holcome, who had run away with her in his automobile and tried to make her marry him by force. And Larry Fenwick, whom she had always admired because he had told her one night that if she wouldn't kiss him she could get out of his car and walk home. What a list!

. . . And, after all, an obsolete list. She was in love now, set for the eternal romance that was to be the synthesis of all romance, yet sad for these men and these moonlights and for the "thrills" she had had—and the kisses. The past—her past, oh, what a joy! She had been exuberantly happy.

Turning over the pages her eyes rested idly on the scattered entries of the past four months. She read the last few carefully.

"*April 1st.*—I know Bill Carstairs hates me because I was so disagreeable, but I hate to be sentimentalized over sometimes. We drove out to the Rockyear Country Club and the most wonderful moon kept shining through the trees. My silver dress is getting tarnished. Funny how one forgets the other nights at Rockyear—with Kenneth Cowan when I loved him so!

"*April 3rd.*—After two hours of Schroeder who, they inform me, has millions, I've decided that this matter of sticking to things wears one out, particularly when the things concerned are men. There's nothing so often overdone and from to-day I swear to be amused. We talked about 'love'—how banal! With how many men have I talked about love?

"*April 11th.*—Patch actually called up to-day! and when he forswore me about a month ago he fairly raged out the door. I'm gradually losing faith in any man being susceptible to fatal injuries.

"*April 20th.*—Spent the day with Anthony. Maybe I'll marry him some time. I kind of like his ideas—he stimulates all the originality in me. Blockhead came around about ten in his new car and took me out Riverside Drive. I liked him to-night: he's so considerate. He knew I didn't want to talk so he was quiet all during the ride.

"*April 21st.*—Woke up thinking of Anthony and sure enough he called and sounded sweet on the phone—so I broke a date for him. To-day I feel I'd break anything for him, including the ten commandments and my neck. He's coming at eight and I shall wear pink and look very fresh and starched——"

She paused here, remembering that after he had gone that night she had undressed with the shivering April air streaming in the windows. Yet it seemed she had not felt the cold, warmed by the profound banalities burning in her heart.

The next entry occurred a few days later:

"*April 24th.*—I want to marry Anthony, because husbands are so often 'husbands' and I must marry a lover.

"There are four general types of husbands.

(1) The husband who always wants to stay in in the evening, has no vices and works for a salary. Totally undesirable!

(2) The atavistic master whose mistress one is, to wait on his pleasure. This sort always considers every pretty woman 'shallow,' a sort of peacock with arrested development.

(3) Next comes the worshipper, the idolater of his wife and all that is his, to the utter oblivion of everything else. This sort demands an emo-

tional actress for a wife. God! it must be an exertion to be thought righteous.

(4) And Anthony—a temporarily passionate lover with wisdom enough to realize when it has flown and that it must fly. And I want to get married to Anthony.

"What grubworms women are to crawl on their bellies through colorless marriages! Marriage was created not to be a background but to need one. Mine is going to be outstanding. It can't, shan't be the setting—it's going to be the performance, the live, lovely, glamourous performance, and the world shall be the scenery. I refuse to dedicate my life to posterity. Surely one owes as much to the current generation as to one's unwanted children. What a fate—to grow rotund and unseemly, to lose my self-love, to think in terms of milk, oatmeal, nurse, diapers.... Dear dream children, how much more beautiful you are, dazzling little creatures who flutter (all dream children must flutter) on golden, golden wings——

Such children, however, poor dear babies, have little in common with the wedded state.

"*June 7th.*—Moral question: Was it wrong to make Bloeckman love me? Because I did really make him. He was almost sweetly sad to-night. How opportune it was that my throat is swollen plunk together and tears were easy to muster. But he's just the past—buried already in my plentiful lavender.

"*June 8th.*—And to-day I've promised not to chew my mouth. Well, I won't, I suppose—but if he'd only asked me not to eat!

"Blowing bubbles—that's what we're doing, Anthony and me. And we blew such beautiful ones to-day, and they'll explode and then we'll blow more and more, I guess—bubbles just as big and just as beautiful, until all the soap and water is used up."

On this note the diary ended. Her eyes wandered up the page, over the June 8th's of 1912, 1910, 1907. The earliest entry was scrawled in the plump, bulbous hand of a sixteen-year-old girl—it was the name, Bob Lamar, and a word she could not decipher. Then she knew what it was—and, knowing, she found her eyes misty with tears. There in a graying blur was the record of her first kiss, faded as its intimate afternoon, on a rainy veranda seven years before. She seemed to remember something one of them had said that day and yet she could not remember. Her tears came faster, until she could scarcely see the page. She was crying, she told herself, because she could remember only the rain and the wet flowers in the yard and the smell of the damp grass.

. . . After a moment she found a pencil and holding it unsteadily drew three parallel lines beneath the last entry. Then she printed FINIS in large capitals, put the book back in the drawer, and crept into bed.

Breath of the Cave

Back in his apartment after the bridal dinner, Anthony snapped out his lights and, feeling impersonal and fragile as a piece of china waiting on a serving table, got into bed. It was a warm night—a sheet was enough for comfort—and through his wide-open windows came sound, evanescent and summery, alive with remote anticipation. He was thinking that the young years behind him, hollow and colorful, had been lived in facile and vacillating cynicism upon the recorded emotions of men long dust. And there was something beyond that; he knew now. There was the union of his soul with Gloria's, whose radiant fire and freshness was the living material of which the dead beauty of books was made.

From the night into his high-walled room there came,

persistently, that evanescent and dissolving sound—something the city was tossing up and calling back again, like a child playing with a ball. In Harlem, the Bronx, Gramercy Park, and along the water-fronts, in little parlors or on pebble-strewn, moon-flooded roofs, a thousand lovers were making this sound, crying little fragments of it into the air. All the city was playing with this sound out there in the blue summer dark, throwing it up and calling it back, promising that, in a little while, life would be beautiful as a story, promising happiness—and by that promise giving it. It gave love hope in its own survival. It could do no more.

It was then that a new note separated itself jarringly from the soft crying of the night. It was a noise from an areaway within a hundred feet from his rear window, the noise of a woman's laughter. It began low, incessant and whining—some servant-maid with her fellow, he thought—and then it grew in volume and became hysterical, until it reminded him of a girl he had seen overcome with nervous laughter at a vaudeville performance. Then it sank, receded, only to rise again and include words—a coarse joke, some bit of obscure horse-play he could not distinguish. It would break off for a moment and he would just catch the low rumble of a man's voice, then begin again—interminably; at first annoying, then strangely terrible. He shivered, and getting up out of bed went to the window. It had reached a high point, tensed and stifled, almost the quality of a scream—then it ceased and left behind it a silence empty and menacing as the greater silence overhead. Anthony stood by the window a moment longer before he returned to his bed. He found himself upset and shaken. Try as he might to strangle his reaction, some animal quality in that unrestrained laughter had grasped at his imagination, and for the first time in four months aroused his old aversion and horror toward all the business of life. The room had grown smothery. He wanted to be out in some cool and bitter breeze, miles above the cities, and to live serene and detached back in the corners of his mind. Life was that sound out there, that ghastly reiterated female sound.

"Oh, my *God!*" he cried, drawing in his breath sharply.

Burying his face in the pillows he tried in vain to concentrate upon the details of the next day.

Morning

In the gray light he found that it was only five o'clock. He regretted nervously that he had awakened so early—he would appear fagged at the wedding. He envied Gloria who could hide her fatigue with careful pigmentation.

In his bathroom he contemplated himself in the mirror and saw that he was unusually white—half a dozen small imperfections stood out against the morning pallor of his complexion, and overnight he had grown the faint stubble of a beard—the general effect, he fancied, was unprepossessing, haggard, half unwell.

On his dressing table were spread a number of articles which he told over carefully with suddenly fumbling fingers—their tickets to California, the book of traveller's checks, his watch, set to the half minute, the key to his apartment, which he must not forget to give to Maury, and, most important of all, the ring. It was of platinum set around with small emeralds; Gloria had insisted on this; she had always wanted an emerald wedding ring, she said.

It was the third present he had given her; first had come the engagement ring, and then a little gold cigarette-case. He would be giving her many things now—clothes and jewels and friends and excitement. It seemed absurd that from now on he would pay for all her meals. It was going to cost: he wondered if he had not underestimated for this trip, and if he had not better cash a larger check. The question worried him.

Then the breathless impendency of the event swept his mind clear of details. This was the day—unsought, unsuspected six months before, but now breaking in yellow light through his east window, dancing along the carpet as though the sun were smiling at some ancient and reiterated gag of his own.

Anthony laughed in a nervous one-syllable snort.

"By God!" he muttered to himself, "I'm as good as married!"

The Ushers

Six young men in Cross Patch's *library growing more and more cheery under the influence of Mumm's Extra Dry, set surreptitiously in cold pails by the bookcases.*

The First Young Man: By golly! Believe me, in my next book I'm going to do a wedding scene that'll knock 'em cold!

The Second Young Man: Met a débutante th'other day said she thought your book was powerful. As a rule young girls cry for this primitive business.

The Third Young Man: Where's Anthony?

The Fourth Young Man: Walking up and down outside talking to himself.

Second Young Man: Lord! Did you see the minister? Most peculiar looking teeth.

Fifth Young Man: Think they're natural. Funny thing people having gold teeth.

Sixth Young Man: They say they love 'em. My dentist told me once a woman came to him and insisted on having two of her teeth covered with gold. No reason at all. All right the way they were.

FOURTH YOUNG MAN: Hear you got out a book, Dicky. 'Gratulations!

DICK: (*Stiffly*) Thanks.

FOURTH YOUNG MAN: (*Innocently*) What is it? College stories?

DICK: (*More stiffly*) No. Not college stories.

FOURTH YOUNG MAN: Pity! Hasn't been a good book about Harvard for years.

DICK: (*Touchily*) Why don't you supply the lack?

THIRD YOUNG MAN: I think I saw a squad of guests turn the drive in a Packard just now.

SIXTH YOUNG MAN: Might open a couple more bottles on the strength of that.

THIRD YOUNG MAN: It was the shock of my life when I heard the old man was going to have a wet wedding. Rabid prohibitionist, you know.

FOURTH YOUNG MAN: (*Snapping his fingers excitedly*) By gad! I knew I'd forgotten something. Kept thinking it was my vest.

DICK: What was it?

FOURTH YOUNG MAN: By gad! By gad!

SIXTH YOUNG MAN: Here! Here! Why the tragedy?

SECOND YOUNG MAN: What'd you forget? The way home?

DICK: (*Maliciously*) He forgot the plot for his book of Harvard stories.

FOURTH YOUNG MAN: No, sir, I forgot the present, by George! I forgot to buy old Anthony a present. I kept putting it off and putting it off, and by gad I've forgotten it! What'll they think?

SIXTH YOUNG MAN: (*Facetiously*) That's probably what's been holding up the wedding.

(THE FOURTH YOUNG MAN *looks nervously at his watch. Laughter.*)

FOURTH YOUNG MAN: By gad! What an ass I am!

SECOND YOUNG MAN: What d'you make of the bridesmaid who thinks she's Nora Bayes? Kept telling me she wished this was a ragtime wedding. Name's Haines or Hampton.

DICK: (*Hurriedly spurring his imagination*) Kane, you mean, Muriel Kane. She's a sort of debt of honor, I believe. Once saved Gloria from drowning, or something of the sort.

SECOND YOUNG MAN: I didn't think she could stop that perpetual swaying long enough to swim. Fill up my glass, will you? Old man and I had a long talk about the weather just now.

MAURY: Who? Old Adam?

SECOND YOUNG MAN: No, the bride's father. He must be with a weather bureau.

DICK: He's my uncle, Otis.

OTIS: Well, it's an honorable profession. (*Laughter.*)

SIXTH YOUNG MAN: Bride your cousin, isn't she?

DICK: Yes, Cable, she is.

CABLE: She certainly is a beauty. Not like you, Dicky. Bet she brings old Anthony to terms.

MAURY: Why are all grooms given the title of "old"? I think marriage is an error of youth.

DICK: Maury, the professional cynic.

MAURY: Why, you intellectual faker!

FIFTH YOUNG MAN: Battle of the highbrows here, Otis. Pick up what crumbs you can.

DICK: Faker yourself! What do *you* know?

MAURY: What do *you* know?

DICK: Ask me anything. Any branch of knowledge.

MAURY: All right. What's the fundamental principle of biology?

DICK: You don't know yourself.

MAURY: Don't hedge!

DICK: Well, natural selection?

MAURY: Wrong.

DICK: I give it up.

MAURY: Ontogony recapitulates phyllogony.

FIFTH YOUNG MAN: Take your base!

MAURY: Ask you another. What's the influence of mice on the clover crop? (*Laughter.*)

FOURTH YOUNG MAN: What's the influence of rats on the Decalogue?

MAURY: Shut up, you saphead. There *is* a connection.

DICK: What is it then?

MAURY: (*Pausing a moment in growing disconcertion*) Why, let's see. I seem to have forgotten exactly. Something about the bees eating the clover.

FOURTH YOUNG MAN: And the clover eating the mice! Haw! Haw!

MAURY: (*Frowning*) Let me just think a minute.

DICK: (*Sitting up suddenly*) Listen!

(*A volley of chatter explodes in the adjoining room. The six young men arise, feeling at their neckties.*)

DICK: (*Weightily*) We'd better join the firing squad. They're going to take the picture, I guess. No, that's afterward.

OTIS: Cable, you take the ragtime bridesmaid.

FOURTH YOUNG MAN: I wish to God I'd sent that present.

MAURY: If you'll give me another minute I'll think of that about the mice.

OTIS: I was usher last month for old Charlie McIntyre and——

(*They move slowly toward the door as the chatter becomes a babel and the practising preliminary to the overture issues in long pious groans from* ADAM PATCH'S *organ.*)

Anthony

There were five hundred eyes boring through the back of his cutaway and the sun glinting on the clergyman's inappropriately bourgeois teeth. With difficulty he restrained a laugh. Gloria was saying something in a clear proud voice and he tried to think that the affair was irrevocable, that every second was significant, that his life was being slashed into two periods and that the face of the world was changing before him. He tried to recapture that ecstatic sensation of ten weeks before. All these emotions eluded him, he did not even feel the physical nervousness of that very morning—it was all one gigantic aftermath. And those gold teeth! He wondered if the clergyman were married; he wondered perversely if a clergyman could perform his own marriage service. . . .

But as he took Gloria into his arms he was conscious of a strong reaction. The blood was moving in his veins now. A languorous and pleasant content settled like a weight upon him, bringing responsibility and possession. He was married.

Gloria

So many, such mingled emotions, that no one of them was separable from the others! She could have wept for her mother, who was crying quietly back there ten feet and for the loveliness of the June sunlight flooding in at the windows. She was beyond all conscious perceptions. Only a sense, colored with delirious wild excitement, that the ultimately important was happening—and a trust, fierce and passionate, burning in her like a prayer, that in a moment she would be forever and securely safe.

Late one night they arrived in Santa Barbara, where

the night clerk at the Hotel Lafcadio refused to admit them, on the grounds that they were not married.

The clerk thought that Gloria was beautiful. He did not think that anything so beautiful as Gloria could be moral.

"Con Amore"

That first half-year—the trip West, the long months' loiter along the California coast, and the gray house near Greenwich where they lived until late autumn made the country dreary—those days, those places, saw the enraptured hours. The breathless idyl of their engagement gave way, first, to the intense romance of the more passionate relationship. The breathless idyl left them, fled on to other lovers; they looked around one day and it was gone, how they scarcely knew. Had either of them lost the other in the days of the idyl, the love lost would have been ever to the loser that dim desire without fulfilment which stands back of all life. But magic must hurry on, and the lovers remain. . . .

The idyl passed, bearing with it its extortion of youth. Came a day when Gloria found that other men no longer bored her; came a day when Anthony discovered that he could sit again late into the evening, talking with Dick of those tremendous abstractions that had once occupied his world. But, knowing they had had the best of love, they clung to what remained. Love lingered—by way of long conversations at night into those stark hours when the mind thins and sharpens and the borrowings from dreams become the stuff of all life, by way of deep and intimate kindnesses they developed toward each other, by way of their laughing at the same absurdities and thinking the same things noble and the same things sad.

It was, first of all, a time of discovery. The things

they found in each other were so diverse, so intermixed and, moreover, so sugared with love as to seem at the time not so much discoveries as isolated phenomena—to be allowed for, and to be forgotten. Anthony found that he was living with a girl of tremendous nervous tension and of the most high-handed selfishness. Gloria knew within a month that her husband was an utter coward toward any one of a million phantasms created by his imagination. Her perception was intermittent, for this cowardice sprang out, became almost obscenely evident, then faded and vanished as though it had been only a creation of her own mind. Her reactions to it were not those attributed to her sex—it roused her neither to disgust nor to a premature feeling of motherhood. Herself almost completely without physical fear, she was unable to understand, and so she made the most of what she felt to be his fear's redeeming feature, which was that though he was a coward under a shock and a coward under a strain—when his imagination was given play—he had yet a sort of dashing recklessness that moved her on its brief occasions almost to admiration, and a pride that usually steadied him when he thought he was observed.

The trait first showed itself in a dozen incidents of little more than nervousness—his warning to a taxi-driver against fast driving, in Chicago; his refusal to take her to a certain tough café she had always wished to visit; these of course admitted the conventional interpretation—that it was of her he had been thinking; nevertheless, their culminative weight disturbed her. But something that occurred in a San Francisco hotel, when they had been married a week, gave the matter certainty.

It was after midnight and pitch dark in their room. Gloria was dozing off and Anthony's even breathing beside her made her suppose that he was asleep, when suddenly she saw him raise himself on his elbow and stare at the window.

"What is it, dearest?" she murmured.

"Nothing"—he had relaxed to his pillow and turned toward her—"nothing, my darling wife."

"Don't say 'wife.' I'm your mistress. Wife's such an ugly word. Your 'permanent mistress' is so much more tangible and desirable. . . . Come into my arms," she added in a rush of tenderness; "I can sleep so well, so well with you in my arms."

Coming into Gloria's arms had a quite definite meaning. It required that he should slide one arm under her shoulder, lock both arms about her, and arrange himself as nearly as possible as a sort of three-sided crib for her luxurious ease. Anthony, who tossed, whose arms went tinglingly to sleep after half an hour of that position, would wait until she was asleep and roll her gently over to her side of the bed—then, left to his own devices, he would curl himself into his usual knots.

Gloria, having attained sentimental comfort, retired into her doze. Five minutes ticked away on Bloeckman's travelling clock; silence lay all about the room, over the unfamiliar, impersonal furniture and the half-oppressive ceiling that melted imperceptibly into invisible walls on both sides. Then there was suddenly a rattling flutter at the window, staccato and loud upon the hushed, pent air.

With a leap Anthony was out of the bed and standing tense beside it.

"Who's there?" he cried in an awful voice.

Gloria lay very still, wide awake now and engrossed not so much in the rattling as in the rigid breathless figure whose voice had reached from the bedside into that ominous dark.

The sound stopped; the room was quiet as before—then Anthony pouring words in at the telephone.

"Some one just tried to get into the room! . . .

"There's some one at the window!" His voice was emphatic now, faintly terrified.

"All right! Hurry!" He hung up the receiver; stood motionless.

. . . There was a rush and commotion at the door, a knocking—Anthony went to open it upon an excited night clerk with three bell-boys grouped staring behind him. Between thumb and finger the night clerk held a wet pen with the threat of a weapon; one of the bell-boys had seized a telephone directory and was looking at it sheepishly. Simultaneously the group was joined by the hastily summoned house-detective, and as one man they surged into the room.

Lights sprang on with a click. Gathering a piece of sheet about her Gloria dove away from sight, shutting her eyes to keep out the horror of this unpremeditated visitation. There was no vestige of an idea in her stricken sensibilities save that her Anthony was at grievous fault.

. . . The night clerk was speaking from the window, his tone half of the servant, half of the teacher reproving a schoolboy.

"Nobody out there," he declared conclusively; "my golly, nobody *could* be out there. This here's a sheer fall to the street of fifty feet. It was the wind you heard, tugging at the blind."

"Oh."

Then she was sorry for him. She wanted only to comfort him and draw him back tenderly into her arms, to tell them to go away because the thing their presence connotated was odious. Yet she could not raise her head for shame. She heard a broken sentence, apologies, conventions of the employee and one unrestrained snicker from a bell-boy.

"I've been nervous as the devil all evening," Anthony was saying; "somehow that noise just shook me—I was only about half awake."

"Sure, I understand," said the night clerk with comfortable tact; "been that way myself."

The door closed; the lights snapped out; Anthony crossed the floor quietly and crept into bed. Gloria, feigning to be heavy with sleep, gave a quiet little sigh and slipped into his arms.

"What was it, dear?"

"Nothing," he answered, his voice still shaken; "I thought there was somebody at the window, so I looked out, but I couldn't see any one and the noise kept up, so I phoned down-stairs. Sorry if I disturbed you, but I'm awfully darn nervous to-night."

Catching the lie, she gave an interior start—he had not gone to the window, nor near the window. He had stood by the bed and then sent in his call of fear.

"Oh," she said—and then: "I'm so sleepy."

For an hour they lay awake side by side, Gloria with her eyes shut so tight that blue moons formed and revolved against backgrounds of deepest mauve, Anthony staring blindly into the darkness overhead.

After many weeks it came gradually out into the light, to be laughed and joked at. They made a tradition to fit over it—whenever that overpowering terror of the night attacked Anthony, she would put her arms about him and croon, soft as a song:

"I'll protect my Anthony. Oh, nobody's ever going to harm my Anthony!"

He would laugh as though it were a jest they played for their mutual amusement, but to Gloria it was never quite a jest. It was, at first, a keen disappointment;

later, it was one of the times when she controlled her temper.

The management of Gloria's temper, whether it was aroused by a lack of hot water for her bath or by a skirmish with her husband, became almost the primary duty of Anthony's day. It must be done just so—by this much silence, by that much pressure, by this much yielding, by that much force. It was in her angers with their attendant cruelties that her inordinate egotism chiefly displayed itself. Because she was brave, because she was "spoiled," because of her outrageous and commendable independence of judgment, and finally because of her arrogant consciousness that she had never seen a girl as beautiful as herself, Gloria had developed into a consistent, practising Nietzschean. This, of course, with overtones of profound sentiment.

There was, for example, her stomach. She was used to certain dishes, and she had a strong conviction that she could not possibly eat anything else. There must be a lemonade and a tomato sandwich late in the morning, then a light lunch with a stuffed tomato. Not only did she require food from a selection of a dozen dishes, but in addition this food must be prepared in just a certain way. One of the most annoying half hours of the first fortnight occurred in Los Angeles, when an unhappy waiter brought her a tomato stuffed with chicken salad instead of celery.

"We always serve it that way, madame," he quavered to the gray eyes that regarded him wrathfully.

Gloria made no answer, but when the waiter had turned discreetly away she banged both fists upon the table until the china and silver rattled.

"Poor Gloria!" laughed Anthony unwittingly, "you can't get what you want ever, can you?"

"I can't eat *stuff!*" she flared up.

"I'll call back the waiter."

"I don't want you to! He doesn't know anything, the darn *fool!*"

"Well, it isn't the hotel's fault. Either send it back, forget it, or be a sport and eat it."

"Shut up!" she said succinctly.

"Why take it out on me?"

"Oh, I'm *not*," she wailed, "but I simply *can't* eat it."

Anthony subsided helplessly.

"We'll go somewhere else," he suggested.

"I don't *want* to go anywhere else. I'm tired of being trotted around to a dozen cafés and not getting *one thing* fit to eat."

"When did we go around to a dozen cafés?"

"You'd *have* to in *this* town," insisted Gloria with ready sophistry.

Anthony, bewildered, tried another tack.

"Why don't you try to eat it? It can't be as bad as you think."

"Just—because—I—don't—like—chicken!"

She picked up her fork and began poking contemptuously at the tomato, and Anthony expected her to begin flinging the stuffings in all directions. He was sure that she was approximately as angry as she had ever been—for an instant he had detected a spark of hate directed as much toward him as toward any one else—and Gloria angry was, for the present, unapproachable.

Then, surprisingly, he saw that she had tentatively raised the fork to her lips and tasted the chicken salad. Her frown had not abated and he stared at her anxiously, making no comment and daring scarcely to breathe. She tasted another forkful—in another moment she was eating. With difficulty Anthony restrained a chuckle; when at length he spoke his words had no possible connection with chicken salad.

This incident, with variations, ran like a lugubrious fugue through the first year of marriage; always it left Anthony baffled, irritated, and depressed. But another rough brushing of temperaments, a question of laundry-bags, he found even more annoying as it ended inevitably in a decisive defeat for him.

One afternoon in Coronado, where they made the longest stay of their trip, more than three weeks, Gloria was arraying herself brilliantly for tea. Anthony, who had been down-stairs listening to the latest rumor bulletins of war in Europe, entered the room, kissed the back of her powdered neck, and went to his dresser. After a great pulling out and pushing in of drawers, evidently unsatisfactory, he turned around to the Unfinished Masterpiece.

"Got any handkerchiefs, Gloria?" he asked.

Gloria shook her golden head.

"Not a one. I'm using one of yours."

"The last one, I deduce." He laughed dryly.

"Is it?" She applied an emphatic though very delicate contour to her lips.

"Isn't the laundry back?"

"I don't know."

Anthony hesitated—then, with sudden discernment, opened the closet door. His suspicions were verified. On the hook provided hung the blue bag furnished by the hotel. This was full of his clothes—he had put them there himself. The floor beneath it was littered with an astonishing mass of finery—lingerie, stockings, dresses, nightgowns, and pajamas—most of it scarcely worn but all of it coming indubitably under the general heading of Gloria's laundry.

He stood holding the closet door open.

"Why, Gloria!"

"What?"

The lip line was being erased and corrected according to some mysterious perspective; not a finger trembled as she manipulated the lip-stick, not a glance wavered in his direction. It was a triumph of concentration.

"Haven't you ever sent out the laundry?"

"Is it there?"

"It most certainly is."

"Well, I guess I haven't, then."

"Gloria," began Anthony, sitting down on the bed and trying to catch her mirrored eyes, "you're a nice fellow, you are! I've sent it out every time it's been sent since we left New York, and over a week ago you promised you'd do it for a change. All you'd have to do would be to cram your own junk into that bag and ring for the chambermaid."

"Oh, why fuss about the laundry?" exclaimed Gloria petulantly, "I'll take care of it."

"I haven't fussed about it. I'd just as soon divide the bother with you, but when we run out of handkerchiefs it's darn near time something's done."

Anthony considered that he was being extraordinarily logical. But Gloria, unimpressed, put away her cosmetics and casually offered him her back.

"Hook me up," she suggested; "Anthony, dearest, I forgot all about it. I meant to, honestly, and I will to-day. Don't be cross with your sweetheart."

What could Anthony do then but draw her down upon his knee and kiss a shade of color from her lips.

"But I don't mind," she murmured with a smile, radiant and magnanimous. "You can kiss all the paint off my lips any time you want."

They went down to tea. They bought some handkerchiefs in a notion store near by. All was forgotten.

But two days later Anthony looked in the closet and saw the bag still hung limp upon its hook and that the gay and vivid pile on the floor had increased surprisingly in height.

"Gloria!" he cried.

"Oh—" Her voice was full of real distress. Despairingly Anthony went to the phone and called the chambermaid.

"It seems to me," he said impatiently, "that you expect me to be some sort of French valet to you."

Gloria laughed, so infectiously that Anthony was unwise enough to smile. Unfortunate man! In some intangible manner his smile made her mistress of the situation—with an air of injured righteousness she went emphatically to the closet and began pushing her laundry violently into the bag. Anthony watched her—ashamed of himself.

"There!" she said, implying that her fingers had been worked to the bone by a brutal taskmaster.

He considered, nevertheless, that he had given her an object-lesson and that the matter was closed, but on the contrary it was merely beginning. Laundry pile followed laundry pile—at long intervals; dearth of handkerchief followed dearth of handkerchief—at short ones; not to mention dearth of sock, of shirt, of everything. And Anthony found at length that either he must send it out himself or go through the increasingly unpleasant ordeal of a verbal battle with Gloria.

Gloria and General Lee

On their way East they stopped two days in Washington, strolling about with some hostility in its atmosphere of harsh repellent light, of distance without freedom, of pomp without splendor—it seemed a pasty-pale and self-conscious city. The second day they made an ill-advised trip to General Lee's old home at Arlington.

The bus which bore them was crowded with hot, unprosperous people, and Anthony, intimate to Gloria, felt a storm brewing. It broke at the Zoo, where the party stopped for ten minutes. The Zoo, it seemed, smelt of monkeys. Anthony laughed; Gloria called down the curse of Heaven upon monkeys, including in her malevolence all the passengers of the bus and their perspiring offspring who had hied themselves monkey-ward.

Eventually the bus moved on to Arlington. There it met other busses and immediately a swarm of women and children were leaving a trail of peanut-shells through the halls of General Lee and crowding at length into the room where he was married. On the wall of this room a pleasing sign announced in large red letters "Ladies' Toilet." At this final blow Gloria broke down.

"I think it's perfectly terrible!" she said furiously, "the idea of letting these people come here! And of encouraging them by making these houses show-places."

"Well," objected Anthony, "if they weren't kept up they'd go to pieces."

"What if they did!" she exclaimed as they sought the wide pillared porch. "Do you think they've left a breath of 1860 here? This has become a thing of 1914."

"Don't you want to preserve old things?"

"But you *can't*, Anthony. Beautiful things grow to a certain height and then they fail and fade off, breathing out memories as they decay. And just as any period decays in our minds, the things of that period should decay too, and in that way they're preserved for a while in the few hearts like mine that react to them. That graveyard at Tarrytown, for instance. The asses who give money to preserve things have spoiled that too. Sleepy Hollow's gone; Washington Irving's dead and his books are rotting in our estimation year by year—then let the graveyard rot too, as it should, as all things should. Trying to preserve a century by keeping its relics up to date is like keeping a dying man alive by stimulants."

"So you think that just as a time goes to pieces its houses ought to go too?"

"Of course! Would you value your Keats letter if the signature was traced over to make it last longer? It's just because I love the past that I want this house to look back on its glamourous moment of youth and beauty, and I want its stairs to creak as if to the footsteps of women with hoop skirts and men in boots and spurs. But they've made it into a blondined, rouged-up old woman of sixty. It hasn't any right to look so prosperous. It might care enough for Lee to drop a brick now and then. How many of these—these *animals*"—she waved her hand around—"get anything from this, for all the histories and guide-books and restorations in existence? How many of them who think that, at best, appreciation is talking in undertones and walking on tiptoes would even come here if it was any trouble? I want it to smell of magnolias instead of peanuts and I want my shoes to crunch on the same gravel that Lee's boots crunched on. There's no beauty without poignancy and there's no poignancy without the feeling that it's going, men, names, books, houses—bound for dust—mortal——"

A small boy appeared beside them and, swinging a handful of banana-peels, flung them valiantly in the direction of the Potomac.

SENTIMENT

Simultaneously with the fall of Liège, Anthony and Gloria arrived in New York. In retrospect the six weeks seemed miraculously happy. They had found to a great extent, as most young couples find in some measure, that they possessed in common many fixed ideas and curiosities and odd quirks of mind; they were essentially companionable.

But it had been a struggle to keep many of their conversations on the level of discussions. Arguments were fatal to Gloria's disposition. She had all her life been associated either with her mental inferiors or with men who, under the almost hostile intimidation of her beauty, had not dared to contradict her; naturally, then, it irritated her when Anthony emerged from the state in which her pronouncements were an infallible and ultimate decision.

He failed to realize, at first, that this was the result partly of her "female" education and partly of her beauty, and he was inclined to include her with her entire sex as curiously and definitely limited. It maddened him to find she had no sense of justice. But he discovered that, when a subject did interest her, her brain tired less quickly than his. What he chiefly missed in her mind was the pedantic teleology—the sense of order and accuracy, the sense of life as a mysteriously correlated piece of patchwork, but he understood after a while that such a quality in her would have been incongruous.

Of the things they possessed in common, greatest of all was their almost uncanny pull at each other's hearts. The day they left the hotel in Coronado she sat down on one of the beds while they were packing, and began to weep bitterly.

"Dearest—" His arms were around her; he pulled her head down upon his shoulder. "What is it, my own Gloria? Tell me."

"We're going away," she sobbed. "Oh, Anthony, it's sort of the first place we've lived together. Our two little beds here—side by side—they'll be always waiting for us, and we're never coming back to 'em any more."

She was tearing at his heart as she always could. Sentiment came over him, rushed into his eyes.

"Gloria, why, we're going on to another room. And two other little beds. We're going to be together all our lives."

Words flooded from her in a low husky voice.

"But it won't be—like our two beds—ever again. Everywhere we go and move on and change, something's lost—something's left behind. You can't ever quite repeat anything, and I've been so yours, here——"

He held her passionately near, discerning far beyond any criticism of her sentiment, a wise grasping of the minute, if only an indulgence of her desire to cry—Gloria the idler, caresser of her own dreams, extracting poignancy from the memorable things of life and youth.

Later in the afternoon when he returned from the station with the tickets he found her asleep on one of the beds, her arm curled about a black object which he could not at first identify. Coming closer he found it was one of his shoes, not a particularly new one, nor clean one, but her face, tear-stained, was pressed against it, and he understood her ancient and most honorable message. There was almost ecstasy in waking her and seeing her smile at him, shy but well aware of her own nicety of imagination.

With no appraisal of the worth or dross of these two things, it seemed to Anthony that they lay somewhere near the heart of love.

The Gray House

It is in the twenties that the actual momentum of life begins to slacken, and it is a simple soul indeed to whom as many things are significant and meaningful at thirty as at ten years before. At thirty an organ-grinder is a more or less moth-eaten man who grinds an organ—and once he was an organ-grinder! The unmistakable stigma of humanity touches all those impersonal and beautiful things that only youth ever grasps in their impersonal glory. A brilliant ball, gay with light romantic laughter, wears through its own silks and satins to show the bare framework of a man-made thing—oh, that eternal hand!—a play, most tragic and most divine, becomes merely a succession of speeches, sweated over by the eternal plagiarist in the clammy hours and acted by men subject to cramps, cowardice, and manly sentiment.

And this time with Gloria and Anthony, this first year of marriage, and the gray house caught them in that stage when the organ-grinder was slowly undergoing his inevitable metamorphosis. She was twenty-three; he was twenty-six.

The gray house was, at first, of sheerly pastoral intent. They lived impatiently in Anthony's apartment for the first fortnight after the return from California, in a stifled atmosphere of open trunks, too many callers, and the eternal laundry-bags. They discussed with their friends the stupendous problem of their future. Dick and Maury would sit with them agreeing solemnly, almost thoughtfully, as Anthony ran through his list of what they "ought" to do, and where they "ought" to live.

"I'd like to take Gloria abroad," he complained, "except for this damn war—and next to that I'd sort of like to have a place in the country, somewhere near New York, of course, where I could write—or whatever I decide to do."

Gloria laughed.

"Isn't he cute?" she required of Maury. "'Whatever he decides to do!' But what am *I* going to do if he works? Maury, will you take me around if Anthony works?"

"Anyway, I'm not going to work yet," said Anthony quickly.

It was vaguely understood between them that on some misty day he would enter a sort of glorified diplomatic service and be envied by princes and prime ministers for his beautiful wife.

"Well," said Gloria helplessly, "I'm sure I don't know. We talk and talk and never get anywhere, and we ask all our friends and they just answer the way we want 'em to. I wish somebody'd take care of us."

"Why don't you go out to—out to Greenwich or something?" suggested Richard Caramel.

"I'd like that," said Gloria, brightening. "Do you think we could get a house there?"

Dick shrugged his shoulders and Maury laughed.

"You two amuse me," he said. "Of all the unpractical people! As soon as a place is mentioned you expect us to pull great piles of photographs out of our pockets showing the different styles of architecture available in bungalows."

"That's just what I don't want," wailed Gloria, "a hot stuffy bungalow, with a lot of babies next door and their father cutting the grass in his shirt sleeves——"

"For Heaven's sake, Gloria," interrupted Maury, "nobody wants to lock you up in a bungalow. Who in God's name brought bungalows into the conversation? But you'll never get a place anywhere unless you go out and hunt for it."

"Go where? You say 'go out and hunt for it,' but where?"

With dignity Maury waved his hand paw-like about the room.

"Out anywhere. Out in the country. There're lots of places."

"Thanks."

"Look here!" Richard Caramel brought his yellow eye rakishly into play. "The trouble with you two is that you're all disorganized. Do you know anything about New York State? Shut up, Anthony, I'm talking to Gloria."

"Well," she admitted finally, "I've been to two or three house parties in Portchester and around in Connecticut—but, of course, that isn't in New York State, is it? And neither is Morristown," she finished with drowsy irrelevance.

There was a shout of laughter.

"Oh, Lord!" cried Dick, "'neither is Morristown!' No, and neither is Santa Barbara, Gloria. Now listen. To begin with, unless you have a fortune there's no use considering any place like Newport or Southhampton or Tuxedo. They're out of the question."

They all agreed to this solemnly.

"And personally I hate New Jersey. Then, of course, there's upper New York, above Tuxedo."

"Too cold," said Gloria briefly. "I was there once in an automobile."

"Well, it seems to me there're a lot of towns like Rye between New York and Greenwich where you could buy a little gray house of some——"

Gloria leaped at the phrase triumphantly. For the first time since their return East she knew what she wanted.

"Oh, *yes!*" she cried. "Oh, *yes!* that's it: a little gray house with sort of white around and a whole lot of swamp maples just as brown and gold as an October picture in a gallery. Where can we find one?"

"Unfortunately, I've mislaid my list of little gray houses with swamp maples around them—but I'll try to find it. Meanwhile you take a piece of paper and write down the names of seven possible towns. And every day this week you take a trip to one of those towns."

"Oh, gosh!" protested Gloria, collapsing mentally, "why won't you do it for us? I hate trains."

"Well, hire a car, and——"

Gloria yawned.

"I'm tired of discussing it. Seems to me all we do is talk about where to live."

"My exquisite wife wearies of thought," remarked Anthony ironically. "She must have a tomato sandwich to stimulate her jaded nerves. Let's go out to tea."

As the unfortunate upshot of this conversation, they took Dick's advice literally, and two days later went out to Rye, where they wandered around with an irritated real-estate agent, like bewildered babes in the wood. They were shown houses at a hundred a month which closely adjoined other houses at a hundred a month; they were shown isolated houses to which they invariably took violent dislikes, though they submitted weakly to the agent's desire that they "look at that stove—some stove!" and to a great shaking of doorposts and tapping of walls, intended evidently to show that the house would not immediately collapse, no matter how convincingly it gave that impression. They gazed through windows into interiors furnished either "commercially" with slab-like chairs and unyielding settees, or "home-like" with the melancholy bric-à-brac of other summers—crossed tennis rackets, fit-form couches, and depressing Gibson girls. With a feeling of guilt they looked at a few really nice houses, aloof, dignified, and cool—at three hundred a month. They went away from Rye thanking the real-estate agent very much indeed.

On the crowded train back to New York the seat behind was occupied by a super-respirating Latin whose last few meals had obviously been composed entirely of garlic. They reached the apartment gratefully, almost hysterically, and Gloria rushed for a hot bath in the reproachless bathroom. So far as the question of a future abode was concerned both of them were incapacitated for a week.

The matter eventually worked itself out with unhoped-for romance. Anthony ran into the living room one afternoon fairly radiating "the idea."

"I've got it," he was exclaiming as though he had just caught a mouse. "We'll get a car."

"Gee whiz! Haven't we got troubles enough taking care of ourselves?"

"Give me a second to explain, can't you? Just let's leave our stuff with Dick and just pile a couple of suitcases in our car, the one we're going to buy—we'll have to have one in the country anyway—and just start out in the direction of New Haven. You see, as we get out of commuting distance from New York, the rents'll get cheaper, and as soon as we find a house we want we'll just settle down."

By his frequent and soothing interpolation of the word "just" he aroused her lethargic enthusiasm. Strutting violently about the room, he simulated a dynamic and irresistible efficiency. "We'll buy a car to-morrow."

Life, limping after imagination's ten-league boots, saw them out of town a week later in a cheap but sparkling new roadster, saw them through the chaotic unintelligible Bronx, then over a wide murky district which alternated cheerless blue-green wastes with suburbs of tremendous and sordid activity. They left New York at eleven and it was well past a hot and beatific noon when they moved rakishly through Pelham.

"These aren't towns," said Gloria scornfully, "these

are just city blocks plumped down coldly into waste acres. I imagine all the men here have their mustaches stained from drinking their coffee too quickly in the morning."

"And play pinochle on the commuting trains."

"What's pinochle?"

"Don't be so literal. How should I know? But it sounds as though they ought to play it."

"I like it. It sounds as if it were something where you sort of cracked your knuckles or something. . . . Let me drive."

Anthony looked at her suspiciously.

"You swear you're a good driver?"

"Since I was fourteen."

He stopped the car cautiously at the side of the road and they changed seats. Then with a horrible grinding noise the car was put in gear, Gloria adding an accompaniment of laughter which seemed to Anthony disquieting and in the worst possible taste.

"Here we go!" she yelled. "Whoo-oop!"

Their heads snapped back like marionettes on a single wire as the car leaped ahead and curved retchingly about a standing milk-wagon, whose driver stood up on his seat and bellowed after them. In the immemorial tradition of the road Anthony retorted with a few brief epigrams as to the grossness of the milk-delivering profession. He cut his remarks short, however, and turned to Gloria with the growing conviction that he had made a grave mistake in relinquishing control and that Gloria was a driver of many eccentricities and of infinite carelessness.

"Remember now!" he warned her nervously, "the man said we oughtn't to go over twenty miles an hour for the first five thousand miles."

She nodded briefly, but evidently intending to accomplish the prohibitive distance as quickly as possible, slightly increased her speed. A moment later he made another attempt.

"See that sign? Do you want to get us pinched?"

"Oh, for Heaven's sake," cried Gloria in exasperation, "you *always* exaggerate things so!"

"Well, I don't want to get arrested."

"Who's arresting you? You're so persistent—just like you were about my cough medicine last night."

"It was for your own good."

"Ha! I might as well be living with mama."

"What a thing to say to me!"

A standing policeman swerved into view, was hastily passed.

"See him?" demanded Anthony.

"Oh, you drive me crazy! He didn't arrest us, did he?"

"When he does it'll be too late," countered Anthony brilliantly.

Her reply was scornful, almost injured.

"Why, this old thing won't *go* over thirty-five."

"It isn't old."

"It is in spirit."

That afternoon the car joined the laundry-bags and Gloria's appetite as one of the trinity of contention. He warned her of railroad tracks; he pointed out approaching automobiles; finally he insisted on taking the wheel and a furious, insulted Gloria sat silently beside him between the towns of Larchmont and Rye.

But it was due to this furious silence of hers that the gray house materialized from its abstraction, for just beyond Rye he surrendered gloomily to it and re-relinquished the wheel. Mutely he beseeched her and Gloria, instantly cheered, vowed to be more careful. But because a discourteous street-car persisted callously in remaining upon its track Gloria ducked down a side-street—and thereafter that afternoon was never able to find her way back to the Post Road. The street they finally mistook for it lost its Post-Road aspect when it had gone five miles from Cos Cob. Its macadam became gravel, then dirt—moreover, it narrowed and developed a border of maple trees, through which filtered the westering sun, making its endless experiments with shadow designs upon the long grass.

"We're lost now," complained Anthony.

"Read that sign!"

"Marietta—Five Miles. What's Marietta?"

"Never heard of it, but let's go on. We can't turn here and there's probably a detour back to the Post Road."

The way became scarred with deepening ruts and insidious shoulders of stone. Three farmhouses faced them momentarily, slid by. A town sprang up in a cluster of dull roofs around a white tall steeple.

Then Gloria, hesitating between two approaches, and making her choice too late, drove over a fire-hydrant and ripped the transmission violently from the car.

It was dark when the real-estate agent of Marietta showed them the gray house. They came upon it just west of the village, where it rested against a sky that was a warm blue cloak buttoned with tiny stars. The gray house had been there when women who kept cats were probably witches, when Paul Revere made false teeth in Boston preparatory to arousing the great commercial people, when our ancestors were gloriously deserting Washington in droves. Since those days the house had been bolstered up in a feeble corner, considerably repartitioned and newly plastered inside, amplified by a kitchen and added to by a side-porch—but, save for where some jovial oaf had roofed the new kitchen with red tin, Colonial it defiantly remained.

"How did you happen to come to Marietta?" demanded the real-estate agent in a tone that was first cousin to suspicion. He was showing them through four spacious and airy bedrooms.

"We broke down," explained Gloria. "I drove over a fire-hydrant and we had ourselves towed to the garage and then we saw your sign."

The man nodded, unable to follow such a sally of spontaneity. There was something subtly immoral in doing anything without several months' consideration.

They signed a lease that night and, in the agent's car, returned jubilantly to the somnolent and dilapidated Marietta Inn, which was too broken for even the chance immoralities and consequent gaieties of a country roadhouse. Half the night they lay awake planning the things they were to do there. Anthony was going to work at an astounding pace on his history and thus ingratiate himself with his cynical grandfather. . . . When the car was repaired they would explore the country and join the nearest "really nice" club, where Gloria would play golf "or something" while Anthony wrote. This, of course, was Anthony's idea—Gloria was sure she wanted but to read and dream and be fed tomato sandwiches and lemonades by some angelic servant still in a shadowy hinterland. Between paragraphs Anthony would come and kiss her as she lay indolently in the hammock. . . . The hammock! a host of new dreams in tune to its imagined rhythm, while the wind stirred it and waves of sun undulated over the shadows of blown wheat, or the dusty road freckled and darkened with quiet summer rain. . . .

And guests—here they had a long argument, both of them trying to be extraordinarily mature and far-sighted. Anthony claimed that they would need people at least every other week-end "as a sort of change." This provoked an involved and extremely sentimental conversation as to whether Anthony did not consider Gloria change enough. Though he assured her that he did, she insisted upon doubting him. . . . Eventually the conversation assumed its eternal monotone: "What then? Oh, what'll we do then?"

"Well, we'll have a dog," suggested Anthony.

"I don't want one. I want a kitty." She went thoroughly and with great enthusiasm into the history, habits, and tastes of a cat she had once possessed. Anthony considered that it must have been a horrible character with neither personal magnetism nor a loyal heart.

Later they slept, to wake an hour before dawn with the gray house dancing in phantom glory before their dazzled eyes.

The Soul of Gloria

For that autumn the gray house welcomed them with a rush of sentiment that falsified its cynical old age. True, there were the laundry-bags, there was Gloria's appetite, there was Anthony's tendency to brood and his imaginative "nervousness," but there were intervals also of an unhoped-for serenity. Close together on the porch they would wait for the moon to stream across the silver acres of farmland, jump a thick wood and tumble waves of radiance at their feet. In such a moonlight Gloria's face was of a pervading, reminiscent white, and with a modicum of effort they would slip off the blinders of custom and each would find in the other almost the quintessential romance of the vanished June.

One night while her head lay upon his heart and their cigarettes glowed in swerving buttons of light through the dome of darkness over the bed, she spoke for the first time and fragmentarily of the men who had hung for brief moments on her beauty.

"Do you ever think of them?" he asked her.

"Only occasionally—when something happens that recalls a particular man."

"What do you remember—their kisses?"

"All sorts of things. . . . Men are different with women."

"Different in what way?"

"Oh, entirely—and quite inexpressibly. Men who had the most firmly rooted reputation for being this way or that would sometimes be surprisingly inconsistent with me. Brutal men were tender, negligible men were astonishingly loyal and lovable, and, often, honorable men took attitudes that were anything but honorable."

"For instance?"

"Well, there was a boy named Percy Wolcott from Cornell who was quite a hero in college, a great athlete, and saved a lot of people from a fire or something like that. But I soon found he was stupid in a rather dangerous way."

"What way?"

"It seems he had some naïve conception of a woman 'fit to be his wife,' a particular conception that I used to run into a lot and that always drove me wild. He demanded a girl who'd never been kissed and who liked to sew and sit home and pay tribute to his self-esteem. And I'll bet a hat if he's gotten an idiot to sit and be stupid with him he's tearing out on the side with some much speedier lady."

"I'd be sorry for his wife."

"I wouldn't. Think what an ass she'd be not to realize it before she married him. He's the sort whose idea of honoring and respecting a woman would be never to give her any excitement. With the best intentions, he was deep in the dark ages."

"What was his attitude toward you?"

"I'm coming to that. As I told you—or did I tell you?—he was mighty good-looking: big brown honest eyes and one of those smiles that guarantee the heart behind it is twenty-karat gold. Being young and credulous, I thought he had some discretion, so I kissed him fervently one night when we were riding around after a dance at the Homestead at Hot Springs. It had been a wonderful week, I remember—with the most luscious trees spread like green lather, sort of, all over the valley and a mist rising out of them on October mornings like bonfires lit to turn them brown——"

"How about your friend with the ideals?" interrupted Anthony.

"It seems that when he kissed me he began to think that perhaps he could get away with a little more, that I needn't be 'respected' like this Beatrice Fairfax glad-girl of his imagination."

"What'd he do?"

"Not much. I pushed him off a sixteen-foot embankment before he was well started."

"Hurt him?" inquired Anthony with a laugh.

"Broke his arm and sprained his ankle. He told the story all over Hot Springs, and when his arm healed a man named Barley who liked me fought him and broke it over again. Oh, it was all an awful mess. He threatened to sue Barley, and Barley—he was from Georgia—was seen buying a gun in town. But before that mama had dragged me North again, much against my will, so I never did find out all that happened—though I saw Barley once in the Vanderbilt lobby."

Anthony laughed long and loud.

"What a career! I suppose I ought to be furious because you've kissed so many men. I'm not, though."

At this she sat up in bed.

"It's funny, but I'm so sure that those kisses left no

mark on me—no taint of promiscuity, I mean—even though a man once told me in all seriousness that he hated to think I'd been a public drinking glass."

"He had his nerve."

"I just laughed and told him to think of me rather as a loving-cup that goes from hand to hand but should be valued none the less."

"Somehow it doesn't bother me—on the other hand it would, of course, if you'd done any more than kiss them. But I believe *you're* absolutely incapable of jealousy except as hurt vanity. Why don't you care what I've done? Wouldn't you prefer it if I'd been absolutely innocent?"

"It's all in the impression it might have made on you. *My* kisses were because the man was good-looking, or because there was a slick moon, or even because I've felt vaguely sentimental and a little stirred. But that's all—it's had utterly no effect on me. But you'd remember and let memories haunt you and worry you."

"Haven't you ever kissed any one like you've kissed me?"

"No," she answered simply. "As I've told you, men have tried—oh, lots of things. Any pretty girl has that experience. . . . You see," she resumed, "it doesn't matter to me how many women you've stayed with in the past, so long as it was merely a physical satisfaction, but I don't believe I could endure the idea of your ever having lived with another woman for a protracted period or even having wanted to marry some possible girl. It's different somehow. There'd be all the little intimacies remembered—and they'd dull that freshness that after all is the most precious part of love."

Rapturously he pulled her down beside him on the pillow.

"Oh, my darling," he whispered, "as if I remembered anything but your dear kisses."

Then Gloria, in a very mild voice:

"Anthony, did I hear anybody say they were thirsty?"

Anthony laughed abruptly and with a sheepish and amused grin got out of bed.

"With just a *little* piece of ice in the water," she added. "Do you suppose I could have that?"

Gloria used the adjective "little" whenever she asked a favor—it made the favor sound less arduous. But Anthony laughed again—whether she wanted a cake of ice or a marble of it, he must go down-stairs to the kitchen. . . . Her voice followed him through the hall: "And just a *little* cracker with just a *little* marmalade on it. . . ."

"Oh, gosh!" sighed Anthony in rapturous slang, "she's wonderful, that girl! She *has* it!"

"When we have a baby," she began one day—this, it had already been decided, was to be after three years—"I want it to look like you."

"Except its legs," he insinuated slyly.

"Oh, yes, except his legs. He's got to have my legs. But the rest of him can be you."

"My nose?"

Gloria hesitated.

"Well, perhaps my nose. But certainly your eyes—and my mouth, and I guess my shape of the face. I wonder; I think he'd be sort of cute if he had my hair."

"My dear Gloria, you've appropriated the whole baby."

"Well, I didn't mean to," she apologized cheerfully.

"Let him have my neck at least," he urged, regarding himself gravely in the glass. "You've often said you liked my neck because the Adam's apple doesn't show, and, besides, your neck's too short."

"Why, it is *not!*" she cried indignantly, turning to the mirror, "it's just right. "I don't believe I've ever seen a better neck."

"It's too short," he repeated teasingly.

"Short?" Her tone expressed exasperated wonder. "Short? You're crazy!" She elongated and contracted it to convince herself of its reptilian sinuousness. "Do you call *that* a short neck?"

"One of the shortest I've ever seen."

For the first time in weeks tears started from Gloria's eyes and the look she gave him had a quality of real pain.

"Oh, Anthony——"

"My Lord, Gloria!" He approached her in bewilderment and took her elbows in his hands. "Don't cry, *please!* Didn't you know I was only kidding? Gloria, look at me! Why, dearest, you've got the longest neck I've ever seen. Honestly."

Her tears dissolved in a twisted smile.

"Well—you shouldn't have said that, then. Let's talk about the b-baby."

Anthony paced the floor and spoke as though rehearsing for a debate.

"To put it briefly, there are two babies we could have, two distinct and logical babies, utterly differentiated. There's the baby that's the combination of the best of both of us. Your body, my eyes, my mind, your intelligence—and then there is the baby which is our worst—my body, your disposition, and my irresolution."

"I like that second baby," she said.

"What I'd really like," continued Anthony, "would be to have two sets of triplets one year apart and then experiment with the six boys——"

"Poor me," she interjected.

"—I'd educate them each in a different country and by a different system and when they were twenty-three I'd call them together and see what they were like."

"Let's have 'em all with my neck," suggested Gloria.

The End of a Chapter

The car was at length repaired and with a deliberate vengeance took up where it left off the business of causing infinite dissension. Who should drive? How fast should Gloria go? These two questions and the eternal recriminations involved ran through the days. They motored to the Post-Road towns, Rye, Portchester, and Greenwich, and called on a dozen friends, mostly Gloria's, who all seemed to be in different stages of having babies and in this respect as well as in others bored her to a point of nervous distraction. For an hour after each visit she would bite her fingers furiously and be inclined to take out her rancor on Anthony.

"I loathe women," she cried in a mild temper. "What on earth can you say to them—except talk 'lady-lady'? I've enthused over a dozen babies that I've wanted only to choke. And every one of those girls is either incipiently jealous and suspicious of her husband if he's charming or beginning to be bored with him if he isn't."

"Don't you ever intend to see any women?"

"I don't know. They never seem clean to me—never—never. Except just a few. Constance Shaw—you know, the Mrs. Merriam who came over to see us last Tuesday—is almost the only one. She's so tall and fresh-looking and stately."

"I don't like them so tall."

Though they went to several dinner dances at various country clubs, they decided that the autumn was too nearly over for them to "go out" on any scale, even had they been so inclined. He hated golf; Gloria liked it only mildly, and though she enjoyed a violent rush that some undergraduates gave her one night and was glad that Anthony should be proud of her beauty, she also perceived that their hostess for the evening, a Mrs. Granby, was somewhat disquieted by the fact that Anthony's classmate, Alec Granby, joined with enthusiasm in the rush. The Granbys never phoned again, and though Gloria laughed, it piqued her not a little.

"You see," she explained to Anthony, "if I wasn't married it wouldn't worry her—but she's been to the movies in her day and she thinks I may be a vampire. But the point is that placating such people requires an effort that I'm simply unwilling to make. . . . And those cute little freshmen making eyes at me and paying me idiotic compliments! I've grown up, Anthony."

Marietta itself offered little social life. Half a dozen farm-estates formed a hectagon around it, but these belonged to ancient men who displayed themselves only as inert, gray-thatched lumps in the back of limousines on their way to the station, whither they were sometimes accompanied by equally ancient and doubly massive wives. The townspeople were a particularly uninteresting type—unmarried females were predominant for the most part—with school-festival horizons and souls bleak as the forbidding white architecture of the three churches. The only native with whom they came into close contact was the broad-hipped, broad-shouldered Swedish girl who came every day to do their work. She was silent and efficient, and Gloria, after finding her weeping violently into her bowed arms upon the kitchen table, developed an uncanny fear of her and stopped complaining about the food. Because of her untold and esoteric grief the girl stayed on.

Gloria's penchant for premonitions and her bursts of vague supernaturalism were a surprise to Anthony. Either some complex, properly and scientifically inhibited in the early years with her Bilphistic mother, or some inherited hypersensitiveness, made her susceptible to any suggestion of the psychic, and, far from gullible about the motives of people, she was inclined to credit any extraordinary happening attributed to the whimsical perambulations of the buried. The desperate squeakings about the old house on windy nights that to Anthony were burglars with revolvers ready in hand represented to Gloria the auras, evil and restive, of dead generations, expiating the inexpiable upon the ancient and romantic hearth. One night, because of two swift bangs downstairs, which Anthony fearfully but unavailingly investigated, they lay awake nearly until dawn asking each other examination-paper questions about the history of the world.

In October Muriel came out for a two weeks' visit. Gloria had called her on long-distance, and Miss Kane ended the conversation characteristically by saying "All-ll-ll righty. I'll be there with bells!" She arrived with a dozen popular songs under her arm.

"You ought to have a phonograph out here in the country," she said, "just a little Vic—they don't cost much. Then whenever you're lonesome you can have Caruso or Al Jolson right at your door."

She worried Anthony to distraction by telling him that "he was the first clever man she had ever known and she got so tired of shallow people." He wondered that people fell in love with such women. Yet he supposed that under a certain impassioned glance even she might take on a softness and promise.

But Gloria, violently showing off her love for Anthony, was diverted into a state of purring content.

Finally Richard Caramel arrived for a garrulous and to Gloria painfully literary week-end, during which he discussed himself with Anthony long after she lay in childlike sleep up-stairs.

"It's been mighty funny, this success and all," said Dick. "Just before the novel appeared I'd been trying, without success, to sell some short stories. Then, after my book came out, I polished up three and had them accepted by one of the magazines that had rejected them before. I've done a lot of them since; publishers don't pay me for my book till this winter."

"Don't let the victor belong to the spoils."

"You mean write trash?" He considered. "If you mean deliberately injecting a slushy fade-out into each one, I'm not. But I don't suppose I'm being so careful. I'm certainly writing faster and I don't seem to be thinking as much as I used to. Perhaps it's because I don't get any conversation, now that you're married and Maury's gone to Philadelphia. Haven't the old urge and ambition. Early success and all that."

"Doesn't it worry you?"

"Frantically. I get a thing I call sentence-fever that must be like buck-fever—it's a sort of intense literary self-consciousness that comes when I try to force myself. But the really awful days aren't when I think I can't write. They're when I wonder whether any writing is worth while at all—I mean whether I'm not a sort of glorified buffoon."

"I like to hear you talk that way," said Anthony with a touch of his old patronizing insolence. "I was afraid you'd gotten a bit idiotic over your work. Read the damnedest interview you gave out——"

Dick interrupted with an agonized expression.

"Good Lord! Don't mention it. Young lady wrote it—most admiring young lady. Kept telling me my work was 'strong,' and I sort of lost my head and made a lot of strange pronouncements. Some of it was good, though, don't you think?"

"Oh, yes; that part about the wise writer writing for the youth of his generation, the critic of the next, and the schoolmaster of ever afterward."

"Oh, I believe a lot of it," admitted Richard Caramel with a faint beam. "It simply was a mistake to give it out."

In November they moved into Anthony's apartment, from which they sallied triumphantly to the Yale-Harvard and Harvard-Princeton football games, to the St. Nicholas ice-skating rink, to a thorough round of the theatres and to a miscellany of entertainments—from small, staid dances to the great affairs that Gloria loved, held in those few houses where lackeys with powdered wigs scurried around in magnificent Anglomania under the direction of gigantic majordomos. Their intention was to go abroad the first of the year or, at any rate, when the war was over. Anthony had actually completed a Chestertonian essay on the twelfth century by way of introduction to his proposed book and Gloria had done some extensive research work on the question of Russian sable coats—in fact the winter was approaching quite comfortably, when the Bilphistic demiurge decided suddenly in mid-December that Mrs. Gilbert's soul had aged sufficiently in its present incarnation. In consequence Anthony took a miserable and hysterical Gloria out to Kansas City, where, in the fashion of mankind, they paid the terrible and mind-shaking deference to the dead.

Mr. Gilbert became, for the first and last time in his life, a truly pathetic figure. That woman he had broken to wait upon his body and play congregation to his mind had ironically deserted him—just when he could not much longer have supported her. Never again would he be able so satisfactorily to bore and bully a human soul.

CHAPTER II

SYMPOSIUM

Gloria had lulled Anthony's mind to sleep. She, who seemed of all women the wisest and the finest, hung like a brilliant curtain across his doorways, shutting out the light of the sun. In those first years what he believed bore invariably the stamp of Gloria; he saw the sun always through the pattern of the curtain.

It was a sort of lassitude that brought them back to Marietta for another summer. Through a golden enervating spring they had loitered, restive and lazily extravagant, along the California coast, joining other parties intermittently and drifting from Pasadena to Coronado, from Coronado to Santa Barbara, with no purpose more apparent than Gloria's desire to dance by different music or catch some infinitesimal variant among the changing colors of the sea. Out of the Pacific there rose to greet them savage rocklands and equally barbaric hostelries built that at tea-time one might drowse into a languid wicker bazaar glorified by the polo costumes of Southhampton and Lake Forest and Newport and Palm Beach. And, as the waves met and splashed and glittered in the most placid of the bays, so they joined this group and that, and with them shifted stations, murmuring ever of those strange unsubstantial gaieties in wait just over the next green and fruitful valley.

A simple healthy leisure class it was—the best of the men not unpleasantly undergraduate—they seemed to be on a perpetual candidates list for some etherealized

"Porcellian" or "Skull and Bones" extended out indefinitely into the world; the women, of more than average beauty, fragilely athletic, somewhat idiotic as hostesses but charming and infinitely decorative as guests. Sedately and gracefully they danced the steps of their selection in the balmy tea hours, accomplishing with a certain dignity the movements so horribly burlesqued by clerk and chorus girl the country over. It seemed ironic that in this lone and discredited offspring of the arts Americans should excel, unquestionably.

Having danced and splashed through a lavish spring, Anthony and Gloria found that they had spent too much money and for this must go into retirement for a certain period. There was Anthony's "work," they said. Almost before they knew it they were back in the gray house, more aware now that other lovers had slept there, other names had been called over the banisters, other couples had sat upon the porch steps watching the gray-green fields and the black bulk of woods beyond.

It was the same Anthony, more restless, inclined to quicken only under the stimulus of several high-balls, faintly, almost imperceptibly, apathetic toward Gloria. But Gloria—she would be twenty-four in August and was in an attractive but sincere panic about it. Six years to thirty! Had she been less in love with Anthony her sense of the flight of time would have expressed itself in a reawakened interest in other men, in a deliberate intention of extracting a transient gleam of romance from every potential lover who glanced at her with lowered brows over a shining dinner table. She said to Anthony one day:

"How I feel is that if I wanted anything I'd take it. That's what I've always thought all my life. But it happens that I want you, and so I just haven't room for any other desires."

They were bound eastward through a parched and lifeless Indiana, and she had looked up from one of her beloved moving picture magazines to find a casual conversation suddenly turned grave.

Anthony frowned out the car window. As the track crossed a country road a farmer appeared momentarily in his wagon; he was chewing on a straw and was apparently the same farmer they had passed a dozen times before, sitting in silent and malignant symbolism. As Anthony turned to Gloria his frown intensified.

"You worry me," he objected; "I can imagine *wanting* another woman under certain transitory circumstances, but I can't imagine taking her."

"But I don't feel that way, Anthony. I can't be bothered resisting things I want. My way is not to want them—to want nobody but you."

"Yet when I think that if you just happened to take a fancy to some one——"

"Oh, don't be an idiot!" she exclaimed. "There'd be nothing casual about it. And I can't even imagine the possibility."

This emphatically closed the conversation. Anthony's unfailing appreciation made her happier in his company than in any one's else. She definitely enjoyed him—she loved him. So the summer began very much as had the one before.

There was, however, one radical change in ménage. The icy-hearted Scandinavian, whose austere cooking and sardonic manner of waiting on table had so depressed Gloria, gave way to an exceedingly efficient Japanese whose name was Tanalahaka, but who confessed that he heeded any summons which included the dissyllable "Tana."

Tana was unusually small even for a Japanese, and displayed a somewhat naïve conception of himself as a man of the world. On the day of his arrival from "R. Gugimoniki, Japanese Reliable Employment Agency," he called Anthony into his room to see the treasures of his trunk. These included a large collection of Japanese post cards, which he was all for explaining to his employer at once, individually and at great length. Among them were half a dozen of pornographic intent and plainly of American origin, though the makers had modestly omitted both their names and the form for mailing. He next brought out some of his own handiwork—a pair of American pants, which he had made himself, and two suits of solid silk underwear. He informed Anthony confidentially as to the purpose for which these latter were reserved. The next exhibit was a rather good copy of an etching of Abraham Lincoln, to whose face he had given an unmistakable Japanese cast. Last came a flute; he had made it himself but it was broken: he was going to fix it soon.

After these polite formalities, which Anthony conjectured must be native to Japan, Tana delivered a long harangue in splintered English on the relation of master and servant from which Anthony gathered that he had worked on large estates but had always quarrelled with the other servants because they were not honest. They had a great time over the word "honest," and in fact became rather irritated with each other, because Anthony persisted stubbornly that Tana was trying to say "hornets," and even went to the extent of buzzing in the manner of a bee and flapping his arms to imitate wings.

After three-quarters of an hour Anthony was released with the warm assurance that they would have other nice chats in which Tana would tell "how we do in my countree."

Such was Tana's garrulous première in the gray

house—and he fulfilled its promise. Though he was conscientious and honorable, he was unquestionably a terrific bore. He seemed unable to control his tongue, sometimes continuing from paragraph to paragraph with a look akin to pain in his small brown eyes.

Sunday and Monday afternoons he read the comic sections of the newspapers. One cartoon which contained a facetious Japanese butler diverted him enormously, though he claimed that the protagonist, who to Anthony appeared clearly Oriental, had really an American face. The difficulty with the funny paper was that when, aided by Anthony, he had spelled out the last three pictures and assimilated their context with a concentration surely adequate for Kant's "Critique," he had entirely forgotten what the first pictures were about.

In the middle of June Anthony and Gloria celebrated their first anniversary by having a "date." Anthony knocked at the door and she ran to let him in. Then they sat together on the couch calling over those names they had made for each other, new combinations of endearments ages old. Yet to this "date" was appended no attenuated good-night with its ecstasy of regret.

Later in June horror leered out at Gloria, struck at her and frightened her bright soul back half a generation. Then slowly it faded out, faded back into that impenetrable darkness whence it had come—taking relentlessly its modicum of youth.

With an infallible sense of the dramatic it chose a little railroad station in a wretched village near Portchester. The station platform lay all day bare as a prairie, exposed to the dusty yellow sun and to the glance of that most obnoxious type of countryman who lives near a metropolis and has attained its cheap smartness without its urbanity. A dozen of these yokels, red-eyed, cheerless as scarecrows, saw the incident. Dimly it passed across their confused and uncomprehending minds, taken at its broadest for a coarse joke, at its subtlest for a "shame." Meanwhile there upon the platform a measure of brightness faded from the world.

With Eric Merriam, Anthony had been sitting over a decanter of Scotch all the hot summer afternoon, while Gloria and Constance Merriam swam and sunned themselves at the Beach Club, the latter under a striped parasol-awning, Gloria stretched sensuously upon the soft hot sand, tanning her inevitable legs. Later they had all four played with inconsequential sandwiches; then Gloria had risen, tapping Anthony's knee with her parasol to get his attention.

"We've got to go, dear."

"Now?" He looked at her unwillingly. At that moment nothing seemed of more importance than to idle on that shady porch drinking mellowed Scotch, while his host reminisced interminably on the byplay of some forgotten political campaign.

"We've really got to go," repeated Gloria. "We can get a taxi to the station. . . . Come on, Anthony!" she commanded a bit more imperiously.

"Now see here—" Merriam, his yarn cut off, made conventional objections, meanwhile provocatively filling his guest's glass with a high-ball that should have been sipped through ten minutes. But at Gloria's annoyed "We really *must!*" Anthony drank it off, got to his feet and made an elaborate bow to his hostess.

"It seems we 'must,'" he said, with little grace.

In a minute he was following Gloria down a garden-walk between tall rose-bushes, her parasol brushing gently the June-blooming leaves. Most inconsiderate, he thought, as they reached the road. He felt with injured naïvete that Gloria should not have interrupted such innocent and harmless enjoyment. The whiskey had both soothed and clarified the restless things in his mind. It occurred to him that she had taken this same attitude several times before. Was he always to retreat from pleasant episodes at a touch of her parasol or a flicker of her eye? His unwillingness blurred to ill will, which rose within him like a resistless bubble. He kept silent, perversely inhibiting a desire to reproach her. They found a taxi in front of the Inn; rode silently to the little station. . . .

Then Anthony knew what he wanted—to assert his will against this cool and impervious girl, to obtain with one magnificent effort a mastery that seemed infinitely desirable.

"Let's go over to see the Barneses," he said without looking at her. "I don't feel like going home."

—Mrs. Barnes, née Rachael Jerryl, had a summer place several miles from Redgate.

"We went there day before yesterday," she answered shortly.

"I'm sure they'd be glad to see us." He felt that that was not a strong enough note, braced himself stubbornly, and added: "I want to see the Barneses. I haven't any desire to go home."

"Well, I haven't any desire to go to the Barneses."

Suddenly they stared at each other.

"Why, Anthony," she said with annoyance, "this is Sunday night and they probably have guests for supper. Why we should go in at this hour——"

"Then why couldn't we have stayed at the Merriams'?" he burst out. "Why go home when we were having a perfectly decent time? They asked us to supper."

"They had to. Give me the money and I'll get the railroad tickets."

"I certainly will not! I'm in no humor for a ride in that damn hot train."

Gloria stamped her foot on the platform.

"Anthony, you act as if you're tight!"

"On the contrary, I'm perfectly sober."

But his voice had slipped into a husky key and she knew with certainty that this was untrue.

"If you're sober you'll give me the money for the tickets."

But it was too late to talk to him that way. In his mind was but one idea—that Gloria was being selfish, that she was always being selfish and would continue to be unless here and now he asserted himself as her master. This was the occasion of all occasions, since for a whim she had deprived him of a pleasure. His determination solidified, approached momentarily a dull and sullen hate.

"I won't go in the train," he said, his voice trembling a little with anger. "We're going to the Barneses."

"I'm not!" she cried. "If you go I'm going home alone."

"Go on, then."

Without a word she turned toward the ticket office; simultaneously he remembered that she had some money with her and that this was not the sort of victory he wanted, the sort he must have. He took a step after her and seized her arm.

"See here!" he muttered, "you're *not* going alone!"

"I certainly am—why, Anthony!" This exclamation as she tried to pull away from him and he only tightened his grasp.

He looked at her with narrowed and malicious eyes.

"Let go!" Her cry had a quality of fierceness. "If you have *any* decency you'll let go."

"Why?" He knew why. But he took a confused and not quite confident pride in holding her there.

"I'm going home, do you understand? And you're going to let me go!"

"No, I'm not."

Her eyes were burning now.

"Are you going to make a scene here?"

"I say you're not going! I'm tired of your eternal selfishness!"

"I only want to go home." Two wrathful tears started from her eyes.

"This time you're going to do what *I* say."

Slowly her body straightened: her head went back in a gesture of infinite scorn.

"I hate you!" Her low words were expelled like venom through her clenched teeth. "Oh, *let* me go! Oh, I *hate* you!" She tried to jerk herself away but he only grasped the other arm. "I hate you! I hate you!"

At Gloria's fury his uncertainty returned, but he felt that now he had gone too far to give in. It seemed that he had always given in and that in her heart she had despised him for it. Ah, she might hate him now, but afterward she would admire him for his dominance.

The approaching train gave out a premonitory siren that tumbled melodramatically toward them down the glistening blue tracks. Gloria tugged and strained to free herself, and words older than the Book of Genesis came to her lips.

"Oh, you brute!" she sobbed. "Oh, you brute! Oh, I hate you! Oh, you brute! Oh——"

On the station platform other prospective passengers were beginning to turn and stare; the drone of the train was audible, it increased to a clamor. Gloria's efforts redoubled, then ceased altogether, and she stood there trembling and hot-eyed at this helpless humiliation, as the engine roared and thundered into the station.

Low, below the flood of steam and the grinding of the brakes came her voice:

"Oh, if there was one *man* here you couldn't do this! You couldn't do this! You coward! You coward, oh, you coward!"

Anthony, silent, trembling himself, gripped her rigidly, aware that faces, dozens of them, curiously unmoved, shadows of a dream, were regarding him. Then the bells distilled metallic crashes that were like physical pain, the smoke-stacks volleyed in slow acceleration at the sky, and in a moment of noise and gray gaseous turbulence the line of faces ran by, moved off, became indistinct—until suddenly there was only the sun slanting east across the tracks and a volume of sound decreasing far off like a train made out of tin thunder. He dropped her arms. He had won.

Now, if he wished, he might laugh. The test was done and he had sustained his will with violence. Let leniency walk in the wake of victory.

"We'll hire a car here and drive back to Marietta," he said with fine reserve.

For answer Gloria seized his hand with both of hers and raising it to her mouth bit deeply into his thumb. He scarcely noticed the pain; seeing the blood spurt he absent-mindedly drew out his handkerchief and wrapped the wound. That too was part of the triumph he supposed—it was inevitable that defeat should thus be resented—and as such was beneath notice.

She was sobbing, almost without tears, profoundly and bitterly.

"I won't go! I won't go! You—can't—make—me—go! You've—you've killed any love I ever had for you, and any respect. But all that's left in me would die before I'd move from this place. Oh, if I'd thought *you'd* lay your hands on me——"

"You're going with me," he said brutally, "if I have to carry you."

He turned, beckoned to a taxicab, told the driver to go to Marietta. The man dismounted and swung the door open. Anthony faced his wife and said between his clenched teeth:

"Will you get in?—or will I *put* you in?"

With a subdued cry of infinite pain and despair she yielded herself up and got into the car.

All the long ride, through the increasing dark of twilight, she sat huddled in her side of the car, her silence broken by an occasional dry and solitary sob. Anthony stared out the window, his mind working dully on the slowly changing significance of what had occurred. Something was wrong—that last cry of Gloria's had struck a chord which echoed posthumously and with incongruous disquiet in his heart. He must be right—yet, she seemed such a pathetic little thing now, broken and dispirited, humiliated beyond the measure of her lot to bear. The sleeves of her dress were torn; her parasol was gone, forgotten on the platform. It was a new costume, he remembered, and she had been so proud of it that very morning when they had left the house. . . . He began wondering if any one they knew had seen the incident. And persistently there recurred to him her cry:

"All that's left in me would die——"

This gave him a confused and increasing worry. It fitted so well with the Gloria who lay in the corner—no longer a proud Gloria, nor any Gloria he had known. He asked himself if it were possible. While he did not believe she would cease to love him—this, of course, was unthinkable—it was yet problematical whether Gloria without her arrogance, her independence, her virginal confidence and courage, would be the girl of his glory, the radiant woman who was precious and charming because she was ineffably, triumphantly herself.

He was very drunk even then, so drunk as not to realize his own drunkenness. When they reached the gray house he went to his own room and, his mind still wrestling helplessly and sombrely with what he had done, fell into a deep stupor on his bed.

It was after one o'clock and the hall seemed extraordinarily quiet when Gloria, wide-eyed and sleepless, traversed it and pushed open the door of his room. He had been too befuddled to open the windows and the air was stale and thick with whiskey. She stood for a moment by his bed, a slender, exquisitely graceful figure in her boyish silk pajamas—then with abandon she flung herself upon him, half waking him in the frantic emotion of her embrace, dropping her warm tears upon his throat.

"Oh, Anthony!" she cried passionately, "oh, my darling, you don't know what you did!"

Yet in the morning, coming early into her room, he knelt down by her bed and cried like a little boy, as though it was his heart that had been broken.

"It seemed, last night," she said gravely, her fingers playing in his hair, "that all the part of me you loved, the part that was worth knowing, all the pride and fire, was gone. I knew that what was left of me would always love you, but never in quite the same way."

Nevertheless, she was aware even then that she would forget in time and that it is the manner of life seldom to strike but always to wear away. After that morning the incident was never mentioned and its deep wound healed with Anthony's hand—and if there was triumph some darker force than theirs possessed it, possessed the knowledge and the victory.

Nietzschean Incident

Gloria's independence, like all sincere and profound qualities, had begun unconsciously, but, once brought to her attention by Anthony's fascinated discovery of it, it assumed more nearly the proportions of a formal code. From her conversation it might be assumed that all her energy and vitality went into a violent affirmation of the negative principle "Never give a damn."

"Not for anything or anybody," she said, "except myself and, by implication, for Anthony. That's the rule of all life and if it weren't I'd be that way anyhow. Nobody'd do anything for me if it didn't gratify them to, and I'd do as little for them."

She was on the front porch of the nicest lady in Marietta when she said this, and as she finished she gave a curious little cry and sank in a dead faint to the porch floor.

The lady brought her to and drove her home in her car. It had occurred to the estimable Gloria that she was probably with child.

She lay upon the long lounge down-stairs. Day was slipping warmly out the window, touching the late roses on the porch pillars.

"All I think of ever is that I love you," she wailed. "I value my body because you think it's beautiful. And this body of mine—of yours—to have it grow ugly and shapeless? It's simply intolerable. Oh, Anthony, I'm not afraid of the pain."

He consoled her desperately—but in vain. She continued:

"And then afterward I might have wide hips and be pale, with all my freshness gone and no radiance in my hair."

He paced the floor with his hands in his pockets, asking:

"Is it certain?"

"*I* don't know anything. I've always hated obstrics, or whatever you call them. I thought I'd have a child some time. But not now."

"Well, for God's sake don't lie there and go to pieces."

Her sobs lapsed. She drew down a merciful silence from the twilight which filled the room. "Turn on the lights," she pleaded. "These days seem so short—June seemed—to—have—longer days when I was a little girl."

The lights snapped on and it was as though blue drapes of softest silk had been dropped behind the windows and the door. Her pallor, her immobility, without grief now, or joy, awoke his sympathy.

"Do you want me to have it?" she asked listlessly.

"I'm indifferent. That is, I'm neutral. If you have it I'll probably be glad. If you don't—well, that's all right too."

"I wish you'd make up your mind one way or the other!"

"Suppose you make up *your* mind."

She looked at him contemptuously, scorning to answer.

"You'd think you'd been singled out of all the women in the world for this crowning indignity."

"What if I do!" she cried angrily. "It isn't an indignity for them. It's their one excuse for living. It's the one thing they're good for. It *is* an indignity for *me*."

"See here, Gloria, I'm with you whatever you do, but for God's sake be a sport about it."

"Oh, don't *fuss* at me!" she wailed.

They exchanged a mute look of no particular significance but of much stress. Then Anthony took a book from the shelf and dropped into a chair.

Half an hour later her voice came out of the intense stillness that pervaded the room and hung like incense on the air.

"I'll drive over and see Constance Merriam to-morrow."

"All right. And I'll go to Tarrytown and see Grampa."

"—You see," she added, "it isn't that I'm afraid—of this or anything else. I'm being true to me, you know."

"I know," he agreed.

The Practical Men

Adam Patch, in a pious rage against the Germans, subsisted on the war news. Pin maps plastered his walls; atlases were piled deep on tables convenient to his hand together with "Photographic Histories of the World War," official Explain-alls, and the "Personal Impressions" of war correspondents and of Privates X, Y, and Z. Several times during Anthony's visit his grandfather's secretary, Edward Shuttleworth, the one-time "Accomplished Gin-physician" of "Pat's Place" in Hoboken, now shod with righteous indignation, would appear with an extra. The old man attacked each paper with untiring fury, tearing out those columns which appeared to him of sufficient pregnancy for preservation and thrusting them into one of his already bulging files.

"Well, what have you been doing?" he asked Anthony blandly. "Nothing? Well, I thought so. I've been intending to drive over and see you, all summer."

"I've been writing. Don't you remember the essay I sent you—the one I sold to The Florentine last winter?"

"Essay? You never sent *me* any essay."

"Oh, yes, I did. We talked about it."

Adam Patch shook his head mildly.

"Oh, no. You never sent *me* any essay. You may have thought you sent it but it never reached me."

"Why, you read it, Grampa," insisted Anthony, somewhat exasperated, "you read it and disagreed with it."

The old man suddenly remembered, but this was made apparent only by a partial falling open of his mouth, displaying rows of gray gums. Eying Anthony with a green and ancient stare he hesitated between confessing his error and covering it up.

"So you're writing," he said quickly. "Well, why don't you go over and write about these Germans? Write something real, something about what's going on, something people can read."

"Anybody can't be a war correspondent," objected Anthony. "You have to have some newspaper willing to buy your stuff. And I can't spare the money to go over as a free-lance."

"I'll send you over," suggested his grandfather surprisingly. "I'll get you over as an authorized correspondent of any newspaper you pick out."

Anthony recoiled from the idea—almost simultaneously he bounded toward it.

"I—don't—know——"

He would have to leave Gloria, whose whole life yearned toward him and enfolded him. Gloria was in trouble. Oh, the thing wasn't feasible—yet—he saw himself in khaki, leaning, as all war correspondents lean, upon a heavy stick, portfolio at shoulder—trying to look like an Englishman. "I'd like to think it over," he confessed. "It's certainly very kind of you. I'll think it over and I'll let you know."

Thinking it over absorbed him on the journey to New York. He had had one of those sudden flashes of illumination vouchsafed to all men who are dominated by a strong and beloved woman, which show them a world of harder men, more fiercely trained and grappling with the abstractions of thought and war. In that world the arms of Gloria would exist only as the hot embrace of a chance mistress, coolly sought and quickly forgotten. . . .

These unfamiliar phantoms were crowding closely about him when he boarded his train for Marietta, in the Grand Central Station. The car was crowded; he secured the last vacant seat and it was only after several minutes that he gave even a casual glance to the man beside him. When he did he saw a heavy lay of jaw and nose, a curved chin and small, puffed-under eyes. In a moment he recognized Joseph Bloeckman.

Simultaneously they both half rose, were half embarrassed, and exchanged what amounted to a half handshake. Then, as though to complete the matter, they both half laughed.

"Well," remarked Anthony without inspiration, "I haven't seen you for a long time." Immediately he regretted his words and started to add: "I didn't know you lived out this way." But Bloeckman anticipated him by asking pleasantly:

"How's your wife? . . ."

"She's very well. How've you been?"

"Excellent." His tone amplified the grandeur of the word.

It seemed to Anthony that during the last year Bloeckman had grown tremendously in dignity. The boiled look was gone, he seemed "done" at last. In addition he was no longer overdressed. The inappropriate facetiousness he had affected in ties had given way to a sturdy dark pattern, and his right hand, which had formerly displayed two heavy rings, was now innocent of ornament and even without the raw glow of a manicure.

This dignity appeared also in his personality. The last aura of the successful travelling-man had faded from him, that deliberate ingratiation of which the lowest form is the bawdy joke in the Pullman smoker. One imagined that, having been fawned upon financially, he had attained aloofness; having been snubbed socially, he had acquired reticence. But whatever had given him weight instead of bulk, Anthony no longer felt a correct superiority in his presence.

"D'you remember Caramel, Richard Caramel? I believe you met him one night."

"I remember. He was writing a book."

"Well, he sold it to the movies. Then they had some scenario man named Jordan work on it. Well, Dick subscribes to a clipping bureau and he's furious because about half the movie reviewers speak of the 'power and strength of William Jordan's "Demon Lover."' Didn't mention old Dick at all. You'd think this fellow Jordan had actually conceived and developed the thing."

Bloeckman nodded comprehensively.

"Most of the contracts state that the original writer's name goes into all the paid publicity. Is Caramel still writing?"

"Oh, yes. Writing hard. Short stories."

"Well, that's fine, that's fine. . . . You on this train often?"

"About once a week. We live in Marietta."

"Is that so? Well, well! I live near Cos Cob myself. Bought a place there only recently. We're only five miles apart."

"You'll have to come and see us." Anthony was surprised at his own courtesy. "I'm sure Gloria'd be delighted to see an old friend. Anybody'll tell you where the house is—it's our second season there."

"Thank you." Then, as though returning a complementary politeness: "How is your grandfather?"

"He's been well. I had lunch with him to-day."

"A great character," said Bloeckman severely. "A fine example of an American."

THE TRIUMPH OF LETHARGY

Anthony found his wife deep in the porch hammock voluptuously engaged with a lemonade and a tomato sandwich and carrying on an apparently cheery conversation with Tana upon one of Tana's complicated themes.

"In my countree," Anthony recognized his invariable preface, "all time—peoples—eat rice—because haven't got. Cannot eat what no have got." Had his nationality not been desperately apparent one would have thought he had acquired his knowledge of his native land from American primary-school geographies.

When the Oriental had been squelched and dismissed to the kitchen, Anthony turned questioningly to Gloria:

"It's all right," she announced, smiling broadly. "And it surprised me more than it does you."

"There's no doubt?"

"None! Couldn't be!"

They rejoiced happily, gay again with reborn irresponsibility. Then he told her of his opportunity to go abroad, and that he was almost ashamed to reject it.

"What do *you* think? Just tell me frankly."

"Why, Anthony!" Her eyes were startled. "Do you want to go? Without me?"

His face fell—yet he knew, with his wife's question, that it was too late. Her arms, sweet and strangling, were around him, for he had made all such choices back in that room in the Plaza the year before. This was an anachronism from an age of such dreams.

"Gloria," he lied, in a great burst of comprehension, "of course I don't. I was thinking you might go as a nurse or something." He wondered dully if his grandfather would consider this.

As she smiled he realized again how beautiful she was, a gorgeous girl of miraculous freshness and sheerly honorable eyes. She embraced his suggestion with luxurious intensity, holding it aloft like a sun of her own making and basking in its beams. She strung together an amazing synopsis for an extravaganza of martial adventure.

After supper, surfeited with the subject, she yawned. She wanted not to talk but only to read "Penrod," stretched upon the lounge until at midnight she fell asleep. But Anthony, after he had carried her romantically up the stairs, stayed awake to brood upon the day, vaguely angry with her, vaguely dissatisfied.

"What am I going to do?" he began at breakfast. "Here we've been married a year and we've just worried around without even being efficient people of leisure."

"Yes, you ought to do something," she admitted, being in an agreeable and loquacious humor. This was not the first of these discussions, but as they usually developed Anthony in the rôle of protagonist, she had come to avoid them.

"It's not that I have any moral compunctions about work," he continued, "but grampa may die to-morrow and he may live for ten years. Meanwhile we're living above our income and all we've got to show for it is a farmer's car and a few clothes. We keep an apartment that we've only lived in three months and a little old house way off in nowhere. We're frequently bored and yet we won't make any effort to know any one except the same crowd who drift around California all summer wearing sport clothes and waiting for their families to die."

"How you've changed!" remarked Gloria. "Once you told me you didn't see why an American couldn't loaf gracefully."

"Well, damn it, I wasn't married. And the old mind was working at top speed and now it's going round and round like a cog-wheel with nothing to catch it. As a matter of fact I think that if I hadn't met you I *would* have done something. But you make leisure so subtly attractive——"

"Oh, it's all my fault——"

"I didn't mean that, and you know I didn't. But here I'm almost twenty-seven and——"

"Oh," she interrupted in vexation, "you make me tired! Talking as though I were objecting or hindering you!"

"I was just discussing it, Gloria. Can't I discuss——"

"I should think you'd be strong enough to settle——"

"—something with you without——"

"—your own problems without coming to me. You *talk* a lot about going to work. I could use more money very easily, but *I'm* not complaining. Whether you work or not I love you." Her last words were gentle as fine snow upon hard ground. But for the moment neither was attending to the other—they were each engaged in polishing and perfecting his own attitude.

"I have worked—some." This by Anthony was an imprudent bringing up of raw reserves. Gloria laughed, torn between delight and derision; she resented his sophistry as at the same time she admired his nonchalance. She would never blame him for being the ineffectual idler so long as he did it sincerely, from the attitude that nothing much was worth doing.

"Work!" she scoffed. "Oh, you sad bird! You bluffer! Work—that means a great arranging of the desk and the lights, a great sharpening of pencils, and 'Gloria, don't sing!' and 'Please keep that damn Tana away from me,' and 'Let me read you my opening sentence,' and 'I won't be through for a long time, Gloria, so don't stay up for me,' and a tremendous consumption of tea or coffee. And that's all. In just about an hour I hear the old pencil stop scratching and look over. You've got out a book and you're 'looking up' something. Then you're reading. Then yawns—then bed and a great tossing about because you're all full of caffeine and can't sleep. Two weeks later the whole performance over again."

With much difficulty Anthony retained a scanty breech-clout of dignity.

"Now that's a *slight* exaggeration. You know *darn well* I sold an essay to The Florentine—and it attracted a lot of attention considering the circulation of The Florentine. And what's more, Gloria, you know I sat up till five o'clock in the morning finishing it."

She lapsed into silence, giving him rope. And if he had not hanged himself he had certainly come to the end of it.

"At least," he concluded feebly, "I'm perfectly willing to be a war correspondent."

But so was Gloria. They were both willing—anxious; they assured each other of it. The evening ended on a note of tremendous sentiment, the majesty of leisure, the ill health of Adam Patch, love at any cost.

"Anthony!" she called over the banister one afternoon a week later, "there's some one at the door."

Anthony, who had been lolling in the hammock on the sun-speckled south porch, strolled around to the front of the house. A foreign car, large and impressive, crouched like an immense and saturnine bug at the foot of the path. A man in a soft pongee suit, with cap to match, hailed him.

"Hello there, Patch. Ran over to call on you."

It was Bloeckman; as always, infinitesimally improved, of subtler intonation, of more convincing ease.

"I'm awfully glad you did." Anthony raised his voice to a vine-covered window: "Glor-i-*a*! We've got a visitor!"

"I'm in the tub," wailed Gloria politely.

With a smile the two men acknowledged the triumph of her alibi.

"She'll be down. Come round here on the side-porch. Like a drink? Gloria's always in the tub—good third of every day."

"Pity she doesn't live on the Sound."

"Can't afford it."

As coming from Adam Patch's grandson, Bloeckman took this as a form of pleasantry. After fifteen minutes filled with estimable brilliancies, Gloria appeared, fresh in starched yellow, bringing atmosphere and an increase of vitality.

"I want to be a successful sensation in the movies," she announced. "I hear that Mary Pickford makes a million dollars annually."

"You could, you know," said Bloeckman. "I think you'd film very well."

"Would you let me, Anthony? If I only play unsophisticated rôles?"

As the conversation continued in stilted commas, Anthony wondered that to him and Bloeckman both this girl had once been the most stimulating, the most tonic personality they had ever known—and now the three sat like overoiled machines, without conflict, without fear, without elation, heavily enamelled little figures secure beyond enjoyment in a world where death and war, dull emotion and noble savagery were covering a continent with the smoke of terror.

In a moment he would call Tana and they would pour into themselves a gay and delicate poison which would restore them momentarily to the pleasurable excitement of childhood, when every face in a crowd had carried its suggestion of splendid and significant transactions taking place somewhere to some magnificent and illimitable purpose. . . . Life was no more than this summer afternoon; a faint wind stirring the lace collar of Gloria's dress; the slow baking drowsiness of the veranda. . . . Intolerably unmoved they all seemed, removed from any romantic imminency of action. Even Gloria's beauty needed wild emotions, needed poignancy, needed death. . . .

". . . Any day next week," Bloeckman was saying to Gloria. "Here—take this card. What they do is to give you a test of about three hundred feet of film, and they can tell pretty accurately from that."

"How about Wednesday?"

"Wednesday's fine. Just phone me and I'll go around with you——"

He was on his feet, shaking hands briskly—then his car was a wraith of dust down the road. Anthony turned to his wife in bewilderment.

"Why, Gloria!"

"You don't mind if I have a trial, Anthony. Just a trial? I've got to go to town Wednesday, *any*how."

"But it's so silly! You don't want to go into the movies—moon around a studio all day with a lot of cheap chorus people."

"Lot of mooning around Mary Pickford does!"

"Everybody isn't a Mary Pickford."

"Well, I can't see how you'd object to my *try*ing."

"I do, though. I hate actors."

"Oh, you make me tired. Do you imagine I have a very thrilling time dozing on this damn porch?"

"You wouldn't mind if you loved me."

"Of course I love you," she said impatiently, making out a quick case for herself. "It's just because I do that I hate to see you go to pieces by just lying around and saying you ought to work. Perhaps if I *did* go into this for a while it'd stir you up so you'd do something."

"It's just your craving for excitement, that's all it is."

"Maybe it is! It's a perfectly natural craving, isn't it?"

"Well, I'll tell you one thing. If you go to the movies I'm going to Europe."

"Well, go on then! *I'm* not stopping you!"

To show she was not stopping him she melted into melancholy tears. Together they marshalled the armies of sentiment—words, kisses, endearments, self-reproaches. They attained nothing. Inevitably they attained nothing. Finally, in a burst of gargantuan emotion each of them sat down and wrote a letter. Anthony's was to his grandfather; Gloria's was to Joseph Bloeckman. It was a triumph of lethargy.

One day early in July Anthony, returned from an afternoon in New York, called up-stairs to Gloria. Receiving no answer he guessed she was asleep and so went into the pantry for one of the little sandwiches that were always prepared for them. He found Tana seated at the kitchen table before a miscellaneous assortment of odds and ends—cigar-boxes, knives, pencils, the tops of cans, and some scraps of paper covered with elaborate figures and diagrams.

"What the devil you doing?" demanded Anthony curiously.

Tana politely grinned.

"I show you," he exclaimed enthusiastically. "I tell——"

"You making a dog-house?"

"No, sa." Tana grinned again. "Make typewutta."

"Typewriter?"

"Yes, sa. I think, oh all time I think, lie in bed think 'bout typewutta."

"So you thought you'd make one, eh?"

"Wait. I tell."

Anthony, munching a sandwich, leaned leisurely against the sink. Tana opened and closed his mouth several times as though testing its capacity for action. Then with a rush he began:

"I been think—typewutta—has, oh, many many many many *thing*. Oh many many many many."

"Many keys. I see."

"No-o? *Yes*—key! Many many many many lettah. Like so a-b-c."

"Yes, you're right."

"Wait. I tell." He screwed his face up in a tremendous effort to express himself: "I been think—many words—end same. Like i-n-g."

"You bet. A whole raft of them."

"So—I make—typewutta—quick. Not so many lettah——"

"That's a great idea, Tana. Save time. You'll make a fortune. Press one key and there's 'ing.' Hope you work it out."

Tana laughed disparagingly.

"Wait. I tell——"

"Where's Mrs. Patch?"

"She out. Wait, I tell—" Again he screwed up his face for action. "*My* typewutta——"

"Where is she?"

"Here—I make." He pointed to the miscellany of junk on the table.

"I mean Mrs. Patch."

"She out." Tana reassured him. "She be back five o'clock, she say."

"Down in the village?"

"No. Went off be-fore lunch. She go Mr. Bloeckman."

Anthony started.

"Went out with Mr. Bloeckman?"

"She be back five."

Without a word Anthony left the kitchen with Tana's disconsolate "I tell" trailing after him. So this was Gloria's idea of excitement, by God! His fists were clenched; within a moment he had worked himself up to a tremendous pitch of indignation. He went to the door and looked out; there was no car in sight and his watch stood at four minutes of five. With furious energy he dashed down to the end of the path—as far as the bend of the road a mile off he could see no car—except—but it was a farmer's flivver. Then, in an undignified pursuit of dignity, he rushed back to the shelter of the house as quickly as he had rushed out.

Pacing up and down the living room he began an angry rehearsal of the speech he would make to her when she came in——

"So this is love!" he would begin—or no, it sounded too much like the popular phrase "So this is Paris!" He must be dignified, hurt, grieved. Anyhow— "So this is what *you* do when I have to go up and trot all day around the hot city on business. No wonder I can't write! No wonder I don't dare let you out of my sight!" He was expanding now, warming to his subject. "I'll tell you," he continued, "I'll tell you—" He paused, catching a familiar ring in the words—then he realized—it was Tana's "I tell."

Yet Anthony neither laughed nor seemed absurd to himself. To his frantic imagination it was already six—seven—eight, and she was never coming! Bloeckman finding her bored and unhappy had persuaded her to go to California with him. . . .

—There was a great to-do out in front, a joyous "Yoho, Anthony!" and he rose trembling, weakly happy to see her fluttering up the path. Bloeckman was following, cap in hand.

"Dearest!" she cried.

"We've been for the best jaunt—all over New York State."

"I'll have to be starting home," said Bloeckman, almost immediately. "Wish you'd both been here when I came."

"I'm sorry I wasn't," answered Anthony dryly.

When he had departed Anthony hesitated. The fear was gone from his heart, yet he felt that some protest was ethically apropos. Gloria resolved his uncertainty.

"I knew you wouldn't mind. He came just before lunch and said he had to go to Garrison on business and wouldn't I go with him. He looked so lonesome, Anthony. And I drove his car all the way."

Listlessly Anthony dropped into a chair, his mind tired—tired with nothing, tired with everything, with the world's weight he had never chosen to bear. He was ineffectual and vaguely helpless here as he had always been. One of those personalities who, in spite of all their words, are inarticulate, he seemed to have inherited only the vast tradition of human failure—that, and the sense of death.

"I suppose I don't care," he answered.

One must be broad about these things, and Gloria being young, being beautiful, must have reasonable privileges. Yet it wearied him that he failed to understand.

Winter

She rolled over on her back and lay still for a moment in the great bed watching the February sun suffer one last attenuated refinement in its passage through the leaded panes into the room. For a time she had no accurate sense of her whereabouts or of the events of the day before, or the day before that; then, like a suspended pendulum, memory began to beat out its story, releasing with each swing a burdened quota of time until her life was given back to her.

She could hear, now, Anthony's troubled breathing beside her; she could smell whiskey and cigarette smoke. She noticed that she lacked complete muscular control; when she moved it was not a sinuous motion with the resultant strain distributed easily over her body—it was a tremendous effort of her nervous system as though each time she were hypnotizing herself into performing an impossible action. . . .

She was in the bathroom, brushing her teeth to get rid of that intolerable taste; then back by the bedside listening to the rattle of Bounds's key in the outer door.

"Wake up, Anthony!" she said sharply.

She climbed into bed beside him and closed her eyes.

Almost the last thing she remembered was a conversation with Mr. and Mrs. Lacy. Mrs. Lacy had said, "Sure you don't want us to get you a taxi?" and Anthony had replied that he guessed they could walk over to Fifth all right. Then they had both attempted, imprudently, to bow—and collapsed absurdly into a battalion of empty milk bottles just outside the door. There must have been two dozen milk bottles standing open-mouthed in the dark. She could conceive of no plausible explanation of those milk bottles. Perhaps they had been attracted by the singing in the Lacy house and had hurried over agape with wonder to see the fun. Well, they'd had the worst of it—though it seemed that she and Anthony never would get up, the perverse things rolled so. . . .

Still, they had found a taxi. "My meter's broken and it'll cost you a dollar and a half to get home," said the taxi-driver. "Well," said Anthony, "I'm young Packy McFarland and if you'll come down here I'll beat you till you can't stand up." . . . At that point the man had driven off without them. They must have found another taxi, for they were in the apartment. . . .

"What time is it?" Anthony was sitting up in bed, staring at her with owlish precision.

This was obviously a rhetorical question. Gloria could think of no reason why she should be expected to know the time.

"Golly, I feel like the devil!" muttered Anthony dispassionately. Relaxing, he tumbled back upon his pillow. "Bring on your grim reaper!"

"Anthony, how'd we finally get home last night?"

"Taxi."

"Oh!" Then, after a pause: "Did you put me to bed?"

"I don't know. Seems to me you put *me* to bed. What day is it?"

"Tuesday."

"Tuesday? I hope so. If it's Wednesday, I've got to start work at that idiotic place. Supposed to be down at nine or some such ungodly hour."

"Ask Bounds," suggested Gloria feebly.

"Bounds!" he called.

Sprightly, sober—a voice from a world that it seemed in the past two days they had left forever, Bounds sprang in short steps down the hall and appeared in the half darkness of the door.

"What day, Bounds?"

"February the twenty-second, I think, sir."

"I mean day of the week."

"Tuesday, sir." "Thanks." After a pause: "Are you ready for breakfast, sir?"

"Yes, and Bounds, before you get it, will you make a

pitcher of water, and set it here beside the bed? I'm a little thirsty."

"Yes, sir."

Bounds retreated in sober dignity down the hallway.

"Lincoln's birthday," affirmed Anthony without enthusiasm, "or St. Valentine's or somebody's. When did we start on this insane party?"

"Sunday night."

"After prayers?" he suggested sardonically.

"We raced all over town in those hansoms and Maury sat up with his driver, don't you remember? Then we came home and he tried to cook some bacon—came out of the pantry with a few blackened remains, insisting it was 'fried to the proverbial crisp.'"

Both of them laughed, spontaneously but with some difficulty, and lying there side by side reviewed the chain of events that had ended in this rusty and chaotic dawn.

They had been in New York for almost four months, since the country had grown too cool in late October. They had given up California this year, partly because of lack of funds, partly with the idea of going abroad should this interminable war, persisting now into its second year, end during the winter. Of late their income had lost elasticity; no longer did it stretch to cover gay whims and pleasant extravagances, and Anthony had spent many puzzled and unsatisfactory hours over a densely figured pad, making remarkable budgets that left huge margins for "amusements, trips, etc.," and trying to apportion, even approximately, their past expenditures.

He remembered a time when in going on a "party" with his two best friends, he and Maury had invariably paid more than their share of the expenses. They would buy the tickets for the theatre or squabble between themselves for the dinner check. It had seemed fitting; Dick, with his naïveté and his astonishing fund of information about himself, had been a diverting, almost juvenile, figure—court jester to their royalty. But this was no longer true. It was Dick who always had money; it was Anthony who entertained within limitations—always excepting occasional wild, wine-inspired, check-cashing parties—and it was Anthony who was solemn about it next morning and told the scornful and disgusted Gloria that they'd have to be "more careful next time."

In the two years since the publication of "The Demon Lover," Dick had made over twenty-five thousand dollars, most of it lately, when the reward of the author of fiction had begun to swell unprecedentedly as a result of the voracious hunger of the motion pictures for plots. He received seven hundred dollars for every story, at that time a large emolument for such a young man—he was not quite thirty—and for every one that contained enough "action" (kissing, shooting, and sacrificing) for the movies, he obtained an additional thousand. His stories varied; there was a measure of vitality and a sort of instinctive technic in all of them, but none attained the personality of "The Demon Lover," and there were several that Anthony considered downright cheap. These, Dick explained severely, were to widen his audience. Wasn't it true that men who had attained real permanence from Shakespeare to Mark Twain had appealed to the many as well as to the elect?

Though Anthony and Maury disagreed, Gloria told him to go ahead and make as much money as he could—that was the only thing that counted anyhow. . . .

Maury, a little stouter, faintly mellower, and more complaisant, had gone to work in Philadelphia. He came to New York once or twice a month and on such occasions the four of them travelled the popular routes from dinner to the theatre, thence to the Frolic or, perhaps, at the urging of the ever-curious Gloria, to one of the cellars of Greenwich Village, notorious through the furious but short-lived vogue of the "new poetry movement."

In January, after many monologues directed at his reticent wife, Anthony determined to "get something to do," for the winter at any rate. He wanted to please his grandfather and even, in a measure, to see how he liked it himself. He discovered during several tentative semi-social calls that employers were not interested in a young man who was only going to "try it for a few months or so." As the grandson of Adam Patch he was received everywhere with marked courtesy, but the old man was a back number now—the heyday of his fame as first an "oppressor" and then an uplifter of the people had been during the twenty years preceding his retirement. Anthony even found several of the younger men who were under the impression that Adam Patch had been dead for some years.

Eventually Anthony went to his grandfather and asked his advice, which turned out to be that he should enter the bond business as a salesman, a tedious suggestion to Anthony, but one that in the end he determined to follow. Sheer money in deft manipulation had fascinations under all circumstances, while almost any side of manufacturing would be insufferably dull. He considered newspaper work but decided that the hours were not ordered for a married man. And he lingered over pleasant fancies of himself either as editor of a brilliant weekly of opinion, an American Mercure de France, or as scintillant producer of satiric comedy and Parisian musical revue. However, the approaches to these latter guilds seemed to be guarded by professional secrets. Men drifted into them by the devious highways of writing and acting. It was palpably impossible to get on a magazine unless you had been on one before.

So in the end he entered, by way of his grandfather's letter, that Sanctum Americanum where sat the president of Wilson, Hiemer and Hardy at his "cleared desk," and issued therefrom employed. He was to begin work on the twenty-third of February.

In tribute to the momentous occasion this two-day revel had been planned, since, he said, after he began working he'd have to get to bed early during the week. Maury Noble had arrived from Philadelphia on a trip that had to do with seeing some man in Wall Street (whom, incidentally, he failed to see), and Richard Caramel had been half persuaded, half tricked into joining them. They had condescended to a wet and fashionable wedding on Monday afternoon, and in the evening had occurred the dénouement: Gloria, going beyond her accustomed limit of four precisely timed cocktails, led them on as gay and joyous a bacchanal as they had ever known, disclosing an astonishing knowledge of ballet steps, and singing songs which she confessed had been taught her by her cook when she was innocent and seventeen. She repeated these by request at intervals throughout the evening with such frank conviviality that Anthony, far from being annoyed, was gratified at this fresh source of entertainment. The occasion was memorable in other ways—a long conversation between Maury and a defunct crab, which he was dragging around on the end of a string, as to whether the crab was fully conversant with the applications of the binomial theorem, and the aforementioned race in two hansom cabs with the sedate and impressive shadows of Fifth Avenue for audience, ending in a labyrinthine escape into the darkness of Central Park. Finally Anthony and Gloria had paid a call on some wild young married people—the Lacys—and collapsed in the empty milk bottles.

Morning now—theirs to add up the checks cashed here and there in clubs, stores, restaurants. Theirs to air the dank staleness of wine and cigarettes out of the tall blue front room, to pick up the broken glass and brush at the stained fabric of chairs and sofas; to give Bounds suits and dresses for the cleaners; finally, to take their smothery half-feverish bodies and faded depressed spirits out into the chill air of February, that life might go on and Wilson, Hiemer and Hardy obtain the services of a vigorous man at nine next morning.

"Do you remember," called Anthony from the bathroom, "when Maury got out at the corner of One Hundred and Tenth Street and acted as a traffic cop, beckoning cars forward and motioning them back? They must have thought he was a private detective."

After each reminiscence they both laughed inordinately, their overwrought nerves responding as acutely and janglingly to mirth as to depression.

Gloria at the mirror was wondering at the splendid color and freshness of her face—it seemed that she had never looked so well, though her stomach hurt her and her head was aching furiously.

The day passed slowly. Anthony, riding in a taxi to his broker's to borrow money on a bond, found that he had only two dollars in his pocket. The fare would cost all of that, but he felt that on this particular afternoon he could not have endured the subway. When the taximetre reached his limit he must get out and walk.

With this his mind drifted off into one of its characteristic day-dreams. . . . In this dream he discovered that the metre was going too fast—the driver had dishonestly adjusted it. Calmly he reached his destination and then nonchalantly handed the man what he justly owed him. The man showed fight, but almost before his hands were up Anthony had knocked him down with one terrific blow. And when he rose Anthony quickly sidestepped and floored him definitely with a crack in the temple.

. . . He was in court now. The judge had fined him five dollars and he had no money. Would the court take his check? Ah, but the court did not know him. Well, he could identify himself by having them call his apartment.

. . . They did so. Yes, it was Mrs. Anthony Patch speaking—but how did she know that this man was her husband? How could she know? Let the police sergeant ask her if she remembered the milk bottles . . .

He leaned forward hurriedly and tapped at the glass. The taxi was only at Brooklyn Bridge, but the metre showed a dollar and eighty cents, and Anthony would never have omitted the ten per cent tip.

Later in the afternoon he returned to the apartment. Gloria had also been out—shopping—and was asleep, curled in a corner of the sofa with her purchase locked securely in her arms. Her face was as untroubled as a little girl's, and the bundle that she pressed tightly to her bosom was a child's doll, a profound and infinitely healing balm to her disturbed and childish heart.

Destiny

It was with this party, more especially with Gloria's part in it, that a decided change began to come over their way of living. The magnificent attitude of not giving a damn altered overnight; from being a mere tenet of Gloria's it became the entire solace and justification for what they chose to do and what consequence it brought. Not to be sorry, not to loose one cry of regret, to live according to a clear code of honor toward each other, and to seek the moment's happiness as fervently and persistently as possible.

"No one cares about us but ourselves, Anthony," she said one day. "It'd be ridiculous for me to go about pretending I felt any obligations toward the world, and as for worrying what people think about me, I simply *don't*, that's all. Since I was a little girl in dancing-school I've been criticised by the mothers of all the little girls who weren't as popular as I was, and I've always looked on criticism as a sort of envious tribute."

This was because of a party in the "Boul' Mich'" one night, where Constance Merriam had seen her as one of a highly stimulated party of four. Constance Merriam, "as an old school friend," had gone to the trouble of inviting her to lunch next day in order to inform her how terrible it was.

"I told her I couldn't see it," Gloria told Anthony. "Eric Merriam is a sort of sublimated Percy Wolcott—you remember that man in Hot Springs I told you about—his idea of respecting Constance is to leave her at home with her sewing and her baby and her book, and such innocuous amusements, whenever he's going on a party that promises to be anything but deathly dull."

"Did you tell her that?"

"I certainly did. And I told her that what she really objected to was that I was having a better time than she was."

Anthony applauded her. He was tremendously proud of Gloria, proud that she never failed to eclipse whatever other women might be in the party, proud that men were always glad to revel with her in great rowdy groups, without any attempt to do more than enjoy her beauty and the warmth of her vitality.

These "parties" gradually became their chief source of entertainment. Still in love, still enormously interested in each other, they yet found as spring drew near that staying at home in the evening palled on them;

books were unreal; the old magic of being alone had long since vanished—instead they preferred to be bored by a stupid musical comedy, or to go to dinner with the most uninteresting of their acquaintances, so long as there would be enough cocktails to keep the conversation from becoming utterly intolerable. A scattering of younger married people who had been their friends in school or college, as well as a varied assortment of single men, began to think instinctively of them whenever color and excitement were needed, so there was scarcely a day without its phone call, its "Wondered what you were doing this evening." Wives, as a rule, were afraid of Gloria—her facile attainment of the centre of the stage, her innocent but nevertheless disturbing way of becoming a favorite with husbands—these things drove them instinctively into an attitude of profound distrust, heightened by the fact that Gloria was largely unresponsive to any intimacy shown her by a woman.

On the appointed Wednesday in February Anthony had gone to the imposing offices of Wilson, Hiemer and Hardy and listened to many vague instructions delivered by an energetic young man of about his own age, named Kahler, who wore a defiant yellow pompadour, and in announcing himself as an assistant secretary gave the impression that it was a tribute to exceptional ability.

"There's two kinds of men here, you'll find," he said. "There's the man who gets to be an assistant secretary or treasurer, gets his name on our folder here, before he's thirty, and there's the man who gets his name there at forty-five. The man who gets his name there at forty-five stays there the rest of his life."

"How about the man who gets it there at thirty?" inquired Anthony politely.

"Why, he gets up here, you see." He pointed to a

list of assistant vice-presidents upon the folder. "Or maybe he gets to be president or secretary or treasurer."

"And what about these over here?"

"Those? Oh, those are the trustees—the men with capital."

"I see."

"Now some people," continued Kahler, "think that whether a man gets started early or late depends on whether he's got a college education. But they're wrong."

"I see."

"I had one; I was Buckleigh, class of nineteen-eleven, but when I came down to the Street I soon found that the things that would help me here weren't the fancy things I learned in college. In fact, I had to get a lot of fancy stuff out of my head."

Anthony could not help wondering what possible "fancy stuff" he had learned at Buckleigh in nineteen-eleven. An irrepressible idea that it was some sort of needlework recurred to him throughout the rest of the conversation.

"See that fellow over there?" Kahler pointed to a youngish-looking man with handsome gray hair, sitting at a desk inside a mahogany railing. "That's Mr. Ellinger, the first vice-president. Been everywhere, seen everything; got a fine education."

In vain did Anthony try to open his mind to the romance of finance; he could think of Mr. Ellinger only as one of the buyers of the handsome leather sets of Thackeray, Balzac, Hugo, and Gibbon that lined the walls of the big bookstores.

Through the damp and uninspiring month of March he was prepared for salesmanship. Lacking enthusiasm he was capable of viewing the turmoil and bustle that surrounded him only as a fruitless circumambient striving toward an incomprehensible goal, tangibly evidenced only by the rival mansions of Mr. Frick and Mr. Carnegie on Fifth Avenue. That these portentous vice-presidents and trustees should be actually the fathers of the "best men" he had known at Harvard seemed to him incongruous.

He ate in an employees' lunch-room up-stairs with an uneasy suspicion that he was being uplifted, wondering through that first week if the dozens of young clerks, some of them alert and immaculate, and just out of college, lived in flamboyant hope of crowding onto that narrow slip of cardboard before the catastrophic thirties. The conversation that interwove with the pattern of the day's work was all much of a piece. One discussed how Mr. Wilson had made his money, what method Mr. Hiemer had employed, and the means resorted to by Mr. Hardy. One related age-old but eternally breathless anecdotes of the fortunes stumbled on precipitously in the Street by a "butcher" or a "bartender," or "a darn *mess*enger boy, by golly!" and then one talked of the current gambles, and whether it was best to go out for a hundred thousand a year or be content with twenty. During the preceding year one of the assistant secretaries had invested all his savings in Bethlehem Steel. The story of his spectacular magnificence, of his haughty resignation in January, and of the triumphal palace he was now building in California, was the favorite office subject. The man's very name had acquired a magic significance, symbolizing as he did the aspirations of all good Americans. Anecdotes were told about him—how one of the vice-presidents had advised him to sell, by golly, but he had hung on, even bought on margin, "and *now* look where he is!"

Such, obviously, was the stuff of life—a dizzy triumph dazzling the eyes of all of them, a gypsy siren to content them with meagre wage and with the arithmetical improbability of their eventual success.

To Anthony the notion became appalling. He felt that to succeed here the idea of success must grasp and limit his mind. It seemed to him that the essential element in these men at the top was their faith that their affairs were the very core of life. All other things being equal, self-assurance and opportunism won out over technical knowledge; it was obvious that the more expert work went on near the bottom—so, with appropriate efficiency, the technical experts were kept there.

His determination to stay in at night during the week did not survive, and a good half of the time he came to work with a splitting, sickish headache and the crowded horror of the morning subway ringing in his ears like an echo of hell.

Then, abruptly, he quit. He had remained in bed all one Monday, and late in the evening, overcome by one of those attacks of moody despair to which he periodically succumbed, he wrote and mailed a letter to Mr. Wilson, confessing that he considered himself ill adapted to the work. Gloria, coming in from the theatre with Richard Caramel, found him on the lounge, silently staring at the high ceiling, more depressed and discouraged than he had been at any time since their marriage.

She wanted him to whine. If he had she would have reproached him bitterly, for she was not a little annoyed, but he only lay there so utterly miserable that she felt sorry for him, and kneeling down she stroked his head, saying how little it mattered, how little anything mattered so long as they loved each other. It was like their first year, and Anthony, reacting to her cool hand, to her voice that was soft as breath itself upon his ear, became almost cheerful, and talked with her of his future plans. He even regretted, silently, before he went to bed that he had so hastily mailed his resignation.

"Even when everything seems rotten you can't trust that judgment," Gloria had said. "It's the sum of all your judgments that counts."

In mid-April came a letter from the real-estate agent in Marietta, encouraging them to take the gray house for another year at a slightly increased rental, and enclosing a lease made out for their signatures. For a week lease and letter lay carelessly neglected on Anthony's desk. They had no intention of returning to Marietta. They were weary of the place, and had been bored most of the preceding summer. Besides, their car had deteriorated to a rattling mass of hypochondriacal metal, and a new one was financially inadvisable.

But because of another wild revel, enduring through four days and participated in, at one time or another, by more than a dozen people, they did sign the lease; to their utter horror they signed it and sent it, and immediately it seemed as though they heard the gray house, drably malevolent at last, licking its white chops and waiting to devour them.

"Anthony, where's that lease?" she called in high alarm one Sunday morning, sick and sober to reality. "Where did you leave it? It was here!"

Then she knew where it was. She remembered the house party they had planned on the crest of their exuberance; she remembered a room full of men to whose less exhilarated moments she and Anthony were of no importance, and Anthony's boast of the transcendent merit and seclusion of the gray house, that it was so isolated that it didn't matter how much noise went on there. Then Dick, who had visited them, cried enthusiastically that it was the best little house imaginable, and that they were idiotic not to take it for another summer. It had been easy to work themselves up to a sense of how hot and deserted the city was getting, of how cool and ambrosial were the charms of Marietta. Anthony had picked up the lease and waved it wildly, found Gloria happily acquiescent, and with one last burst of garrulous decision during which all the men agreed with solemn handshakes that they would come out for a visit . . .

"Anthony," she cried. "we've signed and sent it!"

"What?"

"The lease!"

"What the devil!"

"Oh, *An*thony!" There was utter misery in her voice. For the summer, for eternity, they had built themselves a prison. It seemed to strike at the last roots of their stability. Anthony thought they might arrange it with the real-estate agent. They could no longer afford the double rent, and going to Marietta meant giving up his apartment, his reproachless apartment with the exquisite bath and the rooms for which he had bought his furniture and hangings—it was the closest to a home that he had ever had—familiar with memories of four colorful years.

But it was not arranged with the real-estate agent, nor was it arranged at all. Dispiritedly, without even any talk of making the best of it, without even Gloria's all-sufficing "I don't care," they went back to the house that they now knew heeded neither youth nor love—only those austere and incommunicable memories that they could never share.

The Sinister Summer

There was a horror in the house that summer. It came with them and settled itself over the place like a sombre pall, pervasive through the lower rooms, gradually spreading and climbing up the narrow stairs until it oppressed their very sleep. Anthony and Gloria grew to hate being there alone. Her bedroom, which had seemed so pink and young and delicate, appropriate to her pastel-shaded lingerie tossed here and there on chair and bed, seemed now to whisper with its rustling curtains:

"Ah, my beautiful young lady, yours is not the first daintiness and delicacy that has faded here under the summer suns . . . generations of unloved women have adorned themselves by that glass for rustic lovers who paid no heed. . . . Youth has come into this room in palest blue and left it in the gray cerements of despair, and through long nights many girls have lain awake where that bed stands pouring out waves of misery into the darkness."

Gloria finally tumbled all her clothes and unguents ingloriously out of it, declaring that she had come to live with Anthony, and making the excuse that one of her screens was rotten and admitted bugs. So her room was abandoned to insensitive guests, and they dressed and slept in her husband's chamber, which Gloria considered somehow "good," as though Anthony's presence there had acted as exterminator of any uneasy shadows of the past that might have hovered about its walls.

The distinction between "good" and "bad," ordered early and summarily out of both their lives, had been reinstated in another form. Gloria insisted that any one invited to the gray house must be "good," which, in the case of a girl, meant that she must be either simple and reproachless or, if otherwise, must possess a certain solidity and strength. Always intensely sceptical of her sex, her judgments were now concerned with the question of whether women were or were not clean. By uncleanliness she meant a variety of things, a lack of pride, a slackness in fibre and, most of all, the unmistakable aura of promiscuity.

"Women soil easily," she said, "far more easily than men. Unless a girl's very young and brave it's almost impossible for her to go down-hill without a certain hysterical animality, the cunning, dirty sort of animality. A man's different—and I suppose that's why one of the commonest characters of romance is a man going gallantly to the devil."

She was disposed to like many men, preferably those who gave her frank homage and unfailing entertainment—but often with a flash of insight she told Anthony that some one of his friends was merely using him, and consequently had best be left alone. Anthony customarily demurred, insisting that the accused was a "good one," but he found that his judgment was more fallible than hers, memorably when, as it happened on several occasions, he was left with a succession of restaurant checks for which to render a solitary account.

More from their fear of solitude than from any desire to go through the fuss and bother of entertaining, they filled the house with guests every week-end, and often on through the week. The week-end parties were much the same. When the three or four men invited had arrived, drinking was more or less in order, followed by a hilarious dinner and a ride to the Cradle Beach Country Club, which they had joined because it was inexpensive, lively if not fashionable, and almost a necessity for just such occasions as these. Moreover, it was of no great moment what one did there, and so long as the Patch party were reasonably inaudible, it mattered little whether or not the social dictators of Cradle Beach saw the gay Gloria imbibing cocktails in the supper room at frequent intervals during the evening.

Saturday ended, generally, in a glamourous confusion

—it proving often necessary to assist a muddled guest to bed. Sunday brought the New York papers and a quiet morning of recuperating on the porch—and Sunday afternoon meant good-by to the one or two guests who must return to the city, and a great revival of drinking among the one or two who remained until next day, concluding in a convivial if not hilarious evening.

The faithful Tana, pedagogue by nature and man of all work by profession, had returned with them. Among their more frequent guests a tradition had sprung up about him. Maury Noble remarked one afternoon that his real name was Tannenbaum, and that he was a German agent kept in this country to disseminate Teutonic propaganda through Westchester County, and, after that, mysterious letters began to arrive from Philadelphia addressed to the bewildered Oriental as "Lt. Emile Tannenbaum," containing a few cryptic messages signed "General Staff," and adorned with an atmospheric double column of facetious Japanese. Anthony always handed them to Tana without a smile; hours afterward the recipient could be found puzzling over them in the kitchen and declaring earnestly that the perpendicular symbols were not Japanese, nor anything resembling Japanese.

Gloria had taken a strong dislike to the man ever since the day when, returning unexpectedly from the village, she had discovered him reclining on Anthony's bed, puzzling out a newspaper. It was the instinct of all servants to be fond of Anthony and to detest Gloria, and Tana was no exception to the rule. But he was thoroughly afraid of her and made plain his aversion only in his moodier moments by subtly addressing Anthony with remarks intended for her ear:

"What Miz Pats want dinner?" he would say, looking at his master. Or else he would comment about the bitter selfishness of "'Merican peoples" in such manner that there was no doubt who were the "peoples" referred to.

But they dared not dismiss him. Such a step would have been abhorrent to their inertia. They endured Tana as they endured ill weather and sickness of the body and the estimable Will of God—as they endured all things, even themselves.

In Darkness

One sultry afternoon late in July Richard Caramel telephoned from New York that he and Maury were coming out, bringing a friend with them. They arrived about five, a little drunk, accompanied by a small, stocky man of thirty-five, whom they introduced as Mr. Joe Hull, one of the best fellows that Anthony and Gloria had ever met.

Joe Hull had a yellow beard continually fighting through his skin and a low voice which varied between basso profundo and a husky whisper. Anthony, carrying Maury's suitcase up-stairs, followed into the room and carefully closed the door.

"Who is this fellow?" he demanded.

Maury chuckled enthusiastically.

"Who, Hull? Oh, *he's* all right. He's a good one."

"Yes, but who is he?"

"Hull? He's just a good fellow. He's a prince." His laughter redoubled, culminating in a succession of pleasant catlike grins. Anthony hesitated between a smile and a frown.

"He looks sort of funny to me. Weird-looking clothes"—he paused—"I've got a sneaking suspicion you two picked him up somewhere last night."

"Ridiculous," declared Maury. "Why, I've known him all my life." However, as he capped this statement with another series of chuckles, Anthony was impelled to remark: "The devil you have!"

Later, just before dinner, while Maury and Dick were conversing uproariously, with Joe Hull listening in silence as he sipped his drink, Gloria drew Anthony into the dining room:

"I don't like this man Hull," she said. "I wish he'd use Tana's bathtub."

"I can't very well ask him to."

"Well, I don't want him in ours."

"He seems to be a simple soul."

"He's got on white shoes that look like gloves. I can see his toes right through them. Uh! Who is he, anyway?"

"You've got me."

"Well, I think they've got their nerve to bring him out here. This isn't a Sailor's Rescue Home!"

"They were tight when they phoned. Maury said they've been on a party since yesterday afternoon."

Gloria shook her head angrily, and saying no more returned to the porch. Anthony saw that she was trying to forget her uncertainty and devote herself to enjoying the evening.

It had been a tropical day, and even into late twilight the heat-waves emanating from the dry road were quivering faintly like undulating panes of isinglass. The sky was cloudless, but far beyond the woods in the direction of the Sound a faint and persistent rolling had commenced. When Tana announced dinner the men, at a word from Gloria, remained coatless and went inside.

Maury began a song, which they accomplished in harmony during the first course. It had two lines and was sung to a popular air called Daisy Dear. The lines were:

"The—pan-ic—has—come—over us,
So *ha-a-as*—the moral de*cline!*"

Each rendition was greeted with bursts of enthusiasm and prolonged applause.

"Cheer up, Gloria!" suggested Maury. "You seem the least bit depressed."

"I'm not," she lied.

"Here, Tannenbaum!" he called over his shoulder. "I've filled you a drink. Come on!"

Gloria tried to stay his arm.

"Please don't, Maury!"

"Why not? Maybe he'll play the flute for us after dinner. Here, Tana."

Tana, grinning, bore the glass away to the kitchen. In a few moments Maury gave him another.

"Cheer up, Gloria!" he cried. "For Heaven's sakes everybody, cheer up Gloria."

"Dearest, have another drink," counselled Anthony. "Do, please!"

"Cheer up, Gloria," said Joe Hull easily.

Gloria winced at this uncalled-for use of her first name, and glanced around to see if any one else had noticed it. The word coming so glibly from the lips of a man to whom she had taken an inordinate dislike repelled her. A moment later she noticed that Joe Hull had given Tana another drink, and her anger increased, heightened somewhat from the effects of the alcohol.

"—and once," Maury was saying, "Peter Granby and I went into a Turkish bath in Boston, about two o'clock at night. There was no one there but the proprietor, and we jammed him into a closet and locked the door. Then a fella came in and wanted a Turkish bath. Thought we were the rubbers, by golly! Well, we just picked him up and tossed him into the pool with all his clothes on. Then we dragged him out and laid him on a slab and slapped him until he was black and blue. 'Not so rough, fellows!' he'd say in a little squeaky voice, 'please! . . .'"

—Was this Maury? thought Gloria. From any one else the story would have amused her, but from Maury, the infinitely appreciative, the apotheosis of tact and consideration . . .

"The—pan-ic—has—come—over us,
So *ha-a-as*——"

A drum of thunder from outside drowned out the rest of the song; Gloria shivered and tried to empty her glass, but the first taste nauseated her, and she set it down. Dinner was over and they all marched into the big room, bearing several bottles and decanters. Some one had closed the porch door to keep out the wind, and in consequence circular tentacles of cigar smoke were twisting already upon the heavy air.

"Paging Lieutenant Tannenbaum!" Again it was the changeling Maury. "Bring us the flute!"

Anthony and Maury rushed into the kitchen; Richard Caramel started the phonograph and approached Gloria.

"Dance with your well-known cousin."

"I don't want to dance."

"Then I'm going to carry you around."

As though he were doing something of overpowering importance, he picked her up in his fat little arms and started trotting gravely about the room.

"Set me down, Dick! I'm dizzy!" she insisted.

He dumped her in a bouncing bundle on the couch, and rushed off to the kitchen, shouting "Tana! Tana!"

Then, without warning, she felt other arms around her, felt herself lifted from the lounge. Joe Hull had picked her up and was trying, drunkenly, to imitate Dick.

"Put me down!" she said sharply.

His maudlin laugh, and the sight of that prickly yellow jaw close to her face. stirred her to intolerable disgust.

"At once!"

"The—pan-ic—" he began, but got no further, for

Gloria's hand swung around swiftly and caught him in the cheek. At this he all at once let go of her, and she fell to the floor, her shoulder hitting the table a glancing blow in transit. . . .

Then the room seemed full of men and smoke. There was Tana in his white coat reeling about supported by Maury. Into his flute he was blowing a weird blend of sound that was known, cried Anthony, as the Japanese train-song. Joe Hull had found a box of candles and was juggling them, yelling "One down!" every time he missed, and Dick was dancing by himself in a fascinated whirl around and about the room. It appeared to her that everything in the room was staggering in grotesque fourth-dimensional gyrations through intersecting planes of hazy blue.

Outside, the storm had come up amazingly—the lulls within were filled with the scrape of the tall bushes against the house and the roaring of the rain on the tin roof of the kitchen. The lightning was interminable, letting down thick drips of thunder like pig iron from the heart of a white-hot furnace. Gloria could see that the rain was spitting in at three of the windows—but she could not move to shut them. . . .

. . . She was in the hall. She had said good night but no one had heard or heeded her. It seemed for an instant as though something had looked down over the head of the banister, but she could not have gone back into the living room—better madness than the madness of that clamor. . . . Up-stairs she fumbled for the electric switch and missed it in the darkness; a roomful of lightning showed her the button plainly on the wall. But when the impenetrable black shut down, it again eluded her fumbling fingers, so she slipped off her dress and petticoat and threw herself weakly on the dry side of the half-drenched bed.

She shut her eyes. From down-stairs arose the babel of the drinkers, punctured suddenly by a tinkling shiver of broken glass, and then another, and by a soaring fragment of unsteady, irregular song. . . .

She lay there for something over two hours—so she calculated afterward, sheerly by piecing together the bits of time. She was conscious, even aware, after a long while that the noise down-stairs had lessened, and that the storm was moving off westward, throwing back lingering showers of sound that fell, heavy and lifeless as her soul, into the soggy fields. This was succeeded by a slow, reluctant scattering of the rain and wind, until there was nothing outside her windows but a gentle dripping and the swishing play of a cluster of wet vine against the sill. She was in a state half-way between sleeping and waking, with neither condition predominant . . . and she was harassed by a desire to rid herself of a weight pressing down upon her breast. She felt that if she could cry the weight would be lifted, and forcing the lids of her eyes together she tried to raise a lump in her throat . . . to no avail. . . .

Drip! Drip! Drip! The sound was not unpleasant —like spring, like a cool rain of her childhood, that made cheerful mud in her back yard and watered the tiny garden she had dug with miniature rake and spade and hoe. Drip—dri-ip! It was like days when the rain came out of yellow skies that melted just before twilight and shot one radiant shaft of sunlight diagonally down the heavens into the damp green trees. So cool, so clear and clean—and her mother there at the centre of the world, at the centre of the rain, safe and dry and strong. She wanted her mother now, and her mother was dead, beyond sight and touch forever. And this weight was pressing on her, pressing on her—oh, it pressed on her so!

She became rigid. Some one had come to the door

and was standing regarding her, very quiet except for a slight swaying motion. She could see the outline of his figure distinct against some indistinguishable light. There was no sound anywhere, only a great persuasive silence—even the dripping had ceased . . . only this figure, swaying, swaying in the doorway, an indiscernible and subtly menacing terror, a personality filthy under its varnish, like smallpox spots under a layer of powder. Yet her tired heart, beating until it shook her breasts, made her sure that there was still life in her, desperately shaken, threatened. . . .

The minute or succession of minutes prolonged itself interminably, and a swimming blur began to form before her eyes, which tried with childish persistence to pierce the gloom in the direction of the door. In another instant it seemed that some unimaginable force would shatter her out of existence . . . and then the figure in the doorway—it was Hull, she saw, Hull—turned deliberately and, still slightly swaying, moved back and off, as if absorbed into that incomprehensible light that had given him dimension.

Blood rushed back into her limbs, blood and life together. With a start of energy she sat upright, shifting her body until her feet touched the floor over the side of the bed. She knew what she must do—now, now, before it was too late. She must go out into this cool damp, out, away, to feel the wet swish of the grass around her feet and the fresh moisture on her forehead. Mechanically she struggled into her clothes, groping in the dark of the closet for a hat. She must go from this house where the thing hovered that pressed upon her bosom, or else made itself into stray, swaying figures in the gloom.

In a panic she fumbled clumsily at her coat, found the sleeve just as she heard Anthony's footsteps on the lower stair. She dared not wait; he might not let her go, and even Anthony was part of this weight, part of this evil house and the sombre darkness that was growing up about it. . . .

Through the hall then . . . and down the back stairs, hearing Anthony's voice in the bedroom she had just left——

"Gloria! Gloria!"

But she had reached the kitchen now, passed out through the doorway into the night. A hundred drops, startled by a flare of wind from a dripping tree, scattered on her and she pressed them gladly to her face with hot hands.

"Gloria! Gloria!"

The voice was infinitely remote, muffled and made plaintive by the walls she had just left. She rounded the house and started down the front path toward the road, almost exultant as she turned into it, and followed the carpet of short grass alongside, moving with caution in the intense darkness.

"Gloria!"

She broke into a run, stumbled over the segment of a branch twisted off by the wind. The voice was outside the house now. Anthony, finding the bedroom deserted, had come onto the porch. But this thing was driving her forward; it was back there with Anthony, and she must go on in her flight under this dim and oppressive heaven, forcing herself through the silence ahead as though it were a tangible barrier before her.

She had gone some distance along the barely discernible road, probably half a mile, passed a single deserted barn that loomed up, black and foreboding, the only building of any sort between the gray house and Marietta; then she turned the fork, where the road entered the wood and ran between two high walls of leaves and branches that nearly touched overhead. She noticed suddenly a thin, longitudinal gleam of silver upon the road before her, like a bright sword half embedded in the mud. As she came closer she gave a little cry of satisfaction—it was a wagon-rut full of water, and glancing heavenward she saw a light rift of sky and knew that the moon was out.

"Gloria!"

She started violently. Anthony was not two hundred feet behind her.

"Gloria, wait for me!"

She shut her lips tightly to keep from screaming, and increased her gait. Before she had gone another hundred yards the woods disappeared, rolling back like a dark stocking from the leg of the road. Three minutes' walk ahead of her, suspended in the now high and limitless air, she saw a thin interlacing of attenuated gleams and glitters, centred in a regular undulation on some one invisible point. Abruptly she knew where she would go. That was the great cascade of wires that rose high over the river, like the legs of a gigantic spider whose eye was the little green light in the switch-house, and ran with the railroad bridge in the direction of the station. The station! There would be the train to take her away.

"Gloria, it's me! It's Anthony! Gloria, I won't try to stop you! For God's sake, where are you?"

She made no answer but began to run, keeping on the high side of the road and leaping the gleaming puddles—dimensionless pools of thin, unsubstantial gold. Turning sharply to the left, she followed a narrow wagon road, serving to avoid a dark body on the ground. She looked up as an owl hooted mournfully from a solitary tree. Just ahead of her she could see the trestle that led to the railroad bridge and the steps mounting up to it. The station lay across the river.

Another sound startled her, the melancholy siren of an approaching train, and almost simultaneously, a repeated call, thin now and far away.

"Gloria! Gloria!"

Anthony must have followed the main road. She laughed with a sort of malicious cunning at having eluded him; she could spare the time to wait until the train went by.

The siren soared again, closer at hand, and then, with no anticipatory roar and clamor, a dark and sinuous body curved into view against the shadows far down the high-banked track, and with no sound but the rush of the cleft wind and the clocklike tick of the rails, moved toward the bridge—it was an electric train. Above the engine two vivid blurs of blue light formed incessantly a radiant crackling bar between them, which, like a spluttering flame in a lamp beside a corpse, lit for an instant the successive rows of trees and caused Gloria to draw back instinctively to the far side of the road. The light was tepid—the temperature of warm blood. . . . The clicking blended suddenly with itself in a rush of even sound, and then, elongating in sombre elasticity, the thing roared blindly by her and thundered onto the bridge, racing the lurid shaft of fire it cast into the solemn river alongside. Then it contracted swiftly, sucking in its sound until it left only a reverberant echo, which died upon the farther bank.

Silence crept down again over the wet country; the faint dripping resumed, and suddenly a great shower of drops tumbled upon Gloria, stirring her out of the trance-like torpor which the passage of the train had wrought. She ran swiftly down a descending level to the bank and began climbing the iron stairway to the bridge, remembering that it was something she had always wanted to do, and that she would have the added excitement of traversing the yard-wide plank that ran beside the tracks over the river.

There! This was better. She was at the top now and could see the lands about her as successive sweeps of open country, cold under the moon, coarsely patched and seamed with thin rows and heavy clumps of trees. To her right, half a mile down the river, which trailed away behind the light like the shiny, slimy path of a snail, winked the scattered lights of Marietta. Not two hundred yards away at the end of the bridge squatted the station, marked by a sullen lantern. The oppression was lifted now—the tree-tops below her were rocking the young starlight to a haunted doze. She stretched out her arms with a gesture of freedom. This was what she had wanted, to stand alone where it was high and cool.

"Gloria!"

Like a startled child she scurried along the plank, hopping, skipping, jumping, with an ecstatic sense of her own physical lightness. Let him come now—she no longer feared that, only she must first reach the station, because that was part of the game. She was happy. Her hat, snatched off, was clutched tightly in her hand, and her short curled hair bobbed up and down about her ears. She had thought she would never feel so young again, but this was her night, her world. Triumphantly she laughed as she left the plank, and reaching the wooden platform flung herself down happily beside an iron roof-post.

"Here I am!" she called, gay as the dawn in her elation. "Here I am, Anthony, dear—old, worried Anthony."

"Gloria!" He reached the platform, ran toward her. "Are you all right?" Coming up he knelt and took her in his arms.

"Yes."

"What was the matter? Why did you leave?" he queried anxiously.

"I had to—there was something"—she paused and a flicker of uneasiness lashed at her mind—"there was something sitting on me—here." She put her hand on her breast. "I had to go out and get away from it."

"What do you mean by 'something'?"

"I don't know—that man Hull——"

"Did he bother you?"

"He came to my door, drunk. I think I'd gotten sort of crazy by that time."

"Gloria, dearest——"

Wearily she laid her head upon his shoulder.

"Let's go back," he suggested.

She shivered.

"Uh! No, I couldn't. It'd come and sit on me again." Her voice rose to a cry that hung plaintive on the darkness. "That thing——"

"There—there," he soothed her, pulling her close to him. "We won't do anything you don't want to do. What do you want to do? Just sit here?"

"I want—I want to go away."

"Where?"

"Oh—anywhere."

"By golly, Gloria," he cried, "you're still tight!"

"No, I'm not. I haven't been, all evening. I went up-stairs about, oh, I don't know, about half an hour after dinner . . . Ouch!"

He had inadvertently touched her right shoulder.

"It hurts me. I hurt it some way. I don't know—somebody picked me up and dropped me."

"Gloria, come home. It's late and damp."

"I can't," she wailed. "Oh, Anthony, don't ask me to! I will to-morrow. You go home and I'll wait here for a train. I'll go to a hotel——"

"I'll go with you."

"No, I don't want you with me. I want to be alone. I want to sleep—oh, I want to sleep. And then to-morrow, when you've got all the smell of whiskey and cigarettes out of the house, and everything straight, and Hull is gone, then I'll come home. If I went now, that thing—oh—!" She covered her eyes with her hand; Anthony saw the futility of trying to persuade her.

"I was all sober when you left," he said. "Dick was asleep on the lounge and Maury and I were having a discussion. That fellow Hull had wandered off somewhere. Then I began to realize I hadn't seen you for several hours, so I went up-stairs——"

He broke off as a salutatory "Hello, there!" boomed suddenly out of the darkness. Gloria sprang to her feet and he did likewise.

"It's Maury's voice," she cried excitedly. "If it's Hull with him, keep them away, keep them away!"

"Who's there?" Anthony called.

"Just Dick and Maury," returned two voices reassuringly.

"Where's Hull?"

"He's in bed. Passed out."

Their figures appeared dimly on the platform.

"What the devil are you and Gloria doing here?" inquired Richard Caramel with sleepy bewilderment.

"What are *you* two doing here?"

Maury laughed.

"Damned if I know. We followed you, and had the deuce of a time doing it. I heard you out on the porch yelling for Gloria, so I woke up the Caramel here and got it through his head, with some difficulty, that if there was a search-party we'd better be on it. He slowed me up by sitting down in the road at intervals and asking me what it was all about. We tracked you by the pleasant scent of Canadian Club."

There was a rattle of nervous laughter under the low train-shed.

"How did you track us, really?"

"Well, we followed along down the road and then we suddenly lost you. Seems you turned off at a wagon-trail. After a while somebody hailed us and asked us if we were looking for a young girl. Well, we came up and found it was a little shivering old man, sitting on a fallen tree like somebody in a fairy tale. 'She turned down here,' he said, 'and most steppud on me, goin' somewhere in an awful hustle, and then a fella in short golfin' pants come runnin' along and went after her. He throwed me this.' The old fellow had a dollar bill he was waving around——"

"Oh, the poor old man!" ejaculated Gloria, moved.

"I threw him another and we went on, though he asked us to stay and tell him what it was all about."

"Poor old man," repeated Gloria dismally.

Dick sat down sleepily on a box.

"And now what?" he inquired in the tone of stoic resignation.

"Gloria's upset," explained Anthony. "She and I are going to the city by the next train."

Maury in the darkness had pulled a time-table from his pocket.

"Strike a match."

A tiny flare leaped out of the opaque background illuminating the four faces, grotesque and unfamiliar here in the open night.

"Let's see. Two, two-thirty—no, that's evening. By gad, you won't get a train till five-thirty."

Anthony hesitated.

"Well," he muttered uncertainly, "we've decided to stay here and wait for it. You two might as well go back and sleep."

"You go, too, Anthony," urged Gloria; "I want you

to have some sleep, dear. You've been pale as a ghost all day."

"Why, you little idiot!"

Dick yawned.

"Very well. You stay, we stay."

He walked out from under the shed and surveyed the heavens.

"Rather a nice night, after all. Stars are out and everything. Exceptionally tasty assortment of them."

"Let's see." Gloria moved after him and the other two followed her. "Let's sit out here," she suggested. "I like it much better."

Anthony and Dick converted a long box into a back-rest and found a board dry enough for Gloria to sit on. Anthony dropped down beside her and with some effort Dick hoisted himself onto an apple-barrel near them.

"Tana went to sleep in the porch hammock," he remarked. "We carried him in and left him next to the kitchen stove to dry. He was drenched to the skin."

"That awful little man!" sighed Gloria.

"How do you do!" The voice, sonorous and funereal, had come from above, and they looked up startled to find that in some manner Maury had climbed to the roof of the shed, where he sat dangling his feet over the edge, outlined as a shadowy and fantastic gargoyle against the now brilliant sky.

"It must be for such occasions as this," he began softly, his words having the effect of floating down from an immense height and settling softly upon his auditors, "that the righteous of the land decorate the railroads with bill-boards asserting in red and yellow that 'Jesus Christ is God,' placing them, appropriately enough, next to announcements that 'Gunter's Whiskey is Good.'"

There was gentle laughter and the three below kept their heads tilted upward.

"I think I shall tell you the story of my education," continued Maury, "under these sardonic constellations."

"Do! Please!"

"Shall I, really?"

They waited expectantly while he directed a ruminative yawn toward the white smiling moon.

"Well," he began, "as an infant I prayed. I stored up prayers against future wickedness. One year I stored up nineteen hundred 'Now I lay me's.'"

"Throw down a cigarette," murmured some one.

A small package reached the platform simultaneously with the stentorian command:

"Silence! I am about to unburden myself of many memorable remarks reserved for the darkness of such earths and the brilliance of such skies."

Below, a lighted match was passed from cigarette to cigarette. The voice resumed:

"I was adept at fooling the deity. I prayed immediately after all crimes until eventually prayer and crime became indistinguishable to me. I believed that because a man cried out 'My God!' when a safe fell on him, it proved that belief was rooted deep in the human breast. Then I went to school. For fourteen years half a hundred earnest men pointed to ancient flint-locks and cried to me: 'There's the real thing. These new rifles are only shallow, superficial imitations.' They damned the books I read and the things I thought by calling them immoral; later the fashion changed, and they damned things by calling them 'clever.'

"And so I turned, canny for my years, from the professors to the poets, listening—to the lyric tenor of Swinburne and the tenor robusto of Shelley, to Shakespeare with his first bass and his fine range, to Tennyson with his second bass and his occasional falsetto, to Milton and Marlow, bassos profundo. I gave ear to

Browning chatting, Byron declaiming, and Wordsworth droning. This, at least, did me no harm. I learned a little of beauty—enough to know that it had nothing to do with truth—and I found, moreover, that there was no great literary tradition; there was only the tradition of the eventful death of every literary tradition. . . .

"Then I grew up, and the beauty of succulent illusions fell away from me. The fibre of my mind coarsened and my eyes grew miserably keen. Life rose around my island like a sea, and presently I was swimming.

"The transition was subtle—the thing had lain in wait for me for some time. It has its insidious, seemingly innocuous trap for every one. With me? No—I didn't try to seduce the janitor's wife—nor did I run through the streets unclothed, proclaiming my virility. It is never quite passion that does the business—it is the dress that passion wears. I became bored—that was all. Boredom, which is another name and a frequent disguise for vitality, became the unconscious motive of all my acts. Beauty was behind me, do you understand?—I was grown." He paused. "End of school and college period. Opening of Part Two."

Three quietly active points of light showed the location of his listeners. Gloria was now half sitting, half lying, in Anthony's lap. His arm was around her so tightly that she could hear the beating of his heart. Richard Caramel, perched on the apple-barrel, from time to time stirred and gave off a faint grunt.

"I grew up then, into this land of jazz, and fell immediately into a state of almost audible confusion. Life stood over me like an immoral schoolmistress, editing my ordered thoughts. But, with a mistaken faith in intelligence, I plodded on. I read Smith, who laughed at charity and insisted that the sneer was the highest form of self-expression—but Smith himself replaced charity as an obscurer of the light. I read Jones, who neatly disposed of individualism—and behold! Jones was still in my way. I did not think—I was a battle-ground for the thoughts of many men; rather was I one of those desirable but impotent countries over which the great powers surge back and forth.

"I reached maturity under the impression that I was gathering the experience to order my life for happiness. Indeed, I accomplished the not unusual feat of solving each question in my mind long before it presented itself to me in life—and of being beaten and bewildered just the same.

"But after a few tastes of this latter dish I had had enough. Here! I said, Experience is not worth the getting. It's not a thing that happens pleasantly to a passive you—it's a wall that an active you runs up against. So I wrapped myself in what I thought was my invulnerable scepticism and decided that my education was complete. But it was too late. Protect myself as I might by making no new ties with tragic and predestined humanity, I was lost with the rest. I had traded the fight against love for the fight against loneliness, the fight against life for the fight against death."

He broke off to give emphasis to his last observation —after a moment he yawned and resumed.

"I suppose that the beginning of the second phase of my education was a ghastly dissatisfaction at being used in spite of myself for some inscrutable purpose of whose ultimate goal I was unaware—if, indeed, there *was* an ultimate goal. It was a difficult choice. The schoolmistress seemed to be saying, 'We're going to play football and nothing but football. If you don't want to play football you can't play at all——'

"What was I to do—the playtime was so short!

"You see, I felt that we were even denied what consolation there might have been in being a figment of a corporate man rising from his knees. Do you think that I leaped at this pessimism, grasped it as a sweetly smug superior thing, no more depressing really than, say, a gray autumn day before a fire?—I don't think I did that. I was a great deal too warm for that, and too alive.

"For it seemed to me that there was no ultimate goal for man. Man was beginning a grotesque and bewildered fight with nature—nature, that by the divine and magnificent accident had brought us to where we could fly in her face. She had invented ways to rid the race of the inferior and thus give the remainder strength to fill her higher—or, let us say, her more amusing—though still unconscious and accidental intentions. And, actuated by the highest gifts of the enlightenment, we were seeking to circumvent her. In this republic I saw the black beginning to mingle with the white—in Europe there was taking place an economic catastrophe to save three or four diseased and wretchedly governed races from the one mastery that might organize them for material prosperity.

"We produce a Christ who can raise up the leper—and presently the breed of the leper is the salt of the earth. If any one can find any lesson in that, let him stand forth."

"There's only one lesson to be learned from life, anyway," interrupted Gloria, not in contradiction but in a sort of melancholy agreement.

"What's that?" demanded Maury sharply.

"That there's no lesson to be learned from life."

After a short silence Maury said:

"Young Gloria, the beautiful and merciless lady, first looked at the world with the fundamental sophistication I have struggled to attain, that Anthony never will attain, that Dick will never fully understand."

There was a disgusted groan from the apple-barrel.

Anthony, grown accustomed to the dark, could see plainly the flash of Richard Caramel's yellow eye and the look of resentment on his face as he cried:

"You're crazy! By your own statement I should have attained some experience by trying."

"Trying what?" cried Maury fiercely. "Trying to pierce the darkness of political idealism with some wild, despairing urge toward truth? Sitting day after day supine in a rigid chair and infinitely removed from life staring at the tip of a steeple through the trees, trying to separate, definitely and for all time, the knowable from the unknowable? Trying to take a piece of actuality and give it glamour from your own soul to make for that inexpressible quality it possessed in life and lost in transit to paper or canvas? Struggling in a laboratory through weary years for one iota of relative truth in a mass of wheels or a test tube——"

"Have you?"

Maury paused, and in his answer, when it came, there was a measure of weariness, a bitter overnote that lingered for a moment in those three minds before it floated up and off like a bubble bound for the moon.

"Not I," he said softly. "I was born tired—but with the quality of mother wit, the gift of women like Gloria—to that, for all my talking and listening, my waiting in vain for the eternal generality that seems to lie just beyond every argument and every speculation, to that I have added not one jot."

In the distance a deep sound that had been audible for some moments identified itself by a plaintive mooing like that of a gigantic cow and by the pearly spot of a headlight apparent half a mile away. It was a steam-driven train this time, rumbling and groaning, and as it tumbled by with a monstrous complaint it sent a shower of sparks and cinders over the platform.

"Not one jot!" Again Maury's voice dropped down

to them as from a great height. "What a feeble thing intelligence is, with its short steps, its waverings, its pacings back and forth, its disastrous retreats! Intelligence is a mere instrument of circumstances. There are people who say that intelligence must have built the universe—why, intelligence never built a steam engine! Circumstances built a steam engine. Intelligence is little more than a short foot-rule by which we measure the infinite achievements of Circumstances.

"I could quote you the philosophy of the hour—but, for all we know, fifty years may see a complete reversal of this abnegation that's absorbing the intellectuals to-day, the triumph of Christ over Anatole France—" He hesitated, and then added: "But all I know—the tremendous importance of myself to me, and the necessity of acknowledging that importance to myself—these things the wise and lovely Gloria was born knowing, these things and the painful futility of trying to know anything else.

"Well, I started to tell you of my education, didn't I? But I learned nothing, you see, very little even about myself. And if I had I should die with my lips shut and the guard on my fountain pen—as the wisest men have done since—oh, since the failure of a certain matter—a strange matter, by the way. It concerned some sceptics who thought they were far-sighted, just as you and I. Let me tell you about them by way of an evening prayer before you all drop off to sleep.

"Once upon a time all the men of mind and genius in the world became of one belief—that is to say, of no belief. But it wearied them to think that within a few years after their death many cults and systems and prognostications would be ascribed to them which they had never meditated nor intended. So they said to one another:

"'Let's join together and make a great book that will

last forever to mock the credulity of man. Let's persuade our more erotic poets to write about the delights of the flesh, and induce some of our robust journalists to contribute stories of famous amours. We'll include all the most preposterous old wives' tales now current. We'll choose the keenest satirist alive to compile a deity from all the deities worshipped by mankind, a deity who will be more magnificent than any of them, and yet so weakly human that he'll become a byword for laughter the world over—and we'll ascribe to him all sorts of jokes and vanities and rages, in which he'll be supposed to indulge for his own diversion, so that the people will read our book and ponder it, and there'll be no more nonsense in the world.

"'Finally, let us take care that the book possesses all the virtues of style, so that it may last forever as a witness to our profound scepticism and our universal irony.'

"So the men did, and they died.

"But the book lived always, so beautifully had it been written, and so astounding the quality of imagination with which these men of mind and genius had endowed it. They had neglected to give it a name, but after they were dead it became known as the Bible."

When he concluded there was no comment. Some damp languor sleeping on the air of night seemed to have bewitched them all.

"As I said, I started on the story of my education. But my high-balls are dead and the night's almost over, and soon there'll be an awful jabbering going on everywhere, in the trees and the houses, and the two little stores over there behind the station, and there'll be a great running up and down upon the earth for a few hours— Well," he concluded with a laugh, "thank God we four can all pass to our eternal rest knowing we've left the world a little better for having lived in it."

A breeze sprang up, blowing with it faint wisps of life which flattened against the sky.

"Your remarks grow rambling and inconclusive," said Anthony sleepily. "You expected one of those miracles of illumination by which you say your most brilliant and pregnant things in exactly the setting that should provoke the ideal symposium. Meanwhile Gloria has shown her far-sighted detachment by falling asleep —I can tell that by the fact that she has managed to concentrate her entire weight upon my broken body."

"Have I bored you?" inquired Maury, looking down with some concern.

"No, you have disappointed us. You've shot a lot of arrows but did you shoot any birds?"

"I leave the birds to Dick," said Maury hurriedly. "I speak erratically, in disassociated fragments."

"You can get no rise from me," muttered Dick. "My mind is full of any number of material things. I want a warm bath too much to worry about the importance of my work or what proportion of us are pathetic figures."

Dawn made itself felt in a gathering whiteness eastward over the river and an intermittent cheeping in the near-by trees.

"Quarter to five," sighed Dick; "almost another hour to wait. Look! Two gone." He was pointing to Anthony, whose lids had sagged over his eyes. "Sleep of the Patch family——"

But in another five minutes, despite the amplifying cheeps and chirrups, his own head had fallen forward, nodded down twice, thrice. . . .

Only Maury Noble remained awake, seated upon the station roof, his eyes wide open and fixed with fatigued intensity upon the distant nucleus of morning. He was wondering at the unreality of ideas, at the fading radiance of existence, and at the little absorptions that were creeping avidly into his life, like rats into a ruined house.

He was sorry for no one now—on Monday morning there would be his business, and later there would be a girl of another class whose whole life he was; these were the things nearest his heart. In the strangeness of the brightening day it seemed presumptuous that with this feeble, broken instrument of his mind he had ever tried to think.

There was the sun, letting down great glowing masses of heat; there was life, active and snarling, moving about them like a fly swarm—the dark pants of smoke from the engine, a crisp "all aboard!" and a bell ringing. Confusedly Maury saw eyes in the milk train staring curiously up at him, heard Gloria and Anthony in quick controversy as to whether he should go to the city with her—then another clamor and she was gone and the three men, pale as ghosts, were standing alone upon the platform while a grimy coal-heaver went down the road on top of a motor truck, carolling hoarsely at the summer morning.

CHAPTER III

THE BROKEN LUTE

It is seven-thirty of an August evening. The windows in the living room of the gray house are wide open, patiently exchanging the tainted inner atmosphere of liquor and smoke for the fresh drowsiness of the late hot dusk. There are dying flower scents upon the air, so thin, so fragile, as to hint already of a summer laid away in time. But August is still proclaimed relentlessly by a thousand crickets around the side-porch, and by one who has broken into the house and concealed himself confidently behind a bookcase, from time to time shrieking of his cleverness and his indomitable will.

The room itself is in messy disorder. On the table is a dish of fruit, which is real but appears artificial. Around it are grouped an ominous assortment of decanters, glasses, and heaped ash-trays, the latter still raising wavy smoke-ladders into the stale air—the effect on the whole needing but a skull to resemble that venerable chromo, once a fixture in every "den," which presents the appendages to the life of pleasure with delightful and awe-inspiring sentiment.

After a while the sprightly solo of the supercricket is interrupted rather than joined by a new sound—the melancholy wail of an erratically fingered flute. It is obvious that the musician is practising rather than performing, for from time to time the gnarled strain breaks off and, after an interval of indistinct mutterings, recommences.

Just prior to the seventh false start a third sound contributes to the subdued discord. It is a taxi outside. A minute's silence, then the taxi again, its boisterous retreat almost obliterating the scrape of footsteps on the cinder walk. The door-bell shrieks alarmingly through the house.

From the kitchen enters a small, fatigued Japanese, hastily buttoning a servant's coat of white duck. He opens the front screen-door and admits a handsome young man of thirty, clad in the sort of well-intentioned clothes peculiar to those who serve mankind. To his whole personality clings a well-intentioned air: his glance about the room is compounded of curiosity and a determined optimism; when he looks at Tana the entire burden of uplifting the godless Oriental is in his eyes. His name is FREDERICK E. PARAMORE. *He was at Harvard with* ANTHONY, *where because of the initials of their surnames they were constantly placed next to each other in classes. A fragmentary acquaintance developed—but since that time they have never met.*

Nevertheless, PARAMORE *enters the room with a certain air of arriving for the evening.*

Tana is answering a question.

TANA: (*Grinning with ingratiation*) Gone to Inn for dinnah. Be back half-hour. Gone since ha' past six.

PARAMORE: (*Regarding the glasses on the table*) Have they company?

TANA: Yes. Company. Mistah Caramel, Mistah and Missays Barnes, Miss Kane, all stay here.

PARAMORE: I see. (*Kindly*) They've been having a spree, I see.

TANA: I no un'stan'.

PARAMORE: They've been having a fling.

TANA: Yes, they have drink. Oh, many, many, many drink.

PARAMORE: (*Receding delicately from the subject*) Didn't I hear the sounds of music as I approached the house?

TANA: (*With a spasmodic giggle*) Yes, I play.

PARAMORE: One of the Japanese instruments.

(*He is quite obviously a subscriber to the "National Geographic Magazine."*)

TANA: I play flu-u-ute, Japanese flu-u-ute.

PARAMORE: What song were you playing? One of your Japanese melodies?

TANA: (*His brow undergoing preposterous contraction*) I play train song. How you call?—*railroad* song. So call in my countree. Like train. It go so-o-o; that mean whistle; train start. Then go so-o-o; that mean train go. Go like that. Vera nice song in my countree. Children song.

PARAMORE: It sounded very nice.

(*It is apparent at this point that only a gigantic effort at control restrains* TANA *from rushing upstairs for his post cards, including the six made in America.*)

TANA: I fix high-ball for gentleman?

PARAMORE: No, thanks. I don't use it. (*He smiles.*)

(TANA *withdraws into the kitchen, leaving the intervening door slightly ajar. From the crevice there suddenly issues again the melody of the Japanese train song—this time not a practice, surely, but a performance, a lusty, spirited performance.*

The phone rings. TANA, *absorbed in his harmonics, gives no heed, so* PARAMORE *takes up the receiver.*)

PARAMORE: Hello. . . . Yes. . . . No, he's not here now, but he'll be back any moment. . . . Butterworth? Hello, I didn't quite catch the name. . . . Hello, hello, hello. Hello! . . . Huh!

(*The phone obstinately refuses to yield up any more sound.* PARAMORE *replaces the receiver.*

At this point the taxi motif re-enters, wafting with it a second young man; he carries a suitcase and opens the front door without ringing the bell.)

MAURY: (*In the hall*) Oh, Anthony! Yoho! (*He comes into the large room and sees* PARAMORE) How do?

PARAMORE: (*Gazing at him with gathering intensity*) Is this—is this Maury Noble?

MAURY: That's it. (*He advances, smiling, and holding out his hand*) How are you, old boy? Haven't seen you for years.

(*He has vaguely associated the face with Harvard, but is not even positive about that. The name, if he ever knew it, he has long since forgotten. However, with a fine sensitiveness and an equally commendable charity* PARAMORE *recognizes the fact and tactfully relieves the situation.*)

PARAMORE: You've forgotten Fred Paramore? We were both in old Unc Robert's history class.

MAURY: No, I haven't, Unc—I mean Fred. Fred was —I mean Unc was a great old fellow, wasn't he?

PARAMORE: (*Nodding his head humorously several times*) Great old character. Great old character.

MAURY: (*After a short pause*) Yes—he was. Where's Anthony?

PARAMORE: The Japanese servant told me he was at some inn. Having dinner, I suppose.

MAURY: (*Looking at his watch*) Gone long?

PARAMORE: I guess so. The Japanese told me they'd be back shortly.

MAURY: Suppose we have a drink.

PARAMORE: No, thanks. I don't use it. (*He smiles.*)

MAURY: Mind if I do? (*Yawning as he helps himself from a bottle*) What have you been doing since you left college?

PARAMORE: Oh, many things. I've led a very active life. Knocked about here and there. (*His tone implies anything from lion-stalking to organized crime.*)

MAURY: Oh, been over to Europe?

PARAMORE: No, I haven't—unfortunately.

MAURY: I guess we'll all go over before long.

PARAMORE: Do you really think so?

MAURY: Sure! Country's been fed on sensationalism for more than two years. Everybody getting restless. Want to have some fun.

PARAMORE: Then you don't believe any ideals are at stake?

MAURY: Nothing of much importance. People want excitement every so often.

PARAMORE: (*Intently*) It's very interesting to hear you say that. Now I was talking to a man who'd been over there——

(*During the ensuing testament, left to be filled in by the reader with such phrases as "Saw with his own eyes," "Splendid spirit of France," and "Salvation of civilization,"* MAURY *sits with lowered eyelids, dispassionately bored.*)

MAURY: (*At the first available opportunity*) By the way, do you happen to know that there's a German agent in this very house?

PARAMORE: (*Smiling cautiously*) Are you serious?

MAURY: Absolutely. Feel it my duty to warn you.

PARAMORE: (*Convinced*) A governess?

MAURY: (*In a whisper, indicating the kitchen with his thumb*) *Tana!* That's not his real name. I understand he constantly gets mail addressed to Lieutenant Emile Tannenbaum.

PARAMORE: (*Laughing with hearty tolerance*) You were kidding me.

MAURY: I may be accusing him falsely. But, you haven't told me what you've been doing.

PARAMORE: For one thing—writing.

MAURY: Fiction?

PARAMORE: No. Non-fiction.

MAURY: What's that? A sort of literature that's half fiction and half fact?

PARAMORE: Oh, I've confined myself to fact. I've been doing a good deal of social-service work.

MAURY: Oh!

(*An immediate glow of suspicion leaps into his eyes. It is as though* PARAMORE *had announced himself as an amateur pickpocket.*)

PARAMORE: At present I'm doing service work in Stamford. Only last week some one told me that Anthony Patch lived so near.

(*They are interrupted by a clamor outside, unmistakable as that of two sexes in conversation and laughter. Then there enter the room in a body* ANTHONY, GLORIA, RICHARD CARAMEL, MURIEL KANE, RACHAEL BARNES *and* RODMAN BARNES, *her husband. They surge about* MAURY, *illogically replying* "Fine!" *to his general* "Hello." . . . ANTHONY, *meanwhile, approaches his other guest.*)

ANTHONY: Well, I'll be darned. How are you? Mighty glad to see you.

PARAMORE: It's good to see you, Anthony. I'm stationed in Stamford, so I thought I'd run over. (*Roguishly*) We have to work to beat the devil most of the time, so we're entitled to a few hours' vacation.

(*In an agony of concentration* ANTHONY *tries to recall the name. After a struggle of parturition his memory gives up the fragment* "Fred," *around which he hastily builds the sentence* "Glad you did, Fred!" *Meanwhile the slight hush prefatory to an introduction has fallen upon the company.* MAURY, *who could help, prefers to look on in malicious enjoyment.*)

ANTHONY: (*In desperation*) Ladies and gentlemen, this is—this is Fred.

MURIEL: (*With obliging levity*) Hello, Fred!

(RICHARD CARAMEL *and* PARAMORE *greet each other intimately by their first names, the latter recollecting that* DICK *was one of the men in his class who had never before troubled to speak to him.* DICK *fatuously imagines that* PARAMORE *is some one he has previously met in* ANTHONY'S *house.*

The three young women go up-stairs.)

MAURY: (*In an undertone to* DICK) Haven't seen Muriel since Anthony's wedding.

DICK: She's now in her prime. Her latest is "*I'll* say so!"

(ANTHONY *struggles for a while with* PARAMORE *and at length attempts to make the conversation general by asking every one to have a drink.*)

MAURY: I've done pretty well on this bottle. I've gone from "Proof" down to "Distillery." (*He indicates the words on the label.*)

ANTHONY: (*To* PARAMORE) Never can tell when these two will turn up. Said good-by to them one afternoon at five and darned if they didn't appear about two in the morning. A big hired touring-car from New York drove up to the door and out they stepped, drunk as lords, of course.

(*In an ecstasy of consideration* PARAMORE *regards the cover of a book which he holds in his hand.* MAURY *and* DICK *exchange a glance.*)

DICK: (*Innocently, to* PARAMORE) You work here in town?

PARAMORE: No, I'm in the Laird Street Settlement in Stamford. (*To* ANTHONY) You have no idea of the amount of poverty in these small Connecticut towns. Italians and other immigrants. Catholics mostly, you know, so it's very hard to reach them.

ANTHONY: (*Politely*) Lot of crime?

PARAMORE: Not so much crime as ignorance and dirt.

MAURY: That's my theory: immediate electrocution of all ignorant and dirty people. I'm all for the criminals—give color to life. Trouble is if you started to punish ignorance you'd have to begin in the first families, then you could take up the moving picture people, and finally Congress and the clergy.

PARAMORE: (*Smiling uneasily*) I was speaking of the more fundamental ignorance—of even our language.

MAURY: (*Thoughtfully*) I suppose it is rather hard. Can't even keep up with the new poetry.

PARAMORE: It's only when the settlement work has gone on for months that one realizes how bad things are. As our secretary said to me, your finger-nails never seem dirty until you wash your hands. Of course we're already attracting much attention.

MAURY: (*Rudely*) As your secretary might say, if you stuff paper into a grate it'll burn brightly for a moment.

(*At this point* GLORIA, *freshly tinted and lustful of admiration and entertainment, rejoins the party, followed by her two friends. For several moments the conversation becomes entirely fragmentary.* GLORIA *calls* ANTHONY *aside.*)

GLORIA: Please don't drink much, Anthony.

ANTHONY: Why?

GLORIA: Because you're so simple when you're drunk.

ANTHONY: Good Lord! What's the matter now?

GLORIA: (*After a pause during which her eyes gaze coolly into his*) Several things. In the first place, why do you insist on paying for everything? Both those men have more money than you!

ANTHONY: Why, Gloria! They're my guests!

GLORIA: That's no reason why you should pay for a bottle of champagne Rachael Barnes smashed. Dick tried to fix that second taxi bill, and you wouldn't let him.

ANTHONY: Why, Gloria——

GLORIA: When we have to keep selling bonds to even pay our bills, it's time to cut down on excess generosities. Moreover, I wouldn't be quite so attentive to Rachael Barnes. Her husband doesn't like it any more than I do!

ANTHONY: Why, Gloria——

GLORIA: (*Mimicking him sharply*) "Why, Gloria!" But that's happened a little too often this summer—with every pretty woman you meet. It's grown to be a sort of habit, and I'm *not* going to stand it! If you can play around, I can, too. (*Then, as an afterthought*) By the way, this Fred person isn't a second Joe Hull, is he?

ANTHONY: Heavens, no! He probably came up to get me to wheedle some money out of grandfather for his flock.

(GLORIA *turns away from a very depressed* ANTHONY *and returns to her guests.*

By nine o'clock these can be divided into two classes —those who have been drinking consistently and those who have taken little or nothing. In the second group are the BARNESES, MURIEL, *and* FREDERICK E. PARAMORE.)

MURIEL: I wish I could write. I get these ideas but I never seem to be able to put them in words.

DICK: As Goliath said, he understood how David felt, but he couldn't express himself. The remark was immediately adopted for a motto by the Philistines.

MURIEL: I don't get you. I must be getting stupid in my old age.

GLORIA: (*Weaving unsteadily among the company like an exhilarated angel*) If any one's hungry there's some French pastry on the dining room table.

MAURY: Can't tolerate those Victorian designs it comes in.

MURIEL: (*Violently amused*) *I'll* say you're tight, Maury.

(*Her bosom is still a pavement that she offers to the hoofs of many passing stallions, hoping that their iron shoes may strike even a spark of romance in the darkness. . . .*

Messrs. BARNES *and* PARAMORE *have been engaged in conversation upon some wholesome subject, a subject so wholesome that* MR. BARNES *has been trying for several moments to creep into the more tainted air around the central lounge. Whether* PARAMORE *is lingering in the gray house out of politeness or curiosity, or in order at some future time to make a sociological report on the decadence of American life, is problematical.*)

MAURY: Fred, I imagined you were very broad-minded.

PARAMORE: I am.

MURIEL: Me, too. I believe one religion's as good as another and everything.

PARAMORE: There's some good in all religions.

MURIEL: I'm a Catholic but, as I always say, I'm not working at it.

PARAMORE: (*With a tremendous burst of tolerance*) The Catholic religion is a very—a very powerful religion.

MAURY: Well, such a broad-minded man should consider the raised plane of sensation and the stimulated optimism contained in this cocktail.

PARAMORE: (*Taking the drink, rather defiantly*) Thanks, I'll try—one.

MAURY: One? Outrageous! Here we have a class of 'nineteen ten reunion, and you refuse to be even a little pickled. Come on!

> "*Here's a health to King Charles,*
> *Here's a health to King Charles,*
> *Bring the bowl that you boast——*"

(PARAMORE *joins in with a hearty voice.*)

MAURY: Fill the cup, Frederick. You know everything's subordinated to nature's purposes with us, and her purpose with you is to make you a rip-roaring tippler.

PARAMORE: If a fellow can drink like a gentleman——

MAURY: What is a gentleman, anyway?

ANTHONY: A man who never has pins under his coat lapel.

MAURY: Nonsense! A man's social rank is determined by the amount of bread he eats in a sandwich.

DICK: He's a man who prefers the first edition of a book to the last edition of a newspaper.

RACHAEL: A man who never gives an impersonation of a dope-fiend.

MAURY: An American who can fool an English butler into thinking he's one.

MURIEL: A man who comes from a good family and went to Yale or Harvard or Princeton, and has money and dances well, and all that.

MAURY: At last—the perfect definition! Cardinal Newman's is now a back number.

PARAMORE: I think we ought to look on the question more broad-mindedly. Was it Abraham Lincoln who said that a gentleman is one who never inflicts pain?

MAURY: It's attributed, I believe, to General Ludendorff.

PARAMORE: Surely you're joking.

MAURY: Have another drink.

PARAMORE: I oughtn't to. (*Lowering his voice for* MAURY'S *ear alone*) What if I were to tell you this is the third drink I've ever taken in my life?

(DICK *starts the phonograph, which provokes* MURIEL *to rise and sway from side to side, her elbows against her ribs, her forearms perpendicular to her body and out like fins.*)

MURIEL: Oh, let's take up the rugs and dance!

(*This suggestion is received by* ANTHONY *and* GLORIA *with interior groans and sickly smiles of acquiescence.*)

MURIEL: Come on, you lazy-bones. Get up and move the furniture back.

DICK: Wait till I finish my drink.

MAURY: (*Intent on his purpose toward* PARAMORE) I'll tell you what. Let's each fill one glass, drink it off—and then we'll dance.

(*A wave of protest which breaks against the rock of* MAURY'S *insistence.*)

MURIEL: My head is simply going *round* now.

RACHAEL: (*In an undertone to* ANTHONY) Did Gloria tell you to stay away from me?

ANTHONY: (*Confused*) Why, certainly not. Of course not.

(RACHAEL *smiles at him inscrutably. Two years have given her a sort of hard, well-groomed beauty.*)

MAURY: (*Holding up his glass*) Here's to the defeat of democracy and the fall of Christianity.

MURIEL: Now really!

(*She flashes a mock-reproachful glance at* MAURY *and then drinks.*

They all drink, with varying degrees of difficulty.)

MURIEL: Clear the floor!

(*It seems inevitable that this process is to be gone through, so* ANTHONY *and* GLORIA *join in the great moving of tables, piling of chairs, rolling of carpets, and breaking of lamps. When the furniture has been stacked in ugly masses at the sides, there appears a space about eight feet square.*)

MURIEL: Oh, let's have music!

MAURY: Tana will render the love song of an eye, ear, nose, and throat specialist.

(*Amid some confusion due to the fact that* TANA *has retired for the night, preparations are made for the performance. The pajamaed Japanese, flute in hand, is wrapped in a comforter and placed in a chair atop one of the tables, where he makes a ludicrous and grotesque spectacle.* PARAMORE *is perceptibly drunk and so enraptured with the notion that he increases the effect by simulating funny-paper staggers and even venturing on an occasional hiccough.*)

PARAMORE: (*To* GLORIA) Want to dance with me?

GLORIA: No, sir! Want to do the swan dance. Can you do it?

PARAMORE: Sure. Do them all.

GLORIA: All right. You start from that side of the room and I'll start from this.

MURIEL: Let's go!

(*Then Bedlam creeps screaming out of the bottles:*

TANA *plunges into the recondite mazes of the train song, the plaintive "tootle toot-toot" blending its melancholy cadences with the* "Poor Butter-fly (tink-atink), by the blossoms wait-ing" *of the phonograph.* MURIEL *is too weak with laughter to do more than cling desperately to* BARNES, *who, dancing with the ominous rigidity of an army officer, tramps without humor around the small space.* ANTHONY *is trying to hear* RACHAEL'S *whisper—without attracting* GLORIA'S *attention. . . .*

But the grotesque, the unbelievable, the histrionic incident is about to occur, one of those incidents in which life seems set upon the passionate imitation of the lowest forms of literature. PARAMORE *has been trying to emulate* GLORIA, *and as the commotion reaches its height he begins to spin round and round, more and more dizzily—he staggers, recovers, staggers again and then falls in the direction of the hall . . . almost into the arms of old* ADAM PATCH, *whose approach has been rendered inaudible by the pandemonium in the room.*

ADAM PATCH *is very white. He leans upon a stick. The man with him is* EDWARD SHUTTLEWORTH, *and it is he who seizes* PARAMORE *by the shoulder and deflects the course of his fall away from the venerable philanthropist.*

The time required for quiet to descend upon the room like a monstrous pall may be estimated at two minutes, though for a short period after that the phonograph gags and the notes of the Japanese train song dribble from the end of TANA'S *flute. Of the nine people only* BARNES, PARAMORE, *and* TANA *are unaware of the late-comer's identity. Of the nine not one is aware that* ADAM PATCH *has that morning made a contribution of fifty thousand dollars to the cause of national prohibition.*

It is given to PARAMORE *to break the gathering silence; the high tide of his life's depravity is reached in his incredible remark.*)

PARAMORE: (*Crawling rapidly toward the kitchen on his hands and knees*) I'm not a guest here—I work here.

(*Again silence falls—so deep now, so weighted with intolerably contagious apprehension, that* RACHAEL *gives a nervous little giggle, and* DICK *finds himself telling over and over a line from Swinburne, grotesquely appropriate to the scene:*

"One gaunt bleak blossom of scentless breath."

. . . *Out of the hush the voice of* ANTHONY, *sober and strained, saying something to* ADAM PATCH; *then this, too, dies away.*)

SHUTTLEWORTH: (*Passionately*) Your grandfather thought he would motor over to see your house. I phoned from Rye and left a message.

(*A series of little gasps, emanating, apparently, from nowhere, from no one, fall into the next pause.* ANTHONY *is the color of chalk.* GLORIA'S *lips are parted and her level gaze at the old man is tense and frightened. There is not one smile in the room. Not one? Or does* CROSS PATCH'S *drawn mouth tremble slightly open, to expose the even rows of his thin teeth? He speaks —five mild and simple words.*)

ADAM PATCH: We'll go back now, Shuttleworth——

(*And that is all. He turns, and assisted by his cane goes out through the hall, through the front door, and with hellish portentousness his uncertain footsteps crunch on the gravel path under the August moon.)*

Retrospect

In this extremity they were like two goldfish in a bowl from which all the water had been drawn; they could not even swim across to each other.

Gloria would be twenty-six in May. There was nothing, she had said, that she wanted, except to be young and beautiful for a long time, to be gay and happy, and to have money and love. She wanted what most women want, but she wanted it much more fiercely and passionately. She had been married over two years. At first there had been days of serene understanding, rising to ecstasies of proprietorship and pride. Alternating with these periods had occurred sporadic hates, enduring a short hour, and forgetfulnesses lasting no longer than an afternoon. That had been for half a year.

Then the serenity, the content, had become less jubilant, had become gray—very rarely, with the spur of jealousy or forced separation, the ancient ecstasies returned, the apparent communion of soul and soul, the emotional excitement. It was possible for her to hate Anthony for as much as a full day, to be carelessly incensed at him for as long as a week. Recrimination had displaced affection as an indulgence, almost as an entertainment, and there were nights when they would go to sleep trying to remember who was angry and who should be reserved next morning. And as the second year waned there had entered two new elements. Gloria realized that Anthony had become capable of utter indifference toward her, a temporary indifference, more than half lethargic, but one from which she could no longer stir him by a whispered word, or a certain intimate smile. There were days when her caresses affected him as a sort of suffocation. She was conscious of these things; she never entirely admitted them to herself.

It was only recently that she perceived that in spite of her adoration of him, her jealousy, her servitude, her pride, she fundamentally despised him—and her contempt blended indistinguishably with her other emotions. . . . All this was her love—the vital and feminine illusion that had directed itself toward him one April night, many months before.

On Anthony's part she was, in spite of these qualifications, his sole preoccupation. Had he lost her he would have been a broken man, wretchedly and sentimentally absorbed in her memory for the remainder of life. He seldom took pleasure in an entire day spent alone with her—except on occasions he preferred to have a third person with them. There were times when he felt that if he were not left absolutely alone he would go mad—there were a few times when he definitely hated her. In his cups he was capable of short attractions toward other women, the hitherto-suppressed outcroppings of an experimental temperament.

That spring, that summer, they had speculated upon future happiness—how they were to travel from summer land to summer land, returning eventually to a gorgeous estate and possible idyllic children, then entering diplomacy or politics, to accomplish, for a while, beautiful and important things, until finally as a white-haired (beautifully, silkily, white-haired) couple they were to loll about in serene glory, worshipped by the bourgeoisie of the land. . . . These times were to begin "when we get our money"; it was on such dreams rather than on any satisfaction with their increasingly irregular, increasingly dissipated life that their hope rested. On gray mornings when the jests of the night before had shrunk to ribaldries without wit or dignity, they could, after a fashion, bring out this batch of common hopes and count them over, then smile at each other and repeat, by way of clinching the matter, the terse yet sincere Nietzscheanism of Gloria's defiant "I don't care!"

Things had been slipping perceptibly. There was the money question, increasingly annoying, increasingly ominous; there was the realization that liquor had become a practical necessity to their amusement—not an uncommon phenomenon in the British aristocracy of a hundred years ago, but a somewhat alarming one in a civilization steadily becoming more temperate and more circumspect. Moreover, both of them seemed vaguely weaker in fibre, not so much in what they did as in their subtle reactions to the civilization about them. In Gloria had been born something that she had hitherto never needed—the skeleton, incomplete but nevertheless unmistakable, of her ancient abhorrence, a conscience. This admission to herself was coincidental with the slow decline of her physical courage.

Then, on the August morning after Adam Patch's unexpected call, they awoke, nauseated and tired, dispirited with life, capable only of one pervasive emotion—fear.

Panic

"Well?" Anthony sat up in bed and looked down at her. The corners of his lips were drooping with depression, his voice was strained and hollow.

Her reply was to raise her hand to her mouth and begin a slow, precise nibbling at her finger.

"We've done it," he said after a pause; then, as she was still silent, he became exasperated. "Why don't you say something?"

"What on earth do you want me to say?"

"What are you thinking?"

"Nothing."

"Then stop biting your finger!"

Ensued a short confused discussion of whether or not she had been thinking. It seemed essential to Anthony that she should muse aloud upon last night's disaster. Her silence was a method of settling the responsibility on him. For her part she saw no necessity for speech—the moment required that she should gnaw at her finger like a nervous child.

"I've got to fix up this damn mess with my grandfather," he said with uneasy conviction. A faint newborn respect was indicated by his use of "my grandfather" instead of "grampa."

"You can't," she affirmed abruptly. "You can't—*ever*. He'll never forgive you as long as he lives."

"Perhaps not," agreed Anthony miserably. "Still—I might possibly square myself by some sort of reformation and all that sort of thing——"

"He looked sick," she interrupted, "pale as flour."

"He *is* sick. I told you that three months ago."

"I wish he'd died last week!" she said petulantly. "Inconsiderate old fool!"

Neither of them laughed.

"But just let me say," she added quietly, "the next time I see you acting with any woman like you did with Rachael Barnes last night, I'll leave you—*just—like—that!* I'm simply *not* going to stand it!"

Anthony quailed.

"Oh, don't be absurd," he protested. "You know there's no woman in the world for me except you—none, dearest."

His attempt at a tender note failed miserably—the more imminent danger stalked back into the foreground.

"If I went to him," suggested Anthony, "and said with appropriate biblical quotations that I'd walked too long in the way of unrighteousness and at last seen the light—" He broke off and glanced with a whimsical expression at his wife. "I wonder what he'd do?"

"I don't know."

She was speculating as to whether or not their guests would have the acumen to leave directly after breakfast.

Not for a week did Anthony muster the courage to go to Tarrytown. The prospect was revolting and left alone he would have been incapable of making the trip—but if his will had deteriorated in these past three years, so had his power to resist urging. Gloria compelled him to go. It was all very well to wait a week, she said, for that would give his grandfather's violent animosity time to cool—but to wait longer would be an error—it would give it a chance to harden.

He went, in trepidation . . . and vainly. Adam Patch was not well, said Shuttleworth indignantly. Positive instructions had been given that no one was to see him. Before the ex-"gin-physician's" vindictive eye Anthony's front wilted. He walked out to his taxicab with what was almost a slink—recovering only a little of his self-respect as he boarded the train; glad to escape, boylike, to the wonder palaces of consolation that still rose and glittered in his own mind.

Gloria was scornful when he returned to Marietta. Why had he not forced his way in? That was what she would have done!

Between them they drafted a letter to the old man, and after considerable revision sent it off. It was half an apology, half a manufactured explanation. The letter was not answered.

Came a day in September, a day slashed with alternate sun and rain, sun without warmth, rain without freshness. On that day they left the gray house, which had seen the flower of their love. Four trunks and three monstrous crates were piled in the dismantled room where, two years before, they had sprawled lazily, thinking in terms of dreams, remote, languorous, content. The room echoed with emptiness. Gloria, in a new brown dress edged with fur, sat upon a trunk in silence, and Anthony walked nervously to and fro smoking, as they waited for the truck that would take their things to the city.

"What are those?" she demanded, pointing to some books piled upon one of the crates.

"That's my old stamp collection," he confessed sheepishly. "I forgot to pack it."

"Anthony, it's so silly to carry it around."

"Well, I was looking through it the day we left the apartment last spring, and I decided not to store it."

"Can't you sell it? Haven't we enough junk?"

"I'm sorry," he said humbly.

With a thunderous rattling the truck rolled up to the door. Gloria shook her fist defiantly at the four walls.

"I'm so glad to go!" she cried, "so glad. Oh, my God, how I hate this house!"

So the brilliant and beautiful lady went up with her husband to New York. On the very train that bore them away they quarrelled—her bitter words had the frequency, the regularity, the inevitability of the stations they passed.

"Don't be cross," begged Anthony piteously. "We've got nothing but each other, after all."

"We haven't even that, most of the time," cried Gloria.

"When haven't we?"

"A lot of times—beginning with one occasion on the station platform at Redgate."

"You don't mean to say that——"

"No," she interrupted coolly, "I don't brood over it. It came and went—and when it went it took something with it."

She finished abruptly. Anthony sat in silence, confused, depressed. The drab visions of train-side Mamaroneck, Larchmont, Rye, Pelham Manor, succeeded each other with intervals of bleak and shoddy wastes posing ineffectually as country. He found himself remembering how on one summer morning they two had started from New York in search of happiness. They had never expected to find it, perhaps, yet in itself that quest had been happier than anything he expected forevermore. Life, it seemed, must be a setting up of props around one—otherwise it was disaster. There was no rest, no quiet. He had been futile in longing to drift and dream; no one drifted except to maelstroms, no one dreamed, without his dreams becoming fantastic nightmares of indecision and regret.

Pelham! They had quarrelled in Pelham because Gloria must drive. And when she set her little foot on the accelerator the car had jumped off spunkily, and their two heads had jerked back like marionettes worked by a single string.

The Bronx—the houses gathering and gleaming in the sun, which was falling now through wide refulgent skies and tumbling caravans of light down into the streets. New York, he supposed, was home—the city of luxury and mystery, of preposterous hopes and exotic dreams. Here on the outskirts absurd stucco palaces reared themselves in the cool sunset, poised for an instant in cool unreality, glided off far away, succeeded by the mazed confusion of the Harlem River. The train moved in through the deepening twilight, above and past half a hundred cheerful sweating streets of the upper East Side, each one passing the car window like the space between the spokes of a gigantic wheel, each one with its vigorous colorful revelation of poor children swarming in feverish activity like vivid ants in alleys of red sand. From the tenement windows leaned rotund, moon-shaped mothers, as constellations of this sordid heaven; women like dark imperfect jewels, women like vegetables, women like great bags of abominably dirty laundry.

"I like these streets," observed Anthony aloud. "I always feel as though it's a performance being staged for me; as though the second I've passed they'll all stop leaping and laughing and, instead, grow very sad, remembering how poor they are, and retreat with bowed heads into their houses. You often get that effect abroad, but seldom in this country."

Down in a tall busy street he read a dozen Jewish names on a line of stores; in the door of each stood a dark little man watching the passers from intent eyes—eyes gleaming with suspicion, with pride, with clarity, with cupidity, with comprehension. New York—he could not dissociate it now from the slow, upward creep of this people—the little stores, growing, expanding, consolidating, moving, watched over with hawk's eyes and a bee's attention to detail—they slathered out on all sides. It was impressive—in perspective it was tremendous.

Gloria's voice broke in with strange appropriateness upon his thoughts.

"I wonder where Bloeckman's been this summer."

The Apartment

After the sureties of youth there sets in a period of intense and intolerable complexity. With the soda-jerker this period is so short as to be almost negligible. Men higher in the scale hold out longer in the attempt to preserve the ultimate niceties of relationship, to retain "impractical" ideas of integrity. But by the late twenties the business has grown too intricate, and what has hitherto been imminent and confusing has become gradually remote and dim. Routine comes down like twilight on a harsh landscape, softening it until it is tolerable. The complexity is too subtle, too varied; the values are changing utterly with each lesion of vitality; it has begun to appear that we can learn nothing from the past with which to face the future—so we cease to be impulsive, convincible men, interested in what is ethically true by fine margins, we substitute rules of conduct for ideas of integrity, we value safety above romance, we become, quite unconsciously, pragmatic. It is left to the few to be persistently concerned with the nuances of relationships—and even this few only in certain hours especially set aside for the task.

Anthony Patch had ceased to be an individual of mental adventure, of curiosity, and had become an individual of bias and prejudice, with a longing to be emotionally undisturbed. This gradual change had taken place through the past several years, accelerated by a succession of anxieties preying on his mind. There was, first of all, the sense of waste, always dormant in his heart, now awakened by the circumstances of his position. In his moments of insecurity he was haunted by the suggestion that life might be, after all, significant. In his early twenties the conviction of the futility of effort, of the wisdom of abnegation, had been confirmed by the philosophies he had admired as well as by his association with Maury Noble, and later with his wife. Yet there had been occasions—just before his first meeting with Gloria, for example, and when his grandfather had suggested that he should go abroad as a war correspondent—upon which his dissatisfaction had driven him almost to a positive step.

One day just before they left Marietta for the last time, in carelessly turning over the pages of a Harvard Alumni Bulletin, he had found a column which told him what his contemporaries had been about in this six years since graduation. Most of them were in business, it was true, and several were converting the heathen of China or America to a nebulous protestantism; but a few, he found, were working constructively at jobs that were neither sinecures nor routines. There was Calvin Boyd, for instance, who, though barely out of medical school, had discovered a new treatment for typhus, had shipped abroad and was mitigating some of the civilization that the Great Powers had brought to Servia; there was Eugene Bronson, whose articles in The New Democracy were stamping him as a man with ideas transcending both vulgar timeliness and popular hysteria; there was a man named Daly who had been suspended from the faculty of a righteous university for preaching Marxian doctrines in the classroom: in art, science, politics, he saw the authentic personalities of his time emerging—there was even Severance, the quarter-back, who had given up his life rather neatly and gracefully with the Foreign Legion on the Aisne.

He laid down the magazine and thought for a while about these diverse men. In the days of his integrity he would have defended his attitude to the last—an Epicurus in Nirvana, he would have cried that to struggle was to believe, to believe was to limit. He would as soon have become a churchgoer because the prospect of immortality gratified him as he would have considered entering the leather business because the intensity of the competition would have kept him from unhappiness. But at present he had no such delicate scruples. This autumn, as his twenty-ninth year began, he was inclined to close his mind to many things, to avoid prying deeply into motives and first causes, and mostly to long passionately for security from the world and from himself. He hated to be alone, as has been said he often dreaded being alone with Gloria.

Because of the chasm which his grandfather's visit had opened before him, and the consequent revulsion from his late mode of life, it was inevitable that he should look around in this suddenly hostile city for the friends and environments that had once seemed the warmest and most secure. His first step was a desperate attempt to get back his old apartment.

In the spring of 1912 he had signed a four-year lease at seventeen hundred a year, with an option of renewal. This lease had expired the previous May. When he had first rented the rooms they had been mere potentialities, scarcely to be discerned as that, but Anthony had seen into these potentialities and arranged in the lease that he and the landlord should each spend a certain amount in improvements. Rents had gone up in the past four years, and last spring when Anthony had waived his option the landlord, a Mr. Sohenberg, had realized that he could get a much bigger price for what was now a prepossessing apartment. Accordingly, when Anthony approached him on the subject in September he was met with Sohenberg's offer of a three-year lease at twenty-five hundred a year. This, it seemed to Anthony, was outrageous. It meant that well over a third of their income would be consumed in rent. In vain he argued that his own money, his own ideas on the repartitioning, had made the rooms attractive.

In vain he offered two thousand dollars—twenty-two hundred, though they could ill afford it: Mr. Sohenberg was obdurate. It seemed that two other gentlemen were considering it; just that sort of an apartment was in demand for the moment, and it would scarcely be business to *give* it to Mr. Patch. Besides, though he had never mentioned it before, several of the other tenants had complained of noise during the previous winter—singing and dancing late at night, that sort of thing.

Internally raging Anthony hurried back to the Ritz to report his discomfiture to Gloria.

"I can just see you," she stormed, "letting him back you down!"

"What could I say?"

"You could have told him what he *was*. I wouldn't have *stood* it. No other man in the world would have stood it! You just let people order you around and cheat you and bully you and take advantage of you as if you were a silly little boy. It's absurd!"

"Oh, for Heaven's sake, don't lose your temper."

"I know, Anthony, but you *are* such an ass!"

"Well, possibly. Anyway, we can't afford that apartment. But we can afford it better than living here at the Ritz."

"You were the one who insisted on coming here."

"Yes, because I knew you'd be miserable in a cheap hotel."

"Of course I would!"

"At any rate we've got to find a place to live."

"How much can we pay?" she demanded.

"Well, we can pay even his price if we sell more bonds, but we agreed last night that until I had gotten something definite to do we——"

"Oh, I know all that. I asked you how much we can pay out of just our income."

"They say you ought not to pay more than a fourth."

"How much is a fourth?"

"One hundred and fifty a month."

"Do you mean to say we've got only six hundred dollars coming in every month?" A subdued note crept into her voice.

"Of course!" he answered angrily. "Do you think we've gone on spending more than twelve thousand a year without cutting way into our capital?"

"I knew we'd sold bonds, but—have we spent that much a year? How did we?" Her awe increased.

"Oh, I'll look in those careful account-books we kept," he remarked ironically, and then added: "Two rents a good part of the time, clothes, travel—why, each of those springs in California cost about four thousand dollars. That darn car was an expense from start to finish. And parties and amusements and—oh, one thing or another."

They were both excited now and inordinately depressed. The situation seemed worse in the actual telling Gloria than it had when he had first made the discovery himself.

"You've got to make some money," she said suddenly.

"I know it."

"And you've got to make another attempt to see your grandfather."

"I will."

"When?"

"When we get settled."

This eventuality occurred a week later. They rented a small apartment on Fifty-seventh Street at one hundred and fifty a month. It included bedroom, living-room, kitchenette, and bath, in a thin, white-stone apartment house, and though the rooms were too small to display Anthony's best furniture, they were clean, new, and, in a blonde and sanitary way, not unattractive. Bounds had gone abroad to enlist in the British army, and in his place they tolerated rather than enjoyed the services of a gaunt, big-boned Irishwoman, whom Gloria loathed because she discussed the glories of Sinn Fein as she served breakfast. But they had vowed they would have no more Japanese, and English servants were for the present hard to obtain. Like Bounds, the woman prepared only breakfast. Their other meals they took at restaurants and hotels.

What finally drove Anthony post-haste up to Tarrytown was an announcement in several New York papers that Adam Patch, the multimillionaire, the philanthropist, the venerable uplifter, was seriously ill and not expected to recover.

The Kitten

Anthony could not see him. The doctors' instructions were that he was to talk to no one, said Mr. Shuttleworth—who offered kindly to take any message that Anthony might care to intrust with him, and deliver it to Adam Patch when his condition permitted. But by obvious innuendo he confirmed Anthony's melancholy inference that the prodigal grandson would be particularly unwelcome at the bedside. At one point in the conversation Anthony, with Gloria's positive instructions in mind, made a move as though to brush by the secretary, but Shuttleworth with a smile squared his brawny shoulders, and Anthony saw how futile such an attempt would be.

Miserably intimidated, he returned to New York, where husband and wife passed a restless week. A little incident that occurred one evening indicated to what tension their nerves were drawn.

Walking home along a cross-street after dinner, Anthony noticed a night-bound cat prowling near a railing.

"I always have an instinct to kick a cat," he said idly.

"I like them."

"I yielded to it once."

"When?"

"Oh, years ago; before I met you. One night between the acts of a show. Cold night, like this, and I was a little tight—one of the first times I was ever tight," he added. "The poor little beggar was looking for a place to sleep, I guess, and I was in a mean mood, so it took my fancy to kick it——"

"Oh, the poor kitty!" cried Gloria, sincerely moved.

Inspired with the narrative instinct, Anthony enlarged on the theme.

"It was pretty bad," he admitted. "The poor little beast turned around and looked at me rather plaintively as though hoping I'd pick him up and be kind to him—he was really just a kitten—and before he knew it a big foot launched out at him and caught his little back——"

"Oh!" Gloria's cry was full of anguish.

"It was such a cold night," he continued, perversely, keeping his voice upon a melancholy note. "I guess it expected kindness from somebody, and it got only pain——"

He broke off suddenly—Gloria was sobbing. They had reached home, and when they entered the apartment she threw herself upon the lounge, crying as though he had struck at her very soul.

"Oh, the poor little kitty!" she repeated piteously, "the poor little kitty. So cold——"

"Gloria——"

"Don't come near me! Please, don't come near me. You killed the soft little kitty."

Touched, Anthony knelt beside her.

"Dear," he said. "Oh, Gloria, darling. It isn't true. I invented it—every word of it."

But she would not believe him. There had been something in the details he had chosen to describe that made her cry herself asleep that night, for the kitten, for Anthony, for herself, for the pain and bitterness and cruelty of all the world.

The Passing of an American Moralist

Old Adam died on a midnight of late November with a pious compliment to his God on his thin lips. He, who had been flattered so much, faded out flattering the Omnipotent Abstraction which he fancied he might have angered in the more lascivious moments of his youth. It was announced that he had arranged some sort of an armistice with the deity, the terms of which were not made public, though they were thought to have included a large cash payment. All the newspapers printed his biography, and two of them ran short editorials on his sterling worth, and his part in the drama of industrialism, with which he had grown up. They referred guardedly to the reforms he had sponsored and financed. The memories of Comstock and Cato the Censor were resuscitated and paraded like gaunt ghosts through the columns.

Every newspaper remarked that he was survived by a single grandson, Anthony Comstock Patch, of New York.

The burial took place in the family plot at Tarrytown. Anthony and Gloria rode in the first carriage, too worried to feel grotesque, both trying desperately to glean presage of fortune from the faces of retainers who had been with him at the end.

They waited a frantic week for decency, and then, having received no notification of any kind, Anthony called up his grandfather's lawyer. Mr. Brett was not in—he was expected back in an hour. Anthony left his telephone number.

It was the last day of November, cool and crackling outside, with a lustreless sun peering bleakly in at the windows. While they waited for the call, ostensibly engaged in reading, the atmosphere, within and without, seemed pervaded with a deliberate rendition of the pathetic fallacy. After an interminable while, the bell jingled, and Anthony, starting violently, took up the receiver.

"Hello . . ." His voice was strained and hollow. "Yes—I did leave word. Who is this, please? . . . Yes. . . . Why, it was about the estate. Naturally I'm interested, and I've received no word about the reading of the will—I thought you might not have my address. . . . What? . . . Yes . . ."

Gloria fell on her knees. The intervals between Anthony's speeches were like tourniquets winding on her heart. She found herself helplessly twisting the large buttons from a velvet cushion. Then:

"That's—that's very, very odd—that's very odd—that's very odd. Not even any—ah—mention or any —ah—reason——?"

His voice sounded faint and far away. She uttered a little sound, half gasp, half cry.

"Yes, I'll see. . . . All right, thanks . . . thanks. . . ."

The phone clicked. Her eyes looking along the floor saw his feet cut the pattern of a patch of sunlight on the carpet. She arose and faced him with a gray, level glance just as his arms folded about her.

"My dearest," he whispered huskily. "He did it, God damn him!"

Next Day

"Who are the heirs?" asked Mr. Haight. "You see when you can tell me so little about it——"

Mr. Haight was tall and bent and beetle-browed. He

had been recommended to Anthony as an astute and tenacious lawyer.

"I only know vaguely," answered Anthony. "A man named Shuttleworth, who was a sort of pet of his, has the whole thing in charge as administrator or trustee or something—all except the direct bequests to charity and the provisions for servants and for those two cousins in Idaho."

"How distant are the cousins?"

"Oh, third or fourth, anyway. I never even heard of them."

Mr. Haight nodded comprehensively.

"And you want to contest a provision of the will?"

"I guess so," admitted Anthony helplessly. "I want to do what sounds most hopeful—that's what I want you to tell me."

"You want them to refuse probate to the will?"

Anthony shook his head.

"You've got me. I haven't any idea what 'probate' is. I want a share of the estate."

"Suppose you tell me some more details. For instance, do you know why the testator disinherited you?"

"Why—yes," began Anthony. "You see he was always a sucker for moral reform, and all that——"

"I know," interjected Mr. Haight humorlessly.

"—and I don't suppose he ever thought I was much good. I didn't go into business, you see. But I feel certain that up to last summer I was one of the beneficiaries. We had a house out in Marietta, and one night grandfather got the notion he'd come over and see us. It just happened that there was a rather gay party going on and he arrived without any warning. Well, he took one look, he and this fellow Shuttleworth, and then turned around and tore right back to Tarrytown. After that he never answered my letters or even let me see him."

"He was a prohibitionist, wasn't he?"

"He was everything—regular religious maniac."

"How long before his death was the will made that disinherited you?"

"Recently—I mean since August."

"And you think that the direct reason for his not leaving you the majority of the estate was his displeasure with your recent actions?"

"Yes."

Mr. Haight considered. Upon what grounds was Anthony thinking of contesting the will?

"Why, isn't there something about evil influence?"

"Undue influence is one ground—but it's the most difficult. You would have to show that such pressure was brought to bear so that the deceased was in a condition where he disposed of his property contrary to his intentions——"

"Well, suppose this fellow Shuttleworth dragged him over to Marietta just when he thought some sort of a celebration was probably going on?"

"That wouldn't have any bearing on the case. There's a strong division between advice and influence. You'd have to prove that the secretary had a sinister intention. I'd suggest some other grounds. A will is automatically refused probate in case of insanity, drunkenness"—here Anthony smiled—"or feeble-mindedness through premature old age."

"But," objected Anthony, "his private physician, being one of the beneficiaries, would testify that he wasn't feeble-minded. And he wasn't. As a matter of fact he probably did just what he intended to with his money—it was perfectly consistent with everything he'd ever done in his life——"

"Well, you see, feeble-mindedness is a great deal like undue influence—it implies that the property wasn't disposed of as originally intended. The most common ground is duress—physical pressure."

Anthony shook his head.

"Not much chance on that, I'm afraid. Undue influence sounds best to me."

After more discussion, so technical as to be largely unintelligible to Anthony, he retained Mr. Haight as counsel. The lawyer proposed an interview with Shuttleworth, who, jointly with Wilson, Hiemer and Hardy, was executor of the will. Anthony was to come back later in the week.

It transpired that the estate consisted of approximately forty million dollars. The largest bequest to an individual was of one million, to Edward Shuttleworth, who received in addition thirty thousand a year salary as administrator of the thirty-million-dollar trust fund, left to be doled out to various charities and reform societies practically at his own discretion. The remaining nine millions were proportioned among the two cousins in Idaho and about twenty-five other beneficiaries: friends, secretaries, servants, and employees, who had, at one time or another, earned the seal of Adam Patch's approval.

At the end of another fortnight Mr. Haight, on a retainer's fee of fifteen thousand dollars, had begun preparations for contesting the will.

The Winter of Discontent

Before they had been two months in the little apartment on Fifty-seventh Street, it had assumed for both of them the same indefinable but almost material taint that had impregnated the gray house in Marietta. There was the odor of tobacco always—both of them smoked incessantly; it was in their clothes, their blankets, the curtains, and the ash-littered carpets. Added to this was the wretched aura of stale wine, with its inevitable suggestion of beauty gone foul and revelry remembered in disgust. About a particular set of glass goblets on the sideboard the odor was particularly noticeable, and in the main room the mahogany table was ringed with white circles where glasses had been set down upon it. There had been many parties—people broke things; people became sick in Gloria's bathroom; people spilled wine; people made unbelievable messes of the kitchenette.

These things were a regular part of their existence. Despite the resolutions of many Mondays it was tacitly understood as the week-end approached that it should be observed with some sort of unholy excitement. When Saturday came they would not discuss the matter, but would call up this person or that from among their circle of sufficiently irresponsible friends, and suggest a rendezvous. Only after the friends had gathered and Anthony had set out decanters, would he murmur casually: "I guess I'll have just one high-ball myself——"

Then they were off for two days—realizing on a wintry dawn that they had been the noisiest and most conspicuous members of the noisiest and most conspicuous party at the Boul' Mich', or the Club Ramée, or at other resorts much less particular about the hilarity of their clientèle. They would find that they had, somehow, squandered eighty or ninety dollars, how, they never knew; they customarily attributed it to the general penury of the "friends" who had accompanied them.

It began to be not unusual for the more sincere of their friends to remonstrate with them, in the very course of a party, and to predict a sombre end for them in the loss of Gloria's "looks" and Anthony's "constitution."

The story of the summarily interrupted revel in Marietta had, of course, leaked out in detail—"Muriel doesn't mean to tell every one she knows," said Gloria to Anthony, "but she thinks every one she tells is the only one she's going to tell"—and, diaphanously veiled, the tale had been given a conspicuous place in Town Tattle. When the terms of Adam Patch's will were made public and the newspapers printed items concerning Anthony's suit, the story was beautifully rounded out—to Anthony's infinite disparagement. They began to hear rumors about themselves from all quarters, rumors founded usually on a soupçon of truth, but overlaid with preposterous and sinister detail.

Outwardly they showed no signs of deterioration. Gloria at twenty-six was still the Gloria of twenty; her complexion a fresh damp setting for her candid eyes; her hair still a childish glory, darkening slowly from corn color to a deep russet gold; her slender body suggesting ever a nymph running and dancing through Orphic groves. Masculine eyes, dozens of them, followed her with a fascinated stare when she walked through a hotel lobby or down the aisle of a theatre. Men asked to be introduced to her, fell into prolonged states of sincere admiration, made definite love to her—for she was still a thing of exquisite and unbelievable beauty. And for his part Anthony had rather gained than lost in appearance; his face had taken on a certain intangible air of tragedy, romantically contrasted with his trim and immaculate person.

Early in the winter, when all conversation turned on the probability of America's going into the war, when Anthony was making a desperate and sincere attempt to write, Muriel Kane arrived in New York and came immediately to see them. Like Gloria, she seemed never to change. She knew the latest slang, danced the latest dances, and talked of the latest songs and plays with all the fervor of her first season as a New York drifter. Her coyness was eternally new, eternally ineffectual; her clothes were extreme; her black hair was bobbed, now, like Gloria's.

"I've come up for the midwinter prom at New Haven," she announced, imparting her delightful secret. Though she must have been older then than any of the boys in college, she managed always to secure some sort of invitation, imagining vaguely that at the next party would occur the flirtation which was to end at the romantic altar.

"Where've you been?" inquired Anthony, unfailingly amused.

"I've been at Hot Springs. It's been slick and peppy this fall—more *men!*"

"Are you in love, Muriel?"

"What do you mean 'love'?" This was the rhetorical question of the year. "I'm going to tell you something," she said, switching the subject abruptly. "I suppose it's none of my business, but I think it's time for you two to settle down."

"Why, we are settled down."

"Yes, you are!" she scoffed archly. "Everywhere I go I hear stories of your escapades. Let me tell you, I have an awful time sticking up for you."

"You needn't bother," said Gloria coldly.

"Now, Gloria," she protested, "you know I'm one of your best friends."

Gloria was silent. Muriel continued:

"It's not so much the idea of a woman drinking, but Gloria's so pretty, and so many people know her by sight all around, that it's naturally conspicuous——"

"What have you heard recently?" demanded Gloria, her dignity going down before her curiosity.

"Well, for instance, that that party in Marietta *killed* Anthony's grandfather."

Instantly husband and wife were tense with annoyance.

"Why, I think that's outrageous."

"That's what they say," persisted Muriel stubbornly.

Anthony paced the room. "It's preposterous!" he declared. "The very people we take on parties shout the story around as a great joke—and eventually it gets back to us in some such form as this."

Gloria began running her finger through a stray reddish curl. Muriel licked her veil as she considered her next remark.

"You ought to have a baby."

Gloria looked up wearily.

"We can't afford it."

"All the people in the slums have them," said Muriel triumphantly.

Anthony and Gloria exchanged a smile. They had reached the stage of violent quarrels that were never made up, quarrels that smouldered and broke out again at intervals or died away from sheer indifference—but this visit of Muriel's drew them temporarily together. When the discomfort under which they were living was remarked upon by a third party, it gave them the impetus to face this hostile world together. It was very seldom, now, that the impulse toward reunion sprang from within.

Anthony found himself associating his own existence with that of the apartment's night elevator man, a pale, scraggly bearded person of about sixty, with an air of being somewhat above his station. It was probably because of this quality that he had secured the position; it made him a pathetic and memorable figure of failure. Anthony recollected, without humor, a hoary jest about the elevator man's career being a matter of ups and downs—it was, at any rate, an enclosed life of infinite dreariness. Each time Anthony stepped into the car he waited breathlessly for the old man's "Well, I guess we're going to have some sunshine to-day." Anthony thought how little rain or sunshine he would enjoy shut into that close little cage in the smoke-colored, windowless hall.

A darkling figure, he attained tragedy in leaving the life that had used him so shabbily. Three young gunmen came in one night, tied him up and left him on a pile of coal in the cellar while they went through the trunk room. When the janitor found him next morning he had collapsed from chill. He died of pneumonia four days later.

He was replaced by a glib Martinique negro, with an incongruous British accent and a tendency to be surly, whom Anthony detested. The passing of the old man had approximately the same effect on him that the kitten story had had on Gloria. He was reminded of the cruelty of all life and, in consequence, of the increasing bitterness of his own.

He was writing—and in earnest at last. He had gone to Dick and listened for a tense hour to an elucidation of those minutiæ of procedure which hitherto he had rather scornfully looked down upon. He needed money immediately—he was selling bonds every month to pay their bills. Dick was frank and explicit:

"So far as articles on literary subjects in these obscure magazines go, you couldn't make enough to pay your rent. Of course if a man has the gift of humor, or a chance at a big biography, or some specialized knowledge, he may strike it rich. But for you, fiction's the only thing. You say you need money right away?"

"I certainly do."

"Well, it'd be a year and a half before you'd make any money out of a novel. Try some popular short stories. And, by the way, unless they're exceptionally brilliant they have to be cheerful and on the side of the heaviest artillery to make you any money."

Anthony thought of Dick's recent output, which had been appearing in a well-known monthly. It was concerned chiefly with the preposterous actions of a class of sawdust effigies who, one was assured, were New York society people, and it turned, as a rule, upon questions of the heroine's technical purity, with mock-sociological overtones about the "mad antics of the four hundred."

"But your stories—" exclaimed Anthony aloud, almost involuntarily.

"Oh, that's different," Dick asserted astoundingly. "I have a reputation, you see, so I'm expected to deal with strong themes."

Anthony gave an interior start, realizing with this remark how much Richard Caramel had fallen off. Did he actually think that these amazing latter productions were as good as his first novel?

Anthony went back to the apartment and set to work. He found that the business of optimism was no mean task. After half a dozen futile starts he went to the public library and for a week investigated the files of a popular magazine. Then, better equipped, he accomplished his first story, "The Dictaphone of Fate." It was founded upon one of his few remaining impressions of that six weeks in Wall Street the year before. It purported to be the sunny tale of an office boy who, quite by accident, hummed a wonderful melody into the dictaphone. The cylinder was discovered by the boss's brother, a well-known producer of musical comedy—and then immediately lost. The body of the story was concerned with the pursuit of the missing cylinder and the eventual marriage of the noble office boy (now a successful composer) to Miss Rooney, the virtuous stenographer, who was half Joan of Arc and half Florence Nightingale.

He had gathered that this was what the magazines wanted. He offered, in his protagonists, the customary denizens of the pink-and-blue literary world, immersing them in a saccharine plot that would offend not a single stomach in Marietta. He had it typed in double space—this last as advised by a booklet, "Success as a Writer Made Easy," by R. Meggs Widdlestien, which assured the ambitious plumber of the futility of perspiration, since after a six-lesson course he could make at least a thousand dollars a month.

After reading it to a bored Gloria and coaxing from her the immemorial remark that it was "better than a lot of stuff that gets published," he satirically affixed the nom de plume of "Gilles de Sade," enclosed the proper return envelope, and sent it off.

Following the gigantic labor of conception he decided to wait until he heard from the first story before beginning another. Dick had told him that he might get as much as two hundred dollars. If by any chance it did happen to be unsuited, the editor's letter would, no doubt, give him an idea of what changes should be made.

"It is, without question, the most abominable piece of writing in existence," said Anthony.

The editor quite conceivably agreed with him. He returned the manuscript with a rejection slip. Anthony sent it off elsewhere and began another story. The second one was called "The Little Open Doors"; it was written in three days. It concerned the occult: an estranged couple were brought together by a medium in a vaudeville show.

There were six altogether, six wretched and pitiable

efforts to "write down" by a man who had never before made a consistent effort to write at all. Not one of them contained a spark of vitality, and their total yield of grace and felicity was less than that of an average newspaper column. During their circulation they collected, all told, thirty-one rejection slips, headstones for the packages that he would find lying like dead bodies at his door.

In mid-January Gloria's father died, and they went again to Kansas City—a miserable trip, for Gloria brooded interminably, not upon her father's death, but on her mother's. Russel Gilbert's affairs having been cleared up they came into possession of about three thousand dollars, and a great amount of furniture. This was in storage, for he had spent his last days in a small hotel. It was due to his death that Anthony made a new discovery concerning Gloria. On the journey East she disclosed herself, astonishingly, as a Bilphist.

"Why, Gloria," he cried, "you don't mean to tell me you believe that stuff."

"Well," she said defiantly, "why not?"

"Because it's—it's fantastic. You know that in every sense of the word you're an agnostic. You'd laugh at any orthodox form of Christianity—and then you come out with the statement that you believe in some silly rule of reincarnation."

"What if I do? I've heard you and Maury, and every one else for whose intellect I have the slightest respect, agree that life as it appears is utterly meaningless. But it's always seemed to me that if I were unconsciously learning something here it might not be so meaningless."

"You're not learning anything—you're just getting tired. And if you must have a faith to soften things, take up one that appeals to the reason of some one beside a lot of hysterical women. A person like you oughtn't to accept anything unless it's decently demonstrable."

"I don't care about truth. I want some happiness."

"Well, if you've got a decent mind the second has got to be qualified by the first. Any simple soul can delude himself with mental garbage."

"I don't care," she held out stoutly, "and, what's more, I'm not propounding any doctrine."

The argument faded off, but reoccurred to Anthony several times thereafter. It was disturbing to find this old belief, evidently assimilated from her mother, inserting itself again under its immemorial disguise as an innate idea.

They reached New York in March after an expensive and ill-advised week spent in Hot Springs, and Anthony resumed his abortive attempts at fiction. As it became plainer to both of them that escape did not lie in the way of popular literature, there was a further slipping of their mutual confidence and courage. A complicated struggle went on incessantly between them. All efforts to keep down expenses died away from sheer inertia, and by March they were again using any pretext as an excuse for a "party." With an assumption of recklessness Gloria tossed out the suggestion that they should take all their money and go on a real spree while it lasted—anything seemed better than to see it go in unsatisfactory driblets.

"Gloria, you want parties as much as I do."

"It doesn't matter about me. Everything I do is in accordance with my ideas: to use every minute of these years, when I'm young, in having the best time I possibly can."

"How about after that?"

"After that I won't care."

"Yes, you will."

"Well, I may—but I won't be able to do anything about it. And I'll have had my good time."

"You'll be the same then. After a fashion, we *have* had our good time, raised the devil, and we're in the state of paying for it."

Nevertheless, the money kept going. There would be two days of gaiety, two days of moroseness—an endless, almost invariable round. The sharp pull-ups, when they occurred, resulted usually in a spurt of work for Anthony, while Gloria, nervous and bored, remained in bed or else chewed abstractedly at her fingers. After a day or so of this, they would make an engagement, and then— Oh, what did it matter? This night, this glow, the cessation of anxiety and the sense that if living was not purposeful it was, at any rate, essentially romantic! Wine gave a sort of gallantry to their own failure.

Meanwhile the suit progressed slowly, with interminable examinations of witnesses and marshallings of evidence. The preliminary proceedings of settling the estate were finished. Mr. Haight saw no reason why the case should not come up for trial before summer.

Bloeckman appeared in New York late in March; he had been in England for nearly a year on matters concerned with "Films Par Excellence." The process of general refinement was still in progress—always he dressed a little better, his intonation was mellower, and in his manner there was perceptibly more assurance that the fine things of the world were his by a natural and inalienable right. He called at the apartment, remained only an hour, during which he talked chiefly of the war, and left telling them he was coming again. On his second visit Anthony was not at home, but an absorbed and excited Gloria greeted her husband later in the afternoon.

"Anthony," she began, "would you still object if I went in the movies?"

His whole heart hardened against the idea. As she seemed to recede from him, if only in threat, her presence became again not so much precious as desperately necessary.

"Oh, Gloria——!"

"Blockhead said he'd put me in—only if I'm ever going to do anything I'll have to start now. They only want young women. Think of the money, Anthony!"

"For you—yes. But how about me?"

"Don't you know that anything I have is yours too?"

"It's such a hell of a career!" he burst out, the moral, the infinitely circumspect Anthony, "and such a hell of a bunch. And I'm so utterly tired of that fellow Bloeckman coming here and interfering. I hate theatrical things."

"It isn't theatrical! It's utterly different."

"What am I supposed to do? Chase you all over the country? Live on your money?"

"Then make some yourself."

The conversation developed into one of the most violent quarrels they had ever had. After the ensuing reconciliation and the inevitable period of moral inertia, she realized that he had taken the life out of the project. Neither of them ever mentioned the probability that Bloeckman was by no means disinterested, but they both knew that it lay back of Anthony's objection.

In April war was declared with Germany. Wilson and his cabinet—a cabinet that in its lack of distinction was strangely reminiscent of the twelve apostles—let loose the carefully starved dogs of war, and the press began to whoop hysterically against the sinister morals, sinister philosophy, and sinister music produced by the Teutonic temperament. Those who fancied themselves particularly broad-minded made the exquisite distinction that it was only the German Government which aroused them to hysteria; the rest were worked up to a condition of retching indecency. Any song which contained the word "mother" and the word "kaiser" was assured of a tremendous success. At last every one had something to talk about—and almost every one fully enjoyed it, as though they had been cast for parts in a sombre and romantic play.

Anthony, Maury, and Dick sent in their applications for officers' training-camps and the two latter went about feeling strangely exalted and reproachless; they chattered to each other, like college boys, of war's being the one excuse for, and justification of, the aristocrat, and conjured up an impossible caste of officers, to be composed, it appeared, chiefly of the more attractive alumni of three or four Eastern colleges. It seemed to Gloria that in this huge red light streaming across the nation even Anthony took on a new glamour.

The Tenth Infantry, arriving in New York from Panama, were escorted from saloon to saloon by patriotic citizens, to their great bewilderment. West Pointers began to be noticed for the first time in years, and the general impression was that everything was glorious, but not half so glorious as it was going to be pretty soon, and that everybody was a fine fellow, and every race a great race—always excepting the Germans—and in every strata of society outcasts and scapegoats had but to appear in uniform to be forgiven, cheered, and wept over by relatives, ex-friends, and utter strangers.

Unfortunately, a small and precise doctor decided that there was something the matter with Anthony's blood-pressure. He could not conscientiously pass him for an officers' training-camp.

The Broken Lute

Their third anniversary passed, uncelebrated, unnoticed. The season warmed in thaw, melted into hotter summer, simmered and boiled away. In July the will was offered for probate, and upon the contestation was assigned by the surrogate to trial term for trial. The matter was prolonged into September—there was difficulty in empanelling an unbiassed jury because of the moral sentiments involved. To Anthony's disappointment a verdict was finally returned in favor of the testator, whereupon Mr. Haight caused a notice of appeal to be served upon Edward Shuttleworth.

As the summer waned Anthony and Gloria talked of the things they were to do when the money was theirs, and of the places they were to go to after the war, when they would "agree on things again," for both of them looked forward to a time when love, springing like the phœnix from its own ashes, should be born again in its mysterious and unfathomable haunts.

He was drafted early in the fall, and the examining doctor made no mention of low blood-pressure. It was all very purposeless and sad when Anthony told Gloria one night that he wanted, above all things, to be killed. But, as always, they were sorry for each other for the wrong things at the wrong times. . . .

They decided that for the present she was not to go with him to the Southern camp where his contingent was ordered. She would remain in New York to "use the apartment," to save money, and to watch the progress of the case—which was pending now in the Appellate Division, of which the calendar, Mr. Haight told them, was far behind.

Almost their last conversation was a senseless quarrel about the proper division of the income—at a word either would have given it all to the other. It was typical of the muddle and confusion of their lives that on the October night when Anthony reported at the Grand Central Station for the journey to camp, she arrived only in time to catch his eye over the anxious heads of a gathered crowd. Through the dark light of the enclosed train-sheds their glances stretched across a hysterical area, foul with yellow sobbing and the smells of poor women. They must have pondered upon what they had done to one another, and each must have accused himself of drawing this sombre pattern through which they were tracing tragically and obscurely. At the last they were too far away for either to see the other's tears.

BOOK III

CHAPTER I

A MATTER OF CIVILIZATION

At a frantic command from some invisible source, Anthony groped his way inside. He was thinking that for the first time in more than three years he was to remain longer than a night away from Gloria. The finality of it appealed to him drearily. It was his clean and lovely girl that he was leaving.

They had arrived, he thought, at the most practical financial settlement: she was to have three hundred and seventy-five dollars a month—not too much considering that over half of that would go in rent—and he was taking fifty to supplement his pay. He saw no need for more: food, clothes, and quarters would be provided—there were no social obligations for a private.

The car was crowded and already thick with breath. It was one of the type known as "tourist" cars, a sort of brummagem Pullman, with a bare floor, and straw seats that needed cleaning. Nevertheless, Anthony greeted it with relief. He had vaguely expected that the trip South would be made in a freight-car, in one end of which would stand eight horses and in the other forty men. He had heard the "hommes 40, chevaux 8" story so often that it had become confused and ominous.

As he rocked down the aisle with his barrack-bag slung at his shoulder like a monstrous blue sausage, he saw no vacant seats, but after a moment his eye fell on a single space at present occupied by the feet of a short swarthy Sicilian, who, with his hat drawn over his eyes, hunched defiantly in the corner. As Anthony stopped beside him he stared up with a scowl, evidently intended to be intimidating; he must have adopted it as a defense against this entire gigantic equation. At Anthony's sharp "That seat taken?" he very slowly lifted the feet as though they were a breakable package, and placed them with some care upon the floor. His eyes remained on Anthony, who meanwhile sat down and unbuttoned the uniform coat issued him at Camp Upton the day before. It chafed him under the arms.

Before Anthony could scrutinize the other occupants of the section a young second lieutenant blew in at the upper end of the car and wafted airily down the aisle, announcing in a voice of appalling acerbity:

"There will be no smoking in this car! No smoking! Don't smoke, men, in this car!"

As he sailed out at the other end a dozen little clouds of expostulation arose on all sides.

"Oh, cripe!"

"Jeese!"

"No *smokin'?*"

"Hey, come back here, fella!"

"What's 'ee idea?"

Two or three cigarettes were shot out through the open windows. Others were retained inside, though kept sketchily away from view. From here and there in accents of bravado, of mockery, of submissive humor, a few remarks were dropped that soon melted into the listless and pervasive silence.

The fourth occupant of Anthony's section spoke up suddenly.

"G'by, liberty," he said sullenly. "G'by, everything except bein' an officer's dog."

Anthony looked at him. He was a tall Irishman with an expression moulded of indifference and utter disdain. His eyes fell on Anthony, as though he expected an answer, and then upon the others. Receiving only a defiant stare from the Italian he groaned and spat noisily on the floor by way of a dignified transition back into taciturnity.

A few minutes later the door opened again and the second lieutenant was borne in upon his customary official zephyr, this time singing out a different tiding:

"All right, men, smoke if you want to! My mistake, men! It's all right, men! Go on and smoke—my mistake!"

This time Anthony had a good look at him. He was young, thin, already faded; he was like his own mustache; he was like a great piece of shiny straw. His chin receded, faintly; this was offset by a magnificent and unconvincing scowl, a scowl that Anthony was to connect with the faces of many young officers during the ensuing year.

Immediately every one smoked—whether they had previously desired to or not. Anthony's cigarette contributed to the hazy oxidation which seemed to roll back and forth in opalescent clouds with every motion of the train. The conversation, which had lapsed between the two impressive visits of the young officer, now revived tepidly; the men across the aisle began making clumsy experiments with their straw seats' capacity for comparative comfort; two card games, half-heartedly begun, soon drew several spectators to sitting positions on the arms of seats. In a few minutes Anthony became aware of a persistently obnoxious sound—the small, defiant Sicilian had fallen audibly asleep. It was wearisome to contemplate that animate protoplasm, reasonable by courtesy only, shut up in a car by an incomprehensible civilization, taken somewhere, to do a vague something without aim or significance or consequence. Anthony sighed, opened a newspaper which he had no recollection of buying, and began to read by the dim yellow light.

Ten o'clock bumped stuffily into eleven; the hours clogged and caught and slowed down. Amazingly the train halted along the dark countryside, from time to time indulging in short, deceitful movements backward or forward, and whistling harsh pæans into the high October night. Having read his newspaper through, editorials, cartoons, and war-poems, his eye fell on a half-column headed *Shakespeareville, Kansas.* It seemed that the Shakespeareville Chamber of Commerce had recently held an enthusiastic debate as to whether the American soldiers should be known as "Sammies" or "Battling Christians." The thought gagged him. He dropped the newspaper, yawned, and let his mind drift off at a tangent. He wondered why Gloria had been late. It seemed so long ago already—he had a pang of illusive loneliness. He tried to imagine from what angle she would regard her new position, what place in her considerations he would continue to hold. The thought acted as a further depressant—he opened his paper and began to read again.

The members of the Chamber of Commerce in Shakespeareville had decided upon "Liberty Lads."

For two nights and two days they rattled southward, making mysterious inexplicable stops in what were apparently arid wastes, and then rushing through large cities with a pompous air of hurry. The whimsicalities of this train foreshadowed for Anthony the whimsicalities of all army administration.

In the arid wastes they were served from the baggage-car with beans and bacon that at first he was unable to eat—he dined scantily on some milk chocolate distributed by a village canteen. But on the second day the baggage-car's output began to appear surprisingly palatable. On the third morning the rumor was passed along that within the hour they would arrive at their destination, Camp Hooker.

It had become intolerably hot in the car, and the men were all in shirt sleeves. The sun came in through the windows, a tired and ancient sun, yellow as parchment and stretched out of shape in transit. It tried to enter in triumphant squares and produced only warped splotches—but it was appallingly steady; so much so that it disturbed Anthony not to be the pivot of all the inconsequential sawmills and trees and telegraph poles that were turning around him so fast. Outside it played its heavy tremolo over olive roads and fallow cotton-fields, back of which ran a ragged line of woods broken with eminences of gray rock. The foreground was dotted sparsely with wretched, ill-patched shanties, among which there would flash by, now and then, a specimen of the languid yokelry of South Carolina, or else a strolling darky with sullen and bewildered eyes.

Then the woods moved off and they rolled into a broad space like the baked top of a gigantic cake, sugared with an infinity of tents arranged in geometric figures over its surface. The train came to an uncertain stop, and the sun and the poles and the trees faded, and his universe rocked itself slowly back to its old usualness, with Anthony Patch in the centre. As the men, weary and perspiring, crowded out of the car, he smelt that unforgetable aroma that impregnates all permanent camps—the odor of garbage.

Camp Hooker was an astonishing and spectacular growth, suggesting "A Mining Town in 1870—The Second Week." It was a thing of wooden shacks and whitish-gray tents, connected by a pattern of roads, with hard tan drill-grounds fringed with trees. Here and there stood green Y. M. C. A. houses, unpromising oases, with their muggy odor of wet flannels and closed telephone-booths—and across from each of them there was usually a canteen, swarming with life, presided over indolently by an officer who, with the aid of a side-car, usually managed to make his detail a pleasant and chatty sinecure.

Up and down the dusty roads sped the soldiers of the quartermaster corps, also in side-cars. Up and down drove the generals in their government automobiles, stopping now and then to bring unalert details to attention, to frown heavily upon captains marching at the heads of companies, to set the pompous pace in that gorgeous game of showing off which was taking place triumphantly over the entire area.

The first week after the arrival of Anthony's draft was filled with a series of interminable inoculations and physical examinations, and with the preliminary drilling. The days left him desperately tired. He had been issued the wrong size shoes by a popular, easy-going supply-sergeant, and in consequence his feet were so swollen that the last hours of the afternoon were an acute torture. For the first time in his life he could throw himself down on his cot between dinner and afternoon drill-call, and seeming to sink with each moment deeper into a bottomless bed, drop off immediately to sleep, while the noise and laughter around him faded to a pleasant drone of drowsy summer sound. In the morning he awoke stiff and aching, hollow as a ghost, and hurried forth to meet the other ghostly figures who swarmed in the wan company streets, while a harsh bugle shrieked and spluttered at the gray heavens.

He was in a skeleton infantry company of about a hundred men. After the invariable breakfast of fatty bacon, cold toast, and cereal, the entire hundred would rush for the latrines, which, however well-policed, seemed always intolerable, like the lavatories in cheap hotels. Out on the field, then, in ragged order—the lame man on his left grotesquely marring Anthony's listless efforts to keep in step, the platoon sergeants either showing off violently to impress the officers and recruits, or else quietly lurking in close to the line of march, avoiding both labor and unnecessary visibility.

When they reached the field, work began immediately—they peeled off their shirts for calisthenics. This was the only part of the day that Anthony enjoyed. Lieutenant Kretching, who presided at the antics, was sinewy and muscular, and Anthony followed his movements faithfully, with a feeling that he was doing something of positive value to himself. The other officers and sergeants walked about among the men with the malice of schoolboys, grouping here and there around some unfortunate who lacked muscular control, giving him confused instructions and commands. When they discovered a particularly forlorn, ill-nourished specimen, they would linger the full half-hour making cutting remarks and snickering among themselves.

One little officer named Hopkins, who had been a sergeant in the regular army, was particularly annoying. He took the war as a gift of revenge from the high gods to himself, and the constant burden of his harangues was that these rookies did not appreciate the full gravity and responsibility of "the service." He considered that by a combination of foresight and dauntless efficiency he had raised himself to his current magnificence. He aped the particular tyrannies of every officer under whom he had served in times gone by. His frown was frozen on his brow—before giving a private a pass to go to town he would ponderously weigh the effect of such an absence upon the company, the army, and the welfare of the military profession the world over.

Lieutenant Kretching, blond, dull and phlegmatic, introduced Anthony ponderously to the problems of attention, right face, about face, and at ease. His principal defect was his forgetfulness. He often kept the company straining and aching at attention for five minutes while he stood out in front and explained a new movement—as a result only the men in the centre knew what it was all about—those on both flanks had been too emphatically impressed with the necessity of staring straight ahead.

The drill continued until noon. It consisted of stressing a succession of infinitely remote details, and though Anthony perceived that this was consistent with the logic of war, it none the less irritated him. That the same faulty blood-pressure which would have been indecent in an officer did not interfere with the duties of a private was a preposterous incongruity. Sometimes, after listening to a sustained invective concerned with a dull and, on the face of it, absurd subject known as military "courtesy," he suspected that the dim purpose of the war was to let the regular army officers—men with the mentality and aspirations of schoolboys—have their fling with some real slaughter. He was being grotesquely sacrificed to the twenty-year patience of a Hopkins!

Of his three tent-mates—a flat-faced, conscientious objector from Tennessee, a big, scared Pole, and the disdainful Celt whom he had sat beside on the train—the two former spent the evenings in writing eternal letters home, while the Irishman sat in the tent door whistling over and over to himself half a dozen shrill and monotonous bird-calls. It was rather to avoid an hour of their company than with any hope of diversion that, when the quarantine was lifted at the end of the week, he went into town. He caught one of the swarm of jitneys that overran the camp each evening, and in half an hour was set down in front of the Stonewall Hotel on the hot and drowsy main street.

Under the gathering twilight the town was unexpectedly attractive. The sidewalks were peopled by vividly dressed, overpainted girls, who chattered volubly in low, lazy voices, by dozens of taxi-drivers who assailed passing officers with "Take y' anywheh, *Lieu*tenant," and by an intermittent procession of ragged, shuffling, subservient negroes. Anthony, loitering along through the warm dusk, felt for the first time in years the slow, erotic breath of the South, imminent in the hot softness of the air, in the pervasive lull of thought and time.

He had gone about a block when he was arrested suddenly by a harsh command at his elbow.

"Haven't you been taught to salute officers?"

He looked dumbly at the man who addressed him, a stout, black-haired captain, who fixed him menacingly with brown pop-eyes.

"*Come to attention!*" The words were literally thundered. A few pedestrians near by stopped and stared. A soft-eyed girl in a lilac dress tittered to her companion.

Anthony came to attention.

"What's your regiment and company?"

Anthony told him.

"After this when you pass an officer on the street you straighten up and salute!"

"All right!"

"Say 'Yes, sir!'"

"Yes, sir."

The stout officer grunted, turned sharply, and marched down the street. After a moment Anthony moved on; the town was no longer indolent and exotic; the magic was suddenly gone out of the dusk. His eyes were turned precipitately inward upon the indignity of his position. He hated that officer, every officer—life was unendurable.

After he had gone half a block he realized that the girl in the lilac dress who had giggled at his discomfiture was walking with her friend about ten paces ahead of him. Several times she had turned and stared at Anthony, with cheerful laughter in the large eyes that seemed the same color as her gown.

At the corner she and her companion visibly slackened their pace—he must make his choice between joining them and passing obliviously by. He passed, hesitated, then slowed down. In a moment the pair were abreast of him again, dissolved in laughter now—not such strident mirth as he would have expected in the North from actresses in this familiar comedy, but a soft, low rippling, like the overflow from some subtle joke, into which he had inadvertently blundered.

"How do you do?" he said.

Her eyes were soft as shadows. Were they violet, or was it their blue darkness mingling with the gray hues of dusk?

"Pleasant evening," ventured Anthony uncertainly.

"Sure is," said the second girl.

"Hasn't been a very pleasant evening for you," sighed the girl in lilac. Her voice seemed as much a part of the night as the drowsy breeze stirring the wide brim of her hat.

"He had to have a chance to show off," said Anthony with a scornful laugh.

"Reckon so," she agreed.

They turned the corner and moved lackadaisically up a side street, as if following a drifting cable to which they were attached. In this town it seemed entirely natural to turn corners like that, it seemed natural to be bound nowhere in particular, to be thinking nothing. . . . The side street was dark, a sudden offshoot into a district of wild rose hedges and little quiet houses set far back from the street.

"Where're you going?" he inquired politely.

"Just goin'." The answer was an apology, a question, an explanation.

"Can I stroll along with you?"

"Reckon so."

It was an advantage that her accent was different. He could not have determined the social status of a Southerner from her talk—in New York a girl of a lower class would have been raucous, unendurable—except through the rosy spectacles of intoxication.

Dark was creeping down. Talking little—Anthony in careless, casual questions, the other two with provincial economy of phrase and burden—they sauntered past another corner, and another. In the middle of a block they stopped beneath a lamp-post.

"I live near here," explained the other girl.

"I live around the block," said the girl in lilac.

"Can I see you home?"

"To the corner, if you want to."

The other girl took a few steps backward. Anthony removed his hat.

"You're supposed to salute," said the girl in lilac with a laugh. "All the soldiers salute."

"I'll learn," he responded soberly.

The other girl said, "Well—" hesitated, then added, "call me up to-morrow, Dot," and retreated from the yellow circle of the street-lamp. Then, in silence, Anthony and the girl in lilac walked the three blocks to the small rickety house which was her home. Outside the wooden gate she hesitated.

"Well—thanks."

"Must you go in so soon?"

"I ought to."

"Can't you stroll around a little longer?"

She regarded him dispassionately.

"I don't even know you."

Anthony laughed.

"It's not too late."

"I reckon I better go in."

"I thought we might walk down and see a movie."

"I'd like to."

"Then I could bring you home. I'd have just enough time. I've got to be in camp by eleven."

It was so dark that he could scarcely see her now. She was a dress swayed infinitesimally by the wind, two limpid, reckless eyes . . .

"Why don't you come—Dot? Don't you like movies? Better come."

She shook her head.

"I oughtn't to."

He liked her, realizing that she was temporizing for the effect on him. He came closer and took her hand.

"If we get back by ten, can't you? Just to the movies?"

"Well—I reckon so——"

Hand in hand they walked back toward down-town, along a hazy, dusky street where a negro newsboy was calling an extra in the cadence of the local venders' tradition, a cadence that was as musical as song.

Dot

Anthony's affair with Dorothy Raycroft was an inevitable result of his increasing carelessness about himself. He did not go to her desiring to possess the desirable, nor did he fall before a personality more vital, more compelling than his own, as he had done with Gloria four years before. He merely slid into the matter through his inability to make definite judgments. He could say "No!" neither to man nor woman; borrower and temptress alike found him tender-minded and pliable. Indeed he seldom made decisions at all, and when he did they were but half-hysterical resolves formed in the panic of some aghast and irreparable awakening.

The particular weakness he indulged on this occasion was his need of excitement and stimulus from without. He felt that for the first time in four years he could express and interpret himself anew. The girl promised rest; the hours in her company each evening alleviated the morbid and inevitably futile poundings of his imagination. He had become a coward in earnest—completely the slave of a hundred disordered and prowling thoughts which were released by the collapse of the authentic devotion to Gloria that had been the chief jailer of his insufficiency.

On that first night, as they stood by the gate, he kissed Dorothy and made an engagement to meet her the following Saturday. Then he went out to camp, and with the light burning lawlessly in his tent, he wrote a long letter to Gloria, a glowing letter, full of the sentimental dark, full of the remembered breath of flowers, full of a true and exceeding tenderness—these things he had learned again for a moment in a kiss given and taken under a rich warm moonlight just an hour before.

When Saturday night came he found Dot waiting at the entrance of the Bijou Moving Picture Theatre. She was dressed as on the preceding Wednesday in her lilac gown of frailest organdy, but it had evidently been washed and starched since then, for it was fresh and unrumpled. Daylight confirmed the impression he had received that in a sketchy, faulty way she was lovely. She was clean, her features were small, irregular, but eloquent and appropriate to each other. She was a dark, unenduring little flower—yet he thought he detected in her some quality of spiritual reticence, of strength drawn from her passive acceptance of all things. In this he was mistaken.

Dorothy Raycroft was nineteen. Her father had kept a small, unprosperous corner store, and she had graduated from high school in the lowest fourth of her class two days before he died. At high school she had enjoyed a rather unsavory reputation. As a matter of fact her behavior at the class picnic, where the rumors started, had been merely indiscreet—she had retained her technical purity until over a year later. The boy had been a clerk in a store on Jackson Street, and on the day after the incident he departed unexpectedly to New York. He had been intending to leave for some time, but had tarried for the consummation of his amorous enterprise.

After a while she confided the adventure to a girl friend, and later, as she watched her friend disappear down the sleepy street of dusty sunshine, she knew in a flash of intuition that her story was going out into the world. Yet after telling it she felt much better, and a little bitter, and made as near an approach to character as she was capable of by walking in another direction and meeting another man with the honest intention of gratifying herself again. As a rule things happened to Dot. She was not weak, because there was nothing in her to tell her she was being weak. She was not strong, because she never knew that some of the things she did were brave. She neither defied nor conformed nor compromised.

She had no sense of humor, but, to take its place, a happy disposition that made her laugh at the proper times when she was with men. She had no definite intentions—sometimes she regretted vaguely that her reputation precluded what chance she had ever had for security. There had been no open discovery: her mother was interested only in starting her off on time each morning for the jewelry store where she earned fourteen dollars a week. But some of the boys she had known in high school now looked the other way when they were walking with "nice girls," and these incidents hurt her feelings. When they occurred she went home and cried.

Besides the Jackson Street clerk there had been two other men, of whom the first was a naval officer, who passed through town during the early days of the war. He had stayed over a night to make a connection, and was leaning idly against one of the pillars of the Stonewall Hotel when she passed by. He remained in town four days. She thought she loved him—lavished on him that first hysteria of passion that would have gone to the pusillanimous clerk. The naval officer's uniform—there were few of them in those days—had made the magic. He left with vague promises on his lips, and, once on the train, rejoiced that he had not told her his real name.

Her resultant depression had thrown her into the arms of Cyrus Fielding, the son of a local clothier, who had hailed her from his roadster one day as she passed along the sidewalk. She had always known him by name. Had she been born to a higher stratum he would have known her before. She had descended a little lower—so he met her after all. After a month he had gone away to training-camp, a little afraid of the intimacy, a little relieved in perceiving that she had not cared deeply for him, and that she was not the sort who would ever make trouble. Dot romanticized this affair and conceded to her vanity that the war had taken these men away from her. She told herself that she could have married the naval officer. Nevertheless, it worried her that within eight months there had been three men in her life. She thought with more fear than wonder in her heart that she would soon be like those "bad girls" on Jackson Street at whom she and her gum-chewing, giggling friends had stared with fascinated glances three years before.

For a while she attempted to be more careful. She let men "pick her up"; she let them kiss her, and even allowed certain other liberties to be forced upon her, but she did not add to her trio. After several months the strength of her resolution—or rather the poignant expediency of her fears—was worn away. She grew restless drowsing there out of life and time while the summer months faded. The soldiers she met were either obviously below her or, less obviously, above her—in which case they desired only to use her; they were Yankees, harsh and ungracious; they swarmed in large crowds. . . . And then she met Anthony.

On that first evening he had been little more than a pleasantly unhappy face, a voice, the means with which to pass an hour, but when she kept her engagement with him on Saturday she regarded him with consideration. She liked him. Unknowingly she saw her own tragedies mirrored in his face.

Again they went to the movies, again they wandered along the shadowy, scented streets, hand in hand this time, speaking a little in hushed voices. They passed through the gate—up toward the little porch——

"I can stay a while, can't I?"

"Sh!" she whispered, "we've got to be very quiet. Mother sits up reading Snappy Stories." In confirmation he heard the faint crackling inside as a page was turned. The open-shutter slits emitted horizontal rods of light that fell in thin parallels across Dorothy's skirt.

The street was silent save for a group on the steps of a house across the way, who, from time to time, raised their voices in a soft, bantering song.

> "*—When you wa-ake*
> *You shall ha-ave*
> *All the pretty little hawsiz——*"

Then, as though it had been waiting on a near-by roof for their arrival, the moon came slanting suddenly through the vines and turned the girl's face to the color of white roses.

Anthony had a start of memory, so vivid that before his closed eyes there formed a picture, distinct as a flash-back on a screen—a spring night of thaw set out of time in a half-forgotten winter five years before—another face, radiant, flower-like, upturned to lights as transforming as the stars——

Ah, *la belle dame sans merci* who lived in his heart, made known to him in transitory fading splendor by dark eyes in the Ritz-Carlton, by a shadowy glance from a passing carriage in the Bois de Boulogne! But those nights were only part of a song, a remembered glory—here again were the faint winds, the illusions, the eternal present with its promise of romance.

"Oh," she whispered, "do you love me? Do you love me?"

The spell was broken—the drifted fragments of the stars became only light, the singing down the street diminished to a monotone, to the whimper of locusts in the grass. With almost a sigh he kissed her fervent mouth, while her arms crept up about his shoulders.

The Man-at-Arms

As the weeks dried up and blew away, the range of Anthony's travels extended until he grew to comprehend the camp and its environment. For the first time in his life he was in constant personal contact with the waiters to whom he had given tips, the chauffeurs who had touched their hats to him, the carpenters, plumbers, barbers, and farmers who had previously been remarkable only in the subservience of their professional genuflections. During his first two months in camp he did not hold ten minutes' consecutive conversation with a single man.

On the service record his occupation stood as "student"; on the original questionnaire he had prematurely written "author"; but when men in his company asked his business he commonly gave it as bank clerk—had he told the truth, that he did no work, they would have been suspicious of him as a member of the leisure class.

His platoon sergeant, Pop Donnelly, was a scraggly "old soldier," worn thin with drink. In the past he had spent unnumbered weeks in the guard-house, but recently, thanks to the drill-master famine, he had been elevated to his present pinnacle. His complexion was full of shell-holes—it bore an unmistakable resemblance to those aerial photographs of "the battle-field at Blank." Once a week he got drunk down-town on white liquor, returned quietly to camp and collapsed upon his bunk, joining the company at reveille looking more than ever like a white mask of death.

He nursed the astounding delusion that he was astutely "slipping it over" on the government—he had spent eighteen years in its service at a minute wage, and he was soon to retire (here he usually winked) on the impressive income of fifty-five dollars a month. He looked upon it as a gorgeous joke that he had played upon the dozens who had bullied and scorned him since he was a Georgia country boy of nineteen.

At present there were but two lieutenants—Hopkins and the popular Kretching. The latter was considered a good fellow and a fine leader, until a year later, when he disappeared with a mess fund of eleven hundred dollars and, like so many leaders, proved exceedingly difficult to follow.

Eventually there was Captain Dunning, god of this brief but self-sufficing microcosm. He was a reserve officer, nervous, energetic, and enthusiastic. This latter quality, indeed, often took material form and was visible as fine froth in the corners of his mouth. Like most executives he saw his charges strictly from the front, and to his hopeful eyes his command seemed just such an excellent unit as such an excellent war deserved. For all his anxiety and absorption he was having the time of his life.

Baptiste, the little Sicilian of the train, fell foul of him the second week of drill. The captain had several times ordered the men to be clean-shaven when they fell in each morning. One day there was disclosed an alarming breech of this rule, surely a case of Teutonic connivance—during the night four men had grown hair upon their faces. The fact that three of the four understood a minimum of English made a practical object-lesson only the more necessary, so Captain Dunning resolutely sent a volunteer barber back to the company street for a razor. Whereupon for the safety of democracy a half-ounce of hair was scraped dry from the cheeks of three Italians and one Pole.

Outside the world of the company there appeared, from time to time, the colonel, a heavy man with snarling teeth, who circumnavigated the battalion drill-field upon a handsome black horse. He was a West Pointer, and, mimetically, a gentleman. He had a dowdy wife and a dowdy mind, and spent much of his time in town taking advantage of the army's lately exalted social position. Last of all was the general, who traversed the roads of the camp preceded by his flag—a figure so austere, so removed, so magnificent, as to be scarcely comprehensible.

December. Cool winds at night now, and damp, chilly mornings on the drill-grounds. As the heat faded, Anthony found himself increasingly glad to be alive. Renewed strangely through his body, he worried little and existed in the present with a sort of animal content. It was not that Gloria or the life that Gloria represented was less often in his thoughts—it was simply that she became, day by day, less real, less vivid. For a week they had corresponded passionately, almost hysterically—then by an unwritten agreement they had ceased to write more than twice, and then once, a week. She was bored, she said; if his brigade was to be there a long time she was coming down to join him. Mr. Haight was going to be able to submit a stronger brief than he had expected, but doubted that the appealed case would come up until late spring. Muriel was in the city doing Red Cross work, and they went out together rather often. What would Anthony think if *she* went into the Red Cross? Trouble was she had heard that she might have to bathe negroes in alcohol, and after that she hadn't felt so patriotic. The city was full of soldiers and she'd seen a lot of boys she hadn't laid eyes on for years. . . .

Anthony did not want her to come South. He told himself that this was for many reasons—he needed a rest from her and she from him. She would be bored beyond measure in town, and she would be able to see Anthony for only a few hours each day. But in his heart he feared that it was because he was attracted to Dorothy. As a matter of fact he lived in terror that Gloria should learn by some chance or intention of the relation he had formed. By the end of a fortnight the entanglement began to give him moments of misery at his own faithlessness. Nevertheless, as each day ended he was unable to withstand the lure that would draw him irresistibly out of his tent and over to the telephone at the Y. M. C. A.

"Dot."

"Yes?"

"I may be able to get in to-night."

"I'm so glad."

"Do you want to listen to my splendid eloquence for a few starry hours?"

"Oh, you funny—" For an instant he had a memory of five years before—of Geraldine. Then——

"I'll arrive about eight."

At seven he would be in a jitney bound for the city, where hundreds of little Southern girls were waiting on moonlit porches for their lovers. He would be excited already for her warm retarded kisses, for the amazed quietude of the glances she gave him—glances nearer to worship than any he had ever inspired. Gloria and he had been equals, giving without thought of thanks or obligation. To this girl his very caresses were an inestimable boon. Crying quietly she had confessed to him that he was not the first man in her life; there had been one other—he gathered that the affair had no sooner commenced than it had been over.

Indeed, so far as she was concerned, she spoke the truth. She had forgotten the clerk, the naval officer, the clothier's son, forgotten her vividness of emotion, which is true forgetting. She knew that in some opaque and shadowy existence some one had taken her—it was as though it had occurred in sleep.

Almost every night Anthony came to town. It was too cool now for the porch, so her mother surrendered to them the tiny sitting room, with its dozens of cheaply framed chromos, its yard upon yard of decorative fringe, and its thick atmosphere of several decades in the proximity of the kitchen. They would build a fire—then, happily, inexhaustibly, she would go about the business of love. Each evening at ten she would walk with him to the door, her black hair in disarray, her face pale without cosmetics, paler still under the whiteness of the moon. As a rule it would be bright and silver outside; now and then there was a slow warm rain, too indolent, almost, to reach the ground.

"Say you love me," she would whisper.

"Why, of course, you sweet baby."

"Am I a baby?" This almost wistfully.

"Just a little baby."

She knew vaguely of Gloria. It gave her pain to think of it, so she imagined her to be haughty and proud and cold. She had decided that Gloria must be older than Anthony, and that there was no love between husband and wife. Sometimes she let herself dream that after the war Anthony would get a divorce and they would be married—but she never mentioned this to Anthony, she scarcely knew why. She shared his company's idea that he was a sort of bank clerk—she thought that he was respectable and poor. She would say:

"If I had some money, darlin', I'd give ev'y bit of it to you. . . . I'd like to have about fifty thousand dollars."

"I suppose that'd be plenty," agreed Anthony.

—In her letter that day Gloria had written: "I suppose if we *could* settle for a million it would be better to tell Mr. Haight to go ahead and settle. But it'd seem a pity. . . ."

. . . "We could have an automobile," exclaimed Dot, in a final burst of triumph.

AN IMPRESSIVE OCCASION

Captain Dunning prided himself on being a great reader of character. Half an hour after meeting a man he was accustomed to place him in one of a number of astonishing categories—fine man, good man, smart fellow, theorizer, poet, and "worthless." One day early in February he caused Anthony to be summoned to his presence in the orderly tent.

"Patch," he said sententiously, "I've had my eye on you for several weeks."

Anthony stood erect and motionless.

"And I think you've got the makings of a good soldier."

He waited for the warm glow, which this would naturally arouse, to cool—and then continued:

"This is no child's play," he said, narrowing his brows.

Anthony agreed with a melancholy "No, sir."

"It's a man's game—and we need leaders." Then the climax, swift, sure, and electric: "Patch, I'm going to make you a corporal."

At this point Anthony should have staggered slightly backward, overwhelmed. He was to be one of the quarter million selected for that consummate trust. He was going to be able to shout the technical phrase, "Follow me!" to seven other frightened men.

"You seem to be a man of some education," said Captain Dunning.

"Yes, sir."

"That's good, that's good. Education's a great thing, but don't let it go to your head. Keep on the way you're doing and you'll be a good soldier."

With these parting words lingering in his ears, Corporal Patch saluted, executed a right about face, and left the tent.

Though the conversation amused Anthony, it did generate the idea that life would be more amusing as a sergeant or, should he find a less exacting medical examiner, as an officer. He was little interested in the work, which seemed to belie the army's boasted gallantry. At the inspections one did not dress up to look well, one dressed up to keep from looking badly.

But as winter wore away—the short, snowless winter marked by damp nights and cool, rainy days—he marvelled at how quickly the system had grasped him. He was a soldier—all who were not soldiers were civilians. The world was divided primarily into those two classifications.

It occurred to him that all strongly accentuated classes, such as the military, divided men into two kinds: their own kind—and those without. To the clergyman there were clergy and laity, to the Catholic there were Catholics and non-Catholics, to the negro there were blacks and whites, to the prisoner there were the imprisoned and the free, and to the sick man there were the sick and the well. . . . So, without thinking of it once in his lifetime, he had been a civilian, a layman, a non-Catholic, a Gentile, white, free, and well. . . .

As the American troops were poured into the French and British trenches he began to find the names of many Harvard men among the casualties recorded in the Army and Navy Journal. But for all the sweat and blood the situation appeared unchanged, and he saw no prospect of the war's ending in the perceptible future. In the old chronicles the right wing of one army always defeated the left wing of the other, the left wing being, meanwhile, vanquished by the enemy's right. After that the mercenaries fled. It had been so simple, in those days, almost as if prearranged. . . .

Gloria wrote that she was reading a great deal. What

a mess they had made of their affairs, she said. She had so little to do now that she spent her time imagining how differently things might have turned out. Her whole environment appeared insecure—and a few years back she had seemed to hold all the strings in her own little hand. . . .

In June her letters grew hurried and less frequent. She suddenly ceased to write about coming South.

DEFEAT

March in the country around was rare with jasmine and jonquils and patches of violets in the warming grass. Afterward he remembered especially one afternoon of such a fresh and magic glamour that as he stood in the rifle-pit marking targets he recited "Atalanta in Calydon" to an uncomprehending Pole, his voice mingling with the rip, sing, and splatter of the bullets overhead.

"When the hounds of spring . . ."

Spang!

"Are on winter's traces . . ."

Whirr-r-r-r! . . .

"The mother of months . . ."

"*Hey!* Come to! Mark three-e-e! . . ."

In town the streets were in a sleepy dream again, and together Anthony and Dot idled in their own tracks of the previous autumn until he began to feel a drowsy attachment for this South—a South, it seemed, more of Algiers than of Italy, with faded aspirations pointing back over innumerable generations to some warm, primitive Nirvana, without hope or care. Here there was an inflection of cordiality, of comprehension, in every voice. "Life plays the same lovely and agonizing joke on all of us," they seemed to say in their plaintive pleasant cadence, in the rising inflection terminating on an unresolved minor.

He liked his barber shop, where he was "Hi, corporal!" to a pale, emaciated young man, who shaved him and pushed a cool vibrating machine endlessly over his insatiable head. He liked "Johnston's Gardens" where they danced, where a tragic negro made yearning, aching music on a saxophone until the garish hall became an enchanted jungle of barbaric rhythms and smoky laughter, where to forget the uneventful passage of time upon Dorothy's soft sighs and tender whisperings was the consummation of all aspiration, of all content.

There was an undertone of sadness in her character, a conscious evasion of all except the pleasurable minutiæ of life. Her violet eyes would remain for hours apparently insensate as, thoughtless and reckless, she basked like a cat in the sun. He wondered what the tired, spiritless mother thought of them, and whether in her moments of uttermost cynicism she ever guessed at their relationship.

On Sunday afternoons they walked along the countryside, resting at intervals on the dry moss in the outskirts of a wood. Here the birds had gathered and the clusters of violets and white dogwood; here the hoar trees shone crystalline and cool, oblivious to the intoxicating heat that waited outside; here he would talk, intermittently, in a sleepy monologue, in a conversation of no significance, of no replies.

July came scorching down. Captain Dunning was ordered to detail one of his men to learn blacksmithing. The regiment was filling up to war strength, and he needed most of his veterans for drill-masters, so he selected the little Italian, Baptiste, whom he could most easily spare. Little Baptiste had never had anything to do with horses. His fear made matters worse. He reappeared in the orderly room one day and told Captain Dunning that he wanted to die if he couldn't be relieved. The horses kicked at him, he said; he was no good at the work. Finally he fell on his knees and besought Captain Dunning, in a mixture of broken English and scriptural Italian, to get him out of it. He had not slept for three days; monstrous stallions reared and cavorted through his dreams.

Captain Dunning reproved the company clerk (who had burst out laughing), and told Baptiste he would do what he could. But when he thought it over he decided that he couldn't spare a better man. Little Baptiste went from bad to worse. The horses seemed to divine his fear and take every advantage of it. Two weeks later a great black mare crushed his skull in with her hoofs while he was trying to lead her from her stall.

In mid-July came rumors, and then orders, that concerned a change of camp. The brigade was to move to an empty cantonment, a hundred miles farther south, there to be expanded into a division. At first the men thought they were departing for the trenches, and all evening little groups jabbered in the company street, shouting to each other in swaggering exclamations: "Su-u-ure we are!" When the truth leaked out, it was rejected indignantly as a blind to conceal their real destination. They revelled in their own importance. That night they told their girls in town that they were "going to get the Germans." Anthony circulated for a while among the groups—then, stopping a jitney, rode down to tell Dot that he was going away.

She was waiting on the dark veranda in a cheap white dress that accentuated the youth and softness of her face.

"Oh," she whispered, "I've wanted you so, honey. All this day."

"I have something to tell you."

She drew him down beside her on the swinging seat, not noticing his ominous tone.

"Tell me."

"We're leaving next week."

Her arms seeking his shoulders remained poised upon the dark air, her chin tipped up. When she spoke the softness was gone from her voice.

"Leaving for France?"

"No. Less luck than that. Leaving for some darn camp in Mississippi."

She shut her eyes and he could see that the lids were trembling.

"Dear little Dot, life is so damned hard."

She was crying upon his shoulder.

"So damned hard, so damned hard," he repeated aimlessly; "it just hurts people and hurts people, until finally it hurts them so that they can't be hurt ever any more. That's the last and worst thing it does."

Frantic, wild with anguish, she strained him to her breast.

"Oh, God!" she whispered brokenly, "you can't go way from me. I'd die."

He was finding it impossible to pass off his departure as a common, impersonal blow. He was too near to her to do more than repeat "Poor little Dot. Poor little Dot."

"And then what?" she demanded wearily.

"What do you mean?"

"You're my whole life, that's all. I'd die for you right now if you said so. I'd get a knife and kill myself. You can't leave me here."

Her tone frightened him.

"These things happen," he said evenly.

"Then I'm going with you." Tears were streaming

down her cheeks. Her mouth was trembling in an ecstasy of grief and fear.

"Sweet," he muttered sentimentally, "sweet little girl. Don't you see we'd just be putting off what's bound to happen? I'll be going to France in a few months——"

She leaned away from him and clinching her fists lifted her face toward the sky.

"I want to die," she said, as if moulding each word carefully in her heart.

"Dot," he whispered uncomfortably, "you'll forget. Things are sweeter when they're lost. I know—because once I wanted something and got it. It was the only thing I ever wanted badly, Dot. And when I got it it turned to dust in my hands."

"All right."

Absorbed in himself, he continued:

"I've often thought that if I hadn't got what I wanted things might have been different with me. I might have found something in my mind and enjoyed putting it in circulation. I might have been content with the work of it, and had some sweet vanity out of the success. I suppose that at one time I could have had anything I wanted, within reason, but that was the only thing I ever wanted with any fervor. God! And that taught me you can't have *any*thing, you can't have anything at *all*. Because desire just cheats you. It's like a sunbeam skipping here and there about a room. It stops and gilds some inconsequential object, and we poor fools try to grasp it—but when we do the sunbeam moves on to something else, and you've got the inconsequential part, but the glitter that made you want it is gone—" He broke off uneasily. She had risen and was standing, dry-eyed, picking little leaves from a dark vine.

"Dot——"

"Go way," she said coldly.

"What? Why?"

"I don't want just words. If that's all you have for me you'd better go."

"Why, Dot——"

"What's death to me is just a lot of words to you. You put 'em together so pretty."

"I'm sorry. I was talking about you, Dot."

"Go way from here."

He approached her with arms outstretched, but she held him away.

"You don't want me to go with you," she said evenly; "maybe you're going to meet that—that girl—" She could not bring herself to say wife. "How do I know? Well, then, I reckon you're not my fellow any more. So go way."

For a moment, while conflicting warnings and desires prompted Anthony, it seemed one of those rare times when he would take a step prompted from within. He hesitated. Then a wave of weariness broke against him. It was too late—everything was too late. For years now he had dreamed the world away, basing his decisions upon emotions unstable as water. The little girl in the white dress dominated him, as she approached beauty in the hard symmetry of her desire. The fire blazing in her dark and injured heart seemed to glow around her like a flame. With some profound and uncharted pride she had made herself remote and so achieved her purpose.

"I didn't—mean to seem so callous, Dot."

"It don't matter."

The fire rolled over Anthony. Something wrenched at his bowels, and he stood there helpless and beaten.

"Come with me, Dot—little loving Dot. Oh, come with me. I couldn't leave you now——"

With a sob she wound her arms around him and let him support her weight while the moon, at its perennial labor of covering the bad complexion of the world, showered its illicit honey over the drowsy street.

The Catastrophe

Early September in Camp Boone, Mississippi. The darkness, alive with insects, beat in upon the mosquito-netting, beneath the shelter of which Anthony was trying to write a letter. An intermittent chatter over a poker game was going on in the next tent, and outside a man was strolling up the company street singing a current bit of doggerel about "K-K-K-Katy."

With an effort Anthony hoisted himself to his elbow and, pencil in hand, looked down at his blank sheet of paper. Then, omitting any heading, he began:

I can't imagine what the matter is, Gloria. I haven't had a line from you for two weeks and it's only natural to be worried——

He threw this away with a disturbed grunt and began again:

I don't know what to think, Gloria. Your last letter, short, cold, without a word of affection or even a decent account of what you've been doing, came two weeks ago. It's only natural that I should wonder. If your love for me isn't absolutely dead it seems that you'd at least keep me from worry——

Again he crumpled the page and tossed it angrily through a tear in the tent wall, realizing simultaneously that he would have to pick it up in the morning. He felt disinclined to try again. He could get no warmth into the lines—only a persistent jealousy and suspicion. Since midsummer these discrepancies in Gloria's correspondence had grown more and more noticeable. At first he had scarcely perceived them. He was so inured to the perfunctory "dearest" and "darlings" scattered through her letters that he was oblivious to their presence or absence. But in this last fortnight he had become increasingly aware that there was something amiss.

He had sent her a night-letter saying that he had passed his examinations for an officers' training-camp, and expected to leave for Georgia shortly. She had not answered. He had wired again—when he received no word he imagined that she might be out of town. But it occurred and recurred to him that she was not out of town, and a series of distraught imaginings began to plague him. Supposing Gloria, bored and restless, had found some one, even as he had. The thought terrified him with its possibility—it was chiefly because he had been so sure of her personal integrity that he had considered her so sparingly during the year. And now, as a doubt was born, the old angers, the rages of possession, swarmed back a thousandfold. What more natural than that she should be in love again?

He remembered the Gloria who promised that should she ever want anything, she would take it, insisting that since she would act entirely for her own satisfaction she could go through such an affair unsmirched—it was only the effect on a person's mind that counted, anyhow, she said, and her reaction would be the masculine one, of satiation and faint dislike.

But that had been when they were first married. Later, with the discovery that she could be jealous of Anthony, she had, outwardly at least, changed her mind. There were no other men in the world for her. This he had known only too surely. Perceiving that a certain fastidiousness would restrain her, he had grown lax in preserving the completeness of her love—which, after all, was the keystone of the entire structure.

Meanwhile all through the summer he had been maintaining Dot in a boarding-house down-town. To do this it had been necessary to write to his broker for money. Dot had covered her journey south by leaving her house a day before the brigade broke camp, informing her mother in a note that she had gone to New York. On the evening following Anthony had called as though to see her. Mrs. Raycroft was in a state of collapse and there was a policeman in the parlor. A questionnaire had ensued, from which Anthony had extricated himself with some difficulty.

In September, with his suspicions of Gloria, the company of Dot had become tedious, then almost intolerable. He was nervous and irritable from lack of sleep; his heart was sick and afraid. Three days ago he had gone to Captain Dunning and asked for a furlough, only to be met with benignant procrastination. The division was starting overseas, while Anthony was going to an officers' training-camp; what furloughs could be given must go to the men who were leaving the country.

Upon this refusal Anthony had started to the telegraph office intending to wire Gloria to come South—he reached the door and receded despairingly, seeing the utter impracticability of such a move. Then he had spent the evening quarrelling irritably with Dot, and returned to camp morose and angry with the world. There had been a disagreeable scene, in the midst of which he had precipitately departed. What was to be done with her did not seem to concern him vitally at present—he was completely absorbed in the disheartening silence of his wife. . . .

The flap of the tent made a sudden triangle back upon itself, and a dark head appeared against the night.

"Sergeant Patch?" The accent was Italian, and Anthony saw by the belt that the man was a headquarters orderly.

"Want me?"

"Lady call up headquarters ten minutes ago. Say she have speak with you. Ver' important."

Anthony swept aside the mosquito-netting and stood up. It might be a wire from Gloria telephoned over.

"She say to get you. She call again ten o'clock."

"All right, thanks." He picked up his hat and in a moment was striding beside the orderly through the hot, almost suffocating, darkness. Over in the headquarters shack he saluted a dozing night-service officer.

"Sit down and wait," suggested the lieutenant nonchalantly. "Girl seemed awful anxious to speak to you."

Anthony's hopes fell away.

"Thank you very much, sir." And as the phone squeaked on the side-wall he knew who was calling.

"This is Dot," came an unsteady voice, "I've got to see you."

"Dot, I told you I couldn't get down for several days."

"I've got to see you to-night. It's important."

"It's too late," he said coldly; "it's ten o'clock, and I have to be in camp at eleven."

"All right." There was so much wretchedness compressed into the two words that Anthony felt a measure of compunction.

"What's the matter?"

"I want to tell you good-by."

"Oh, don't be a little idiot!" he exclaimed. But his spirits rose. What luck if she should leave town this very night! What a burden from his soul. But he said: "You can't possibly leave before to-morrow."

Out of the corner of his eye he saw the night-service officer regarding him quizzically. Then, startlingly, came Dot's next words:

"I don't mean 'leave' that way."

Anthony's hand clutched the receiver fiercely. He

felt his nerves turning cold as if the heat was leaving his body.

"What?"

Then quickly in a wild broken voice he heard:

"Good-by—oh, good-by!"

Cul-*lup!* She had hung up the receiver. With a sound that was half a gasp, half a cry, Anthony hurried from the headquarters building. Outside, under the stars that dripped like silver tassels through the trees of the little grove, he stood motionless, hesitating. Had she meant to kill herself?—oh, the little fool! He was filled with bitter hate toward her. In this dénouement he found it impossible to realize that he had ever begun such an entanglement, such a mess, a sordid mélange of worry and pain.

He found himself walking slowly away, repeating over and over that it was futile to worry. He had best go back to his tent and sleep. He needed sleep. God! Would he ever sleep again? His mind was in a vast clamor and confusion; as he reached the road he turned around in a panic and began running, not toward his company but away from it. Men were returning now—he could find a taxicab. After a minute two yellow eyes appeared around a bend. Desperately he ran toward them.

"Jitney! Jitney!" . . . It was an empty Ford. . . . "I want to go to town."

"Cost you a dollar."

"All right. If you'll just hurry——"

After an interminable time he ran up the steps of a dark ramshackle little house, and through the door, almost knocking over an immense negress who was walking, candle in hand, along the hall.

"Where's my wife?" he cried wildly.

"She gone to bed."

Up the stairs three at a time, down the creaking passage. The room was dark and silent, and with trembling fingers he struck a match. Two wide eyes looked up at him from a wretched ball of clothes on the bed.

"Ah, I knew you'd come," she murmured brokenly.

Anthony grew cold with anger.

"So it was just a plan to get me down here, get me in trouble!" he said. "God damn it, you've shouted 'wolf' once too often!"

She regarded him pitifully.

"I had to see you. I couldn't have lived. Oh, I had to see you——"

He sat down on the side of the bed and slowly shook his head.

"You're no good," he said decisively, talking unconsciously as Gloria might have talked to him. "This sort of thing isn't fair to me, you know."

"Come closer." Whatever he might say Dot was happy now. He cared for her. She had brought him to her side.

"Oh, God," said Anthony hopelessly. As weariness rolled along its inevitable wave his anger subsided, receded, vanished. He collapsed suddenly, fell sobbing beside her on the bed.

"Oh, my darling," she begged him, "don't cry! Oh, don't cry!"

She took his head upon her breast and soothed him, mingled her happy tears with the bitterness of his. Her hand played gently with his dark hair.

"I'm such a little fool," she murmured brokenly, "but I love you, and when you're cold to me it seems as if it isn't worth while to go on livin'."

After all, this was peace—the quiet room with the mingled scent of women's powder and perfume, Dot's hand soft as a warm wind upon his hair, the rise and fall of her bosom as she took breath—for a moment it was as though it were Gloria there, as though he were at rest in some sweeter and safer home than he had ever known.

An hour passed. A clock began to chime in the hall. He jumped to his feet and looked at the phosphorescent hands of his wrist watch. It was twelve o'clock.

He had trouble in finding a taxi that would take him out at that hour. As he urged the driver faster along the road he speculated on the best method of entering camp. He had been late several times recently, and he knew that were he caught again his name would probably be stricken from the list of officer candidates. He wondered if he had not better dismiss the taxi and take a chance on passing the sentry in the dark. Still, officers often rode past the sentries after midnight. . . .

"Halt!" The monosyllable came from the yellow glare that the headlights dropped upon the changing road. The taxi-driver threw out his clutch and a sentry walked up, carrying his rifle at the port. With him, by an ill chance, was the officer of the guard.

"Out late, sergeant."

"Yes, sir. Got delayed."

"Too bad. Have to take your name."

As the officer waited, note-book and pencil in hand, something not fully intended crowded to Anthony's lips, something born of panic, of muddle, of despair.

"Sergeant R. A. Foley," he answered breathlessly.

"And the outfit?"

"Company Q, Eighty-third Infantry."

"All right. You'll have to walk from here, sergeant."

Anthony saluted, quickly paid his taxi-driver, and set off for a run toward the regiment he had named. When he was out of sight he changed his course, and with his heart beating wildly, hurried to his company, feeling that he had made a fatal error of judgment.

Two days later the officer who had been in command of the guard recognized him in a barber shop down-town. In charge of a military policeman he was taken back to the camp, where he was reduced to the ranks without trial, and confined for a month to the limits of his company street.

With this blow a spell of utter depression overtook him, and within a week he was again caught down-town, wandering around in a drunken daze, with a pint of boot-leg whiskey in his hip pocket. It was because of a sort of craziness in his behavior at the trial that his sentence to the guard-house was for only three weeks.

Nightmare

Early in his confinement the conviction took root in him that he was going mad. It was as though there were a quantity of dark yet vivid personalities in his mind, some of them familiar, some of them strange and terrible, held in check by a little monitor, who sat aloft somewhere and looked on. The thing that worried him was that the monitor was sick, and holding out with difficulty. Should he give up, should he falter for a moment, out would rush these intolerable things—only Anthony could know what a state of blackness there would be if the worst of him could roam his consciousness unchecked.

The heat of the day had changed, somehow, until it was a burnished darkness crushing down upon a devastated land. Over his head the blue circles of ominous uncharted suns, of unnumbered centres of fire, revolved interminably before his eyes as though he were lying constantly exposed to the hot light and in a state of feverish coma. At seven in the morning something phantasmal, something almost absurdly unreal that he knew was his mortal body, went out with seven other prisoners and two guards to work on the camp roads. One day they loaded and unloaded quantities of gravel, spread it, raked it—the next day they worked with huge barrels of red-hot tar, flooding the gravel with black, shining pools of molten heat. At night, locked up in the guard-house, he would lie without thought, without courage to compass thought, staring at the irregular beams of the ceiling overhead until about three o'clock, when he would slip into a broken, troubled sleep.

During the work hours he labored with uneasy haste, attempting, as the day bore toward the sultry Mississippi sunset, to tire himself physically so that in the evening he might sleep deeply from utter exhaustion. . . . Then one afternoon in the second week he had a feeling that two eyes were watching him from a place a few feet beyond one of the guards. This aroused him to a sort of terror. He turned his back on the eyes and shovelled feverishly, until it became necessary for him to face about and go for more gravel. Then they entered his vision again, and his already taut nerves tightened up to the breaking-point. The eyes were leering at him. Out of a hot silence he heard his name called in a tragic voice, and the earth tipped absurdly back and forth to a babel of shouting and confusion.

When next he became conscious he was back in the guard-house, and the other prisoners were throwing him curious glances. The eyes returned no more. It was many days before he realized that the voice must have been Dot's, that she had called out to him and made some sort of disturbance. He decided this just previous to the expiration of his sentence, when the cloud that oppressed him had lifted, leaving him in a deep, dispirited lethargy. As the conscious mediator, the monitor who kept that fearsome ménage of horror, grew stronger, Anthony became physically weaker. He was scarcely able to get through the two days of toil, and when he was released, one rainy afternoon, and returned to his company, he reached his tent only to fall into a heavy doze, from which he awoke before dawn, aching and unrefreshed. Beside his cot were two letters that had been awaiting him in the orderly tent for some time. The first was from Gloria; it was short and cool:

The case is coming to trial late in November. Can you possibly get leave?

I've tried to write you again and again but it just seems to make things worse. I want to see you about several matters, but you know that you have once prevented me from coming and I am disinclined to try again. In view of a number of things it seems necessary that we have a conference. I'm very glad about your appointment.

GLORIA.

He was too tired to try to understand—or to care. Her phrases, her intentions, were all very far away in an incomprehensible past. At the second letter he scarcely glanced; it was from Dot—an incoherent, tear-swollen scrawl, a flood of protest, endearment, and grief. After a page he let it slip from his inert hand and drowsed back into a nebulous hinterland of his own. At drill-call he awoke with a high fever and fainted when he tried to leave his tent—at noon he was sent to the base hospital with influenza.

He was aware that this sickness was providential. It saved him from a hysterical relapse—and he recovered in time to entrain on a damp November day for New York, and for the interminable massacre beyond.

When the regiment reached Camp Mills, Long Island, Anthony's single idea was to get into the city and see Gloria as soon as possible. It was now evident that an armistice would be signed within the week, but rumor had it that in any case troops would continue to be shipped to France until the last moment. Anthony was appalled at the notion of the long voyage, of a tedious debarkation at a French port, and of being kept abroad for a year, possibly, to replace the troops who had seen actual fighting.

His intention had been to obtain a two-day furlough, but Camp Mills proved to be under a strict influenza quarantine—it was impossible for even an officer to leave except on official business. For a private it was out of the question.

The camp itself was a dreary muddle, cold, windswept, and filthy, with the accumulated dirt incident to the passage through of many divisions. Their train came in at seven one night, and they waited in line until one while a military tangle was straightened out somewhere ahead. Officers ran up and down ceaselessly, calling orders and making a great uproar. It turned out that the trouble was due to the colonel, who was in a righteous temper because he was a West Pointer, and the war was going to stop before he could get overseas. Had the militant governments realized the number of broken hearts among the older West Pointers during that week, they would indubitably have prolonged the slaughter another month. The thing was pitiable!

Gazing out at the bleak expanse of tents extending for miles over a trodden welter of slush and snow, Anthony saw the impracticability of trudging to a telephone that night. He would call her at the first opportunity in the morning.

Aroused in the chill and bitter dawn he stood at reveille and listened to a passionate harangue from Captain Dunning:

"You men may think the war is over. Well, let me

tell you, it isn't! Those fellows aren't going to sign the armistice. It's another trick, and we'd be crazy to let anything slacken up here in the company, because, let me tell you, we're going to sail from here within a week, and when we do we're going to see some real fighting." He paused that they might get the full effect of his pronouncement. And then: "If you think the war's over, just talk to any one who's been in it and see if *they* think the Germans are all in. They don't. Nobody does. I've talked to the people that *know*, and they say there'll be, anyways, a year longer of war. *They* don't think it's over. So you men better not get any foolish ideas that it is."

Doubly stressing this final admonition, he ordered the company dismissed.

At noon Anthony set off at a run for the nearest canteen telephone. As he approached what corresponded to the down-town of the camp, he noticed that many other soldiers were running also, that a man near him had suddenly leaped into the air and clicked his heels together. The tendency to run became general, and from little excited groups here and there came the sounds of cheering. He stopped and listened—over the cold country whistles were blowing and the chimes of the Garden City churches broke suddenly into reverberatory sound.

Anthony began to run again. The cries were clear and distinct now as they rose with clouds of frosted breath into the chilly air:

"*Germany's surrendered! Germany's surrendered!*"

The False Armistice

That evening in the opaque gloom of six o'clock Anthony slipped between two freight-cars, and once over the railroad, followed the track along to Garden City, where he caught an electric train for New York. He stood some chance of apprehension—he knew that the military police were often sent through the cars to ask for passes, but he imagined that to-night the vigilance would be relaxed. But, in any event, he would have tried to slip through, for he had been unable to locate Gloria by telephone, and another day of suspense would have been intolerable.

After inexplicable stops and waits that reminded him of the night he had left New York, over a year before, they drew into the Pennsylvania Station, and he followed the familiar way to the taxi-stand, finding it grotesque and oddly stimulating to give his own address.

Broadway was a riot of light, thronged as he had never seen it with a carnival crowd which swept its glittering way through scraps of paper, piled ankle-deep on the sidewalks. Here and there, elevated upon benches and boxes, soldiers addressed the heedless mass, each face in which was clear cut and distinct under the white glare overhead. Anthony picked out half a dozen figures—a drunken sailor, tipped backward and supported by two other gobs, was waving his hat and emitting a wild series of roars; a wounded soldier, crutch in hand, was borne along in an eddy on the shoulders of some shrieking civilians; a dark-haired girl sat cross-legged and meditative on top of a parked taxicab. Here surely the victory had come in time, the climax had been scheduled with the uttermost celestial foresight. The great rich nation had made triumphant war, suffered enough for poignancy but not enough for bitterness—hence the carnival, the feasting, the triumph. Under these bright lights glittered the faces of peoples whose glory had long since passed away, whose very civilizations were dead—men whose ancestors had heard the news of victory in Babylon, in Nineveh, in Bagdad, in Tyre, a hundred generations before; men whose ancestors had seen a flower-decked, slave-adorned cortege drift with its wake of captives down the avenues of Imperial Rome. . . .

Past the Rialto, the glittering front of the Astor, the jewelled magnificence of Times Square . . . a gorgeous alley of incandescence ahead. . . . Then—was it years later?—he was paying the taxi-driver in front of a white building on Fifty-seventh Street. He was in the hall—ah, there was the negro boy from Martinique, lazy, indolent, unchanged.

"Is Mrs. Patch in?"

"I have just came on, sah," the man announced with his incongruous British accent.

"Take me up——"

Then the slow drone of the elevator, the three steps to the door, which swung open at the impetus of his knock.

"Gloria!" His voice was trembling. No answer. A faint string of smoke was rising from a cigarette-tray—a number of Vanity Fair sat astraddle on the table.

"Gloria!"

He ran into the bedroom, the bath. She was not there. A negligée of robin's-egg blue laid out upon the bed diffused a faint perfume, illusive and familiar. On a chair were a pair of stockings and a street dress; an open powder box yawned upon the bureau. She must just have gone out.

The telephone rang abruptly and he started—answered it with all the sensations of an impostor.

"Hello. Is Mrs. Patch there?"

"No, I'm looking for her myself. Who is this?"

"This is Mr. Crawford."

"This is Mr. Patch speaking. I've just arrived unexpectedly, and I don't know where to find her."

"Oh." Mr. Crawford sounded a bit taken aback. "Why, I imagine she's at the Armistice Ball. I know she intended going, but I didn't think she'd leave so early."

"Where's the Armistice Ball?"

"At the Astor."

"Thanks."

Anthony hung up sharply and rose. Who was Mr. Crawford? And who was it that was taking her to the ball? How long had this been going on? All these questions asked and answered themselves a dozen times, a dozen ways. His very proximity to her drove him half frantic.

In a frenzy of suspicion he rushed here and there about the apartment, hunting for some sign of masculine occupation, opening the bathroom cupboard, searching feverishly through the bureau drawers. Then he found something that made him stop suddenly and sit down on one of the twin beds, the corners of his mouth drooping as though he were about to weep. There in a corner of her drawer, tied with a frail blue ribbon, were all the letters and telegrams he had written her during the year past. He was suffused with happy and sentimental shame.

"I'm not fit to touch her," he cried aloud to the four walls. "I'm not fit to touch her little hand."

Nevertheless, he went out to look for her.

In the Astor lobby he was engulfed immediately in a crowd so thick as to make progress almost impossible. He asked the direction of the ballroom from half a dozen people before he could get a sober and intelligible answer. Eventually, after a last long wait, he checked his military overcoat in the hall.

It was only nine but the dance was in full blast. The panorama was incredible. Women, women everywhere

—girls gay with wine singing shrilly above the clamor of the dazzling confetti-covered throng; girls set off by the uniforms of a dozen nations; fat females collapsing without dignity upon the floor and retaining self-respect by shouting "Hurraw for the Allies!"; three women with white hair dancing hand in hand around a sailor, who revolved in a dizzying spin upon the floor, clasping to his heart an empty bottle of champagne.

Breathlessly Anthony scanned the dancers, scanned the muddled lines trailing in single file in and out among the tables, scanned the horn-blowing, kissing, coughing, laughing, drinking parties under the great full-bosomed flags which leaned in glowing color over the pageantry and the sound.

Then he saw Gloria. She was sitting at a table for two directly across the room. Her dress was black, and above it her animated face, tinted with the most glamourous rose, made, he thought, a spot of poignant beauty on the room. His heart leaped as though to a new music. He jostled his way toward her and called her name just as the gray eyes looked up and found him. For that instant as their bodies met and melted, the world, the revel, the tumbling whimper of the music faded to an ecstatic monotone hushed as a song of bees.

"Oh, my Gloria!" he cried.

Her kiss was a cool rill flowing from her heart.

CHAPTER II

A MATTER OF ÆSTHETICS

On the night when Anthony had left for Camp Hooker one year before, all that was left of the beautiful Gloria Gilbert—her shell, her young and lovely body—moved up the broad marble steps of the Grand Central Station with the rhythm of the engine beating in her ears like a dream, and out onto Vanderbilt Avenue, where the huge bulk of the Biltmore overhung the street and, down at its low, gleaming entrance, sucked in the many-colored opera-cloaks of gorgeously dressed girls. For a moment she paused by the taxi-stand and watched them—wondering that but a few years before she had been of their number, ever setting out for a radiant Somewhere, always just about to have that ultimate passionate adventure for which the girls' cloaks were delicate and beautifully furred, for which their cheeks were painted and their hearts higher than the transitory dome of pleasure that would engulf them, coiffure, cloak, and all.

It was growing colder and the men passing had flipped up the collars of their overcoats. This change was kind to her. It would have been kinder still had everything changed, weather, streets, and people, and had she been whisked away, to wake in some high, fresh-scented room, alone, and statuesque within and without, as in her virginal and colorful past.

Inside the taxicab she wept impotent tears. That she had not been happy with Anthony for over a year mattered little. Recently his presence had been no more than what it would awake in her of that memorable June. The Anthony of late, irritable, weak, and poor, could do no less than make her irritable in turn—and bored with everything except the fact that in a highly imaginative and eloquent youth they had come together in an ecstatic revel of emotion. Because of this mutually vivid memory she would have done more for Anthony than for any other human—so when she got into the taxicab she wept passionately, and wanted to call his name aloud.

Miserable, lonesome as a forgotten child, she sat in the quiet apartment and wrote him a letter full of confused sentiment:

. . . I can almost look down the tracks and see you going but without you, dearest, dearest, I can't see or hear or feel or think. Being apart—whatever has happened or will happen to us—is like begging for mercy from a storm, Anthony; it's like growing old. I want to kiss you so—in the back of your neck where your old black hair starts. Because I love you and whatever we do or say to each other, or have done, or have said, you've got to feel how much I do, how inanimate I am when you're gone. I can't even hate the damnable presence of PEOPLE, *those people in the station who haven't any right to live—I can't resent them even though they're dirtying up our world, because I'm engrossed in wanting you so.*

If you hated me, if you were covered with sores like a leper, if you ran away with another woman or starved me or beat me—how absurd this sounds—I'd still want you, I'd still love you. I KNOW, *my darling.*

It's late—I have all the windows open and the air outside is just as soft as spring, yet, somehow, much more young and frail than spring. Why do they make spring a young girl, why does that illusion dance and yodel its way for three months through the world's preposterous barrenness. Spring is a lean old plough horse with its ribs showing—it's a pile of refuse in a field, parched by the sun and the rain to an ominous cleanliness.

In a few hours you'll wake up, my darling—and you'll be miserable, and disgusted with life. You'll be in Delaware or Carolina or somewhere and so unimportant. I don't believe there's any one alive who can contemplate themselves as an impermanent institution, as a luxury or an unnecessary evil. Very few of the people who accentuate the futility of life remark the futility of themselves. Perhaps they think that in proclaiming the evil of living they somehow salvage their own worth from the ruin—but they don't, even you and I. . . .

. . . Still I can see you. There's blue haze about the trees where you'll be passing, too beautiful to be predominant. No, the fallow squares of earth will be most frequent—they'll be along beside the track like dirty coarse brown sheets drying in the sun, alive, mechanical, abominable. Nature, slovenly old hag, has been sleeping in them with every old farmer or negro or immigrant who happened to covet her. . . .

So you see that now you're gone I've written a letter all full of contempt and despair. And that just means that I love you, Anthony, with all there is to love with in your

GLORIA.

When she had addressed the letter she went to her twin bed and lay down upon it, clasping Anthony's pillow in her arms as though by sheer force of emotion she could metamorphize it into his warm and living body. Two o'clock saw her dry-eyed, staring with steady persistent grief into the darkness, remembering, remembering unmercifully, blaming herself for a hundred fancied unkindnesses, making a likeness of Anthony akin to some martyred and transfigured Christ. For a time she thought of him as he, in his more sentimental moments, probably thought of himself.

At five she was still awake. A mysterious grinding noise that went on every morning across the areaway told her the hour. She heard an alarm clock ring, and saw a light make a yellow square on an illusory blank wall opposite. With the half-formed resolution of following him South immediately, her sorrow grew remote and unreal, and moved off from her as the dark moved westward. She fell asleep.

When she awoke the sight of the empty bed beside her brought a renewal of misery, dispelled shortly, however, by the inevitable callousness of the bright morning. Though she was not conscious of it, there was relief in eating breakfast without Anthony's tired and worried face opposite her. Now that she was alone she lost all desire to complain about the food. She would change her breakfasts, she thought—have a lemonade and a tomato sandwich instead of the sempiternal bacon and eggs and toast.

Nevertheless, at noon when she had called up several of her acquaintances, including the martial Muriel, and found each one engaged for lunch, she gave way to a quiet pity for herself and her loneliness. Curled on the bed with pencil and paper she wrote Anthony another letter.

Late in the afternoon arrived a special delivery, mailed from some small New Jersey town, and the familiarity of the phrasing, the almost audible undertone of worry and discontent, were so familiar that they comforted her. Who knew? Perhaps army discipline would harden Anthony and accustom him to the idea of work. She had immutable faith that the war would be over before he was called upon to fight, and meanwhile the suit would be won, and they could begin again, this time on a different basis. The first thing different would be that she would have a child. It was unbearable that she should be so utterly alone.

It was a week before she could stay in the apartment with the probability of remaining dry-eyed. There seemed little in the city that was amusing. Muriel had been shifted to a hospital in New Jersey, from which she took a metropolitan holiday only every other week, and with this defection Gloria grew to realize how few were the friends she had made in all these years of New

York. The men she knew were in the army. "Men she knew"?—she had conceded vaguely to herself that all the men who had ever been in love with her were her friends. Each one of them had at a certain considerable time professed to value her favor above anything in life. But now—where were they? At least two were dead, half a dozen or more were married, the rest scattered from France to the Philippines. She wondered whether any of them thought of her, and how often, and in what respect. Most of them must still picture the little girl of seventeen or so, the adolescent siren of nine years before.

The girls, too, were gone far afield. She had never been popular in school. She had been too beautiful, too lazy, not sufficiently conscious of being a Farmover girl and a "Future Wife and Mother" in perpetual capital letters. And girls who had never been kissed hinted, with shocked expressions on their plain but not particularly wholesome faces, that Gloria had. Then these girls had gone east or west or south, married and become "people," prophesying, if they prophesied about Gloria, that she would come to a bad end—not knowing that no endings were bad, and that they, like her, were by no means the mistresses of their destinies.

Gloria told over to herself the people who had visited them in the gray house at Marietta. It had seemed at the time that they were always having company—she had indulged in an unspoken conviction that each guest was ever afterward slightly indebted to her. They owed her a sort of moral ten dollars apiece, and should she ever be in need she might, so to speak, borrow from them this visionary currency. But they were gone, scattered like chaff, mysteriously and subtly vanished in essence or in fact.

By Christmas Gloria's conviction that she should

join Anthony had returned, no longer as a sudden emotion, but as a recurrent need. She decided to write him word of her coming, but postponed the announcement upon the advice of Mr. Haight, who expected almost weekly that the case was coming up for trial.

One day, early in January, as she was walking on Fifth Avenue, bright now with uniforms and hung with the flags of the virtuous nations, she met Rachael Barnes, whom she had not seen for nearly a year. Even Rachael, whom she had grown to dislike, was a relief from ennui, and together they went to the Ritz for tea.

After a second cocktail they became enthusiastic. They liked each other. They talked about their husbands, Rachael in that tone of public vainglory, with private reservations, in which wives are wont to speak.

"Rodman's abroad in the Quartermaster Corps. He's a captain. He was bound he would go, and he didn't think he could get into anything else."

"Anthony's in the Infantry." The words in their relation to the cocktail gave Gloria a sort of glow. With each sip she approached a warm and comforting patriotism.

"By the way," said Rachael half an hour later, as they were leaving, "can't you come up to dinner to-morrow night? I'm having two awfully sweet officers who are just going overseas. I think we ought to do all we can to make it attractive for them."

Gloria accepted gladly. She took down the address—recognizing by its number a fashionable apartment building on Park Avenue.

"It's been awfully good to have seen you, Rachael."

"It's been wonderful. I've wanted to."

With these three sentences a certain night in Marietta two summers before, when Anthony and Rachael had been unnecessarily attentive to each other, was forgiven

—Gloria forgave Rachael, Rachael forgave Gloria. Also it was forgiven that Rachael had been witness to the greatest disaster in the lives of Mr. and Mrs. Anthony Patch——

Compromising with events time moves along.

The Wiles of Captain Collins

The two officers were captains of the popular craft, machine gunnery. At dinner they referred to themselves with conscious boredom as members of the "Suicide Club"—in those days every recondite branch of the service referred to itself as the Suicide Club. One of the captains—Rachael's captain, Gloria observed—was a tall horsy man of thirty with a pleasant mustache and ugly teeth. The other, Captain Collins, was chubby, pink-faced, and inclined to laugh with abandon every time he caught Gloria's eye. He took an immediate fancy to her, and throughout dinner showered her with inane compliments. With her second glass of champagne Gloria decided that for the first time in months she was thoroughly enjoying herself.

After dinner it was suggested that they all go somewhere and dance. The two officers supplied themselves with bottles of liquor from Rachael's sideboard—a law forbade service to the military—and so equipped they went through innumerable fox trots in several glittering caravanseries along Broadway, faithfully alternating partners—while Gloria became more and more uproarious and more and more amusing to the pink-faced captain, who seldom bothered to remove his genial smile at all.

At eleven o'clock to her great surprise she was in the minority for staying out. The others wanted to return to Rachael's apartment—to get some more liquor, they said. Gloria argued persistently that Captain Collins's flask was half full—she had just seen it—then catching Rachael's eye she received an unmistakable wink. She deduced, confusedly, that her hostess wanted to get rid of the officers and assented to being bundled into a taxicab outside.

Captain Wolf sat on the left with Rachael on his knees. Captain Collins sat in the middle, and as he settled himself he slipped his arm about Gloria's shoulder. It rested there lifelessly for a moment and then tightened like a vise. He leaned over her.

"You're awfully pretty," he whispered.

"Thank you kindly, sir." She was neither pleased nor annoyed. Before Anthony came so many arms had done likewise that it had become little more than a gesture, sentimental but without significance.

Up in Rachael's long front room a low fire and two lamps shaded with orange silk gave all the light, so that the corners were full of deep and somnolent shadows. The hostess, moving about in a dark-figured gown of loose chiffon, seemed to accentuate the already sensuous atmosphere. For a while they were all four together, tasting the sandwiches that waited on the tea table—then Gloria found herself alone with Captain Collins on the fireside lounge; Rachael and Captain Wolf had withdrawn to the other side of the room, where they were conversing in subdued voices.

"I wish you weren't married," said Collins, his face a ludicrous travesty of "in all seriousness."

"Why?" She held out her glass to be filled with a high-ball.

"Don't drink any more," he urged her, frowning.

"Why not?"

"You'd be nicer—if you didn't."

Gloria caught suddenly the intended suggestion of the remark, the atmosphere he was attempting to create.

She wanted to laugh—yet she realized that there was nothing to laugh at. She had been enjoying the evening, and she had no desire to go home—at the same time it hurt her pride to be flirted with on just that level.

"Pour me another drink," she insisted.

"Please——"

"Oh, don't be ridiculous!" she cried in exasperation.

"Very well." He yielded with ill grace.

Then his arm was about her again, and again she made no protest. But when his pink cheek came close she leaned away.

"You're awfully sweet," he said with an aimless air.

She began to sing softly, wishing now that he would take down his arm. Suddenly her eye fell on an intimate scene across the room—Rachael and Captain Wolf were engrossed in a long kiss. Gloria shivered slightly—she knew not why. . . . Pink face approached again.

"You shouldn't look at them," he whispered. Almost immediately his other arm was around her . . . his breath was on her cheek. Again absurdity triumphed over disgust, and her laugh was a weapon that needed no edge of words.

"Oh, I thought you were a sport," he was saying.

"What's a sport?"

"Why, a person that likes to—to enjoy life."

"Is kissing you generally considered a joyful affair?"

They were interrupted as Rachael and Captain Wolf appeared suddenly before them.

"It's late, Gloria," said Rachael—she was flushed and her hair was dishevelled. "You'd better stay here all night."

For an instant Gloria thought the officers were being

dismissed. Then she understood, and, understanding, got to her feet as casually as she was able.

Uncomprehendingly Rachael continued:

"You can have the room just off this one. I can lend you everything you need."

Collins's eyes implored her like a dog's; Captain Wolf's arm had settled familiarly around Rachael's waist; they were waiting.

But the lure of promiscuity, colorful, various, labyrinthine, and ever a little odorous and stale, had no call or promise for Gloria. Had she so desired she would have remained, without hesitation, without regret; as it was she could face coolly the six hostile and offended eyes that followed her out into the hall with forced politeness and hollow words.

"*He* wasn't even sport enough to try to take me home," she thought in the taxi, and then with a quick surge of resentment: "How *utter*ly common!"

Gallantry

In February she had an experience of quite a different sort. Tudor Baird, an ancient flame, a young man whom at one time she had fully intended to marry, came to New York by way of the Aviation Corps, and called upon her. They went several times to the theatre, and within a week, to her great enjoyment, he was as much in love with her as ever. Quite deliberately she brought it about, realizing too late that she had done a mischief. He reached the point of sitting with her in miserable silence whenever they went out together.

A Scroll and Keys man at Yale, he possessed the correct reticences of a "good egg," the correct notions of chivalry and *noblesse oblige*—and, of course but unfortunately, the correct biases and the correct lack of ideas—all those traits which Anthony had taught her to despise, but which, nevertheless, she rather admired. Unlike the majority of his type, she found that he was not a bore. He was handsome, witty in a light way, and when she was with him she felt that because of some quality he possessed—call it stupidity, loyalty, sentimentality, or something not quite as definite as any of the three—he would have done anything in his power to please her.

He told her this among other things, very correctly and with a ponderous manliness that masked a real suffering. Loving him not at all she grew sorry for him and kissed him sentimentally one night because he was so charming, a relic of a vanishing generation which lived a priggish and graceful illusion and was being replaced by less gallant fools. Afterward she was glad she had kissed him, for next day when his plane fell fifteen hundred feet at Mineola a piece of a gasolene engine smashed through his heart.

Gloria Alone

When Mr. Haight told her that the trial would not take place until autumn she decided that without telling Anthony she would go into the movies. When he saw her successful, both histrionically and financially, when he saw that she could have her will of Joseph Bloeckman, yielding nothing in return, he would lose his silly prejudices. She lay awake half one night planning her career and enjoying her successes in anticipation, and the next morning she called up "Films Par Excellence." Mr. Bloeckman was in Europe.

But the idea had gripped her so strongly this time that she decided to go the rounds of the moving picture employment agencies. As so often had been the case, her sense of smell worked against her good intentions.

The employment agency smelt as though it had been dead a very long time. She waited five minutes inspecting her unprepossessing competitors—then she walked briskly out into the farthest recesses of Central Park and remained so long that she caught a cold. She was trying to air the employment agency out of her walking suit.

In the spring she began to gather from Anthony's letters—not from any one in particular but from their culminative effect—that he did not want her to come South. Curiously repeated excuses that seemed to haunt him by their very insufficiency occurred with Freudian regularity. He set them down in each letter as though he feared he had forgotten them the last time, as though it were desperately necessary to impress her with them. And the dilutions of his letters with affectionate diminutives began to be mechanical and unspontaneous—almost as though, having completed the letter, he had looked it over and literally stuck them in, like epigrams in an Oscar Wilde play. She jumped to the solution, rejected it, was angry and depressed by turns—finally she shut her mind to it proudly, and allowed an increasing coolness to creep into her end of the correspondence.

Of late she had found a good deal to occupy her attention. Several aviators whom she had met through Tudor Baird came into New York to see her and two other ancient beaux turned up, stationed at Camp Dix. As these men were ordered overseas they, so to speak, handed her down to their friends. But after another rather disagreeable experience with a potential Captain Collins she made it plain that when any one was introduced to her he should be under no misapprehensions as to her status and personal intentions.

When summer came she learned, like Anthony, to watch the officers' casualty list, taking a sort of melancholy pleasure in hearing of the death of some one with whom she had once danced a german and in identifying by name the younger brothers of former suitors—thinking, as the drive toward Paris progressed, that here at length went the world to inevitable and well-merited destruction.

She was twenty-seven. Her birthday fled by scarcely noticed. Years before it had frightened her when she became twenty, to some extent when she reached twenty-six—but now she looked in the glass with calm self-approval seeing the British freshness of her complexion and her figure boyish and slim as of old.

She tried not to think of Anthony. It was as though she were writing to a stranger. She told her friends that he had been made a corporal and was annoyed when they were politely unimpressed. One night she wept because she was sorry for him—had he been even slightly responsive she would have gone to him without hesitation on the first train—whatever he was doing he needed to be taken care of spiritually, and she felt that now she would be able to do even that. Recently, without his continual drain upon her moral strength she found herself wonderfully revived. Before he left she had been inclined through sheer association to brood on her wasted opportunities—now she returned to her normal state of mind, strong, disdainful, existing each day for each day's worth. She bought a doll and dressed it; one week she wept over "Ethan Frome"; the next she revelled in some novels of Galsworthy's, whom she liked for his power of recreating, by spring in darkness, that illusion of young romantic love to which women look forever forward and forever back.

In October Anthony's letters multiplied, became

almost frantic—then suddenly ceased. For a worried month it needed all her powers of control to refrain from leaving immediately for Mississippi. Then a telegram told her that he had been in the hospital and that she could expect him in New York within ten days. Like a figure in a dream he came back into her life across the ballroom on that November evening—and all through long hours that held familiar gladness she took him close to her breast, nursing an illusion of happiness and security she had not thought that she would know again.

Discomfiture of the Generals

After a week Anthony's regiment went back to the Mississippi camp to be discharged. The officers shut themselves up in the compartments on the Pullman cars and drank the whiskey they had bought in New York, and in the coaches the soldiers got as drunk as possible also—and pretended whenever the train stopped at a village that they were just returned from France, where they had practically put an end to the German army. As they all wore overseas caps and claimed that they had not had time to have their gold service stripes sewed on, the yokelry of the seaboard were much impressed and asked them how they liked the trenches—to which they replied "Oh, *boy!*" with great smacking of tongues and shaking of heads. Some one took a piece of chalk and scrawled on the side of the train, "We won the war—now we're going home," and the officers laughed and let it stay. They were all getting what swagger they could out of this ignominious return.

As they rumbled on toward camp, Anthony was uneasy lest he should find Dot awaiting him patiently at the station. To his relief he neither saw nor heard anything of her and thinking that were she still in town she would certainly attempt to communicate with him, he concluded that she had gone—whither he neither knew nor cared. He wanted only to return to Gloria—Gloria reborn and wonderfully alive. When eventually he was discharged he left his company on the rear of a great truck with a crowd who had given tolerant, almost sentimental, cheers for their officers, especially for Captain Dunning. The captain, on his part, had addressed them with tears in his eyes as to the pleasure, etc., and the work, etc., and time not wasted, etc., and duty, etc. It was very dull and human; having given ear to it Anthony, whose mind was freshened by his week in New York, renewed his deep loathing for the military profession and all it connoted. In their childish hearts two out of every three professional officers considered that wars were made for armies and not armies for wars. He rejoiced to see general and field-officers riding desolately about the barren camp deprived of their commands. He rejoiced to hear the men in his company laugh scornfully at the inducements tendered them to remain in the army. They were to attend "schools." He knew what these "schools" were.

Two days later he was with Gloria in New York.

Another Winter

Late one February afternoon Anthony came into the apartment and groping through the little hall, pitch-dark in the winter dusk, found Gloria sitting by the window. She turned as he came in.

"What did Mr. Haight have to say?" she asked listlessly.

"Nothing," he answered, "usual thing. Next month, perhaps."

She looked at him closely; her ear attuned to his voice caught the slightest thickness in the dissyllable.

"You've been drinking," she remarked dispassionately.

"Couple glasses."

"Oh."

He yawned in the armchair and there was a moment's silence between them. Then she demanded suddenly:

"Did you go to Mr. Haight? Tell me the truth."

"No." He smiled weakly. "As a matter of fact I didn't have time."

"I thought you didn't go. . . . He sent for you."

"I don't give a damn. I'm sick of waiting around his office. You'd think he was doing *me* a favor." He glanced at Gloria as though expecting moral support, but she had turned back to her contemplation of the dubious and unprepossessing out-of-doors.

"I feel rather weary of life to-day," he offered tentatively. Still she was silent. "I met a fellow and we talked in the Biltmore bar."

The dusk had suddenly deepened but neither of them made any move to turn on the lights. Lost in heaven knew what contemplation, they sat there until a flurry of snow drew a languid sigh from Gloria.

"What've you been doing?" he asked, finding the silence oppressive.

"Reading a magazine—all full of idiotic articles by prosperous authors about how terrible it is for poor people to buy silk shirts. And while I was reading it I could think of nothing except how I wanted a gray squirrel coat—and how we can't afford one."

"Yes, we can."

"Oh, no."

"Oh, yes! If you want a fur coat you can have one."

Her voice coming through the dark held an implication of scorn.

"You mean we can sell another bond?"

"If necessary. I don't want you to go without things. We have spent a lot, though, since I've been back."

"Oh, shut up!" she said in irritation.

"Why?"

"Because I'm sick and tired of hearing you talk about what we've spent or what we've done. You came back two months ago and we've been on some sort of a party practically every night since. We've both wanted to go out, and we've gone. Well, you haven't heard me complain, have you? But all you do is whine, whine, whine. I don't care any more what we do or what becomes of us and at least I'm consistent. But I will *not* tolerate your complaining and calamity-howling——"

"You're not very pleasant yourself sometimes, you know."

"I'm under no obligations to be. You're not making any attempt to make things different."

"But I am——"

"Huh! Seems to me I've heard that before. This morning you weren't going to touch another thing to drink until you'd gotten a position. And you didn't even have the spunk to go to Mr. Haight when he sent for you about the suit."

Anthony got to his feet and switched on the lights.

"See here!" he cried, blinking, "I'm getting sick of that sharp tongue of yours."

"Well, what are you going to do about it?"

"Do you think *I'm* particularly happy?" he continued, ignoring her question. "Do you think I don't know we're not living as we ought to?"

In an instant Gloria stood trembling beside him.

"I won't *stand* it!" she burst out. "I won't be lectured to. You and your suffering! You're just a pitiful weakling and you always have been!"

They faced one another idiotically, each of them unable to impress the other, each of them tremendously, achingly, bored. Then she went into the bedroom and shut the door behind her.

His return had brought into the foreground all their pre-bellum exasperations. Prices had risen alarmingly and in perverse ratio their income had shrunk to a little over half of its original size. There had been the large retainer's fee to Mr. Haight; there were stocks bought at one hundred, now down to thirty and forty and other investments that were not paying at all. During the previous spring Gloria had been given the alternative of leaving the apartment or of signing a year's lease at two hundred and twenty-five a month. She had signed it. Inevitably as the necessity for economy had increased they found themselves as a pair quite unable to save. The old policy of prevarication was resorted to. Weary of their incapabilities they chattered of what they would do—oh—to-morrow, of how they would "stop going on parties" and of how Anthony would go to work. But when dark came down Gloria, accustomed to an engagement every night, would feel the ancient restlessness creeping over her. She would stand in the doorway of the bedroom, chewing furiously at her fingers and sometimes meeting Anthony's eyes as he glanced up from his book. Then the telephone, and her nerves would relax, she would answer it with ill-concealed eagerness. Some one was coming up "for just a few minutes"—and oh, the weariness of pretense, the appearance of the wine table, the revival of their jaded spirits—and the awakening, like the mid-point of a sleepless night in which they moved.

As the winter passed with the march of the returning troops along Fifth Avenue they became more and more aware that since Anthony's return their relations had entirely changed. After that reflowering of tenderness and passion each of them had returned into some solitary dream unshared by the other and what endearments passed between them passed, it seemed, from empty heart to empty heart, echoing hollowly the departure of what they knew at last was gone.

Anthony had again made the rounds of the metropolitan newspapers and had again been refused encouragement by a motley of office boys, telephone girls, and city editors. The word was: "We're keeping any vacancies open for our own men who are still in France." Then, late in March, his eye fell on an advertisement in the morning paper and in consequence he found at last the semblance of an occupation.

YOU CAN SELL! ! !

Why not earn while you learn?

Our salesmen make $50–$200 *weekly.*

There followed an address on Madison Avenue, and instructions to appear at one o'clock that afternoon. Gloria, glancing over his shoulder after one of their usual late breakfasts, saw him regarding it idly.

"Why don't you try it?" she suggested.

"Oh—it's one of these crazy schemes."

"It might not be. At least it'd be experience."

At her urging he went at one o'clock to the appointed address, where he found himself one of a dense miscellany of men waiting in front of the door. They ranged from a messenger-boy evidently misusing his company's time to an immemorial individual with a gnarled body and a gnarled cane. Some of the men were seedy, with sunken cheeks and puffy pink eyes—others were young, possibly still in high school. After a jostled fifteen minutes during which they all eyed one another with apathetic suspicion there appeared a smart young shepherd clad in a "waist-line" suit and wearing the manner of an assistant rector who herded them up-stairs into a large room, which resembled a school-room and contained innumerable desks. Here the prospective salesmen sat down—and again waited. After an interval a platform at the end of the hall was clouded with half a dozen sober but sprightly men who, with one exception, took seats in a semicircle facing the audience.

The exception was the man who seemed the soberest, the most sprightly and the youngest of the lot, and who advanced to the front of the platform. The audience scrutinized him hopefully. He was rather small and rather pretty, with the commercial rather than the thespian sort of prettiness. He had straight blond bushy brows and eyes that were almost preposterously honest, and as he reached the edge of his rostrum he seemed to throw these eyes out into the audience, simultaneously extending his arm with two fingers outstretched. Then while he rocked himself to a state of balance an expectant silence settled over the hall. With perfect assurance the young man had taken his listeners in hand and his words when they came were steady and confident and of the school of "straight from the shoulder."

"Men!"—he began, and paused. The word died with a prolonged echo at the end of the hall, the faces regarding him, hopefully, cynically, wearily, were alike arrested, engrossed. Six hundred eyes were turned slightly upward. With an even graceless flow that reminded Anthony of the rolling of bowling balls he launched himself into the sea of exposition.

"This bright and sunny morning you picked up your favorite newspaper and you found an advertisement which made the plain, unadorned statement that *you* could sell. That was all it said—it didn't say 'what,' it didn't say 'how,' it didn't say 'why.' It just made one single solitary assertion that *you* and *you* and *you*"—business of pointing—"could sell. Now my job isn't to make a success of you, because every man is born a success, he makes himself a failure; it's not to teach you how to talk, because each man is a natural orator and only makes himself a clam; my business is to tell you one thing in a way that will make you *know* it—it's to tell you that *you* and *you* and *you* have the heritage of money and prosperity waiting for you to come and claim it."

At this point an Irishman of saturnine appearance rose from his desk near the rear of the hall and went out.

"That man thinks he'll go look for it in the beer parlor around the corner. (Laughter.) He won't find it there. Once upon a time I looked for it there myself (laughter), but that was before I did what every one of you men no matter how young or how old, how poor or how rich (a faint ripple of satirical laughter), can do. It was before I found—my*self!*

"Now I wonder if any of you men know what a 'Heart Talk' is. A 'Heart Talk' is a little book in which I started, about five years ago, to write down what I had discovered were the principal reasons for a man's failure and the principal reasons for a man's success—frcm John D. Rockerfeller back to John D. Napoleon (laughter), and before that, back in the days when Abel sold his birthright for a mess of pottage. There are now one hundred of these 'Heart Talks.' Those of you who are sincere, who are interested in our proposition, above all who are dissatisfied with the way things are breaking for you at present will be handed one to take home with you as you go out yonder door this afternoon.

"Now in my own pocket I have four letters just received concerning 'Heart Talks.' These letters have names signed to them that are familiar in every household in the U. S. A. Listen to this one from Detroit:

DEAR MR. CARLETON:

I want to order three thousand more copies of "Heart Talks" for distribution among my salesmen. They have done more for getting work out of the men than any bonus proposition ever considered. I read them myself constantly, and I desire to heartily congratulate you on getting at the roots of the biggest problem that faces our generation to-day—the problem of salesmanship. The rock bottom on which the country is founded is the problem of salesmanship. With many felicitations I am

Yours very cordially,

HENRY W. TERRAL.

He brought the name out in three long booming triumphancies—pausing for it to produce its magical effect. Then he read two more letters, one from a manufacturer of vacuum cleaners and one from the president of the Great Northern Doily Company.

"And now," he continued, "I'm going to tell you in a few words what the proposition is that's going to *make* those of you who go into it in the right spirit. Simply put, it's this: 'Heart Talks' have been incorporated as a company. We're going to put these little pamphlets into the hands of every big business organization, every salesman, and every man who *knows*—I don't say 'thinks,' I say '*knows*'—that he can sell! We are offering some of the stock of the 'Heart Talks' concern upon the market, and in order that the distribution may be as wide as possible, and in order also that we can furnish a living, concrete, flesh-and-blood example of what salesmanship is, or rather what it may be, we're going to give those of you who are the real thing a chance to sell that stock. Now, I don't care what you've tried to sell before or how you've tried to sell it. It don't matter how old you are or how young you are. I only want to know two things—first, do you *want* success, and, second, will you work for it?

"My name is Sammy Carleton. Not 'Mr.' Carleton, but just plain Sammy. I'm a regular no-nonsense man with no fancy frills about me. I want you to call me Sammy.

"Now this is all I'm going to say to you to-day. To-morrow I want those of you who have thought it over and have read the copy of 'Heart Talks' which will be given to you at the door, to come back to this same room at this same time, then we'll go into the proposition further and I'll explain to you what I've found the principles of success to be. I'm going to make you *feel* that *you* and *you* and *you* can sell!"

Mr. Carleton's voice echoed for a moment through the hall and then died away. To the stamping of many feet Anthony was pushed and jostled with the crowd out of the room.

FURTHER ADVENTURES WITH "HEART TALKS"

With an accompaniment of ironic laughter Anthony told Gloria the story of his commercial adventure. But she listened without amusement.

"You're going to give up again?" she demanded coldly.

"Why—you don't expect me to——"

"I never expected anything of you."

He hesitated.

"Well—I can't see the slightest benefit in laughing myself sick over this sort of affair. If there's anything older than the old story, it's the new twist."

It required an astonishing amount of moral energy on Gloria's part to intimidate him into returning, and when he reported next day, somewhat depressed from his perusal of the senile bromides skittishly set forth in "Heart Talks on Ambition," he found only fifty of the original three hundred awaiting the appearance of the vital and compelling Sammy Carleton. Mr. Carleton's powers of vitality and compulsion were this time exercised in elucidating that magnificent piece of speculation—how to sell. It seemed that the approved method was to state one's proposition and then to say not "And now, will you buy?"—this was not the way—oh, no!—the way was to state one's proposition and then, having reduced one's adversary to a state of exhaustion, to deliver oneself of the categorical imperative: "Now see here! You've taken up my time explaining this matter to you. You've admitted my points—all I want to ask is how many do you want?"

As Mr. Carleton piled assertion upon assertion Anthony began to feel a sort of disgusted confidence in him. The man appeared to know what he was talking about. Obviously prosperous, he had risen to the position of instructing others. It did not occur to Anthony that the type of man who attains commercial success seldom knows how or why, and, as in his grandfather's case, when he ascribes reasons, the reasons are generally inaccurate and absurd.

Anthony noted that of the numerous old men who had answered the original advertisement, only two had returned, and that among the thirty odd who assembled on the third day to get actual selling instructions from Mr. Carleton, only one gray head was in evidence. These thirty were eager converts; with their mouths they followed the working of Mr. Carleton's mouth; they swayed in their seats with enthusiasm, and in the intervals of his talk they spoke to each other in tense approving whispers. Yet of the chosen few who, in the words of Mr. Carleton, "were determined to get those deserts that rightly and truly belonged to them," less than half a dozen combined even a modicum of personal appearance with that great gift of being a "pusher." But they were told that they were all natural pushers —it was merely necessary that they should believe with a sort of savage passion in what they were selling. He even urged each one to buy some stock himself, if possible, in order to increase his own sincerity.

On the fifth day then, Anthony sallied into the street with all the sensations of a man wanted by the police. Acting according to instructions he selected a tall office building in order that he might ride to the top story and work downward, stopping in every office that had a name on the door. But at the last minute he hesitated. Perhaps it would be more practicable to acclimate himself to the chilly atmosphere which he felt was awaiting him by trying a few offices on, say, Madison Avenue. He went into an arcade that seemed only semi-prosperous, and seeing a sign which read Percy B. Weatherbee, Architect, he opened the door heroically and entered. A starchy young woman looked up questioningly.

"Can I see Mr. Weatherbee?" He wondered if his voice sounded tremulous.

She laid her hand tentatively on the telephone-receiver.

"What's the name, please?"

"He wouldn't—ah—know me. He wouldn't know my name."

"What's your business with him? You an insurance agent?"

"Oh, no, nothing like that!" denied Anthony hurriedly. "Oh, no. It's a—it's a personal matter." He wondered if he should have said this. It had all sounded so simple when Mr. Carleton had enjoined his flock: "Don't allow yourself to be kept out! Show them you've made up your mind to talk to them, and they'll listen."

The girl succumbed to Anthony's pleasant, melancholy face, and in a moment the door to the inner room opened and admitted a tall, splay-footed man with slicked hair. He approached Anthony with ill-concealed impatience.

"You wanted to see me on a personal matter?"

Anthony quailed.

"I wanted to talk to you," he said defiantly.

"About what?"

"It'll take some time to explain."

"Well, what's it about?" Mr. Weatherbee's voice indicated rising irritation.

Then Anthony, straining at each word, each syllable, began:

"I don't know whether or not you've ever heard of a series of pamphlets called 'Heart Talks'——"

"Good grief!" cried Percy B. Weatherbee, Architect, "are you trying to touch my heart?"

"No, it's business. 'Heart Talks' have been incorporated and we're putting some shares on the market——"

His voice faded slowly off, harassed by a fixed and contemptuous stare from his unwilling prey. For another minute he struggled on, increasingly sensitive, entangled in his own words. His confidence oozed from him in great retching emanations that seemed to be sections of his own body. Almost mercifully Percy B. Weatherbee, Architect, terminated the interview:

"Good grief!" he exploded in disgust, "and you call that a *personal* matter!" He whipped about and strode into his private office, banging the door behind him. Not daring to look at the stenographer, Anthony in some shameful and mysterious way got himself from the room. Perspiring profusely he stood in the hall wondering why they didn't come and arrest him; in every hurried look he discerned infallibly a glance of scorn.

After an hour and with the help of two strong whiskies he brought himself up to another attempt. He walked into a plumber's shop, but when he mentioned his business the plumber began pulling on his coat in a great hurry, gruffly announcing that he had to go to lunch. Anthony remarked politely that it was futile to try to sell a man anything when he was hungry, and the plumber heartily agreed.

This episode encouraged Anthony; he tried to think that had the plumber not been bound for lunch he would at least have listened.

Passing by a few glittering and formidable bazaars he entered a grocery store. A talkative proprietor told him that before buying any stocks he was going to see how the armistice affected the market. To Anthony this seemed almost unfair. In Mr. Carleton's salesman's Utopia the only reason prospective buyers ever gave for not purchasing stock was that they doubted it to be a promising investment. Obviously a man in that state was almost ludicrously easy game, to be brought down merely by the judicious application of the correct selling points. But these men—why, actually they weren't considering buying anything at all.

Anthony took several more drinks before he approached his fourth man, a real-estate agent; nevertheless, he was floored with a coup as decisive as a syllogism. The real-estate agent said that he had three brothers in the investment business. Viewing himself as a breaker-up of homes Anthony apologized and went out.

After another drink he conceived the brilliant plan of selling the stock to the bartenders along Lexington

Avenue. This occupied several hours, for it was necessary to take a few drinks in each place in order to get the proprietor in the proper frame of mind to talk business. But the bartenders one and all contended that if they had any money to buy bonds they would not be bartenders. It was as though they had all convened and decided upon that rejoinder. As he approached a dark and soggy five o'clock he found that they were developing a still more annoying tendency to turn him off with a jest.

At five, then, with a tremendous effort at concentration he decided that he must put more variety into his canvassing. He selected a medium-sized delicatessen store, and went in. He felt, illuminatingly, that the thing to do was to cast a spell not only over the storekeeper but over all the customers as well—and perhaps through the psychology of the herd instinct they would buy as an astounded and immediately convinced whole.

"Af'ernoon," he began in a loud thick voice. "Ga l'il prop'sition."

If he had wanted silence he obtained it. A sort of awe descended upon the half-dozen women marketing and upon the gray-haired ancient who in cap and apron was slicing chicken.

Anthony pulled a batch of papers from his flapping brief case and waved them cheerfully.

"Buy a bon'," he suggested, "good as liberty bon'!" The phrase pleased him and he elaborated upon it. "Better'n liberty bon'. Every one these bon's worth *two* liberty bon's." His mind made a hiatus and skipped to his peroration, which he delivered with appropriate gestures, these being somewhat marred by the necessity of clinging to the counter with one or both hands. "Now see here. You taken up my time. I don't want know *why* you won't buy. I just want you say *why*. Want you say *how many!*"

At this point they should have approached him with check-books and fountain pens in hand. Realizing that they must have missed a cue Anthony, with the instincts of an actor, went back and repeated his finale.

"Now see here! You taken up my time. You followed prop'sition. You agreed 'th reasonin'? Now, all I want from *you* is, how many lib'ty bon's?"

"See here!" broke in a new voice. A portly man whose face was adorned with symmetrical scrolls of yellow hair had come out of a glass cage in the rear of the store and was bearing down upon Anthony. "See here, you!"

"How many?" repeated the salesman sternly. "You taken up my time——"

"Hey, you!" cried the proprietor, "I'll have you taken up by the police."

"You mos' cert'nly won't!" returned Anthony with fine defiance. "All I want know is how many."

From here and there in the store went up little clouds of comment and expostulation.

"How terrible!"

"He's a raving maniac."

"He's disgracefully drunk."

The proprietor grasped Anthony's arm sharply.

"Get out, or I'll call a policeman."

Some relics of rationality moved Anthony to nod and replace his bonds clumsily in the case.

"How many?" he reiterated doubtfully.

"The whole force if necessary!" thundered his adversary, his yellow mustache trembling fiercely.

"Sell 'em all a bon'."

With this Anthony turned, bowed gravely to his late auditors, and wabbled from the store. He found a taxicab at the corner and rode home to the apartment. There he fell sound asleep on the sofa, and so Gloria found him, his breath filling the air with an unpleasant pungency, his hand still clutching his open brief case.

Except when Anthony was drinking, his range of sensation had become less than that of a healthy old man and when prohibition came in July he found that, among those who could afford it, there was more drinking than ever before. One's host now brought out a bottle upon the slightest pretext. The tendency to display liquor was a manifestation of the same instinct that led a man to deck his wife with jewels. To have liquor was a boast, almost a badge of respectability.

In the mornings Anthony awoke tired, nervous, and worried. Halcyon summer twilights and the purple chill of morning alike left him unresponsive. Only for a brief moment every day in the warmth and renewed life of a first high-ball did his mind turn to those opalescent dreams of future pleasure—the mutual heritage of the happy and the damned. But this was only for a little while. As he grew drunker the dreams faded and he became a confused spectre, moving in odd crannies of his own mind, full of unexpected devices, harshly contemptuous at best and reaching sodden and dispirited depths. One night in June he had quarrelled violently with Maury over a matter of the utmost triviality. He remembered dimly next morning that it had been about a broken pint bottle of champagne. Maury had told him to sober up and Anthony's feelings had been hurt, so with an attempted gesture of dignity he had risen from the table and seizing Gloria's arm half led, half shamed her into a taxicab outside, leaving Maury with three dinners ordered and tickets for the opera.

This sort of semi-tragic fiasco had become so usual that when they occurred he was no longer stirred into making amends. If Gloria protested—and of late she was more likely to sink into a contemptuous silence—he would either engage in a bitter defense of himself or else stalk dismally from the apartment. Never since the incident on the station platform at Redgate had he laid his hands on her in anger—though he was withheld often only by some instinct that itself made him tremble with rage. Just as he still cared more for her than for any other creature, so did he more intensely and frequently hate her.

So far, the judges of the Appellate Division had failed to hand down a decision, but after another postponement they finally affirmed the decree of the lower court—two justices dissenting. A notice of appeal was served upon Edward Shuttleworth. The case was going to the court of last resort, and they were in for another interminable wait. Six months, perhaps a year. It had grown enormously unreal to them, remote and uncertain as heaven.

Throughout the previous winter one small matter had been a subtle and omnipresent irritant—the question of Gloria's gray fur coat. At that time women enveloped in long squirrel wraps could be seen every few yards along Fifth Avenue. The women were converted to the shape of tops. They seemed porcine and obscene; they resembled kept women in the concealing richness, the feminine animality of the garment. Yet—Gloria wanted a gray squirrel coat.

Discussing the matter—or, rather, arguing it, for even more than in the first year of their marriage did every discussion take the form of bitter debate full of such phrases as "most certainly," "utterly outrageous," "it's so, nevertheless," and the ultra-emphatic "regardless"—they concluded that they could not afford it. And so gradually it began to stand as a symbol of their growing financial anxiety.

To Gloria the shrinkage of their income was a remarkable phenomenon, without explanation or precedent—that it could happen at all within the space of five years seemed almost an intended cruelty, conceived and executed by a sardonic God. When they were married seventy-five hundred a year had seemed ample for a young couple, especially when augmented by the expectation of many millions. Gloria had failed to realize that it was decreasing not only in amount but in purchasing power until the payment of Mr. Haight's retaining fee of fifteen thousand dollars made the fact suddenly and startlingly obvious. When Anthony was drafted they had calculated their income at over four hundred a month, with the dollar even then decreasing in value, but on his return to New York they discovered an even more alarming condition of affairs. They were receiving only forty-five hundred a year from their investments. And though the suit over the will moved ahead of them like a persistent mirage and the financial danger-mark loomed up in the near distance they found, nevertheless, that living within their income was impossible.

So Gloria went without the squirrel coat and every day upon Fifth Avenue she was a little conscious of her well-worn, half-length leopard skin, now hopelessly old-fashioned. Every other month they sold a bond, yet when the bills were paid it left only enough to be gulped down hungrily by their current expenses. Anthony's calculations showed that their capital would last about seven years longer. So Gloria's heart was very bitter, for in one week, on a prolonged hysterical party during which Anthony whimsically divested himself of coat, vest, and shirt in a theatre and was assisted out by a posse of ushers, they spent twice what the gray squirrel coat would have cost.

It was November, Indian summer rather, and a warm,

warm night—which was unnecessary, for the work of the summer was done. Babe Ruth had smashed the home-run record for the first time and Jack Dempsey had broken Jess Willard's cheek-bone out in Ohio. Over in Europe the usual number of children had swollen stomachs from starvation, and the diplomats were at their customary business of making the world safe for new wars. In New York City the proletariat were being "disciplined," and the odds on Harvard were generally quoted at five to three. Peace had come down in earnest, the beginning of new days.

Up in the bedroom of the apartment on Fifty-seventh Street Gloria lay upon her bed and tossed from side to side, sitting up at intervals to throw off a superfluous cover and once asking Anthony, who was lying awake beside her, to bring her a glass of ice-water. "Be sure and put ice in it," she said with insistence; "it isn't cold enough the way it comes from the faucet."

Looking through the frail curtains she could see the rounded moon over the roofs and beyond it on the sky the yellow glow from Times Square—and watching the two incongruous lights, her mind worked over an emotion, or rather an interwoven complex of emotions, that had occupied it through the day, and the day before that and back to the last time when she could remember having thought clearly and consecutively about anything—which must have been while Anthony was in the army.

She would be twenty-nine in February. The month assumed an ominous and inescapable significance—making her wonder, through these nebulous half-fevered hours whether after all she had not wasted her faintly tired beauty, whether there was such a thing as use for any quality bounded by a harsh and inevitable mortality.

Years before, when she was twenty-one, she had written in her diary: "Beauty is only to be admired, only to be loved—to be harvested carefully and then flung at a chosen lover like a gift of roses. It seems to me, so far as I can judge clearly at all, that my beauty should be used like that. . . ."

And now, all this November day, all this desolate day, under a sky dirty and white, Gloria had been thinking that perhaps she had been wrong. To preserve the integrity of her first gift she had looked no more for love. When the first flame and ecstasy had grown dim, sunk down, departed, she had begun preserving—what? It puzzled her that she no longer knew just what she was preserving—a sentimental memory or some profound and fundamental concept of honor. She was doubting now whether there had been any moral issue involved in her way of life—to walk unworried and unregretful along the gayest of all possible lanes and to keep her pride by being always herself and doing what it seemed beautiful that she should do. From the first little boy in an Eton collar whose "girl" she had been, down to the latest casual man whose eyes had grown alert and appreciative as they rested upon her, there was needed only that matchless candor she could throw into a look or clothe with an inconsequent clause—for she had talked always in broken clauses—to weave about her immeasurable illusions, immeasurable distances, immeasurable light. To create souls in men, to create fine happiness and fine despair she must remain deeply proud—proud to be inviolate, proud also to be melting, to be passionate and possessed.

She knew that in her breast she had never wanted children. The reality, the earthiness, the intolerable sentiment of child-bearing, the menace to her beauty—had appalled her. She wanted to exist only as a conscious flower, prolonging and preserving itself. Her sentimentality could cling fiercely to her own illusions, but her ironic soul whispered that motherhood was also the privilege of the female baboon. So her dreams were of ghostly children only—the early, the perfect symbols of her early and perfect love for Anthony.

In the end then, her beauty was all that never failed her. She had never seen beauty like her own. What it meant ethically or æsthetically faded before the gorgeous concreteness of her pink-and-white feet, the clean perfectness of her body, and the baby mouth that was like the material symbol of a kiss.

She would be twenty-nine in February. As the long night waned she grew supremely conscious that she and beauty were going to make use of these next three months. At first she was not sure for what, but the problem resolved itself gradually into the old lure of the screen. She was in earnest now. No material want could have moved her as this fear moved her. No matter for Anthony, Anthony the poor in spirit, the weak and broken man with bloodshot eyes, for whom she still had moments of tenderness. No matter. She would be twenty-nine in February—a hundred days, so many days; she would go to Bloeckman to-morrow.

With the decision came relief. It cheered her that in some manner the illusion of beauty could be sustained, or preserved perhaps in celluloid after the reality had vanished. Well—to-morrow.

The next day she felt weak and ill. She tried to go out, and saved herself from collapse only by clinging to a mail box near the front door. The Martinique elevator boy helped her up-stairs, and she waited on the bed for Anthony's return without energy to unhook her brassière.

For five days she was down with influenza, which,

just as the month turned the corner into winter, ripened into double pneumonia. In the feverish perambulations of her mind she prowled through a house of bleak unlighted rooms hunting for her mother. All she wanted was to be a little girl, to be efficiently taken care of by some yielding yet superior power, stupider and steadier than herself. It seemed that the only lover she had ever wanted was a lover in a dream.

"Odi Profanum Vulgus"

One day in the midst of Gloria's illness there occurred a curious incident that puzzled Miss McGovern, the trained nurse, for some time afterward. It was noon, but the room in which the patient lay was dark and quiet. Miss McGovern was standing near the bed mixing some medicine, when Mrs. Patch, who had apparently been sound asleep, sat up and began to speak vehemently:

"Millions of people," she said, "swarming like rats, chattering like apes, smelling like all hell . . . monkeys! Or lice, I suppose. For one really exquisite palace . . . on Long Island, say—or even in Greenwich . . . for one palace full of pictures from the Old World and exquisite things—with avenues of trees and green lawns and a view of the blue sea, and lovely people about in slick dresses . . . I'd sacrifice a hundred thousand of them, a million of them." She raised her hand feebly and snapped her fingers. "I care nothing for them—understand me?"

The look she bent upon Miss McGovern at the conclusion of this speech was curiously elfin, curiously intent. Then she gave a short little laugh polished with scorn, and tumbling backward fell off again to sleep.

Miss McGovern was bewildered. She wondered what were the hundred thousand things that Mrs. Patch would sacrifice for her palace. Dollars, she supposed—yet it had not sounded exactly like dollars.

The Movies

It was February, seven days before her birthday, and the great snow that had filled up the cross-streets as dirt fills the cracks in a floor had turned to slush and was being escorted to the gutters by the hoses of the street-cleaning department. The wind, none the less bitter for being casual, whipped in through the open windows of the living room bearing with it the dismal secrets of the areaway and clearing the Patch apartment of stale smoke in its cheerless circulation.

Gloria, wrapped in a warm kimona, came into the chilly room and taking up the telephone receiver called Joseph Bloeckman.

"Do you mean Mr. Joseph *Black?*" demanded the telephone girl at "Films Par Excellence."

"Bloeckman, Joseph Bloeckman. B-l-o——"

"Mr. Joseph Bloeckman has changed his name to Black. Do you want him?"

"Why—yes." She remembered nervously that she had once called him "Blockhead" to his face.

His office was reached by courtesy of two additional female voices; the last was a secretary who took her name. Only with the flow through the transmitter of his own familiar but faintly impersonal tone did she realize that it had been three years since they had met. And he had changed his name to Black.

"Can you see me?" she suggested lightly. "It's on a business matter, really. I'm going into the movies at last—if I can."

"I'm awfully glad. I've always thought you'd like it."

"Do you think you can get me a trial?" she demanded with the arrogance peculiar to all beautiful women, to all women who have ever at any time considered themselves beautiful.

He assured her that it was merely a question of when she wanted the trial. Any time? Well, he'd phone later in the day and let her know a convenient hour. The conversation closed with conventional padding on both sides. Then from three o'clock to five she sat close to the telephone—with no result.

But next morning came a note that contented and excited her:

My dear Gloria:

Just by luck a matter came to my attention that I think will be just suited to you. I would like to see you start with something that would bring you notice. At the same time if a very beautiful girl of your sort is put directly into a picture next to one of the rather shop-worn stars with which every company is afflicted, tongues would very likely wag. But there is a "flapper" part in a Percy B. Debris production that I think would be just suited to you and would bring you notice. Willa Sable plays opposite Gaston Mears in a sort of character part and your part I believe would be her younger sister.

Anyway Percy B. Debris who is directing the picture says if you'll come to the studios day after to-morrow (Thursday) he will run off a test. If ten o'clock is suited to you I will meet you there at that time.

With all good wishes

Ever Faithfully

JOSEPH BLACK.

Gloria had decided that Anthony was to know nothing of this until she had obtained a definite position, and accordingly she was dressed and out of the apartment next morning before he awoke. Her mirror had given her, she thought, much the same account as ever. She wondered if there were any lingering traces of her sickness. She was still slightly under weight, and she had fancied, a few days before, that her cheeks were a trifle thinner—but she felt that those were merely transitory conditions and that on this particular day she looked as fresh as ever. She had bought and charged a new hat, and as the day was warm she had left the leopard skin coat at home.

At the "Films Par Excellence" studios she was announced over the telephone and told that Mr. Black would be down directly. She looked around her. Two girls were being shown about by a little fat man in a slash-pocket coat, and one of them had indicated a stack of thin parcels, piled breast-high against the wall, and extending along for twenty feet.

"That's studio mail," explained the fat man. "Pictures of the stars who are with 'Films Par Excellence.'"

"Oh."

"Each one's autographed by Florence Kelley or Gaston Mears or Mack Dodge—" He winked confidentially. "At least when Minnie McGlook out in Sauk Center gets the picture she wrote for, she *thinks* it's autographed."

"Just a stamp?"

"Sure. It'd take 'em a good eight-hour day to autograph half of 'em. They say Mary Pickford's studio mail costs her fifty thousand a year."

"Say!"

"Sure. Fifty thousand. But it's the best kinda advertising there is——"

They drifted out of earshot and almost immediately Bloeckman appeared—Bloeckman, a dark suave gentleman, gracefully engaged in the middle forties, who greeted her with courteous warmth and told her she had not changed a bit in three years. He led the way into a great hall, as large as an armory and broken intermittently with busy sets and blinding rows of unfamiliar light. Each piece of scenery was marked in large white letters "Gaston Mears Company," "Mack Dodge Company," or simply "Films Par Excellence."

"Ever been in a studio before?"

"Never have."

She liked it. There was no heavy closeness of grease-paint, no scent of soiled and tawdry costumes which years before had revolted her behind the scenes of a musical comedy. This work was done in the clean mornings; the appurtenances seemed rich and gorgeous and new. On a set that was joyous with Manchu hangings a perfect Chinaman was going through a scene according to megaphone directions as the great glittering machine ground out its ancient moral tale for the edification of the national mind.

A red-headed man approached them and spoke with familiar deference to Bloeckman, who answered:

"Hello, Debris. Want you to meet Mrs. Patch. . . . Mrs. Patch wants to go into pictures, as I explained to you. . . . All right, now, where do we go?"

Mr. Debris—the great Percy B. Debris, thought Gloria—showed them to a set which represented the interior of an office. Some chairs were drawn up around the camera, which stood in front of it, and the three of them sat down.

"Ever been in a studio before?" asked Mr. Debris, giving her a glance that was surely the quintessence of keenness. "No? Well, I'll explain exactly what's going to happen. We're going to take what we call a test in order to see how your features photograph and whether you've got natural stage presence and how you respond to coaching. There's no need to be nervous over it.

I'll just have the camera-man take a few hundred feet in an episode I've got marked here in the scenario. We can tell pretty much what we want to from that."

He produced a typewritten continuity and explained to her the episode she was to enact. It developed that one Barbara Wainwright had been secretly married to the junior partner of the firm whose office was there represented. Entering the deserted office one day by accident she was naturally interested in seeing where her husband worked. The telephone rang and after some hesitation she answered it. She learned that her husband had been struck by an automobile and instantly killed. She was overcome. At first she was unable to realize the truth, but finally she succeeded in comprehending it, and went into a dead faint on the floor.

"Now that's all we want," concluded Mr. Debris. "I'm going to stand here and tell you approximately what to do, and you're to act as though I wasn't here, and just go on do it your own way. You needn't be afraid we're going to judge this too severely. We simply want to get a general idea of your screen personality."

"I see."

"You'll find make-up in the room in back of the set. Go light on it. Very little red."

"I see," repeated Gloria, nodding. She touched her lips nervously with the tip of her tongue.

The Test

As she came into the set through the real wooden door and closed it carefully behind her, she found herself inconveniently dissatisfied with her clothes. She should have bought a "misses'" dress for the occasion —she could still wear them, and it might have been a good investment if it had accentuated her airy youth.

Her mind snapped sharply into the momentous present as Mr. Debris's voice came from the glare of the white lights in front.

"You look around for your husband. . . . Now —you don't see him . . . you're curious about the office. . . ."

She became conscious of the regular sound of the camera. It worried her. She glanced toward it involuntarily and wondered if she had made up her face correctly. Then, with a definite effort she forced herself to act—and she had never felt that the gestures of her body were so banal, so awkward, so bereft of grace or distinction. She strolled around the office, picking up articles here and there and looking at them inanely. Then she scrutinized the ceiling, the floor, and thoroughly inspected an inconsequential lead pencil on the desk. Finally, because she could think of nothing else to do, and less than nothing to express, she forced a smile.

"All right. Now the phone rings. Ting-a-ling-a-ling! Hesitate, and then answer it."

She hesitated—and then, too quickly, she thought, picked up the receiver.

"Hello."

Her voice was hollow and unreal. The words rang in the empty set like the ineffectualities of a ghost. The absurdities of their requirements appalled her— Did they expect that on an instant's notice she could put herself in the place of this preposterous and unexplained character?

". . . No . . . no. . . . Not yet! Now listen: 'John Sumner has just been knocked over by an automobile and instantly killed!'"

Gloria let her baby mouth drop slowly open. Then:

"Now hang up! With a bang!"

She obeyed, clung to the table with her eyes wide and staring. At length she was feeling slightly encouraged and her confidence increased.

"My God!" she cried. Her voice was good, she thought. "Oh, my God!"

"Now faint."

She collapsed forward to her knees and throwing her body outward on the ground lay without breathing.

"All right!" called Mr. Debris. "That's enough, thank you. That's plenty. Get up—that's enough."

Gloria arose, mustering her dignity and brushing off her skirt.

"Awful!" she remarked with a cool laugh, though her heart was bumping tumultuously. "Terrible, wasn't it?"

"Did you mind it?" said Mr. Debris, smiling blandly. "Did it seem hard? I can't tell anything about it until I have it run off."

"Of course not," she agreed, trying to attach some sort of meaning to his remark—and failing. It was just the sort of thing he would have said had he been trying not to encourage her.

A few moments later she left the studio. Bloeckman had promised that she should hear the result of the test within the next few days. Too proud to force any definite comment she felt a baffling uncertainty and only now when the step had at last been taken did she realize how the possibility of a successful screen career had played in the back of her mind for the past three years. That night she tried to tell over to herself the elements that might decide for or against her. Whether or not she had used enough make-up worried her, and as the part was that of a girl of twenty, she wondered if she had not been just a little too grave. About her acting she was least of all satisfied. Her entrance had been abominable—in fact not until she reached the phone had she displayed a shred of poise—and then the test had been over. If they had only realized! She wished that she could try it again. A mad plan to call up in the morning and ask for a new trial took possession of her, and as suddenly faded. It seemed neither politic nor polite to ask another favor of Bloeckman.

The third day of waiting found her in a highly nervous condition. She had bitten the insides of her mouth until they were raw and smarting, and burnt unbearably when she washed them with listerine. She had quarrelled so persistently with Anthony that he had left the apartment in a cold fury. But because he was intimidated by her exceptional frigidity, he called up an hour afterward, apologized and said he was having dinner at the Amsterdam Club, the only one in which he still retained membership.

It was after one o'clock and she had breakfasted at eleven, so, deciding to forego luncheon, she started for a walk in the Park. At three there would be a mail. She would be back by three.

It was an afternoon of premature spring. Water was drying on the walks and in the Park little girls were gravely wheeling white doll-buggies up and down under the thin trees while behind them followed bored nursery-maids in two's, discussing with each other those tremendous secrets that are peculiar to nursery-maids.

Two o'clock by her little gold watch. She should have a new watch, one made in a platinum oblong and incrusted with diamonds—but those cost even more than squirrel coats and of course they were out of her reach now, like everything else—unless perhaps the right letter was awaiting her . . . in about an hour . . . fifty-eight minutes exactly. Ten to get there left forty-eight . . . forty-seven now. . .

Little girls soberly wheeling their buggies along the damp sunny walks. The nursery-maids chattering in pairs about their inscrutable secrets. Here and there a raggedy man seated upon newspapers spread on a drying bench, related not to the radiant and delightful afternoon but to the dirty snow that slept exhausted in obscure corners, waiting for extermination. . . .

Ages later, coming into the dim hall she saw the Martinique elevator boy standing incongruously in the light of the stained-glass window.

"Is there any mail for us?" she asked.

"Up-stays, madame."

The switchboard squawked abominably and Gloria waited while he ministered to the telephone. She sickened as the elevator groaned its way up—the floors passed like the slow lapse of centuries, each one ominous, accusing, significant. The letter, a white leprous spot, lay upon the dirty tiles of the hall. . . .

My dear Gloria:

We had the test run off yesterday afternoon, and Mr. Debris seemed to think that for the part he had in mind he needed a younger woman. He said that the acting was not bad, and that there was a small character part supposed to be a very haughty rich widow that he thought you might——

Desolately Gloria raised her glance until it fell out across the areaway. But she found she could not see the opposite wall, for her gray eyes were full of tears. She walked into the bedroom, the letter crinkled tightly in her hand, and sank down upon her knees before the long mirror on the wardrobe floor. This was her twenty-ninth birthday, and the world was melting away before her eyes. She tried to think that it had been the make-up, but her emotions were too profound, too overwhelming for any consolation that the thought conveyed.

She strained to see until she could feel the flesh on her temples pull forward. Yes—the cheeks were ever so faintly thin, the corners of the eyes were lined with tiny wrinkles. The eyes were different. Why, they were different! . . . And then suddenly she knew how tired her eyes were.

"Oh, my pretty face," she whispered, passionately grieving. "Oh, my pretty face! Oh, I don't want to live without my pretty face! Oh, what's *happened?*"

Then she slid toward the mirror and, as in the test, sprawled face downward upon the floor—and lay there sobbing. It was the first awkward movement she had ever made.

CHAPTER III

NO MATTER!

WITHIN another year Anthony and Gloria had become like players who had lost their costumes, lacking the pride to continue on the note of tragedy—so that when Mrs. and Miss Hulme of Kansas City cut them dead in the Plaza one evening, it was only that Mrs. and Miss Hulme, like most people, abominated mirrors of their atavistic selves.

Their new apartment, for which they paid eighty-five dollars a month, was situated on Claremont Avenue, which is two blocks from the Hudson in the dim hundreds. They had lived there a month when Muriel Kane came to see them late one afternoon.

It was a reproachless twilight on the summer side of spring. Anthony lay upon the lounge looking up One Hundred and Twenty-seventh Street toward the river, near which he could just see a single patch of vivid green trees that guaranteed the brummagem umbrageousness of Riverside Drive. Across the water were the Palisades, crowned by the ugly framework of the amusement park —yet soon it would be dusk and those same iron cobwebs would be a glory against the heavens, an enchanted palace set over the smooth radiance of a tropical canal.

The streets near the apartment, Anthony had found, were streets where children played—streets a little nicer than those he had been used to pass on his way to Marietta, but of the same general sort, with an occasional hand organ or hurdy-gurdy, and in the cool of the evening many pairs of young girls walking down to the corner drug-store for ice cream soda and dreaming unlimited dreams under the low heavens.

Dusk in the streets now, and children playing, shouting up incoherent ecstatic words that faded out close to the open window—and Muriel, who had come to find Gloria, chattering to him from an opaque gloom over across the room.

"Light the lamp, why don't we?" she suggested. "It's getting *ghost*ly in here."

With a tired movement he arose and obeyed; the gray window-panes vanished. He stretched himself. He was heavier now, his stomach was a limp weight against his belt; his flesh had softened and expanded. He was thirty-two and his mind was a bleak and disordered wreck.

"Have a little drink, Muriel?"

"Not me, thanks. I don't use it any more. What're you doing these days, Anthony?" she asked curiously.

"Well, I've been pretty busy with this lawsuit," he answered indifferently. "It's gone to the Court of Appeals—ought to be settled up one way or another by autumn. There's been some objection as to whether the Court of Appeals has jurisdiction over the matter."

Muriel made a clicking sound with her tongue and cocked her head on one side.

"Well, you tell 'em! I never heard of anything taking so long."

"Oh, they all do," he replied listlessly; "all will cases. They say it's exceptional to have one settled under four or five years."

"Oh . . ." Muriel daringly changed her tack, "why don't you go to work, you la-azy!"

"At what?" he demanded abruptly.

"Why, at anything, I suppose. You're still a young man."

"If that's encouragement, I'm much obliged," he answered dryly—and then with sudden weariness: "Does it bother you particularly that I don't want to work?"

"It doesn't bother me—but, it does bother a lot of people who claim——"

"Oh, God!" he said brokenly, "it seems to me that for three years I've heard nothing about myself but wild stories and virtuous admonitions. I'm tired of it. If you don't want to see us, let us alone. I don't bother my former 'friends.' But I need no charity calls, and no criticism disguised as good advice—" Then he added apologetically: "I'm sorry—but really, Muriel, you mustn't talk like a lady slum-worker even if you are visiting the lower middle classes." He turned his bloodshot eyes on her reproachfully—eyes that had once been a deep, clear blue, that were weak now, strained, and half-ruined from reading when he was drunk.

"Why do you say such awful things?" she protested. "You talk as if you and Gloria were in the middle classes."

"Why pretend we're not? I hate people who claim to be great aristocrats when they can't even keep up the appearances of it."

"Do you think a person has to have money to be aristocratic?"

Muriel . . . the horrified democrat . . .!

"Why, of course. Aristocracy's only an admission that certain traits which we call fine—courage and honor and beauty and all that sort of thing—can best be developed in a favorable environment, where you don't have the warpings of ignorance and necessity."

Muriel bit her lower lip and waved her head from side to side.

"Well, all *I* say is that if a person comes from a good family they're always nice people. That's the trouble with you and Gloria. You think that just because things aren't going your way right now all your old friends are trying to avoid you. You're too sensitive——"

"As a matter of fact," said Anthony, "you know nothing at all about it. With me it's simply a matter of pride, and for once Gloria's reasonable enough to agree that we oughtn't go where we're not wanted. And people don't want us. We're too much the ideal bad examples."

"Nonsense! You can't park your pessimism in my little sun parlor. I think you ought to forget all those morbid speculations and go to work."

"Here I am, thirty-two. Suppose I did start in at some idiotic business. Perhaps in two years I might rise to fifty dollars a week—with luck. That's *if* I could get a job at all; there's an awful lot of unemployment. Well, suppose I made fifty a week. Do you think I'd be any happier? Do you think that if I don't get this money of my grandfather's life will be *endurable?*"

Muriel smiled complacently.

"Well," she said, "that may be clever but it isn't common sense."

A few minutes later Gloria came in seeming to bring with her into the room some dark color, indeterminate and rare. In a taciturn way she was happy to see Muriel. She greeted Anthony with a casual "Hi!"

"I've been talking philosophy with your husband," cried the irrepressible Miss Kane.

"We took up some fundamental concepts," said Anthony, a faint smile disturbing his pale cheeks, paler still under two days' growth of beard.

Oblivious to his irony Muriel rehashed her contention. When she had done, Gloria said quietly:

"Anthony's right. It's no fun to go around when you have the sense that people are looking at you in a certain way."

He broke in plaintively:

"Don't you think that when even Maury Noble, who was my best friend, won't come to see us it's high time to stop calling people up?" Tears were standing in his eyes.

"That was your fault about Maury Noble," said Gloria coolly.

"It wasn't."

"It most certainly was."

Muriel intervened quickly:

"I met a girl who knew Maury, the other day, and she says he doesn't drink any more. He's getting pretty cagey."

"Doesn't?"

"Practically not at all. He's making *piles* of money. He's sort of changed since the war. He's going to marry a girl in Philadelphia who has millions, Ceci Larrabee—anyhow, that's what Town Tattle said."

"He's thirty-three," said Anthony, thinking aloud. "But it's odd to imagine his getting married. I used to think he was so brilliant."

"He was," murmured Gloria, "in a way."

"But brilliant people don't settle down in business—or do they? Or what do they do? Or what becomes of everybody you used to know and have so much in common with?"

"You drift apart," suggested Muriel with the appropriate dreamy look.

"They change," said Gloria. "All the qualities that they don't use in their daily lives get cobwebbed up."

"The last thing he said to me," recollected Anthony,

"was that he was going to work so as to forget that there was nothing worth working for."

Muriel caught at this quickly.

"That's what *you* ought to do," she exclaimed triumphantly. "Of course I shouldn't think anybody would want to work for nothing. But it'd give you something to do. What do you do with yourselves, anyway? Nobody ever sees you at Montmartre or—or anywhere. Are you economizing?"

Gloria laughed scornfully, glancing at Anthony from the corners of her eyes.

"Well," he demanded, "what are you laughing at?"

"You know what I'm laughing at," she answered coldly.

"At that case of whiskey?"

"Yes"—she turned to Muriel—"he paid seventy-five dollars for a case of whiskey yesterday."

"What if I did? It's cheaper that way than if you get it by the bottle. You needn't pretend that you won't drink any of it."

"At least I don't drink in the daytime."

"That's a fine distinction!" he cried, springing to his feet in a weak rage. "What's more, I'll be damned if you can hurl that at me every few minutes!"

"It's true."

"It is *not!* And I'm getting sick of this eternal business of criticising me before visitors!" He had worked himself up to such a state that his arms and shoulders were visibly trembling. "You'd think everything was my fault. You'd think you hadn't encouraged me to spend money—and spent a lot more on yourself than I ever did by a long shot."

Now Gloria rose to her feet.

"I *won't* let you talk to me that way!"

"All right, then; by Heaven, you don't have to!"

In a sort of rush he left the room. The two women heard his steps in the hall and then the front door banged. Gloria sank back into her chair. Her face was lovely in the lamplight, composed, inscrutable.

"Oh—!" cried Muriel in distress. "Oh, what *is* the matter?"

"Nothing particularly. He's just drunk."

"Drunk? Why, he's perfectly sober. He talked——"

Gloria shook her head.

"Oh, no, he doesn't show it any more unless he can hardly stand up, and he talks all right until he gets excited. He talks much better than he does when he's sober. But he's been sitting here all day drinking—except for the time it took him to walk to the corner for a newspaper."

"Oh, how terrible!" Muriel was sincerely moved. Her eyes filled with tears. "Has this happened much?"

"Drinking, you mean?"

"No, this—leaving you?"

"Oh, yes. Frequently. He'll come in about midnight—and weep and ask me to forgive him."

"And do you?"

"I don't know. We just go on."

The two women sat there in the lamplight and looked at each other, each in a different way helpless before this thing. Gloria was still pretty, as pretty as she would ever be again—her cheeks were flushed and she was wearing a new dress that she had bought—imprudently—for fifty dollars. She had hoped she could persuade Anthony to take her out to-night, to a restaurant or even to one of the great, gorgeous moving picture palaces where there would be a few people to look at her, at whom she could bear to look in turn. She wanted this because she knew her cheeks were flushed and because her dress was new and becomingly fragile. Only very occasionally, now, did they receive any invitations. But she did not tell these things to Muriel.

"Gloria, dear, I wish we could have dinner together, but I promised a man—and it's seven-thirty already. I've got to *tear*."

"Oh, I couldn't, anyway. In the first place I've been ill all day. I couldn't eat a thing."

After she had walked with Muriel to the door, Gloria came back into the room, turned out the lamp, and leaning her elbows on the window sill looked out at Palisades Park, where the brilliant revolving circle of the Ferris wheel was like a trembling mirror catching the yellow reflection of the moon. The street was quiet now; the children had gone in—over the way she could see a family at dinner. Pointlessly, ridiculously, they rose and walked about the table; seen thus, all that they did appeared incongruous—it was as though they were being jiggled carelessly and to no purpose by invisible overhead wires.

She looked at her watch—it was eight o'clock. She had been pleased for a part of the day—the early afternoon—in walking along that Broadway of Harlem, One Hundred and Twenty-fifth Street, with her nostrils alert to many odors, and her mind excited by the extraordinary beauty of some Italian children. It affected her curiously—as Fifth Avenue had affected her once, in the days when, with the placid confidence of beauty, she had known that it was all hers, every shop and all it held, every adult toy glittering in a window, all hers for the asking. Here on One Hundred and Twenty-fifth Street there were Salvation Army bands and spectrum-shawled old ladies on door-steps and sugary, sticky candy in the grimy hands of shiny-haired children—and the late sun striking down on the sides of the tall tenements. All very rich and racy and savory, like a dish by a provident French chef that one could not help enjoying, even though one knew that the ingredients were probably left-overs. . . .

Gloria shuddered suddenly as a river siren came moaning over the dusky roofs, and leaning back in till the ghostly curtains fell from her shoulder, she turned on the electric lamp. It was growing late. She knew there was some change in her purse, and she considered whether she would go down and have some coffee and rolls where the liberated subway made a roaring cave of Manhattan Street or eat the devilled ham and bread in the kitchen. Her purse decided for her. It contained a nickel and two pennies.

After an hour the silence of the room had grown unbearable, and she found that her eyes were wandering from her magazine to the ceiling, toward which she stared without thought. Suddenly she stood up, hesitated for a moment, biting at her finger—then she went to the pantry, took down a bottle of whiskey from the shelf and poured herself a drink. She filled up the glass with ginger ale, and returning to her chair finished an article in the magazine. It concerned the last revolutionary widow, who, when a young girl, had married an ancient veteran of the Continental Army and who had died in 1906. It seemed strange and oddly romantic to Gloria that she and this woman had been contemporaries.

She turned a page and learned that a candidate for Congress was being accused of atheism by an opponent. Gloria's surprise vanished when she found that the charges were false. The candidate had merely denied the miracle of the loaves and fishes. He admitted, under pressure, that he gave full credence to the stroll upon the water.

Finishing her first drink, Gloria got herself a second.

After slipping on a negligée and making herself comfortable on the lounge, she became conscious that she was miserable and that the tears were rolling down her cheeks. She wondered if they were tears of self-pity, and tried resolutely not to cry, but this existence without hope, without happiness, oppressed her, and she kept shaking her head from side to side, her mouth drawn down tremulously in the corners, as though she were denying an assertion made by some one, somewhere. She did not know that this gesture of hers was years older than history, that, for a hundred generations of men, intolerable and persistent grief has offered that gesture, of denial, of protest, of bewilderment, to something more profound, more powerful than the God made in the image of man, and before which that God, did he exist, would be equally impotent. It is a truth set at the heart of tragedy that this force never explains, never answers—this force intangible as air, more definite than death.

Richard Caramel

Early in the summer Anthony resigned from his last club, the Amsterdam. He had come to visit it hardly twice a year, and the dues were a recurrent burden. He had joined it on his return from Italy because it had been his grandfather's club and his father's, and because it was a club that, given the opportunity, one indisputably joined—but as a matter of fact he had preferred the Harvard Club, largely because of Dick and Maury. However, with the decline of his fortunes, it had seemed an increasingly desirable bauble to cling to. . . . It was relinquished at the last, with some regret. . . .

His companions numbered now a curious dozen. Several of them he had met in a place called "Sammy's," on Forty-third Street, where, if one knocked on the door and were favorably passed on from behind a grating, one could sit around a great round table drinking fairly good whiskey. It was here that he encountered a man named Parker Allison, who had been exactly the wrong sort of rounder at Harvard, and who was running through a large "yeast" fortune as rapidly as possible. Parker Allison's notion of distinction consisted in driving a noisy red-and-yellow racing-car up Broadway with two glittering, hard-eyed girls beside him. He was the sort who dined with two girls rather than with one—his imagination was almost incapable of sustaining a dialogue.

Besides Allison there was Pete Lytell, who wore a gray derby on the side of his head. He always had money and he was customarily cheerful, so Anthony held aimless, long-winded conversation with him through many afternoons of the summer and fall. Lytell, he found, not only talked but reasoned in phrases. His philosophy was a series of them, assimilated here and there through an active, thoughtless life. He had phrases about Socialism—the immemorial ones; he had phrases pertaining to the existence of a personal deity—something about one time when he had been in a railroad accident; and he had phrases about the Irish problem, the sort of woman he respected, and the futility of prohibition. The only time his conversation ever rose superior to these muddled clauses, with which he interpreted the most rococo happenings in a life that had been more than usually eventful, was when he got down to the detailed discussion of his most animal existence: he knew, to a subtlety, the foods, the liquor, and the women that he preferred.

He was at once the commonest and the most remarkable product of civilization. He was nine out of ten people that one passes on a city street—and he was a hairless ape with two dozen tricks. He was the hero of a thousand romances of life and art—and he was a virtual moron, performing staidly yet absurdly a series of complicated and infinitely astounding epics over a span of threescore years.

With such men as these two Anthony Patch drank and discussed and drank and argued. He liked them because they knew nothing about him, because they lived in the obvious and had not the faintest conception of the inevitable continuity of life. They sat not before a motion picture with consecutive reels, but at a musty old-fashioned travelogue with all values stark and hence all implications confused. Yet they themselves were not confused, because there was nothing in them to be confused—they changed phrases from month to month as they changed neckties.

Anthony, the courteous, the subtle, the perspicacious, was drunk each day—in Sammy's with these men, in the apartment over a book, some book he knew, and, very rarely, with Gloria, who, in his eyes, had begun to develop the unmistakable outlines of a quarrelsome and unreasonable woman. She was not the Gloria of old, certainly—the Gloria who, had she been sick, would have preferred to inflict misery upon every one around her rather than confess that she needed sympathy or assistance. She was not above whining now; she was not above being sorry for herself. Each night when she prepared for bed she smeared her face with some new unguent which she hoped illogically would give back the glow and freshness to her vanishing beauty. When Anthony was drunk he taunted her about this. When he was sober he was polite to her, on occasions even tender; he seemed to show for short hours a trace of that old quality of understanding too well to blame—that quality which was the best of him and had worked swiftly and ceaselessly toward his ruin.

But he hated to be sober. It made him conscious of the people around him, of that air of struggle, of greedy ambition, of hope more sordid than despair, of incessant passage up or down, which in every metropolis is most in evidence through the unstable middle class. Unable to live with the rich he thought that his next choice would have been to live with the very poor. Anything was better than this cup of perspiration and tears.

The sense of the enormous panorama of life, never strong in Anthony, had become dim almost to extinction. At long intervals now some incident, some gesture of Gloria's, would take his fancy—but the gray veils had come down in earnest upon him. As he grew older those things faded—after that there was wine.

There was a kindliness about intoxication—there was that indescribable gloss and glamour it gave, like the memories of ephemeral and faded evenings. After a few high-balls there was magic in the tall glowing Arabian night of the Bush Terminal Building—its summit a peak of sheer grandeur, gold and dreaming against the inaccessible sky. And Wall Street, the crass, the banal—again it was the triumph of gold, a gorgeous sentient spectacle; it was where the great kings kept the money for their wars. . . .

. . . The fruit of youth or of the grape, the transitory magic of the brief passage from darkness to darkness—the old illusion that truth and beauty were in some way entwined.

As he stood in front of Delmonico's lighting a cigarette one night he saw two hansoms drawn up close to the curb, waiting for a chance drunken fare. The outmoded cabs were worn and dirty—the cracked patent leather wrinkled like an old man's face, the cushions faded to a brownish lavender; the very horses were ancient and weary, and so were the white-haired men who sat aloft, cracking their whips with a grotesque affectation of gallantry. A relic of vanished gaiety!

Anthony Patch walked away in a sudden fit of depression, pondering the bitterness of such survivals. There was nothing, it seemed, that grew stale so soon as pleasure.

On Forty-second Street one afternoon he met Richard Caramel for the first time in many months, a prosperous, fattening Richard Caramel, whose face was filling out to match the Bostonian brow.

"Just got in this week from the coast. Was going to call you up, but I didn't know your new address."

"We've moved."

Richard Caramel noticed that Anthony was wearing a soiled shirt, that his cuffs were slightly but perceptibly frayed, that his eyes were set in half-moons the color of cigar smoke.

"So I gathered," he said, fixing his friend with his bright-yellow eye. "But where and how is Gloria? My God, Anthony, I've been hearing the dog-gonedest stories about you two even out in California—and when I get back to New York I find you've sunk absolutely out of sight. Why don't you pull yourself together?"

"Now, listen," chattered Anthony unsteadily, "I can't stand a long lecture. We've lost money in a dozen ways, and naturally people have talked—on account of the lawsuit, but the thing's coming to a final decision this winter, surely——"

"You're talking so fast that I can't understand you," interrupted Dick calmly.

"Well, I've said all I'm going to say," snapped Anthony. "Come and see us if you like—or don't!"

With this he turned and started to walk off in the

crowd, but Dick overtook him immediately and grasped his arm.

"Say, Anthony, don't fly off the handle so easily! You know Gloria's my cousin, and you're one of my oldest friends, so it's natural for me to be interested when I hear that you're going to the dogs—and taking her with you."

"I don't want to be preached to."

"Well, then, all right— How about coming up to my apartment and having a drink? I've just got settled. I've bought three cases of Gordon gin from a revenue officer."

As they walked along he continued in a burst of exasperation:

"And how about your grandfather's money—you going to get it?"

"Well," answered Anthony resentfully, "that old fool Haight seems hopeful, especially because people are tired of reformers right now—you know it might make a slight difference, for instance, if some judge thought that Adam Patch made it harder for him to get liquor."

"You can't do without money," said Dick sententiously. "Have you tried to write any—lately?"

Anthony shook his head silently.

"That's funny," said Dick. "I always thought that you and Maury would write some day, and now he's grown to be a sort of tight-fisted aristocrat, and you're——"

"I'm the bad example."

"I wonder why?"

"You probably think you know," suggested Anthony, with an effort at concentration. "The failure and the success both believe in their hearts that they have accurately balanced points of view, the success because he's succeeded, and the failure because he's failed. The successful man tells his son to profit by his father's good fortune, and the failure tells *his* son to profit by his father's mistakes."

"I don't agree with you," said the author of "A Shave-tail in France." "I used to listen to you and Maury when we were young, and I used to be impressed because you were so consistently cynical, but now—well, after all, by God, which of us three has taken to the—to the intellectual life? I don't want to sound vainglorious, but—it's me, and I've always believed that moral values existed, and I always will."

"Well," objected Anthony, who was rather enjoying himself, "even granting that, you know that in practice life never presents problems as clear cut, does it?"

"It does to me. There's nothing I'd violate certain principles for."

"But how do you know when you're violating them? You have to guess at things just like most people do. You have to apportion the values when you look back. You finish up the portrait then—paint in the details and shadows."

Dick shook his head with a lofty stubbornness.

"Same old futile cynic," he said. "It's just a mode of being sorry for yourself. You don't do anything—so nothing matters."

"Oh, I'm quite capable of self-pity," admitted Anthony, "nor am I claiming that I'm getting as much fun out of life as you are."

"You say—at least you used to—that happiness is the only thing worth while in life. Do you think you're any happier for being a pessimist?"

Anthony grunted savagely. His pleasure in the conversation began to wane. He was nervous and craving for a drink.

"My golly!" he cried, "where do you live? I can't keep walking forever."

"Your endurance is all mental, eh?" returned Dick sharply. "Well, I live right here."

He turned in at the apartment house on Forty-ninth Street, and a few minutes later they were in a large new room with an open fireplace and four walls lined with books. A colored butler served them gin rickeys, and an hour vanished politely with the mellow shortening of their drinks and the glow of a light mid-autumn fire.

"The arts are very old," said Anthony after a while. With a few glasses the tension of his nerves relaxed and he found that he could think again.

"Which art?"

"All of them. Poetry is dying first. It'll be absorbed into prose sooner or later. For instance, the beautiful word, the colored and glittering word, and the beautiful simile belong in prose now. To get attention poetry has got to strain for the unusual word, the harsh, earthy word that's never been beautiful before. Beauty, as the sum of several beautiful parts, reached its apotheosis in Swinburne. It can't go any further—except in the novel, perhaps."

Dick interrupted him impatiently:

"You know these new novels make me tired. My God! Everywhere I go some silly girl asks me if I've read 'This Side of Paradise.' Are our girls really like that? If it's true to life, which I don't believe, the next generation is going to the dogs. I'm sick of all this shoddy realism. I think there's a place for the romanticist in literature."

Anthony tried to remember what he had read lately of Richard Caramel's. There was "A Shave-tail in France," a novel called "The Land of Strong Men," and several dozen short stories, which were even worse. It had become the custom among young and clever reviewers to mention Richard Caramel with a smile of scorn. "Mr." Richard Caramel, they called him. His corpse was dragged obscenely through every literary supplement. He was accused of making a great fortune by writing trash for the movies. As the fashion in books shifted he was becoming almost a byword of contempt.

While Anthony was thinking this, Dick had got to his feet and seemed to be hesitating at an avowal.

"I've gathered quite a few books," he said suddenly.

"So I see."

"I've made an exhaustive collection of good American stuff, old and new. I don't mean the usual Longfellow-Whittier thing—in fact, most of it's modern."

He stepped to one of the walls and, seeing that it was expected of him, Anthony arose and followed.

"Look!"

Under a printed tag *Americana* he displayed six long rows of books, beautifully bound and, obviously, carefully chosen.

"And here are the contemporary novelists."

Then Anthony saw the joker. Wedged in between Mark Twain and Dreiser were eight strange and inappropriate volumes, the works of Richard Caramel—"The Demon Lover," true enough . . . but also seven others that were execrably awful, without sincerity or grace.

Unwillingly Anthony glanced at Dick's face and caught a slight uncertainty there.

"I've put my own books in, of course," said Richard Caramel hastily, "though one or two of them are uneven—I'm afraid I wrote a little too fast when I had that magazine contract. But I don't believe in false modesty. Of course some of the critics haven't paid so much attention to me since I've been established—but, after all, it's not the critics that count. They're just sheep."

For the first time in so long that he could scarcely remember, Anthony felt a touch of the old pleasant contempt for his friend. Richard Caramel continued:

"My publishers, you know, have been advertising me as the Thackeray of America—because of my New York novel."

"Yes," Anthony managed to muster, "I suppose there's a good deal in what you say."

He knew that his contempt was unreasonable. He knew that he would have changed places with Dick unhesitatingly. He himself had tried his best to write with his tongue in his cheek. Ah, well, then—can a man disparage his life-work so readily? . . .

—And that night while Richard Caramel was hard at toil, with great hittings of the wrong keys and screwings up of his weary, unmatched eyes, laboring over his trash far into those cheerless hours when the fire dies down, and the head is swimming from the effect of prolonged concentration—Anthony, abominably drunk, was sprawled across the back seat of a taxi on his way to the flat on Claremont Avenue.

The Beating

As winter approached it seemed that a sort of madness seized upon Anthony. He awoke in the morning so nervous that Gloria could feel him trembling in the bed before he could muster enough vitality to stumble into the pantry for a drink. He was intolerable now except under the influence of liquor, and as he seemed to decay and coarsen under her eyes, Gloria's soul and body shrank away from him; when he stayed out all night, as he did several times, she not only failed to be sorry but even felt a measure of dismal relief. Next day he would be faintly repentant, and would remark in a gruff, hang-dog fashion that he guessed he was drinking a little too much.

For hours at a time he would sit in the great armchair that had been in his apartment, lost in a sort of stupor—even his interest in reading his favorite books seemed to have departed, and though an incessant bickering went on between husband and wife, the one subject upon which they ever really conversed was the progress of the will case. What Gloria hoped in the tenebrous depths of her soul, what she expected that great gift of money to bring about, is difficult to imagine. She was being bent by her environment into a grotesque similitude of a housewife. She who until three years before had never made coffee, prepared sometimes three meals a day. She walked a great deal in the afternoons, and in the evenings she read—books, magazines, anything she found at hand. If now she wished for a child, even a child of the Anthony who sought her bed blind drunk, she neither said so nor gave any show or sign of interest in children. It is doubtful if she could have made it clear to any one what it was she wanted, or indeed what there was to want—a lonely, lovely woman, thirty now, retrenched behind some impregnable inhibition born and coexistent with her beauty.

One afternoon when the snow was dirty again along Riverside Drive, Gloria, who had been to the grocer's, entered the apartment to find Anthony pacing the floor in a state of aggravated nervousness. The feverish eyes he turned on her were traced with tiny pink lines that reminded her of rivers on a map. For a moment she received the impression that he was suddenly and definitely old.

"Have you any money?" he inquired of her precipitately.

"What? What do you mean?"

"Just what I said. Money! Money! Can't you speak English?"

She paid no attention but brushed by him and into the pantry to put the bacon and eggs in the ice-box. When his drinking had been unusually excessive he was invariably in a whining mood. This time he followed her and, standing in the pantry door, persisted in his question.

"You heard what I said. Have you any money?"

She turned about from the ice-box and faced him.

"Why, Anthony, you must be crazy! You know I haven't any money—except a dollar in change."

He executed an abrupt about-face and returned to the living room, where he renewed his pacing. It was evident that he had something portentous on his mind—he quite obviously wanted to be asked what was the matter. Joining him a moment later she sat upon the long lounge and began taking down her hair. It was no longer bobbed, and it had changed in the last year from a rich gold dusted with red to an unresplendent light brown. She had bought some shampoo soap and meant to wash it now; she had considered putting a bottle of peroxide into the rinsing water.

"—Well?" she implied silently.

"That darn bank!" he quavered. "They've had my account for over ten years—ten *years*. Well, it seems they've got some autocratic rule that you have to keep over five hundred dollars there or they won't carry you. They wrote me a letter a few months ago and told me I'd been running too low. Once I gave out two bum checks—remember? that night in Reisenweber's?—but I made them good the very next day. Well, I promised old Halloran—he's the manager, the greedy Mick—that I'd watch out. And I thought I was going all right; I kept up the stubs in my check-book pretty regular. Well, I went in there to-day to cash a check, and Halloran came up and told me they'd have to close my account. Too many bad checks, he said, and I never had more than five hundred to my credit—and that only for a day or so at a time. And by God! What do you think he said then?"

"What?"

"He said this was a good time to do it because I didn't have a damn penny in there!"

"You didn't?"

"That's what he told me. Seems I'd given these Bedros people a check for sixty for that last case of liquor—and I only had forty-five dollars in the bank. Well, the Bedros people deposited fifteen dollars to my account and drew the whole thing out."

In her ignorance Gloria conjured up a spectre of imprisonment and disgrace.

"Oh, they won't do anything," he assured her. "Bootlegging's too risky a business. They'll send me a bill for fifteen dollars and I'll pay it."

"Oh." She considered a moment. "—Well, we can sell another bond."

He laughed sarcastically.

"Oh, yes, that's always easy. When the few bonds we have that are paying any interest at all are only worth between fifty and eighty cents on the dollar. We lose about half the bond every time we sell."

"What else can we do?"

"Oh, we'll sell something—as usual. We've got paper worth eighty thousand dollars at par." Again he laughed unpleasantly. "Bring about thirty thousand on the open market."

"I distrusted those ten per cent investments."

"The deuce you did!" he said. "You pretended you

did, so you could claw at me if they went to pieces, but you wanted to take a chance as much as I did."

She was silent for a moment as if considering, then:

"Anthony," she cried suddenly, "two hundred a month is worse than nothing. Let's sell all the bonds and put the thirty thousand dollars in the bank—and if we lose the case we can live in Italy for three years, and then just die." In her excitement as she talked she was aware of a faint flush of sentiment, the first she had felt in many days.

"Three years," he said nervously, "three years! You're crazy. Mr. Haight'll take more than that if we lose. Do you think he's working for charity?"

"I forgot that."

"—And here it is Saturday," he continued, "and I've only got a dollar and some change, and we've got to live till Monday, when I can get to my broker's. . . . And not a drink in the house," he added as a significant afterthought.

"Can't you call up Dick?"

"I did. His man says he's gone down to Princeton to address a literary club or some such thing. Won't be back till Monday."

"Well, let's see— Don't you know some friend you might go to?"

"I tried a couple of fellows. Couldn't find anybody in. I wish I'd sold that Keats letter like I started to last week."

"How about those men you play cards with in that Sammy place?"

"Do you think I'd ask *them?*" His voice rang with righteous horror. Gloria winced. He would rather contemplate her active discomfort than feel his own skin crawl at asking an inappropriate favor. "I thought of Muriel," he suggested.

"She's in California."

"Well, how about some of those men who gave you such a good time while I was in the army? You'd think they might be glad to do a little favor for you."

She looked at him contemptuously, but he took no notice.

"Or how about your old friend Rachael—or Constance Merriam?"

"Constance Merriam's been dead a year, and I wouldn't ask Rachael."

"Well, how about that gentleman who was so anxious to help you once that he could hardly restrain himself, Bloeckman?"

"Oh—!" He had hurt her at last, and he was not too obtuse or too careless to perceive it.

"Why not him?" he insisted callously.

"Because—he doesn't like me any more," she said with difficulty, and then as he did not answer but only regarded her cynically: "If you want to know why, I'll tell you. A year ago I went to Bloeckman—he's changed his name to Black—and asked him to put me into pictures."

"You went to Bloeckman?"

"Yes."

"Why didn't you tell me?" he demanded incredulously, the smile fading from his face.

"Because you were probably off drinking somewhere. He had them give me a test, and they decided that I wasn't young enough for anything except a character part."

"A character part?"

"The 'woman of thirty' sort of thing. I wasn't thirty, and I didn't think I—looked thirty."

"Why, damn him!" cried Anthony, championing her violently with a curious perverseness of emotion, "why——"

"Well, that's why I can't go to him."

"Why, the insolence!" insisted Anthony nervously, "the insolence!"

"Anthony, that doesn't matter now; the thing is we've got to live over Sunday and there's nothing in the house but a loaf of bread and a half-pound of bacon and two eggs for breakfast." She handed him the contents of her purse. "There's seventy, eighty, a dollar fifteen. With what you have that makes about two and a half altogether, doesn't it? Anthony, we can get along on that. We can buy lots of food with that—more than we can possibly eat."

Jingling the change in his hand he shook his head.

"No. I've got to have a drink. I'm so darn nervous that I'm shivering." A thought struck him. "Perhaps Sammy'd cash a check. And then Monday I could rush down to the bank with the money."

"But they've closed your account."

"That's right, that's right—I'd forgotten. I'll tell you what: I'll go down to Sammy's and I'll find somebody there who'll lend me something. I hate like the devil to ask them, though. . . ." He snapped his fingers suddenly. "I know what I'll do. I'll hock my watch. I can get twenty dollars on it, and get it back Monday for sixty cents extra. It's been hocked before—when I was at Cambridge."

He had put on his overcoat, and with a brief good-by he started down the hall toward the outer door.

Gloria got to her feet. It had suddenly occurred to her where he would probably go first.

"Anthony!" she called after him, "hadn't you better leave two dollars with me? You'll only need carfare."

The outer door slammed—he had pretended not to hear her. She stood for a moment looking after him;

then she went into the bathroom among her tragic unguents and began preparations for washing her hair.

Down at Sammy's he found Parker Allison and Pete Lytell sitting alone at a table, drinking whiskey sours. It was just after six o'clock, and Sammy, or Samuele Bendiri, as he had been christened, was sweeping an accumulation of cigarette butts and broken glass into a corner.

"Hi, Tony!" called Parker Allison to Anthony. Sometimes he addressed him as Tony, at other times it was Dan. To him all Anthonys must sail under one of these diminutives.

"Sit down. What'll you have?"

On the subway Anthony had counted his money and found that he had almost four dollars. He could pay for two rounds at fifty cents a drink—which meant that he would have six drinks. Then he would go over to Sixth Avenue and get twenty dollars and a pawn ticket in exchange for his watch.

"Well, roughnecks," he said jovially, "how's the life of crime?"

"Pretty good," said Allison. He winked at Pete Lytell. "Too bad you're a married man. We've got some pretty good stuff lined up for about eleven o'clock, when the shows let out. Oh, boy! Yes, sir—too bad he's married—isn't it, Pete?"

"'Sa shame."

At half past seven, when they had completed the six rounds, Anthony found that his intentions were giving audience to his desires. He was happy and cheerful now—thoroughly enjoying himself. It seemed to him that the story which Pete had just finished telling was unusually and profoundly humorous—and he decided, as he did every day at about this point, that they were "damn good fellows, by golly!" who would do a lot more for him than any one else he knew. The pawn-shops would remain open until late Saturday nights, and he felt that if he took just one more drink he would attain a gorgeous rose-colored exhilaration.

Artfully, he fished in his vest pockets, brought up his two quarters, and stared at them as though in surprise.

"Well, I'll be darned," he protested in an aggrieved tone, "here I've come out without my pocketbook."

"Need some cash?" asked Lytell easily.

"I left my money on the dresser at home. And I wanted to buy you another drink."

"Oh—knock it." Lytell waved the suggestion away disparagingly. "I guess we can blow a good fella to all the drinks he wants. What'll you have—same?"

"I tell you," suggested Parker Allison, "suppose we send Sammy across the street for some sandwiches and eat dinner here."

The other two agreed.

"Good idea."

"Hey, Sammy, wantcha do somep'm for us. . . ."

Just after nine o'clock Anthony staggered to his feet and, bidding them a thick good night, walked unsteadily to the door, handing Sammy one of his two quarters as he passed out. Once in the street he hesitated uncertainly and then started in the direction of Sixth Avenue, where he remembered to have frequently passed several loan offices. He went by a news-stand and two drug-stores—and then he realized that he was standing in front of the place which he sought, and that it was shut and barred. Unperturbed he continued; another one, half a block down, was also closed—so were two more across the street, and a fifth in the square below. Seeing a faint light in the last one, he began to knock on the glass door; he desisted only when a watchman appeared in the back of the shop and motioned him angrily to move on. With growing discouragement, with growing befuddlement, he crossed the street and walked back toward Forty-third. On the corner near Sammy's he paused undecided—if he went back to the apartment, as he felt his body required, he would lay himself open to bitter reproach; yet, now that the pawnshops were closed, he had no notion where to get the money. He decided finally that he might ask Parker Allison, after all—but he approached Sammy's only to find the door locked and the lights out. He looked at his watch; nine-thirty. He began walking.

Ten minutes later he stopped aimlessly at the corner of Forty-third Street and Madison Avenue, diagonally across from the bright but nearly deserted entrance to the Biltmore Hotel. Here he stood for a moment, and then sat down heavily on a damp board amid some débris of construction work. He rested there for almost half an hour, his mind a shifting pattern of surface thoughts, chiefest among which were that he must obtain some money and get home before he became too sodden to find his way.

Then, glancing over toward the Biltmore, he saw a man standing directly under the overhead glow of the porte-cochère lamps beside a woman in an ermine coat. As Anthony watched, the couple moved forward and signalled to a taxi. Anthony perceived by the infallible identification that lurks in the walk of a friend that it was Maury Noble.

He rose to his feet.

"Maury!" he shouted.

Maury looked in his direction, then turned back to the girl just as the taxi came up into place. With the chaotic idea of borrowing ten dollars, Anthony began to run as fast as he could across Madison Avenue and along Forty-third Street.

As he came up Maury was standing beside the yawning door of the taxicab. His companion turned and looked curiously at Anthony.

"Hello, Maury!" he said, holding out his hand. "How are you?"

"Fine, thank you."

Their hands dropped and Anthony hesitated. Maury made no move to introduce him, but only stood there regarding him with an inscrutable feline silence.

"I wanted to see you—" began Anthony uncertainly. He did not feel that he could ask for a loan with the girl not four feet away, so he broke off and made a perceptible motion of his head as if to beckon Maury to one side.

"I'm in rather a big hurry, Anthony."

"I know—but can you, can you—" Again he hesitated.

"I'll see you some other time," said Maury.

"It's important."

"I'm sorry, Anthony."

Before Anthony could make up his mind to blurt out his request, Maury had turned coolly to the girl, helped her into the car and, with a polite "good evening," stepped in after her. As he nodded from the window it seemed to Anthony that his expression had not changed by a shade or a hair. Then with a fretful clatter the taxi moved off, and Anthony was left standing there alone under the lights.

Anthony went on into the Biltmore, for no reason in particular except that the entrance was at hand, and ascending the wide stair found a seat in an alcove. He was furiously aware that he had been snubbed; he was as hurt and angry as it was possible for him to be when in that condition. Nevertheless, he was stubbornly preoccupied with the necessity of obtaining some money before he went home, and once again he told over on his fingers the acquaintances he might conceivably call on in this emergency. He thought, eventually, that he might approach Mr. Howland, his broker, at his home.

After a long wait he found that Mr. Howland was out. He returned to the operator, leaning over her desk and fingering his quarter as though loath to leave unsatisfied.

"Call Mr. Bloeckman," he said suddenly. His own words surprised him. The name had come from some crossing of two suggestions in his mind.

"What's the number, please?"

Scarcely conscious of what he did, Anthony looked up Joseph Bloeckman in the telephone directory. He could find no such person, and was about to close the book when it flashed into his mind that Gloria had mentioned a change of name. It was the matter of a minute to find Joseph Black—then he waited in the booth while central called the number.

"Hello-o. Mr. Bloeckman—I mean Mr. Black in?"

"No, he's out this evening. Is there any message?" The intonation was cockney; it reminded him of the rich vocal deferences of Bounds.

"Where is he?"

"Why, ah, who is this, please, sir?"

"This Mr. Patch. Matter of vi'al importance."

"Why, he's with a party at the Boul' Mich', sir."

"Thanks."

Anthony got his five cents change and started for the Boul' Mich', a popular dancing resort on Forty-fifth Street. It was nearly ten but the streets were dark and sparsely peopled until the theatres should eject their spawn an hour later. Anthony knew the Boul' Mich', for he had been there with Gloria during the year before, and he remembered the existence of a rule that patrons must be in evening dress. Well, he would not go up-stairs—he would send a boy up for Bloeckman and wait for him in the lower hall. For a moment he did not doubt that the whole project was entirely natural and graceful. To his distorted imagination Bloeckman had become simply one of his old friends.

The entrance hall of the Boul' Mich' was warm. There were high yellow lights over a thick green carpet, from the centre of which a white stairway rose to the dancing floor.

Anthony spoke to the hallboy:

"I want to see Mr. Bloeckman—Mr. Black," he said. "He's up-stairs—have him paged."

The boy shook his head.

"'Sagainsa rules to have him paged. You know what table he's at?"

"No. But I've got see him."

"Wait an' I'll getcha waiter."

After a short interval a head waiter appeared, bearing a card on which were charted the table reservations. He darted a cynical look at Anthony—which, however, failed of its target. Together they bent over the card-board and found the table without difficulty—a party of eight, Mr. Black's own.

"Tell him Mr. Patch. Very, very important."

Again he waited, leaning against the banister and listening to the confused harmonies of "Jazz-mad" which came floating down the stairs. A check-girl near him was singing:

"Out in—the shimmee sanitarium
The jazz-mad nuts reside.
Out in—the shimmee sanitarium
I left my blushing bride.
She went and shook herself insane,
So let her shiver back again——"

Then he saw Bloeckman descending the staircase, and took a step forward to meet him and shake hands.

"You wanted to see me?" said the older man coolly.

"Yes," answered Anthony, nodding, "personal matter. Can you jus' step over here?"

Regarding him narrowly Bloeckman followed Anthony to a half bend made by the staircase where they were beyond observation or earshot of any one entering or leaving the restaurant.

"Well?" he inquired.

"Wanted talk to you."

"What about?"

Anthony only laughed—a silly laugh; he intended it to sound casual.

"What do you want to talk to me about?" repeated Bloeckman.

"Wha's hurry, old man?" He tried to lay his hand in a friendly gesture upon Bloeckman's shoulder, but the latter drew away slightly. "How've been?"

"Very well, thanks. . . . See here, Mr. Patch, I've got a party up-stairs. They'll think it's rude if I stay away too long. What was it you wanted to see me about?"

For the second time that evening Anthony's mind made an abrupt jump, and what he said was not at all what he had intended to say.

"Un'erstand you kep' my wife out of the movies."

"What?" Bloeckman's ruddy face darkened in parallel planes of shadows.

"You heard me."

"Look here, Mr. Patch," said Bloeckman, evenly and without changing his expression, "you're drunk. You're disgustingly and insultingly drunk."

"Not too drunk talk to you," insisted Anthony with a leer. "Firs' place, my wife wants nothin' whatever do with you. Never did. Un'erstand me?"

"Be quiet!" said the older man angrily. "I should think you'd respect your wife enough not to bring her into the conversation under these circumstances."

"Never you min' how I expect my wife. One thing —you leave her alone. You go to hell!"

"See here—I think you're a little crazy!" exclaimed Bloeckman. He took two paces forward as though to pass by, but Anthony stepped in his way.

"Not so fas', you Goddam Jew."

For a moment they stood regarding each other, Anthony swaying gently from side to side, Bloeckman almost trembling with fury.

"Be careful!" he cried in a strained voice.

Anthony might have remembered then a certain look Bloeckman had given him in the Biltmore Hotel years before. But he remembered nothing, nothing——

"I'll say it again, you God——"

Then Bloeckman struck out, with all the strength in the arm of a well-conditioned man of forty-five, struck out and caught Anthony squarely in the mouth. Anthony cracked up against the staircase, recovered himself and made a wild drunken swing at his opponent, but Bloeckman, who took exercise every day and knew something of sparring, blocked it with ease and struck him twice in the face with two swift smashing jabs. Anthony gave a little grunt and toppled over onto the green plush carpet, finding, as he fell, that his mouth was full of blood and seemed oddly loose in front. He struggled to his feet, panting and spitting, and then as he started toward Bloeckman, who stood a few feet away, his fists clenched but not up, two waiters who had appeared from nowhere seized his arms and held him, helpless. In back of them a dozen people had miraculously gathered.

"I'll kill him," cried Anthony, pitching and straining from side to side. "Let me kill——"

"Throw him out!" ordered Bloeckman excitedly, just as a small man with a pockmarked face pushed his way hurriedly through the spectators.

"Any trouble, Mr. Black?"

"This bum tried to blackmail me!" said Bloeckman, and then, his voice rising to a faintly shrill note of pride: "He got what was coming to him!"

The little man turned to a waiter.

"Call a policeman!" he commanded.

"Oh, no," said Bloeckman quickly. "I can't be bothered. Just throw him out in the street. . . . Ugh! What an outrage!" He turned and with conscious dignity walked toward the wash-room just as six brawny hands seized upon Anthony and dragged him toward the door. The "bum" was propelled violently to the sidewalk, where he landed on his hands and knees with a grotesque slapping sound and rolled over slowly onto his side.

The shock stunned him. He lay there for a moment in acute distributed pain. Then his discomfort became centralized in his stomach, and he regained consciousness to discover that a large foot was prodding him.

"You've got to move on, y' bum! Move on!"

It was the bulky doorman speaking. A town car had stopped at the curb and its occupants had disembarked—that is, two of the women were standing on the dashboard, waiting in offended delicacy until this obscene obstacle should be removed from their path.

"Move on! Or else I'll *throw* y'on!"

"Here—I'll get him."

This was a new voice; Anthony imagined that it was somehow more tolerant, better disposed than the first. Again arms were about him, half lifting, half dragging him into a welcome shadow four doors up the street and propping him against the stone front of a millinery shop.

"Much obliged," muttered Anthony feebly. Some one pushed his soft hat down upon his head and he winced.

"Just sit still, buddy, and you'll feel better. Those guys sure give you a bump."

"I'm going back and kill that dirty—" He tried to get to his feet but collapsed backward against the wall.

"You can't do nothin' now," came the voice. "Get 'em some other time. I'm tellin' you straight, ain't I? I'm helpin' you."

Anthony nodded.

"An' you better go home. You dropped a tooth to-night, buddy. You know that?"

Anthony explored his mouth with his tongue, verifying the statement. Then with an effort he raised his hand and located the gap.

"I'm agoin' to get you home, friend. Whereabouts do you live——"

"Oh, by God! By God!" interrupted Anthony, clenching his fists passionately. "I'll show the dirty bunch. You help me show 'em and I'll fix it with you. My grandfather's Adam Patch, of Tarrytown——"

"Who?"

"Adam Patch, by God!"

"You wanna go all the way to Tarrytown?"

"No."

"Well, you tell me where to go, friend, and I'll get a cab."

Anthony made out that his Samaritan was a short, broad-shouldered individual, somewhat the worse for wear.

"Where d'you live, hey?"

Sodden and shaken as he was, Anthony felt that his address would be poor collateral for his wild boast about his grandfather.

"Get me a cab," he commanded, feeling in his pockets.

A taxi drove up. Again Anthony essayed to rise, but his ankle swung loose, as though it were in two sections. The Samaritan must needs help him in—and climb in after him.

"See here, fella," said he, "you're soused and you're bunged up, and you won't be able to get in your house 'less somebody carries you in, so I'm going with you, and I know you'll make it all right with me. Where d'you live?"

With some reluctance Anthony gave his address. Then, as the cab moved off, he leaned his head against the man's shoulder and went into a shadowy, painful torpor. When he awoke, the man had lifted him from the cab in front of the apartment on Claremont Avenue and was trying to set him on his feet.

"Can y' walk?"

"Yes—sort of. You better not come in with me." Again he felt helplessly in his pockets. "Say," he continued, apologetically, swaying dangerously on his feet, "I'm afraid I haven't got a cent."

"Huh?"

"I'm cleaned out."

"Sa-a-ay! Didn't I hear you promise you'd fix it with me? Who's goin' to pay the taxi bill?" He turned to the driver for confirmation. "Didn't you hear him say he'd fix it? All that about his grandfather?"

"Matter of fact," muttered Anthony imprudently, "it was you did all the talking; however, if you come round, to-morrow——"

At this point the taxi-driver leaned from his cab and said ferociously:

"Ah, poke him one, the dirty cheap skate. If he wasn't a bum they wouldn'ta throwed him out."

In answer to this suggestion the fist of the Samaritan

shot out like a battering-ram and sent Anthony crashing down against the stone steps of the apartment-house, where he lay without movement, while the tall buildings rocked to and fro above him. . . .

After a long while he awoke and was conscious that it had grown much colder. He tried to move himself but his muscles refused to function. He was curiously anxious to know the time, but he reached for his watch, only to find the pocket empty. Involuntarily his lips formed an immemorial phrase:

"What a night!"

Strangely enough, he was almost sober. Without moving his head he looked up to where the moon was anchored in mid-sky, shedding light down into Claremont Avenue as into the bottom of a deep and uncharted abyss. There was no sign or sound of life save for the continuous buzzing in his own ears, but after a moment Anthony himself broke the silence with a distinct and peculiar murmur. It was the sound that he had consistently attempted to make back there in the Boul' Mich', when he had been face to face with Bloeckman—the unmistakable sound of ironic laughter. And on his torn and bleeding lips it was like a pitiful retching of the soul.

Three weeks later the trial came to an end. The seemingly endless spool of legal red tape having unrolled over a period of four and a half years, suddenly snapped off. Anthony and Gloria and, on the other side, Edward Shuttleworth and a platoon of beneficiaries testified and lied and ill-behaved generally in varying degrees of greed and desperation. Anthony awoke one morning in March realizing that the verdict was to be given at four that afternoon, and at the thought he got up out of his bed and began to dress. With his extreme nervousness there was mingled an unjustified optimism as to the outcome. He believed that the decision of the lower court would be reversed, if only because of the reaction, due to excessive prohibition, that had recently set in against reforms and reformers. He counted more on the personal attacks that they had levelled at Shuttleworth than on the more sheerly legal aspects of the proceedings.

Dressed, he poured himself a drink of whiskey and then went into Gloria's room, where he found her already wide awake. She had been in bed for a week, humoring herself, Anthony fancied, though the doctor had said that she had best not be disturbed.

"Good morning," she murmured, without smiling. Her eyes seemed unusually large and dark.

"How do you feel?" he asked grudgingly. "Better?"

"Yes."

"Much?"

"Yes."

"Do you feel well enough to go down to court with me this afternoon?"

She nodded.

"Yes. I want to. Dick said yesterday that if the weather was nice he was coming up in his car and take me for a ride in Central Park—and look, the room's all full of sunshine."

Anthony glanced mechanically out the window and then sat down upon the bed.

"God, I'm nervous!" he exclaimed.

"Please don't sit there," she said quickly.

"Why not?"

"You smell of whiskey. I can't stand it."

He got up absent-mindedly and left the room. A little later she called to him and he went out and brought her some potato salad and cold chicken from the delicatessen.

At two o'clock Richard Caramel's car arrived at the door and, when he phoned up, Anthony took Gloria down in the elevator and walked with her to the curb.

She told her cousin that it was sweet of him to take her riding. "Don't be simple," Dick replied disparagingly. "It's nothing."

But he did not mean that it was nothing and this was a curious thing. Richard Caramel had forgiven many people for many offenses. But he had never forgiven his cousin, Gloria Gilbert, for a statement she had made just prior to her wedding, seven years before. She had said that she did not intend to read his book.

Richard Caramel remembered this—he had remembered it well for seven years.

"What time will I expect you back?" asked Anthony.

"We won't come back," she answered, "we'll meet you down there at four."

"All right," he muttered, "I'll meet you."

Up-stairs he found a letter waiting for him. It was a mimeographed notice urging "the boys" in condescendingly colloquial language to pay the dues of the American Legion. He threw it impatiently into the waste-basket and sat down with his elbows on the window sill, looking down blindly into the sunny street.

Italy—if the verdict was in their favor it meant Italy. The word had become a sort of talisman to him, a land where the intolerable anxieties of life would fall away like an old garment. They would go to the watering-places first and among the bright and colorful crowds forget the gray appendages of despair. Marvellously renewed, he would walk again in the Piazza di Spogna at twilight, moving in that drifting flotsam of dark women and ragged beggars, of austere, barefooted friars. The thought of Italian women stirred him faintly—when his purse hung heavy again even romance might fly back to perch upon it—the romance of blue canals in Venice, of the golden green hills of Fiesole after rain, and of women, women who changed, dissolved, melted into other women and receded from his life, but who were always beautiful and always young.

But it seemed to him that there should be a difference in his attitude. All the distress that he had ever known, the sorrow and the pain, had been because of women. It was something that in different ways they did to him, unconsciously, almost casually—perhaps finding him tender-minded and afraid, they killed the things in him that menaced their absolute sway.

Turning about from the window he faced his reflection in the mirror, contemplating dejectedly the wan, pasty face, the eyes with their crisscross of lines like shreds of dried blood, the stooped and flabby figure whose very sag was a document in lethargy. He was thirty-three—he looked forty. Well, things would be different.

The door-bell rang abruptly and he started as though he had been dealt a blow. Recovering himself, he went into the hall and opened the outer door. It was Dot.

The Encounter

He retreated before her into the living room, comprehending only a word here and there in the slow flood of sentences that poured from her steadily, one after the other, in a persistent monotone. She was decently and shabbily dressed—a somehow pitiable little hat adorned with pink and blue flowers covered and hid her dark hair. He gathered from her words that several days before she had seen an item in the paper concerning the lawsuit, and had obtained his address from the clerk of the Appellate Division. She had called up the apartment and had been told that Anthony was out by a woman to whom she had refused to give her name.

In the living room he stood by the door regarding her with a sort of stupefied horror as she rattled on. . . . His predominant sensation was that all the civilization and convention around him was curiously unreal. . . . She was in a milliner's shop on Sixth Avenue, she said. It was a lonesome life. She had been sick for a long while after he left for Camp Mills; her mother had come down and taken her home again to Carolina. . . . She had come to New York with the idea of finding Anthony.

She was appallingly in earnest. Her violet eyes were red with tears; her soft intonation was ragged with little gasping sobs.

That was all. She had never changed. She wanted him now, and if she couldn't have him she must die. . . .

"You'll have to get out," he said at length, speaking with tortuous intensity. "Haven't I enough to worry me now without you coming here? My *God!* You'll have to get *out!*"

Sobbing, she sat down in a chair.

"I love you," she cried; "I don't care what you say to me! I love you."

"I don't care!" he almost shrieked; "get out—oh, get out! Haven't you done me harm enough? Haven't—you—done—*enough?*"

"Hit me!" she implored him—wildly, stupidly. "Oh, hit me, and I'll kiss the hand you hit me with!"

His voice rose until it was pitched almost at a scream. "I'll kill you!" he cried. "If you don't get out I'll kill you, I'll kill you!"

There was madness in his eyes now, but, unintimidated, Dot rose and took a step toward him.

"Anthony! Anthony!——"

He made a little clicking sound with his teeth and

drew back as though to spring at her—then, changing his purpose, he looked wildly about him on the floor and wall.

"I'll kill you!" he was muttering in short, broken gasps. "I'll *kill* you!" He seemed to bite at the word as though to force it into materialization. Alarmed at last she made no further movement forward, but meeting his frantic eyes took a step back toward the door. Anthony began to race here and there on his side of the room, still giving out his single cursing cry. Then he found what he had been seeking—a stiff oaken chair that stood beside the table. Uttering a harsh, broken shout, he seized it, swung it above his head and let it go with all his raging strength straight at the white, frightened face across the room . . . then a thick, impenetrable darkness came down upon him and blotted out thought, rage, and madness together—with almost a tangible snapping sound the face of the world changed before his eyes. . . .

Gloria and Dick came in at five and called his name. There was no answer—they went into the living room and found a chair with its back smashed lying in the doorway, and they noticed that all about the room there was a sort of disorder—the rugs had slid, the pictures and bric-à-brac were upset upon the centre table. The air was sickly sweet with cheap perfume.

They found Anthony sitting in a patch of sunshine on the floor of his bedroom. Before him, open, were spread his three big stamp-books, and when they entered he was running his hands through a great pile of stamps that he had dumped from the back of one of them. Looking up and seeing Dick and Gloria he put his head critically on one side and motioned them back.

"Anthony!" cried Gloria tensely, "we've won! They reversed the decision!"

"Don't come in," he murmured wanly, "you'll muss them. I'm sorting, and I know you'll step in them. Everything always gets mussed."

"What are you doing?" demanded Dick in astonishment. "Going back to childhood? Don't you realize you've won the suit? They've reversed the decision of the lower courts. You're worth thirty millions!"

Anthony only looked at him reproachfully.

"Shut the door when you go out." He spoke like a pert child.

With a faint horror dawning in her eyes, Gloria gazed at him——

"Anthony!" she cried, "what is it? What's the matter? Why didn't you come—why, what *is* it?"

"See here," said Anthony softly, "you two get out—now, both of you. Or else I'll tell my grandfather."

He held up a handful of stamps and let them come drifting down about him like leaves, varicolored and bright, turning and fluttering gaudily upon the sunny air: stamps of England and Ecuador, Venezuela and Spain—Italy. . . .

Together with the Sparrows

That exquisite heavenly irony which has tabulated the demise of so many generations of sparrows doubtless records the subtlest verbal inflections of the passengers of such ships as *The Berengaria*. And doubtless it was listening when the young man in the plaid cap crossed the deck quickly and spoke to the pretty girl in yellow.

"That's him," he said, pointing to a bundled figure seated in a wheel chair near the rail. "That's Anthony Patch. First time he's been on deck."

"Oh—that's him?"

"Yes. He's been a little crazy, they say, ever since he got his money, four or five months ago. You see, the other fellow, Shuttleworth, the religious fellow, the one that didn't get the money, he locked himself up in a room in a hotel and shot himself——"

"Oh, he *did*——"

"But I guess Anthony Patch don't care much. He got his thirty million. And he's got his private physician along in case he doesn't feel just right about it. Has *she* been on deck?" he asked.

The pretty girl in yellow looked around cautiously.

"She was here a minute ago. She had on a Russian-sable coat that must have cost a small fortune." She frowned and then added decisively: "I can't stand her, you know. She seems sort of—sort of dyed and *unclean*, if you know what I mean. Some people just have that look about them whether they are or not."

"Sure, I know," agreed the man with the plaid cap. "She's not bad-looking, though." He paused. "Wonder what he's thinking about—his money, I guess, or maybe he's got remorse about that fellow Shuttleworth."

"Probably. . . ."

But the man in the plaid cap was quite wrong. Anthony Patch, sitting near the rail and looking out at the sea, was not thinking of his money, for he had seldom in his life been really preoccupied with material vainglory, nor of Edward Shuttleworth, for it is best to look on the sunny side of these things. No—he was concerned with a series of reminiscences, much as a general might look back upon a successful campaign and analyze his victories. He was thinking of the hardships, the insufferable tribulations he had gone through. They had tried to penalize him for the mistakes of his youth. He had been exposed to ruthless misery, his very craving for romance had been punished, his friends had deserted him—even Gloria had turned against him. He had been alone, alone—facing it all.

Only a few months before people had been urging him to give in, to submit to mediocrity, to go to work. But he had known that he was justified in his way of life—and he had stuck it out stanchly. Why, the very friends who had been most unkind had come to respect him, to know he had been right all along. Had not the Lacys and the Merediths and the Cartwright-Smiths called on Gloria and him at the Ritz-Carlton just a week before they sailed?

Great tears stood in his eyes, and his voice was tremulous as he whispered to himself.

"I showed them," he was saying. "It was a hard fight, but I didn't give up and I came through!"

A los PIES del MAESTRO

DEVOCIONAL DIARIO

COMPILADO POR
Audie G. Lewis

SELECCIONES DE
LO MEJOR DE
CHARLES
SPURGEON

La misión de Editorial Vida es ser la compañía líder en comunicación cristiana que satisfaga las necesidades de las personas, con recursos cuyo contenido glorifique al Señor Jesucristo y promueva principios bíblicos.

A LOS PIES DEL MAESTRO
Edición en español publicada por
Editorial Vida – 2006
Miami, Florida

Originally published in the USA under the title:
At the Master's Feet: A Daily Devotional

Traducción: *Wendy Bello y Rebeca Fernández*
Edición: *Elizabeth Fraguela M.*
Diseño interior: *artserv*
Diseño de cubierta: *Cindy Davis*

ISBN 978-0-8297-4729-4

Categoría: Motivación / Devocional

IMPRESO EN ESTADOS UNIDOS DE AMÉRICA
PRINTED IN THE UNITED STATES OF AMERICA

12 13 14 15 ❖ 10 9 8 7 6

Este libro devocional está dedicado a los hombres y mujeres que han rendido sus vidas a Jesucristo. Al igual que Charles Spurgeon, son más felices cuando están sentados a los pies del Maestro.

Prólogo

Charles H. Spurgeon le predicó aproximadamente a diez millones de personas durante sus más de cuarenta años de ministerio antes de reunirse con el Señor en 1892. Cientos vinieron a Cristo bajo su influencia evangélica mientras sirvió como pastor en la Capilla New Park Street y el Tabernáculo Metropolitano en Londres, Inglaterra. Sin la ayuda de micrófonos u otra tecnología moderna, Charles Spurgeon pastoreó un rebaño de más de seis mil miembros, la congregación más grande de la que se tuviera noticia hasta antes de su ministerio. Durante ese mismo período ayudó a fundar más de cuarenta iglesias y supervisó el Colegio de pastores y el Orfanato Stockwell. A lo largo de su vida influenció grandemente las vidas de muchos grandes líderes cristianos como por ejemplo Dwight Moody, Hudson Taylor, George Mueller y Oswald Chambers. Alrededor del mundo se han vendido millones de copias de los escritos de Spurgeon, incluyendo una reduplicación constante de más de dos mil de sus mejores sermones. Aunque a menudo se le llama el «príncipe de los predicadores» sus palabras, llenas de una perspicacia dada por Dios, han bendecido a más laicos que a pastores.

Es nuestra esperanza que con la compilación de este devocional, muchos, muchos más laicos, pastores y futuros cristianos se animen y fortalezcan con la comprensión espiritual que hemos recopilado de lo mejor de lo mejor de los eternos sermones de Charles Spurgeon. Al final de cada página también hemos incluido una cita extra de las Escrituras que corresponde a un libro del Antiguo o el Nuevo

Testamento. Si se sigue esta lectura diaria adicional, el lector podrá completar la lectura de la Biblia completa en un año. ¡Que Dios continúe bendiciendo a cada uno de los lectores mientras se sientan con este gran pastor a los pies del Maestro!

AUDIE Y HEATHER LEWIS

Introducción

Al recordar mi historia, ni siquiera soñé que al abrir mi boca por primera vez para Cristo en una forma tan humilde, tendría el honor de traer a miles a los pies de Jesús. ¡Bendito, bendito sea su nombre! Suya es la gloria por esto. No puedo evitar pensar que debe haber otro muchacho aquí a quien, al igual que yo, él pueda llamar por su gracia a servirle. Cuando los diáconos de la iglesia de New Park Street me enviaron una carta para que fuera a predicar a Londres, yo la devolví al día siguiente diciéndoles que se habían equivocado, que yo era un muchacho de diecinueve años, que vivía feliz entre las personas muy pobres y humildes de Cambridgeshire que me amaban, y que no imaginaba que ellos quisieran que yo predicara en Londres. Pero ellos me la devolvieron y dijeron que todo eso lo sabían y que yo tenía que ir. ¡Ah, qué tremenda historia ha sido desde entonces la bondad y el cariño del Señor!

CHARLES HADDON SPURGEON
DEL SERMÓN «LOS PANES DEL JOVEN»

Adhiérase a la Palabra de Dios

[Los de Berea] eran de sentimientos más nobles que los de Tesalónica, de modo que recibieron el mensaje con toda avidez y todos los días examinaban las Escrituras para ver si era verdad lo que se les anunciaba.
HECHOS 17:11

Les recomiendo una escrupulosa obediencia a todos, especialmente a aquellos jóvenes que recientemente han hecho profesión de fe en Cristo. No sean como sus padres, porque la generación que está saliendo del escenario ni lee su Biblia, ni le interesa conocer la voluntad del Señor. Si las personas escudriñaran las Escrituras, deberíamos encontrarlas juntas en unidad, pero la Palabra de Dios es el libro menos leído del mundo, en proporción con su circulación. Se distribuye por todas partes, pero escasamente se lee en alguna parte con cuidado y atención, y con una sincera determinación a seguir sus preceptos a toda costa. Ustedes vienen y nos escuchan, y nosotros les damos pequeños pedazos tomados de aquí y de allá, pero no se llevan una amplia noción de la misma como un todo. ¿Cómo podrían llevársela? Los ministros cometen errores y ustedes los siguen sin preguntar. Uno elige este líder y el otro aquel, según las diferentes opiniones e incluso diferentes sectas, lo cual no debería ser, y no sería así si todos nos aferráramos a las normas de la verdad inspirada. Si se leyera la Biblia y se orara sobre ella, muchos errores morirían una muerte rápida y otros quedarían seriamente lisiados. Si en el pasado ustedes hubieran leído ese libro inspirado, muchos errores nunca habrían surgido. Por lo tanto, escudriñen el libro de Dios, y asegúrense de prestarle atención. Adhiéranse a la palabra de Dios a toda costa.

A través de la Biblia en un año: Mateo 1–2

Él suplirá para todas tus necesidades

Así que mi Dios les proveerá de todo lo que necesiten, conforme a las gloriosas riquezas que tiene en Cristo Jesús.

FILIPENSES 4:19

Si *él* te suplirá, de verdad estarás suplido, porque la capacidad de Dios es infinita. Él es infinitamente sabio en cuanto al método de sus acciones e infinitamente poderoso en cuando a las acciones en sí. Él nunca duerme ni se cansa, él nunca está ausente en ningún lugar sino que siempre está listo para ayudar. Quizá tus necesidades lleguen en momentos inesperados, pueden ocurrir a la media noche del desaliento o en el mediodía del regocijo, pero Dios siempre está cercano para suplir la necesidad sorpresiva. Él está presente en todas partes y es omnipotente en todas partes, y él puede suplir todas tus necesidades, en todo lugar, en todo tiempo y en el mayor grado. Recuerda que «la omnipotencia tiene siervos en todas partes» y que siempre que Dios quiere mandarte ayuda, lo puede hacer sin detenerse a preguntar: «¿Cómo se hará?» Lo único que él tiene que hacer es desearlo y todos los poderes del cielo y la tierra se subordinan a tu necesidad. Con un Ayudante así, ¿qué motivos tienes para dudar?

A través de la Biblia en un año: Mateo 3–4

Sacerdotes del Altísimo

Pero ustedes son linaje escogido, real sacerdocio, nación santa, pueblo que pertenece a Dios, para que proclamen las obras maravillosas de aquel que los llamó de las tinieblas a su luz admirable.

1 PEDRO 2:9

¡Alguien como Jesús en alguien como yo! ¡El Rey de gloria en el seno de un pecador! Esto es un milagro de la gracia, sin embargo, es lo suficientemente sencillo. Una fe humilde, que se arrepiente, abre la puerta y Jesús entra de una vez en el corazón. El amor cierra la puerta con la mano de la penitencia, la vigilancia santa mantiene alejados a los intrusos. Y así se cumple la promesa: «Mira que estoy a la puerta y llamo. Si alguno oye mi voz y abre la puerta, entraré, y cenaré con él, y él conmigo» (Apocalipsis 3:20). La meditación, la contemplación, la oración, la alabanza y la obediencia diaria mantienen la casa en orden para el Señor. Y luego viene la consagración de toda nuestra naturaleza para su uso como un templo, la dedicación del espíritu, el alma y el cuerpo y de todos sus poderes como vasijas santas del santuario. Es como escribir «santidad al Señor» en todo lo que nos rodea, hasta que nuestras ropas del diario se conviertan en vestiduras, nuestras comidas en sacramentos, nuestra vida en un ministerio y nosotros mismos en sacerdotes del Altísimo. ¡Qué suprema condescendencia de este morar dentro de nosotros! Él nunca moró en un ángel pero reside en un espíritu contrito. Hay un mundo de significado en las palabras del Redentor «Yo en ellos». Que las conozcamos como las traduce Pablo: «Cristo en ustedes, la esperanza de gloria».

A través de la Biblia en un año: Mateo 5–6

El discípulo a quien Jesús amó

En esto conocemos lo que es el amor: en que Jesucristo entregó su vida por nosotros. Así también nosotros debemos entregar la vida por nuestros hermanos.

1 Juan 3:16

Si tú anhelas ser «el discípulo a quien Jesús amó», empieza pronto. Yo supongo que Juan tendría entre veinte y veinticinco años cuando se convirtió; sea como sea, era un hombre bastante joven. Todas las imágenes que hemos recibido de él, aunque no les concedo gran valor, no obstante, coinciden con el hecho de su juventud. La piedad juvenil tiene la oportunidad más ventajosa de convertirse en piedad eminente. Si empiezas pronto a andar con Cristo, mejorarás tu paso y el hábito crecerá en ti. El que se hizo cristiano en los últimos años de su vida, escasamente alcanzará el primer grado por falta de tiempo y por la influencia entorpecedora de viejos hábitos. Pero el que comienza pronto está sembrando en buen terreno, con un aspecto soleado y debe llegar a la madurez.

Si quieres convertirte en el hombre a quien Jesús ama, cultiva un afecto fuerte y deja que tu naturaleza sea tierna y gentil. El hombre que de forma habitual está de mal humor y enojado, no puede andar con Dios. Un hombre de temperamento presuroso y violento que nunca trata de corregirlo o el hombre en quien hay un recuerdo malévolo de las heridas, como un fuego que arde en las ascuas, no puede ser el compañero y amigo de Jesús, cuyo espíritu es de naturaleza opuesta. El Señor aprueba un corazón lastimero, compasivo, desinteresado y generoso. Debes estar dispuesto a dar no solo tu comodidad, sino hasta tu vida por los hermanos. Vive en el gozo de otros, como hasta los santos hacen en el cielo. Así te convertirás en un hombre muy amado.

A través de la Biblia en un año: Mateo 7–8

Nuestro significado para Dios

Cuando contemplo tus cielos, obra de tus dedos, la luna y las estrellas que allí fijaste, me pregunto: «¿Qué es el hombre, para que en él pienses? ¿Qué es el ser humano, para que lo tomes en cuenta?»
SALMOS 8:3-4

Alza tus ojos a los cielos y cuenta las estrellas. Escucha al astrónomo cuando te dice que esas pequeñas motas de luz son mundos poderosos, algunos de ellos infinitamente superiores a este mundo nuestro y que en el cielo resplandecen millones y millones de mundos así y que quizá todos estos millones que podemos ver son solo una pequeña esquina, una pequeña duna de los mundos que Dios ha hecho, mientras que a lo largo del espacio ilimitado pudieran haber leguas de mundos, si se me permite la expresión, tan innumerables como la arena que circunda la costa de la profundidad. Y ahora, un hombre en un mundo ¡qué pequeño! Un hombre en las miríadas de mundos, un hombre en el universo ¡qué insignificante! Y he aquí el amor, que Dios amara tanto a una criatura tan insignificante. Porque, ¿qué es Dios en comparación con los mundos, su número y su probable extensión en el espacio? Dios es infinitamente mayor que todas las ideas que sugerimos con semejantes comparaciones. Dios mismo es mayor que todo el espacio. Ningún concepto de la grandeza que haya cruzado jamás la mente de las facultades más amplias nos permitiría entender la grandeza de Dios como él es en realidad. Sin embargo, este ser grande y glorioso, que llena todas las cosas y las sustenta con su poder, se digna a mirarnos, no con su pena, ten esto en cuenta, sino con el amor de su alma que es la esencia de sí mismo, porque él es amor. «¡En esto consiste el amor!»

A través de la Biblia en un año: Mateo 9–10

Lo que acosa a todos los hombres

Para que sean hijos de su Padre que está en el cielo. Él hace que salga el sol sobre malos y buenos, y que llueva sobre justos e injustos.
MATEO 5:45

Entre nosotros y otros hombres hay muchas diferencias, pero compartimos con ellos las enfermedades comunes, los trabajos, las pérdidas y las necesidades de nuestra raza caída. Estamos fuera de la entrada del Edén con el resto de la familia de Adán. Podemos ser amados de Dios y, no obstante, ser pobres. El amor de Dios por Lázaro no impidió que este estuviera en la puerta del hombre rico, ni tampoco que los perros lamieran sus heridas. Los santos pueden enfermarse al igual que otros hombres. Job, David y Ezequías experimentaron enfermedades dolorosas. Los santos van al hospital al igual que los pecadores, porque están sujetos a los mismos accidentes y dolencias. Los piadosos escapan a enfermedades como las que los hombres traen sobre sí mismos a causa de los vicios y, por lo general, el pueblo de Dios tiene una gran ventaja sobre los incautos y los reprobados en cuanto a la salud. Pero, no obstante, en este aspecto, los mejores de los hombres son solo hombres y a menudo se dirá: «Señor, el que amas está enfermo». Los elementos tienen el mismo poder sobre el cuerpo de los piadosos que sobre los demás, sobre ellos sopla el siroco y el frío penetra sus vestimentas, el sol los abrasa en la crueldad del calor del verano o la fría humedad amenaza la llama de la vida. En este aspecto, algo sucede a todos, aunque no sin diferencias misteriosas y bendecidas. Alrededor de los piadosos no hay ninguna pantalla que los cubra del sufrimiento físico, no están viviendo en la tierra de Gosén para que la luz anime su morada mientras que la densa niebla se cierne sobre el resto de la tierra.

A través de la Biblia en un año: Mateo 11–12

El amigo firme de la verdad

Consideró que el oprobio por causa del Mesías era una mayor riqueza que los tesoros de Egipto, porque tenía la mirada puesta en la recompensa.
HEBREOS 11:26

En la actualidad, la verdad que Dios ha revelado parece de menor importancia a los hombres que sus propios pensamientos y sueños y a los que todavía creen en la fiel palabra de Cristo se les debe decir: «fui forastero, y me dieron alojamiento» (Mateo 25:35). Cuando ves las verdad revelada, como fue, andando en pieles de cabra y de oveja, desamparada, afligida, atormentada y sin que nadie dijera nada bueno sobre esta, entonces llegó la hora de reconocerla —porque es la verdad de Cristo— y de demostrar tu fidelidad al considerar el reproche que Cristo recibió como una riqueza mayor que todos los tesoros de Egipto. Oh, desprecio a todos los que solo creen lo que todos los demás creen tan solo porque deben estar a tono con la mayoría. No son más que peces muertos que la corriente se llevará a un fin vergonzoso. Así como los peces vivos nadan contra la corriente, también los cristianos vivos buscan la verdad de Cristo en contra de la corriente y lo establecido por las épocas, desafiando tanto la ignorancia como la cultura de las edades. Es el honor del creyente, la hidalguía de un cristiano, ser el amigo firme de la verdad cuando todos los otros hombres la han desechado.

A través de la Biblia en un año: Mateo 13–14

Obedecer y confiar

Que el Dios de la esperanza los llene de toda alegría y paz a ustedes que creen en él, para que rebosen de esperanza por el poder del Espíritu Santo.
ROMANOS 15:13

La lección valiosa es que confíes en él. Si todo el poder es de él, apóyate en él. No nos apoyamos en Cristo lo suficiente. Él nunca se hundirá bajo tu peso. Cristo llevó todas las cargas que los hombres tendrían que cargar y sin duda alguna también lleva las tuyas. Con cuánta frecuencia nos agotamos al caminar cuando debiéramos dejarnos llevar, quiero decir, cargamos nuestros problemas cuando pudiéramos llevarlos a Cristo. Nos agobiamos, gemimos y lloramos y nuestras dificultades no disminuyen, pero cuando las dejamos con aquel que cuida de nosotros y comenzamos a confiar, como un niño confía en su padre, ¡cuán alegres y fuertes en espíritu nos volvemos!

El cielo es el lugar de descanso para nosotros, no este mundo de tentación y pecado. No obstante, prepárate para sufrir o servir. Vigila y espera en la puerta del Maestro para cumplir con su orden. Nunca dejes que tu espíritu esté averiado para el servicio cristiano, ni los días de la semana y mucho menos en el día del Señor. Debemos vivir de tal manera que si nos llamaran a morir en cualquier momento, no necesitemos hacer una oración, sino que estemos listos para el cielo, listos para una vida de servicio o para una muerte de gloria. La verdadera manera de vivir un cristiano en este mundo es estar siempre como quisiera estar si Cristo viniera en ese momento y hay una manera para vivir ese estilo: sencillamente depender de la sangre y la justicia de Jesucristo y luego ir a servirle cada día, por amor a él, diciéndole: «Señor, muéstrame lo que quieres que haga».

A través de la Biblia en un año: Mateo 15–16

Cristo murió por los pecadores

Esta justicia de Dios llega, mediante la fe en Jesucristo, a todos los que creen. De hecho, no hay distinción, pues todos han pecado y están privados de la gloria de Dios.
ROMANOS 3:22-23

El apóstol dice aquí que «no hay distinción», no obstante, él no quiere decir que todos los hombres sean iguales en todos los aspectos. Existen muchas e importantes diferencias entre los hombres. Sería bastante impropio e injusto decir que no hay diferencias de carácter incluso entre los hombres no regenerados porque sin dudas existen muchas variedades y grados de pecadores. Existen algunos que, por así decirlo, se han vendido para hacer lo malo y hay otros que, al parecer, guardaron los mandamientos de Dios desde su juventud.

Entonces, existen diferencias de carácter entre los hombres y, sin dudas, hay diferencias de disposiciones que se muestran desde muy temprano. Algunos niños resultan tiernos y dóciles desde un principio, mientras que otros manifiestan una actitud apasionada y rebelde. Es muy probable que todos conozcamos amigos que todavía no se han convertido pero que son amables, afectuosos, considerados, bondadosos, tienen casi todo lo que pudiéramos desear excepto la única cosa necesaria. ¡Dios quiera que pronto también tengan eso! Qué pena, hay otros cuya actitud es lo contrario, parecen dispuestos a todo lo que es malo.

Hay un punto en el que no hay diferencias y es que «todos han pecado». Todos hemos perdido el derecho de reclamar justicia propia, todos debemos ser hechos justos mediante la atribución de la justicia de Cristo y todos los que tengan esa justicia deben creer en el Señor Jesucristo, porque hay un camino de salvación, y solo uno, y no importa cualquier otra diferencia que pudiera existir, en este aspecto no hay diferencia; si vamos a ser salvos, tenemos que ser salvos de esta única manera.

A través de la Biblia en un año: Mateo 17-18

Marchar en paz

Según tu palabra, Soberano Señor, ya puedes despedir a tu siervo en paz. Porque han visto mis ojos tu salvación.
LUCAS 2:29–30

La base de la esperanza de Simeón para una partida en paz era «según tu palabra» y con certeza ninguna Escritura es de interpretación privada ni está reservada para un creyente con exclusión del resto. Las promesas de Dios, que «son "sí" en Cristo», son seguras para toda la simiente, la promesa no se ha hecho para algunos de los hijos, sino que todos los nacidos de la gracia son herederos. Si Simeón, como un creyente en el Señor, tenía la promesa de que partiría en paz, yo también tengo una promesa similar si estoy en Cristo.

En la muerte, cada creyente debe partir con el mismo sentido que partió Simeón. La palabra que se utiliza aquí es sugerente y alentadora: podría aplicarse ya sea a escapar de confinamiento o a la liberación de los afanes. El hombre cristiano en el estado actual es como un pájaro en una jaula: su cuerpo encarcela su alma. Pero viene el día en que el gran Maestro abrirá la puerta de la jaula y liberará a sus prisioneros, que cantarán todo el tiempo en un éxtasis más allá de la imaginación. Simeón miraba la muerte como una manera de quedar en libertad, una liberación de una terrible detención, un escape de la cautividad, una liberación de la esclavitud. A nosotros se nos otorgará igual redención. Dios, quien nos encomendó que aspiráramos a la santidad y a la espiritualidad y a la semejanza a él, nunca puso esas aspiraciones en nosotros para burlarse. Su intención es gratificar esos deseos santos o de lo contrario no los hubiera incitado.

A través de la Biblia en un año: Mateo 19–20

Ciudadanos del cielo en la tierra

En cambio, nosotros somos ciudadanos del cielo.
FILIPENSES 3:20

¿Qué quiere decir que somos ciudadanos del cielo? Bueno, pues primero, que estamos bajo el gobierno del cielo. Cristo, el rey del cielo, reina en nuestros corazones; las leyes de la gloria son las leyes de nuestras conciencias; nuestra oración diaria es: «hágase tu voluntad en la tierra como en el cielo». Recibimos libremente las proclamaciones que se emiten desde el trono de gloria; obedecemos alegremente los decretos del Gran Rey. Para Cristo no estamos sin ley. El Espíritu de Dios gobierna en nuestros cuerpos mortales, la gracia reina por medio de la justicia y llevamos el yugo fácil de Jesús. Ay, que él se sienta en nuestros corazones como Rey, igual que Salomón en su trono de oro. Somos tuyos, Jesús, así como todo lo que tenemos; gobierna tú sin rival.

Que nuestras vidas sean conformadas a la gloria de nuestra ciudadanía. En el cielo son santos, así que nosotros debemos serlo si nuestra ciudadanía no es una mera pretensión. Allí son felices, así que nosotros debemos regocijarnos siempre en el Señor. En el cielo son obedientes, así debemos serlo nosotros, siguiendo la menor amonestación de la voluntad divina. En el cielo son activos, así debemos ser nosotros, alabando y sirviendo a Dios día y noche. En el cielo hay paz, así que nosotros debemos encontrar reposo en Cristo y estar en paz incluso ahora. En el cielo se regocijan al estar ante el rostro de Cristo; así debemos nosotros estar siempre meditando en él, estudiando su belleza y deseando examinar las verdades que él ha enseñado. En el cielo están llenos de amor, y nosotros debemos amarnos unos a otros como hermanos. En el cielo tienen una dulce comunión unos con otros; así nosotros, aunque somos muchos, somos un cuerpo, miembros los unos de los otros.

A través de la Biblia en un año: Mateo 21–22

Ser ricos para Dios

No acumulen para sí tesoros en la tierra, donde la polilla y el óxido destruyen, y donde los ladrones se meten a robar. Más bien, acumulen para sí tesoros en el cielo, donde ni la polilla ni el óxido carcomen, ni los ladrones se meten a robar. Porque donde esté tu tesoro, allí estará también tu corazón.

MATEO 6:19–21

Hombres cristianos, nunca deben codiciar la estima del mundo; el amor de este mundo no está en conformidad con el amor de Dios. «Si alguien ama al mundo, no tiene el amor del Padre» (1 Juan 2:15). Traten sus sonrisas como tratan sus amenazas, con silencioso desdén. Mejor estén dispuestos a sufrir burla que a tener aprobación, consideren la cruz de Cristo mayor riqueza que todos los tesoros de Egipto. Los hombres de este mundo fueron hechos para ponernos en sus puestos de honor, porque somos extranjeros y ciudadanos de otro país.

Además, como extranjeros, no nos corresponde acumular los tesoros de este mundo. Si somos extranjeros, los tesoros de este mundo son como pedazos de papel, de poco valor para nosotros; y debemos almacenar nuestros tesoro en el cielo, «donde ni la polilla ni el óxido carcomen, ni los ladrones se meten a robar» (Mateo 6:20). El dinero de este mundo no está vigente en el paraíso, y cuando lleguemos a su bienaventurada costa, si se pueden experimentar remordimientos, debemos desear haber acumulado más tesoros en la tierra de nuestra paternidad, en la querida patria más allá de los cielos. Transporta tus joyas a un país más seguro que este mundo; sé más bien rico para Dios que para los hombres.

A través de la Biblia en un año: Mateo 23–24

Violencia sagrada

La oración del justo es poderosa y eficaz.
SANTIAGO 5:16

Nunca desistas en tus oraciones. Ningún tiempo es malo para orar. El resplandor de la luz del día no debe tentarte a desistir y la oscuridad de la medianoche no debe hacerte interrumpir tu clamor. Yo sé que uno de los objetivos principales de Satanás es hacer que los cristianos dejen de orar, porque si él pudiera aunque fuera una vez levantar el arma de la oración, fácilmente nos vencería y nos tomaría como su presa. Pero mientras sigamos clamando al Altísimo, Satanás no puede devorar ni a la más débil de las ovejas del rebaño. La oración, la oración poderosa, prevalecerá si se le da el tiempo necesario.

Y aunque nunca desistas de confiar ni de orar, crece con más fervor en ambas. Deja que tu fe esté aun más dispuesta a renunciar a toda dependencia que no sea en Dios, y deja que tu clamor se vuelva más y más vehemente. La puerta de la misericordia no se abre con cualquier toque, el que prevalezca debe sujetar bien la aldaba y dejarla caer una y otra vez, y otra vez y otra vez. Como dice el viejo refrán puritano: «Las oraciones frías piden denegación, las oraciones que prevalecen son las oraciones calientes». Trae tus oraciones a la puerta del cielo como si fueran un antiguo ariete y ábrela a la fuerza con violencia sagrada porque «el reino de los cielos sufre violencia, y los violentos lo arrebatan» (RVR, 1960). El que vaya a prevalecer con Dios debe ocuparse de que toda su fuerza caiga sobre sus oraciones.

A través de la Biblia en un año: Mateo 25–26

En este mundo

Yo les he dicho estas cosas para que en mí hallen paz. En este mundo afrontarán aflicciones, pero ¡anímense! Yo he vencido al mundo.

JUAN 16:33

El creyente está en dos lugares y vive dos vidas. En el texto se habla de dos lugares: «en mí» y «en este mundo». La vida más noble de un santo está «escondida con Cristo en Dios»; esta es su nueva vida, su vida espiritual, su vida incorruptible, su vida eterna. Amado, regocíjate si estás en Cristo, y disfruta el privilegio que pertenece a esa condición: «en mí hallen paz». No estés satisfecho sin ella, es tu derecho por medio de tu relación con el Príncipe de Paz. Estás en Cristo y por eso tu vida siempre está a salvo y siempre debes estar tranquilo. Tus mayores intereses están todos seguros porque están garantizados por el pacto del cual Jesús es la garantía. Tu tesoro, tu porción eterna, está almacenada en él, en el cielo, donde ni el óxido ni los ladrones pueden entrar. Por lo tanto, anímate.

Estás lamentablemente consciente de que también tienes otra vida, moras en medio de hombres malos, o como dice el texto, estás «en este mundo». Aunque mores en el dulce aislamiento de la vida doméstica, aunque tu familia haya sido visitada con gracia y tus seres queridos sean todos creyentes, aun allí ocurren cosas que te hacen sentir que estás «en este mundo», un mundo de pecado y tristeza. Todavía no estás en el cielo, no sueñes con que lo estás. Sería una lástima que un marinero esperara que el mar fuera tan estable como la tierra, porque el mar siempre será el mar y el mundo será el mundo para ti mientras estés en él.

A través de la Biblia en un año: Mateo 27-28

Trabaja para él

Hermanos míos, ¿de qué le sirve a uno alegar que tiene fe, si no tiene obras?
SANTIAGO 2:14

Muy pocos de nosotros podemos soportar el dolor, quizá somos menos los que podemos soportar la tergiversación, la calumnia y la ingratitud. Quizá estos son avispones que pican como con fuego; hay hombres que se han vuelto locos debido a escándalos crueles provenientes de lenguas venenosas. Cristo, en la vida, soportó estos y otros sufrimientos. Amémoslo mientras pensamos cuánto él nos debe haber amado. ¿Tratarían de saturar sus almas con el amor de Cristo? Admiren el poder de su amor y luego oren para que puedan tener un amor de alguna manera similar a este en poder.

A veces nos preguntamos por qué la iglesia de Dios crece tan lentamente, pero yo no me lo pregunto cuando recuerdo cuán escasa consagración a Cristo hay en la iglesia de Dios. Jesús fue un «varón de dolores, hecho para el sufrimiento» (Isaías 53:3), pero muchos de sus discípulos, quienes profesan ser de él completamente, están viviendo para sí mismos. Hay hombres ricos que se llaman a sí mismos santos y se creen que lo son, cuyos tesoros están acumulados para sí mismos y sus familias. Quizá tú tengas que confesar que no estás hacienda nada, no dejes que este día termine sin que hayas comenzado a hacer algo para tu Señor. Estamos hablando de que la iglesia haga esto o aquello, ¿qué es la iglesia? La iglesia es solo un conglomerado de personas, y si se va hacer algún bien, deben realizarlo las personas, y si todas las personas son holgazanas, no hay trabajo hecho por la iglesia. Puede que exista la apariencia de este, pero en realidad no se hace ningún trabajo. Hermano, hermana, ¿qué estás haciendo para Jesús? Te encargo, por las marcas de los clavos en sus manos, ¡que trabajes para él!

A través de la Biblia en un año: Génesis 1-4

Dios es soberano

El Señor le respondió a Job desde la tempestad. Le dijo: «¿Quién es éste, que oscurece mi consejo con palabras carentes de sentido? Prepárate a hacerme frente; yo te cuestionaré, y tú me responderás. ¿Dónde estabas cuando puse las bases de la tierra? ¡Dímelo, si de veras sabes tanto!»

JOB 38:1-4

El Dios de las Escrituras es un Dios soberano; es decir, es un Dios que tiene autoridad y poder absolutos para hacer exactamente lo que le plazca. Por encima de Dios no hay ley, sobre su brazo no hay necesidad, él no conoce otra regla que no sea su propia voluntad libre y poderosa. Y aunque él no puede ser injusto y no puede hacer nada que no sea bueno, no obstante, su naturaleza es absolutamente libre, para bien es la libertad de la naturaleza de Dios. La voluntad del hombre no puede controlar a Dios, ni tampoco los deseos del hombre, ni el destino en el que creen los supersticiosos; él es Dios, hace lo que quiera en los ejércitos del cielo y en este mundo inferior.

Él también es un Dios, quien no da cuenta de sus asuntos; hace a sus criaturas como quiere hacerlas y hace con ellas como le parece. Y si alguna de estas se resiente por sus actos, él les dice: «¿Quién eres tú para pedirle cuentas a Dios? ¿Acaso le dirá la olla de barro al que la modeló: "¿Por qué me hiciste así?" ¿No tiene derecho el alfarero de hacer del mismo barro unas vasijas para usos especiales y otras para fines ordinarios?"» (Romanos 9:20-21). Dios es bueno; pero Dios es soberano, absoluto, no hay nada que lo pueda controlar. La monarquía de este mundo no es una monarquía constitucional ni limitada, no es tiránica sino que está absolutamente en las manos de un Dios que es toda sabiduría.

A través de la Biblia en un año: Génesis 5–8

Que el nombre de Cristo permanezca

Pues aún son inmaduros. Mientras haya entre ustedes celos y contiendas, ¿no serán inmaduros? ¿Acaso no se estarán comportando según criterios meramente humanos? Cuando uno afirma: "Yo sigo a Pablo", y otro: "Yo sigo a Apolos", ¿no es porque están actuando con criterios humanos? Después de todo, ¿qué es Apolos? ¿Y qué es Pablo? Nada más que servidores por medio de los cuales ustedes llegaron a creer, según lo que el Señor le asignó a cada uno. Yo sembré, Apolos regó, pero Dios ha dado el crecimiento.

1 Corintios 3:3-6

¿Quieres que le pongan tu nombre a todo lo que haces? Procura que Dios no te permita satisfacer tu deseo y luego te diga: «Ahí tienes, has hecho eso para ti, así que puedes premiarte a ti mismo por eso». Siempre que puedas, mantén tu nombre fuera de todo el trabajo que haces para el Señor. Yo solía ver que en París no había un puente o edificio público que no tuviera la letra N en algún lugar. Ahora, ve por toda la ciudad y encuentra una N si puedes. Napoleón esperaba que su fama viviera en un mármol imperecedero, pero al fin y al cabo escribió su nombre en la arena; y si alguno de nosotros piensa, en nuestro ministerio, que el asunto importante es que nuestro nombre sea prominente, vamos por el camino equivocado. Cuando a George Whitefield se le pidió que comenzara un nuevo grupo religioso, él dijo: «No condeno a mi hermano Wesley por lo que ha hecho, pero no puedo hacer lo mismo; que mi nombre perezca, pero que el nombre de Cristo perdure para siempre y siempre».

A través de la Biblia en un año: Génesis 9–12

Obediencia en las cosas pequeñas

Su señor le respondió: «¡Hiciste bien, siervo bueno y fiel! En lo poco has sido fiel; te pondré a cargo de mucho más. ¡Ven a compartir la felicidad de tu señor!»

MATEO 25:21

A menudo las mejores pruebas de la verdad de nuestra religión son las cosas pequeñas por Cristo. La obediencia en las cosas pequeñas tiene mucho que ver con el carácter de un sirviente. Uno emplea a un sirviente en la casa y sabe muy bien si será un sirviente malo o bueno, si las actividades principales del día están bien atendidas: las comidas cocinadas, las camas listas, la casa barrida, si atiende la puerta; pero la diferencia entre un sirviente que hace al hogar feliz y otro que es una plaga yace en varios asuntos pequeños los cuales, por ventura, no podrías anotar en un papel pero constituyen una gran comodidad o incomodidad doméstica y, por lo tanto, determinan el valor de un siervo. Así creo yo que sucede en la vida cristiana. Me imagino que la mayoría de nosotros nunca omitiría los asuntos más críticos de la ley; como hombres cristianos intentamos mantener integridad y rectitud en nuestras acciones, y tratamos de ordenar nuestras familias en el temor de Dios en cuanto a los asuntos grandes. Pero el espíritu de obediencia se manifiesta más al buscar al Señor en los detalles pequeños, se ve al mantener nuestros ojos en el Señor. El espíritu verdaderamente obediente desea conocer la voluntad del Señor acerca de todo y de haber algún punto que al mundo le pareciera trivial, esa es la razón misma por la cual el espíritu obediente dice: «Cuidaré de este para demostrar a mi Señor que incluso en las minucias yo deseo someter mi alma a su agrado».

A través de la Biblia en un año: Génesis 13–16

Persevera hasta la madurez

Hermanos míos, considérense muy dichosos cuando tengan que enfrentarse con diversas pruebas, pues ya saben que la prueba de su fe produce constancia. Y la constancia debe llevar a feliz término la obra, para que sean perfectos e íntegros, sin que les falte nada.
SANTIAGO 1:2-4

A veces, si la misericordia llegara a un creyente inmediatamente después de que la pidiera, sería demasiado pronto, pero Dios mide el tiempo para que llegue solo en el momento más adecuado y mejor. Quizá todavía no estés listo para la bendición. Has pedido carne fuerte pero todavía eres un bebé y, por lo tanto, debes estar contento con la leche durante un tiempo más. Has pedido las pruebas, privilegios y trabajos de un hombre pero todavía eres solo un niño que está creciendo para convertirse en un hombre, y tu buen Padre te dará lo que pides pero te lo dará de manera que no sea una carga para ti sino un beneficio. Si viniera ahora, tal vez implicaría responsabilidades que no podrías abarcar, pero al venir poco a poco, estarás preparado para esta.

No dudo que también existan razones en nuestro futuro de por qué nuestras oraciones no son contestadas. Las demoras en la oración podrían resultar en una especie de escuela de entrenamiento para nosotros. Mira por ejemplo el caso del apóstol. La «espina en la carne» era muy dolorosa y aunque él era un apóstol escogido, no tenía respuesta. Tres veces clamó pero la «espina en la carne» no se quitó. Y fue bueno que así sucediera porque Pablo necesitaba que se le enseñara ternura para que pudiera escribir esas epístolas amorosas y, por lo tanto, recibió una respuesta de otra clase: «Te basta con mi gracia».

A través de la Biblia en un año: Génesis 17–20

El Dios de las Escrituras

No se engañen: de Dios nadie se burla. Cada uno cosecha lo que siembra. El que siembra para agradar a su naturaleza pecaminosa, de esa misma naturaleza cosechará destrucción; el que siembra para agradar al Espíritu, del Espíritu cosechará vida eterna.

GÁLATAS 6:7-8

Y ahora declaramos que el Dios de las santas Escrituras es un Dios de justicia inflexible, no es el Dios al que algunos de ustedes adoran. Ustedes adoran a un dios que pestañea ante los grandes pecados, ustedes creen en un dios que llama a sus delitos pecadillos y pequeñas faltas. Algunos de ustedes adoran a un dios que no castiga el pecado sino que es tan débilmente misericordioso y tan despiadadamente débil que deja pasar las transgresiones y la iniquidad y nunca ejerce castigo. Ustedes creen en un dios que, si un hombre peca, no pide castigo por su delito. Piensan que unas pocas buenas obras de su parte lo apaciguarán, que es tan débil como gobernante que unas pocas palabras bien dichas delante de él, en oración, tendrán el mérito suficiente como para revocar la sentencia, si es que ustedes creen que de alguna manera él establece una sentencia. Su dios no es Dios, es un dios tan falso como el dios de los griegos o el de la antigua Nínive. El Dios de las Escrituras es rigurosamente severo en la justicia y de ninguna manera exonerará al culpable. «Jehová es tardo para la ira y grande en poder, y no tendrá por inocente al culpable» (Nahúm 1:3, RVR 1960). El Dios de las Escrituras es un gobernante que, cuando sus súbditos se rebelan, señala su crimen y nunca los perdona hasta haberlos castigado, ya sea a ellos mismos o a un sustituto.

A través de la Biblia en un año: Génesis 21–24

Ámense los unos a los otros

Queridos hermanos, ya que Dios nos ha amado así, también nosotros debemos amarnos los unos a los otros. Nadie ha visto jamás a Dios, pero si nos amamos los unos a los otros, Dios permanece entre nosotros, y entre nosotros su amor se ha manifestado plenamente.

1 JUAN 4:11-12

Cristiano, por el amor que Dios te ha manifestado, estás obligado a amar a tus compañeros cristianos. Debes amarlos aunque tengan muchas debilidades. Tú también tienes algunas y si no puedes amar a alguien porque tiene un temperamento brusco, quizá esa persona responda que no te puede amar porque tú tienes un espíritu lánguido. Jesús te amó con todas tus debilidades, así que ama a tus hermanos débiles. Me dices que no puedes amar porque tal hermano te ha ofendido ¡pero tú también ofendiste a Cristo! ¿Qué? ¿Acaso debe Cristo perdonar tus miles de ofensas aunque tú no perdones a tu hermano? Al fin y al cabo, ¿qué pasó? «Bueno, no me trató con respeto». Ah, es eso, ¡un pobre gusano quiere que lo traten con respeto! «Pero me habló en tono desdeñoso y hay una hermana aquí, será una mujer cristiana pero dijo algo muy cruel sobre mí». Bueno, sí, ¿y qué importa? Cuando las personas han hablado mal de mí y han sido muy, muy falsos al hacerlo, yo he pensado a menudo que quizá de haberme conocido mejor, hubieran encontrado algo verdadero que decir, y por tanto yo debo ser como a veces decimos de un muchacho al que le han dado sin que lo merezca: «sí se lo merecía, si no ahora, alguna que otra vez, por alguna otra cosa». En lugar de enojarte, sonríe ante la ofensa. ¿Quiénes somos para esperar que todo el mundo nos honre cuando nadie honró a nuestro Señor? Estemos listos de una vez para perdonar hasta setenta veces siete.

A través de la Biblia en un año Génesis 25-28

¿Cómo pueden trabajar los muertos?

En otro tiempo ustedes estaban muertos en sus transgresiones y pecados.
EFESIOS 2:1

La vida espiritual no es el resultado del trabajo, ¿cómo pueden los muertos trabajar para la vida? ¿No se deben despertar primero y luego, no trabajarían más bien de la vida que para la vida? La vida es un don y otorgársela a cualquier hombre debe ser un acto de Dios. El evangelio predica la vida que Jesucristo nos da. Pecador, ¡mira a dónde tienes que buscar! Dependes por completo de la voz que vivifica, de aquel que es la resurrección y la vida. «Esto», diría alguno, «es muy desalentador para nosotros». Así se espera que sea. Es bueno desanimar a los hombres cuando están actuando de acuerdo a principios equivocados. Siempre y cuando pienses que tu salvación puede afectarse por tus propios esfuerzos, méritos o cualquier otra cosa que pueda salir de ti mismo, vas por el camino equivocado y es nuestro deber desanimarte. Recuerda que la declaración de Dios es «que todo el que cree en él no se pierda, sino que tenga vida eterna». Si, por lo tanto, se te permite venir y entregarte a la sangre y a la justicia de Jesucristo, inmediatamente tienes la vida eterna que nunca te podrían brindar todas tus oraciones, lágrimas, arrepentimiento, asistencia a la iglesia, asistencia a la capilla y sacramentos. Jesús te la puede dar libremente en este momento, pero tú no puedes producirla por ti mismo.

Puedes imitarla y engañarte a ti mismo, puede que adornes el cadáver y hagas parecer que estuvieras vivo y puedes galvanizarlo en un movimiento irregular, pero la vida es un fuego divino y tú mismo no puedes aquietar la llama o encenderla; solo a Dios le corresponde avivar y por tanto, te insto a que solo busques a Dios en Jesucristo.

A través de la Biblia en un año: Génesis 29–32

Ten cuidado con el pecado

Porque la paga del pecado es muerte, mientras que la dádiva de Dios es vida eterna en Cristo Jesús, nuestro Señor.
ROMANOS 6:23

Ahora bien, esta tendencia es la misma en cualquier caso: «la paga del pecado es muerte» en cualquier lugar y para todo el mundo. Es así no solo donde puedes verlo operando en el cuerpo sino también donde no puedes verlo. Tal vez te sorprendas cuando te diga que la paga del pecado es muerte incluso en el hombre que tiene vida eterna. El pecado tiene el mismo carácter mortífero en uno y en otro, y solo se existe un antídoto. Tú, mi hermano cristiano, no puedes caer en el pecado sin que este te resulte venenoso, al igual que le sucede a todos los demás, de hecho, para ti es más venenoso que para los que ya están endurecidos por este. Si pecas, esto destruye tu gozo, tu poder en la oración, tu confianza en Dios. Si has pasado noches de frivolidad con personas mundanas, has sentido la influencia mortífera de su compañía. ¿Y qué de tus oraciones por las noches? No puedes acercarte a Dios. La operación del pecado sobre tu espíritu es más que dañina a tu comunión con Dios. Eres como un hombre que ha tomado una droga nociva cuyo humo está aturdiendo el cerebro y adormeciendo el corazón. Si tú, siendo un hijo de Dios, caes en cualquiera de los pecados que tan fácilmente te asedian, estoy seguro que nunca verás que esos pecados despiertan tu gracia ni aumentan tu fe, por el contrario, te harán más y más daño y así será continuamente.

A través de la Biblia en un año: Génesis 33–36

Vivir más allá de nosotros mismos

Por lo tanto, siempre que tengamos la oportunidad, hagamos bien a todos, y en especial a los de la familia de la fe.
GÁLATAS 6:10

Al convertirnos en hacedores del bien, se nos conoce como hijos del buen Dios. «Dichosos los que trabajan por la paz, porque serán llamados hijos de Dios» (Mateo 5:9). Un hombre es hijo de Dios cuando vive más allá de sí mismo interesándose siempre en los demás, cuando su alma no está confinada al círculo estrecho de sus propias narices, sino que anda bendiciendo a los que le rodean sin importar cuán indignos sean. Los verdaderos hijos de Dios nunca ven a una persona perdida sin intentar salvarla, nunca oyen de un sufrimiento sin anhelar impartir consuelo. «No opriman al extranjero, pues ya lo han experimentado en carne propia», le dijo el Señor a Israel (Éxodo 23:9); y lo mismo pasa con nosotros, que una vez fuimos cautivos e incluso ahora nuestro Amigo más selecto sigue siendo un Extranjero por amor a quien amamos a todos los hombres que sufren. Cuando Cristo está en nosotros, buscamos oportunidades de llevar a pródigos, a extranjeros y marginados a la casa del gran Padre. Nuestro amor se extiende a toda la humanidad y nuestra mano no se cierra para nadie: si es así, somos como Dios, al igual que los niños pequeños son como su padre. ¡Qué dulce resultado da aceptar al Hijo de Dios como nuestro Salvador mediante la fe! Él mora en nosotros y nosotros lo contemplamos en santa comunión de manera que «todos nosotros, que con el rostro descubierto reflejamos como en un espejo la gloria del Señor, somos transformados a su semejanza con más y más gloria por la acción del Señor, que es el Espíritu» (2 Corintios 3:18).

A través de la Biblia en un año: Génesis 37–40

El Dios de la compasión

Jesús lloró.

JUAN 11:35

Debemos llorar, porque Jesús lloró. Jesús lloró por otros. No sé si alguna vez él lloró por sí mismo. Sus lágrimas fueron compasivas. Él personificó el mandamiento: «Lloren con los que lloran» (Romanos 12:15). El que puede guardarlo todo dentro del radio de su propio ser, tiene un alma estrecha. Un alma verdadera, un alma cristiana, vive en las almas y cuerpos de otros hombre así como en la suya propia. Un alma perfectamente cristiana considera que el mundo entero es demasiado estrecho para su morada, porque esta vive y ama, vive amando y ama porque vive.

Un mar de lágrimas delante del Dios tres veces santo hará mucho más que las enormes listas de peticiones a nuestros senadores. «Jesús lloró» y sus lágrimas fueron armas poderosas contra el pecado y la muerte. Por favor, observa que no dice que Jesús vociferó sino que «Jesús lloró». Le harás más bien a quienes te ofenden, más bien a ti mismo y más bien a las mejores causas si la compasión lo humedece todo.

Por último, si has llorado, imita a tu Salvador y ¡haz algo! Si el capítulo que tenemos delante concluyera con «Jesús lloró», sería un capítulo pobre. Imagínate que leyéramos que después de ellos haber ido a la tumba: «Jesús lloró y siguió con sus tareas diarias». Yo habría sentido muy poco consuelo en el pasaje. De no haber nada más que lágrimas, habría sido una gran disminución de la actitud acostumbrada de nuestro bendito Señor. ¡Lágrimas! ¿Qué son por sí solas? Agua salada. Una taza de estas le sirve de muy poco a alguien. Pero amados, «Jesús lloró» y luego ordenó: «Quiten la piedra». Él gritó: «¡Lázaro, sal fuera!»

A través de la Biblia en un año: Génesis 41–44

Nunca te rindas

¿Acaso Dios no hará justicia a sus escogidos, que claman a él día y noche? ¿Se tardará mucho en responderles?

LUCAS 18:7

Mientras haya un espacio para la oración y una promesa de respuesta, el creyente no debe dar lugar al desánimo. «Ve otra vez», le dijo Elías a su siervo siete veces. Debe haber sido agotador para el profeta tener que esperar tanto. Él no se paró una sola vez y oró a Dios como en el Carmelo y luego bajó el fuego de inmediato para continuar el sacrificio; sino una y otra vez, y poniéndose en una postura más humilde, con la cara entre sus rodillas, él le ruega al Señor, no por fuego, que era algo inusual, sino por agua, que es el regalo común de los cielos. Y, no obstante, aunque él implora lo que el mismo Señor había prometido, no vino de una vez. Y cuando su siervo regresó, cuatro, cinco y seis veces, la respuesta era la misma, no había señal de lluvia sino que los cielos bronceados miraban a una tierra que estaba tan seca como un horno. «¡Vuelve otra vez!», dijo el profeta y a la séptima vez, ¡mira! Apareció una nube tan pequeña como una mano y esta nube fue la precursora de una tormenta y de una inundación. Cristiano, ve de nuevo siete veces. Incluso más, me aventuro a decir setenta veces siete, porque Dios debe mantener su promesa. El cielo y la tierra pasarán pero ni una jota de la palabra de Jehová puede fallar. «La hierba se seca y la flor se marchita, pero la palabra de nuestro Dios permanece para siempre» (Isaías 40:8). ¿Suplicas tú esa Palabra duradera? No dejes que los pensamientos tenebrosos te lleven al desánimo. Sigue confiando, sigue orando, aumenta tu fervor con la esperanza de que la bendición está por venir.

A través de la Biblia en un año: Génesis 45–47

El poder de la iglesia

El Hijo es el resplandor de la gloria de Dios, la fiel imagen de lo que él es, y el que sostiene todas las cosas con su palabra poderosa.

HEBREOS 1:3

El verdadero poder de la iglesia descansa en Cristo personalmente. Puede que tengas todas las estrellas que hacen brillar la Vía Láctea con todo su brillo combinado, pero no tienen poder para acabar con el mal ni conquistar el pecado. Las estrellas de la iglesia brillan porque Dios las hace brillar. Su brillo no es propio, es una luz prestada mediante la cual son radiantes. Pero el poder que vence al mal, que cura al corazón endurecido, que penetra la conciencia y que mata al pecado reinante, es solo del Señor. «de su boca salía una aguda espada de dos filos» (Apocalipsis 1:16). Por lo tanto, no te glories en el hombre porque su poder le pertenece a Dios.

El poder descansa en la palabra de Cristo: «de su boca salía una aguda espada de dos filos». «El que reciba mi palabra, que la proclame con fidelidad … afirma el Señor» (Jeremías 23:28). El verdadero evangelio perturba e inquieta a las personas: ante el evangelio falso pueden morir para destrucción. Saca la espada, está hecha para herir, déjala ejercer su filo saludable. El evangelio tiene dos filos para que nadie juegue con él. Cuando alguien piense en pasar sus dedos por el reverso de este, se cortará hasta el hueso. Ya sea que estimemos sus amenazas o sus promesas, este corta el pecado. Sepamos por lo tanto que el poder de la iglesia no descansa en ningún otro lugar que en la misma Palabra mientras el propio Jesús la expresa. Sigamos, pues, su palabra pura, no adulterada, afilada y oremos a él para que la envíe con poder de su boca a los corazones y conciencias de los hombres.

A través de la Biblia en un año: Génesis 48–50

Batallas en la guerra de la vida

Sabemos, en efecto, que la ley es espiritual. Pero yo soy meramente humano, y estoy vendido como esclavo al pecado. No entiendo lo que me pasa, pues no hago lo que quiero, sino lo que aborrezco.
ROMANOS 7:14-15

Lo que hice fue mirar a Cristo en la pequeña capilla y recibí vida eterna. Miré a Jesús, él me miró y fuimos uno para siempre. En ese momento mi alegría sobrepasó todos los límites, así como antes la pena me llevó a un extremo de dolor. Yo descansaba perfectamente en Cristo, estaba satisfecho con él y mi corazón estaba contento; pero no supe que su gracia era vida eterna hasta que comencé a leer las Escrituras y a conocer más completamente el valor de la joya que Dios me había dado. Al domingo siguiente fui a la misma capilla y era muy natural que lo hiciera. Pero después de eso nunca regresé, por esta razón: durante mi primera semana la nueva vida que estaba en mí se vio obligada a luchar por su existencia y yo, con todo vigor, seguía librando un conflicto con la vieja naturaleza. Yo sabía que esto era una señal especial de la morada de la gracia en mi alma. Pero en esa misma capilla escuché un sermón: «¡Soy un pobre miserable! ¿Quién me librará de este cuerpo mortal?» (Romanos 7:24), y el predicador declaró que Pablo no era cristiano cuando tuvo esa experiencia. Yo, que era un bebé, tenía el conocimiento suficiente como para no creer una afirmación tan absurda. Este conflicto es una de las evidencias más seguras de mi nuevo nacimiento; la lucha se vuelve más y más intensa. Cada victoria sobre el pecado rebela otro ejército de tendencias malignas y nunca soy capaz de enfundar mi espada ni de cesar en mi oración y mi vigilancia.

A través de la Biblia en un año: Marcos 1–2

Después de ser llamados

Al pasar vio a Leví, hijo de Alfeo, sentado a la mesa donde cobraba impuestos. –Sígueme –le dijo Jesús. Y Leví se levantó y lo siguió. Sucedió que, estando Jesús a la mesa en casa de Leví, muchos recaudadores de impuestos y pecadores se sentaron con él y sus discípulos, pues ya eran muchos los que lo seguían.

MARCOS 2:14-15

No había pasado mucho tiempo desde que Mateo fuera llamado y llevado a seguir al Señor Jesús cuando se dijo a sí mismo: «¿Qué puedo hacer ahora por mi nuevo Amo?» Leví hizo una gran fiesta en su casa y le dijo al Señor Jesús: «Tú me has invitado a seguirte y estoy tratando de hacerlo, y una manera de seguirte es dar una gran fiesta en mi casa esta noche y traer a mis antiguos compañeros. ¿Vendrás? Y luego, cuando estén todos felices alrededor de mi mesa, ¿harás por ellos lo que has hecho por mí?»

Ahora bien, ¿ha sucedido así contigo, mi querido amigo? ¿Has llevado a otros a Jesús? ¿Has llevado a tus hijos a Jesús? ¿Fueron tus oraciones el medio para que tu cónyuge se entregara a Jesús? ¿Fueron tus súplicas el medio para que tus hermanos se entregaran a Jesús? Si no, has fallado en cumplir aquello que debiera ser la obra de tu vida. Pídele al Señor que ahora te ayude a comenzar esta obra con alguna persona de tu propio círculo con quien sea más probable que hables con la mayor influencia y poder. Deja que cada hombre, según su llamamiento, sienta: «Aquel que me invitó a seguirlo me ha invitado para que otros, por mediación mía, sean también llevados a seguirle a él».

A través de la Biblia en un año: Marcos 3–4

No te burles del libro

No piensen que he venido a anular la ley o los profetas; no he venido a anularlos sino a darles cumplimiento. Les aseguro que mientras existan el cielo y la tierra, ni una letra ni una tilde de la ley desaparecerán hasta que todo se haya cumplido.

MATEO 5:17-18

Déjame llamar tu atención al hecho de que cuando Jesús resucitó, era tan sensible a las Escrituras como lo fue antes de su muerte. Él les dijo que «tenía que cumplirse todo lo que está escrito acerca de mí en la ley de Moisés, en los profetas y en los salmos. Entonces les abrió el entendimiento para que comprendieran las Escrituras. —Esto es lo que está escrito —les explicó—: que el Cristo padecerá y resucitará al tercer día» (Lucas 24:44-46). Busca a Jesús donde puedas, él es el antagonista de aquellos que disminuirían la autoridad de las Santas Escrituras. «Está escrito» es su arma contra Satanás, su argumento contra los hombres malvados. En este momento los cultos se burlan del Libro y acusan de bibliolatría a aquellos de nosotros que reverenciamos la divina Palabra, pero en esto ellos no obtienen ayuda de la enseñanza ni del ejemplo de Jesús. De los labios de Jesucristo nunca salió ninguna palabra derogatoria sobre las Escrituras; sino que él eternamente manifestó la consideración más reverente por cada punto y coma de este volumen inspirado. Ya que nuestro Salvador, no solo antes de su muerte sino después de esta, se ocupó de recomendarnos las Escrituras, evitemos con todo nuestro corazón todas las enseñanzas en las cuales el Espíritu Santo quede en un segundo plano.

A través de la Biblia en un año: Marcos 5–6

Ejercitados y entrenados para la guerra

Por último, fortalézcanse con el gran poder del Señor. Pónganse toda la armadura de Dios para que puedan hacer frente a las artimañas del diablo. Porque nuestra lucha no es contra seres humanos, sino contra poderes, contra autoridades, contra potestades que dominan este mundo de tinieblas, contra fuerzas espirituales malignas en las regiones celestiales.

EFESIOS 6:10-12

Debemos considerar la iglesia cristiana no como una hostería lujosa en la cual los caballeros cristianos moran a sus anchas en su propio hostal sino como barracas en las que los soldados se reúnen para ejercitarse y prepararse para la guerra. Debemos considerar la iglesia cristiana no como una asociación para la admiración y el consuelo mutuos sino como un ejército con banderas que marcha a pelear para lograr victorias para Cristo, a invadir las fortalezas de los enemigos y para añadir provincia tras provincia al reino del Redentor.

Puede que veamos a las personas convertidas cuando se reúnen con los miembros de la iglesia como el trigo en el granero. Gracias a Dios que está ahí y que hasta el momento la cosecha ha recompensado al sembrador; pero todavía más inspirador para el alma es cuando consideramos que cada uno de esos creyentes pudiera ser un centro vivo para la extensión del reino de Jesús, porque entonces los veremos sembrando los valles fértiles de nuestra tierra y prometiendo desde antes traer treinta, otros cuarenta, otros cincuenta y algunos hasta cien. Las capacidades de la vida son enormes, uno se convierte en mil en un espacio maravillosamente corto. En poco tiempo unos pocos granos de trigo serán suficientes para sembrar el mundo entero y unos pocos santos verdaderos pudieran ser suficientes para la conversión de todas las naciones.

A través de la Biblia en un año: Marcos 7–8

Solo se requiere un pago

Él fue traspasado por nuestras rebeliones, y molido por nuestras iniquidades; sobre él recayó el castigo, precio de nuestra paz, y gracias a sus heridas fuimos sanados. Todos andábamos perdidos, como ovejas; cada uno seguía su propio camino, pero el Señor hizo recaer sobre él la iniquidad de todos nosotros.

ISAÍAS 53:5-6

Este es tu consuelo: que no te puedes morir. ¿Cómo puedes perecer si Jesús ocupó tu lugar? Si Cristo pagó tu deuda de antaño, ¿se te puede exigir otra vez? Una vez pagada, está cancelada por completo, gustosamente hemos aceptado el recibo y ahora podemos clamar con el apóstol: «¿Quién acusará a los que Dios ha escogido? Dios es el que justifica. ¿Quién condenará? Cristo Jesús es el que murió, e incluso resucitó, y está a la derecha de Dios e intercede por nosotros» (Romanos 8:33-34). Aquí yace el sostén principal de la confianza de todo creyente. Saber que Cristo murió por cada creyente que ha puesto su confianza en su bendita mediación. Si Jesús murió por mí, entonces no me pueden condenar por los pecados que él expió. Dios no puede castigar dos veces por una misma ofensa. Él no puede exigir dos pagos por una deuda.

A través de la Biblia en un año: Marcos 9–10

Instruido por la aflicción

Ahora me alegro en medio de mis sufrimientos por ustedes, y voy completando en mí mismo lo que falta de las aflicciones de Cristo, en favor de su cuerpo, que es la iglesia.

Colosenses 1:24

A menudo la aflicción nos revela verdades y nos abre a la verdad. No sé cuál de las dos es más difícil. La experiencia descubre verdades que de otra manera estaban cerradas para nosotros. El comentarista nunca deja claro muchos de los pasajes de las Escrituras sino que deben explicarse mediante la experiencia. Muchos textos se escriben con una tinta secreta que debe acercarse al fuego de la adversidad para hacerse visible. Yo he oído decir que de día las estrellas pueden verse desde un pozo aunque parados en la tierra firme no haya ninguna visible en el cielo y estoy seguro de que cuando estés en las profundidades de los problema, podrás discernir muchas verdades que como las estrellas no verías en ningún otro lugar. Además, yo dije que nos abre a la verdad así como que nos revela la verdad. Somos superficiales en nuestras creencias: a menudo estamos empapados con la verdad y, no obstante, esta se nos resbala al igual que el agua corre por encima de una losa de mármol. Sin embargo, la aflicción, por así decirlo, nos labra y nos penetra y abre nuestros corazones de manera que la verdad impregne nuestra naturaleza más profunda y la empape como la lluvia a la tierra labrada. Bendito el hombre que recibe la verdad de Dios en su interior, nunca la perderá sino que será la vida de su espíritu. La aflicción, cuando la santifica el Espíritu Santo, hace que los cristianos glorifiquen mucha a Dios mediante su experiencia de la fidelidad del Señor para con ellos.

A través de la Biblia en un año: Marcos 11–12

El huerto del creyente

¿A qué se parece el reino de Dios? —continuó Jesús—. ¿Con qué voy a compararlo? Se parece a un grano de mostaza que un hombre sembró en su huerto. Creció hasta convertirse en un árbol, y las aves anidaron en sus ramas.

LUCAS 13:18-19

Algunos cristianos no tienen huerto, ninguna esfera de servicio personal. Pertenecen al clan de los cristianos y anhelan ver que todo el grupo salga y cultive al mundo pero no se involucran de manera personal. Es encantador entrar en calor con los discursos misioneros y sentir fervor por la salvación de todas las naciones, pero después de todo, el resultado neto de un ímpetu teórico general por el mundo entero, no equivale a mucho.

El deber de todo creyente en Cristo es tener un huerto que embellecer y labrar, al igual que lo fue para Adán, el primer hombre. En las Escuelas Dominicales hay millones de niños: ¡gracias a Dios por eso! Pero, ¿tienes una clase para ti? ¡Toda la iglesia tiene que entrar en acción por Cristo! ¡Una teoría gloriosa! ¿Estás tú ocupado por tu Señor? Será un momento maravilloso cuando cada creyente tenga su porción y la esté sembrando con la semilla de la verdad. El lugar desierto y solitario florecerá como la rosa cuando cada cristiano cultive su propia parcela de rosas. Enseña a tus hijos, habla a tus vecinos, busca la conversión de aquellos a quienes Dios te ha encargado de manera especial.

A través de la Biblia en un año: Marcos 13-14

Aprende y luego ve

Ya el segador recibe su salario y recoge el fruto para vida eterna. Ahora tanto el sembrador como el segador se alegran juntos.

JUAN 4:36

Él salió de su soledad y comenzó a sembrar. Eso es lo que quiero decir. Al principio, un cristiano muy sabiamente vive bajo techo. Ahí dentro se necesita mucha limpieza y fregado. Cuando las abejas salen de sus células, se pasan los primeros días de su vida en la colmena limpiando y dejando todo en orden. No salen a buscar miel hasta primero haber terminado con todo el trabajo de casa. Quisiera que todos los cristianos hicieran sus tareas domésticas tan pronto como fuera posible. Quiero decir, relacionarse con asuntos experimentales como el pecado que mora en uno y la gracia vencedora. Pero después de eso, el sembrador salió a sembrar. Él no estaba contento con su experiencia privada pero salió a sembrar. Hay muchas personas que se sienten miserables porque siempre están en casa. Sal, hermano; sal, hermana. Aunque tu experiencia es importante, solo tiene importancia como plataforma para una utilidad verdadera. Arréglalo todo adentro para que puedas trabajar afuera.

A través de la Biblia en un año: Marcos 15—16

Telarañas barridas

Es más, todo lo considero pérdida por razón del incomparable valor de conocer a Cristo Jesús, mi Señor. Por él lo he perdido todo, y lo tengo por estiércol, a fin de ganar a Cristo y encontrarme unido a él. No quiero mi propia justicia que procede de la ley, sino la que se obtiene mediante la fe en Cristo, la justicia que procede de Dios, basada en la fe.
FILIPENSES 3:8-9

Hay una autojusticia ahí arriba en tu frente, como una corona, tendrás que quitarla. Estás cubierto con las hermosas vestimentas de tus buenas obras, quítalas, hermano. Ninguna tiene mérito ante los ojos de Dios hasta que hayas confiado en su Hijo. Todo lo que has hecho y todo lo que piensas son solo como telarañas que hay que barrer. Ahí está la puerta por la cual deben entrar los más arruinados y tú debes pasar por la misma puerta. No existe un camino privado para los caballeros como tú; no hay camino real al cielo, excepto ese único camino real que está abierto para el principal de los pecadores. ¡Abajo, señor Orgullo! He aquí un hombre que nació de padres cristianos y quizá ha prestado atención a la lógica mentirosa de la era actual que dice: «Los hijos nacidos de padres cristianos no necesitan la conversión; hay algo bueno en ellos por naturaleza». Yo les digo, señores, que empiezo a temblar al pensar en los hijos de padres piadosos porque creo que son los que más posibilidades tienen de ser engañados; a menudo se hacen ilusiones de que están convertidos, cuando no lo están y los admiten en las iglesias cuando todavía no son convertidos. En lugar de alardear de sus piadosos antepasados, por muy alto que sea el privilegio que esto represente, deben recordar que la regeneración no es por sangre ni de nacimiento, ni por la voluntad del hombre, sino de Dios. Para ellos, así como para todos los demás, se aplican las palabras de Cristo: «Debes nacer de nuevo».

A través de la Biblia en un año: Éxodo 1–4

El manto de amor de Dios

Sepan que el Señor honra al que le es fiel; el Señor me escucha cuando lo llamo.
SALMOS 4:3

Entiendes, entonces, que Dios discierne la piedad en los hombres. Hay mucha escoria en todos nosotros, pero Dios espía cualquier oro que pudiera haber, si en el mineral hay algún oro, Dios preserva el terrón debido al metal precioso que este contiene. Yo sé que no eres perfecto. Quizá en este momento estés sufriendo por una gran falta, si es así, me alegra que tengas la piedad que hace que uno sufra por el pecado. Sé que no eres lo que quieres ser o anhelas ser o debes ser. No obstante, temes al Señor y confías en él y lo amas. Así que el Señor puede ver todo eso, él conoce el bien que hay en ti. Él se echa tu pecado a sus espaldas, pero aquello que es de su gracia, lo aparta para sí y te aparta para sí por el bien que hay en ti. Sí me gusta notar en las Escrituras que aunque el pueblo de Dios se describe como un pueblo muy imperfecto, y aunque el Señor nunca es gentil con el pecado, no obstante, él es siempre muy gentil con ellos. Si hay algo bueno en ellos, él lo saca a la luz y es muy misericordioso y su amor cubre con un mantel miles de sus errores y faltas.

A través de la Biblia en un año: Éxodo 5–8

Victoria por medio de Jesús

Sin embargo, en todo esto somos más que vencedores
por medio de aquel que nos amó.
ROMANOS 8:37

¿Estás indefenso? ¿Estás sin consuelo? Este es un día en el que el Señor vendrá para aliviarte. ¿Necesitas fortaleza para romper las cadenas del hábito? Incluso, ¿necesitas poder para arrepentirte? ¿Necesitas ayuda para sentir tu desamparo? ¿Lo necesitas todo? Conozco a algunos que confían en Cristo para el perdón pero su dificultad principal es cómo ser santos. Yo me deleito grandemente en aquellos que buscan y que este es su pensamiento principal; no tanto para escapar al castigo como para evitar el pecado en el futuro. Bueno, si estás luchando contra el mal en el nombre de Jesucristo, no te desanimes, lo dominarás porque este es el día de salvación y está escrito: «Le pondrás por nombre Jesús, porque él salvará a su pueblo de sus pecados». ¿Le estoy hablando a un borracho? ¿Tiene esta copa embriagadora para ti una extraña fascinación y has vuelto a tomar luego de repudiarte muchas veces a ti mismo por hacerlo? No necesitas seguir siendo su esclavo porque este es un día de salvación de ese pecado: mediante la fe en Cristo serás librado de esa trampa mortal. ¿Has sido tentado por alguna otra iniquidad que te tiene obsesionado? ¿Tiene un cierto vicio puesto sus ojos monstruosos en ti y te hechiza al punto que no puedes refrenarte? Regocíjate, entonces, porque este es el día de salvación del pecado. Ni un santo ni un pecador tiene que sentarse bajo el poder de ningún pecado porque en el nombre de Cristo podemos vencer el poder del mal.

A través de la Biblia en un año: Éxodo 9–12

Obediencia en todas las cosas

Así Josué salvó a la prostituta Rajab, a toda su familia y todas sus posesiones, por haber escondido a los mensajeros que él había enviado a Jericó. Y desde entonces, Rajab y su familia viven con el pueblo de Israel.

JOSUÉ 6:25

Ahora bien, esta es una pregunta que nunca pretendo responder en lugar de ninguna otra persona porque no tengo la intención de hacerla por mi cuenta. Si un creyente va a perecer o no porque obvie algún deber conocido o una ordenanza de las Escrituras, es una pregunta que solo el egoísmo presentaría. ¿Debemos hacer solo aquello que procure nuestro progreso o que asegure nuestra salvación? ¿Somos egoístas hasta ese punto? ¿Dice un hijo amoroso: «Si me niego a hacer la voluntad de mi padre, no seguiré siendo su hijo? ¿No seguirá él alimentándome y vistiéndome?» Solo un hijo malvado hablaría así. El hijo verdadero pregunta: «¿Qué quiere mi padre que yo haga? Lo haré alegremente por amor a él. ¿Qué me prohíbe mi padre? Porque lo que él me prohíba será abominable para mí». Colócate por encima de todas las preguntas con respecto a lo esencial y a lo que no lo es y aprende a obedecer en todas las cosas; aunque solo sea atar un cordón rojo a la ventana, o bañarte en agua, haz lo que se te pida y en nada te rebeles contra la palabra del Señor.

A través de la Biblia en un año: Éxodo 13–16

Obediencia precisa

De acuerdo respondió Rajab. Que sea tal como ustedes han dicho. Luego los despidió; ellos partieron, y ella ató el cordón rojo a la ventana.
JOSUÉ 2:21

A ella se le dijo que atara el cordón rojo a la ventana y lo hizo; hubo obediencia exacta. No era cualquier cordón, un hilo, sino un cordón rojo. Ella no lo sustituyó por uno azul, verde o blanco. La orden era ese cordón rojo, no otro y ella tomó ese cordón en particular. La obediencia a Dios se apreciará mucho en los asuntos pequeños. El amor siempre se deleita al ocuparse de las pequeñas cosas y, por lo tanto, hace que las cosas pequeñas sean grandes. Escuché de un puritano al que acusaron por ser demasiado preciso, pero su respuesta fue excelente: «Yo sirvo a un Dios preciso». El Señor, nuestro Dios, es un Dios celoso y es muy celoso de sus mandamientos. Parecía que el error de Moisés al golpear la piedra en lugar de hablarle, era un error pequeño, no obstante, él no pudo entrar al descanso prometido debido a su ofensa. Una acción pequeña puede implicar un gran principio y nos corresponde a nosotros ser muy cautelosos y cuidadosos, buscar cuál es la voluntad del Maestro y nunca hacer un alto ni dudar por alguna razón sino hacer su voluntad tan pronto como la sepamos. La vida cristiana debiera ser un mosaico de obediencias minuciosas. Los soldados de Cristo debieran ser famosos por su disciplina exacta.

A través de la Biblia en un año: Éxodo 17–20

Los que aman más

—¡Es el Señor! —dijo a Pedro el discípulo a quien Jesús amaba.
JUAN 21:7

¿Cuál fue la vida de Juan? Primero, fue una vida de comunión íntima. Juan estaba dondequiera que Cristo estuviera. Otros discípulos quedan fuera pero Pedro, Santiago y Juan estaban presentes. Cuando todos los discípulos se sentaron a la mesa, ni tan siquiera Pedro era el más cercano al Señor, pero Juan apoyó su cabeza en su regazo. Su relación era muy íntima y querida. Jesús y Juan eran como una repetición de David y Jonatán. Si tú eres un hombre muy querido, vivirás en Jesús, tu comunión con él será de día en día.

La vida de Juan fue una senda de instrucción especial. A él le enseñaron cosas que los demás no sabían, porque no podían soportarlas. Al final de su vida, él fue favorecido con visiones que ni tan siquiera Pablo, que ni por un ápice se quedaba detrás del jefe de los apóstoles, había visto nunca. Debido a la grandeza del amor del Señor, él le mostró a Juan cosas del futuro y levantó el velo para que pudiera ver el reino y la gloria. Los que más aman, verán más y los que más rinden su corazón a la doctrina, aprenderán más.

A través de la Biblia en un año: Éxodo 21–24

Por toda la eternidad

Yo les doy vida eterna, y nunca perecerán, ni nadie podrá arrebatármelas de la mano.
JUAN 10:28

No puedo avanzar una pulgada sin orar en el camino, ni mantener la pulgada que gano sin vigilar y permanecer firme. Solo la gracia puede preservarme y perfeccionarme. La vieja naturaleza acabará con la nueva naturaleza si le es posible; y hasta este momento la única razón por la que mi nueva naturaleza no está muerta es esta: porque no puede morir. De haber podido morir, hace mucho tiempo que habría sido asesinada, pero Jesús dijo: «A mis ovejas les doy vida eterna» y «el que cree en mí tiene vida eterna» y por lo tanto el creyente no puede morir. La única religión que te salvará es aquella que no puedes dejar porque te posee y no te dejará. Tener a Cristo viviendo en ti y la verdad incrustada en tu misma naturaleza, ay señores, esta es la cosa que salva el alma y nada menos que esto. Está escrito en el texto: «Porque tanto amó Dios al mundo, que dio a su Hijo unigénito, para que todo el que cree en él no se pierda, sino que tenga vida eterna». ¿Qué es esto sino una vida que durará hasta tus sesenta años y hasta diez más, una vida que eclipsará esas estrellas y aquella luna; una vida que coexistirá con la vida del Padre Eterno? Mientras haya un Dios, el creyente no solo existirá sino que vivirá.

A través de la Biblia en un año: Éxodo 25–28

Con una encomienda divina

Pero ustedes son linaje escogido, real sacerdocio, nación santa, pueblo que pertenece a Dios, para que proclamen las obras maravillosas de aquel que los llamó de las tinieblas a su luz admirable.

1 PEDRO 2:9

Los impíos no pueden comprender a los píos, se burlan de ellos, convierten su gloria en vergüenza porque ellos mismos aman la vanidad y buscan la mentira. Las personas entre quienes el hombre piadoso mora, no lo comprenden; Dios ha hecho que él sea un extraño y forastero entre ellos. Los que han nacido dos veces tienen una vida que aquellos que solo han nacido una vez no pueden comprender. Los que han recibido el Espíritu de Dios tienen un nuevo espíritu dentro de sí que es tan peculiar que la mente carnal no puede percibir lo que es. Las cosas espirituales tienen que discernirse espiritualmente. Cuando un hombre se ha convertido en una nueva criatura en Cristo, las viejas criaturas a su alrededor no pueden entenderlo. Lo miran y ven que actúa por motivos que no pueden entender, ven que hay fuerzas que ellos no reconocen que lo mantienen bajo control, que le inhiben energía de las cuales ellos no son partícipes y que él busca algo que ellos no desean; así que el cristiano se convierte de cierta manera como Cristo mismo, de quien el poeta canta: «El mundo judío no conoció a su Rey, el Hijo eterno de Dios. «El mundo no nos conoce, precisamente porque no lo conoció a él» (1 Juan 3:1).

A través de la Biblia en un año: Éxodo 29–32

Sé piadoso y no temas

Pase lo que pase, compórtense de una manera digna del evangelio de Cristo. De este modo, ya sea que vaya a verlos o que, estando ausente, sólo tenga noticias de ustedes, sabré que siguen firmes en un mismo propósito, luchando unánimes por la fe del evangelio y sin temor alguno a sus adversarios.

FILIPENSES 1:27-28

Dios sabe lo que es la piedad, porque él la ha creado, la sostiene, ha prometido perfeccionarla y se deleita en ella. Con tal de que Dios te entienda, ¿qué importa si tus semejantes te comprenden o no? Si él conoce esa oración secreta que tú tienes, no busques que otros la conozcan. Si tu motivo concienzudo se discierne en el cielo, que no te importe aunque sea denunciado en la tierra. Si tus propósitos, los grandes principios que te bambolean, son aquellos que te atreves a confesar en el gran día del juicio, no necesitas detenerte a confesarlos delante de una generación chancera y burlona. Sé piadoso y no temas, si te malentienden, recuerda que si tu carácter queda enterrado como muerto entre los hombres, habrá «una resurrección de reputaciones» así como de los cuerpos. «Entonces los justos brillarán en el reino de su Padre como el sol. El que tenga oídos, que oiga» (Mateo 13:43).

A través de la Biblia en un año: Éxodo 33-36

Perfectos en Cristo Jesús

¡Soy un pobre miserable! ¿Quién me librará de este cuerpo mortal? ¡Gracias a Dios por medio de Jesucristo nuestro Señor!
ROMANOS 7:24-25

Cristiano acongojado, seca tus lágrimas. ¿Estás llorando a causa del pecado? ¿Por qué lloras? Llora por tu pecado pero no llores por temor al castigo. ¿Te ha dicho el maligno que serás condenado? Dile en su cara que miente. Ay, pobre creyente afligido, ¿estás llorando por tus corrupciones? Mira a tu perfecto Señor, y recuerda, estás completo en él. Para Dios eres tan perfecto como si nunca hubieras pecado; incluso más, más que eso, el Señor, nuestra justicia, te ha puesto una vestimenta divina para que tengas algo más que la justicia del hombre, tienes la justicia de Dios. Oh, tú que sufres por causa del pecado innato y por la depravación, recuerda, ninguno de tus pecados puede condenarte. Has aprendido a odiar el pecado pero has aprendido que el pecado no es tuyo, fue puesto sobre la cabeza de Cristo. Ven, anímate, tu posición no está en ti mismo, está en Cristo; tu aceptación no está en ti mismo sino en tu Señor. Con todo tu pecado, hoy eres tan aceptado como en tu santificación; igualmente Dios te acepta hoy, con todas tus iniquidades, como lo serás cuando estés delante de su trono, libre de toda corrupción. Te suplico que te aferres a este precioso pensamiento, ¡perfección en Cristo! Porque eres perfecto en Jesucristo. Anímate, no temas morir, la muerte no tiene nada terrible para ti; Cristo le ha sacado toda la hiel al aguijón de la muerte.

A través de la Biblia en un año: Éxodo 37–40

No siembres remordimiento

Alrededor de las cinco de la tarde, salió y encontró a otros más que estaban sin trabajo. Les preguntó: «¿Por qué han estado aquí desocupados todo el día?» «Porque nadie nos ha contratado», contestaron. Él les dijo: «Vayan también ustedes a trabajar en mi viñedo».

MATEO 20:6-7

He esperado bastante por un tiempo favorable, pero recuerdo que Salomón dijo: «Quien vigila al viento, no siembra; quien contempla las nubes, no cosecha» (Eclesiastés 11:4). ¿Puedo ver aquí a algunos que han sido miembros de la iglesia durante años aunque todavía no han hecho nada para el Señor? Si has sido un siervo de Dios durante muchos años y aún realmente no has trabajado por la salvación de las almas, quiero que ahora sencillamente te digas: «Vamos, realmente tengo que trabajar en esto». Pronto irás a casa y cuando tu Maestro te diga: «¿Sembraste algo para mí?», tendrás que responderle: «No, Señor, comí mucho. Fui al tabernáculo y disfruté los servicios». «Pero, ¿sembraste algo?» «No, Señor, acaparé mucho; almacené una gran cantidad de la buena semilla». «Pero, ¿sembraste algo?», te volverá a preguntar él y esa será una pregunta terrible para aquellos que nunca salieron a sembrar.

No sé cuán lejos estarás yendo, pero que quede escrito para ti hoy: «Los sembradores salieron a sembrar»; salieron con la determinación de que por el poder del vivo Espíritu de Dios, aquellos que son redimidos por la sangre preciosa de Jesús darían a conocer su evangelio a los hijos de los hombres, sembrando esa buena semilla en cualquier lugar en el que tengan la oportunidad, confiando en Dios para hacer que la semilla crezca y se multiplique.

A través de la Biblia en un año: Lucas 1–2

Salvados para servir

Ustedes me llaman Maestro y Señor, y dicen bien, porque lo soy. Pues si yo, el Señor y el Maestro, les he lavado los pies, también ustedes deben lavarse los pies los unos a los otros.
JUAN 13:13–14

Al tomar el cuenco, la jarra y la toalla para lavar los pies de sus discípulos, puedes ver la humildad de su disposición. Y enseguida, después de esto, lo ves entregándose a sí mismo, su cuerpo, su alma y su espíritu para servirnos. Y qué si digo que incluso en este mismo momento, como el Hijo del hombre en el cielo, él sigue haciendo una especie de servicio para su pueblo. Por amor a Sión él no guarda silencio y por amor a Jerusalén él no descansa sino que sigue intercediendo por aquellos cuyos nombres lleva en su corazón. Escuchen pues, todos ustedes, y que todo el que lo escuche aclame ese hecho misericordioso. Sean santos o pecadores, ya salvos o sedientos del conocimiento de la salvación, debe aceptarse la idea de que la encomienda de Cristo no era engrandecerse a sí mismo sino beneficiarnos a nosotros. Él no vino a ser servido, sino a servir. ¿No te viene esto bien a ti, pobre pecador, tú que nunca le serviste, tú que no podrías, como estás, ministrarle a él? Bueno, él no vino a buscar tu servicio, él vino a dar sus servicios, no para que primero tú le muestres honor sino para mostrarte misericordia. ¡Lo necesitas tanto! Y ya que él no ha venido a buscar tesoros sino a conceder riquezas inescrutables, no para buscar muestras de salud sino ejemplos de enfermedad sobre los cuales el arte sanadora de su gracia pueda operar, de seguro hay esperanza para ti.

A través de la Biblia en un año: Lucas 3–4

Que no sea así

Él respondió: Entonces te ruego, padre, que mandes a Lázaro a la casa de mi padre, para que advierta a mis cinco hermanos y no vengan ellos también a este lugar de tormento.

LUCAS 16:27-28

En mi imaginación, oro para que solo sea en mi imaginación, veo que algunos de ustedes mueren sin ser salvos; y los veo pasar al otro mundo no perdonados, y por primera vez su alma se percata de cuál fue la experiencia del hombre rico de quien el Salvador dijo: «En el infierno levantó los ojos», como si antes hubiera estado dormido y acabara de despertarse a su verdadera condición. «Levantó los ojos» y miró a su alrededor pero no podía ver nada, excepto aquello que le causaba abatimiento y horror; no había huellas de gozo ni esperanza, ninguna pista de alivio o paz. Entonces, en medio de la tristeza terrible llegó el sonido de preguntas como: «¿Dónde estás, pecador? Hace una semana estabas en una casa de oración y el predicar te instó a que buscaras al Señor pero tú lo dejaste para después. ¿Dónde estás ahora? Dijiste que no existía un lugar como el infierno y, ¿qué dices ahora? ¿Dónde estás? Despreciaste al cielo y rechazaste a Jesús, ¿dónde estás ahora?» ¡Que el Señor en su misericordia nos libre a todos de eso!

A través de la Biblia en un año: Lucas 5–6

Una vida santificada

Es Dios quien nos ha hecho para este fin y nos ha dado
su Espíritu como garantía de sus promesas.
2 Corintios 5:5

Cuando Dios le da una nueva naturaleza a su pueblo, la vida que surge de esa nueva naturaleza brota de esta espontáneamente. Las higueras no dan higos unos días y espinas otros, sino que son fieles a su naturaleza en todas las estaciones. El que ha descubierto en qué consiste el cristianismo sabe que es mucho más una vida que un acto, una forma o una profesión. A pesar de que amo mucho el credo de la cristiandad, estoy listo para decir que el verdadero cristianismo es mucho más una vida que un credo. Es un credo y tiene sus ceremonias pero es principalmente una vida. Es una chispa divina de la propia llama del cielo que cae en el seno humano y quema por dentro, que consume mucho de lo que yace en el alma y que al final, como una vida celestial, arde para que la vean y la perciban los que la rodean. Bajo el poder del Espíritu Santo que mora dentro, una persona regenerada se vuelve como el arbusto en Horeb, que resplandecía con la Divinidad. El Dios dentro de él lo hace brillar para que el lugar a su alrededor sea terreno santo y aquellos que lo miren sientan el poder de su vida santificada.

A través de la Biblia en un año: Lucas 7–8

Apóstoles de la incredulidad

Así que los otros discípulos le dijeron: —¡Hemos visto al Señor! —Mientras no vea yo la marca de los clavos en sus manos, y meta mi dedo en las marcas y mi mano en su costado, no lo creeré —repuso Tomás.

JUAN 20:25

Amado, tu Señor resucitado quiere que seas feliz. Cuando él estaba aquí en la tierra dijo: «No se angustien», él hoy te dice lo mismo. A él no le agradan las angustias de su pueblo. A él le encanta que creas en él y descanses. Amado, encuentra, si puedes, una ocasión en la que Jesús inculcara duda o prometiera que los hombres morarían en incertidumbre. Los apóstoles de la incredulidad están en todas partes hoy y se imaginan que están sirviendo a Dios al difundir lo que ellos llaman «dudas honestas». ¡Esto es la muerte para todo gozo! ¡Veneno para toda paz! El Salvador no lo hizo así. Él les haría tomar medidas extraordinarias para deshacerse de sus dudas. La eliminación de sus dudas en cuanto a la resurrección de nuestro Señor necesitaba que ellos lo tocaran y, por lo tanto, él se los ofreció. Amado, tú que estás afligido y contrariado con pensamientos y que por esa causa no consigues consuelo en tu religión debido a tu desconfianza, tu Señor hará que te acerques a él y pongas a prueba su evangelio de cualquier manera que te satisfaga. Él no puede soportar tu duda. Él apela tiernamente diciendo: «¡Hombre de poca fe! ¿Por qué dudaste?» (Mateo 14:31). Él te haría creer en la realidad substancial de su religión y que lo tocaras y vieras: confía en él de manera grande y sencilla, como confía un niño en su madre y no conoce el miedo.

A través de la Biblia en un año: Lucas 9–10

Amor inescrutable

En esto consiste el amor: no en que nosotros hayamos amado a Dios, sino en que él nos amó y envió a su Hijo para que fuera ofrecido como sacrificio por el perdón de nuestros pecados.

1 JUAN 4:10

¿Acaso no hay circunstancias y escenarios que de vez en cuando transpiren delante de nosotros y nos inspiren una exclamación como la del apóstol: «En esto consiste el amor»? Cuando vemos la devoción de una madre a sus hijos, cuando vemos el afecto de un amigo hacia otro y alcanzamos a ver en las diferentes relaciones humanas algo de la bondad que existe en los corazones humanos, hemos dicho: «¡En esto consiste el amor!» Voy a pedirte que mires y consideres la maravilla que el apóstol descubrió y que lo hizo exclamar con manos levantadas: «¡En esto consiste el amor!»

Cuando Dios ama a aquellos que lo aman, parece estar de acuerdo a la ley de la naturaleza, pero cuando él ama a aquellos que no lo aman, esto debe estar por encima de todas las leyes, está de acuerdo, sin dudas, con la regla extraordinaria de la gracia y solo la gracia. No había ni un hombre en la tierra que amara a Dios. No había ninguno que hiciera el bien, ni uno y, no obstante, el Señor puso los ojos de su amor seleccionador en pecadores que no tenían la más remota idea de amarlo a él. En un corazón no renovado no hay más amor para Dios de lo que hay vida en un pedazo de granito. En un alma perdida no hay más amor a Dios que el fuego que hay en las profundidades de las olas del océano; y aquí yace la maravilla, en que cuando no teníamos amor para Dios, él nos amó.

A través de la Biblia en un año: Lucas 11—12

Listos y esperando

Por lo tanto, manténganse despiertos, porque no saben qué día vendrá su Señor.
MATEO 24:42

En un momento en el que ellos no pensaban, vino el Hijo del Hombre. Sin embargo, ahora que tenemos las palabras de las Escrituras para asegurarnos de que él vendrá pronto y que su premio está con él y su obra delante de él, ¡cuán pocos lo esperan! Desde el mismo momento en que la venida de algún príncipe extranjero o el advenimiento de algún suceso importante se divulga entre la gente, estos se buscan y se anticipan. Pero Jesús, para tu venida, para tu glorioso advenimiento, ¿dónde están aquellos que esfuerzan sus ojos para percibir los primeros rayos del sol naciente? Hay muy pocos de tus seguidores que esperan tu aparición. Nos encontramos con unos pocos hombres que andan como si supieran que el tiempo es corto y que el Maestro pudiera regresar cuando el gallo cante o a media noche o en la vigilia del día. Conocemos a unos pocos discípulos amados que con corazones anhelantes pasan agradablemente las horas tediosas mientras preparan canciones para recibirte, ¡oh, Enmanuel! Señor, aumenta el número de aquellos que te buscan y anhelan y oran y esperan, y que vigilan las horas tediosas de la noche en espera de la mañana que traerá tu venida.

A través de la Biblia en un año: Lucas 13–14

Orgullo agradecido

Pero gracias a él ustedes están unidos a Cristo Jesús, a quien Dios ha hecho nuestra sabiduría —es decir, nuestra justificación, santificación y redención— para que, como está escrito: «El que se quiera enorgullecer, que se enorgullezca en el Señor».

1 Corintios 1:30-31

Cuando agradeces a Dios por las buenas cosas que ha hecho por ti, agradécele no solo por guardarte del pecado sino también por permitirte hacer su voluntad. Ningún hombre tiene el derecho de darse el crédito a sí mismo por su propia integridad, porque si es cristiano, la integridad es el don de la gracia de Dios y la obra del Espíritu de Dios dentro de él. Si en tu juventud sí te formaste un juicio cándido y honesto de la Palabra de Dios y luego quemaste todos los puentes y rompiste toda conexión con aquello que quedaba detrás de ti, si te atreviste a echar tu suerte con el despreciado pueblo de Dios, bendícelo por eso y considera que te hizo un gran favor al permitirte actuar así; y si, cuando has sido tentado con grandes sobornos, has sido capaz de decir: «Aléjate de mí, Satanás» y seguir de cerca los talones de Cristo, dale a Dios la gloria por eso y bendice su santo nombre. En un caso así, la virtud es su propia recompensa. Ser obediente a Cristo es una de las mayores bendiciones que Dios pudiera haber derramado sobre cualquier hombre. Hay algunos de nosotros que tienen que agradecer a Dios que cuando hubo momentos de aprieto, no nos atrevimos a ceder; sino que cuando los amigos y los enemigos por igual señalaban otro camino, nosotros vimos cuál era el camino del Maestro y lo seguimos por su gracia. Tendremos que agradecerle esto por toda la eternidad.

A través de la Biblia en un año: Lucas 15–16

Maná del cielo

¡Cuán dulces son a mi paladar tus palabras! ¡Son más dulces que la miel a mi boca!
SALMOS 119:103

Los mejores de nosotros necesitan instrucción. No es sabio que la gente cristiana esté tan ocupada con la obra de Cristo que no puedan escuchar las palabras de Cristo. Debemos alimentarnos o no podremos alimentar a otros. La sinagoga no debe estar desierta si es una sinagoga en la que Cristo está presente. Y, a veces, cuando el Maestro está presente, qué poder hay en la palabra: no es la elocuencia del predicador, ni la fluidez del lenguaje ni lo novedoso de la idea. Hay una influencia secreta, una influencia tranquila que entra en el alma y la somete a la majestad del amor divino. Uno siente la energía vital de la Palabra divina, y no es la palabra del hombre para ti sino la voz de Dios que te despierta y que suena en las recámaras de tu espíritu y hace que todo su ser viva delante de sus ojos. En tales ocasiones el sermón es como el maná del cielo o como el pan y el vino con los que Melquisedec recibió a Abraham, tú te alegras y te fortaleces y te marchas renovado.

A través de la Biblia en un año: Lucas 17–18

Una perspectiva de negocios duradera

No te afanes acumulando riquezas; no te obsesiones con ellas.
PROVERBIOS 23:4

Yo conocí bien a tu padre. Él comenzó su vida como habría querido que aquellos jóvenes comenzaran y anduvo penosamente hasta el fin de los años que tenía asignado y nunca tuvo tiempo para pensar en la religión. Era un caballero tan raro y sensible, ¡un hombre tan sabio! «Lo que yo quiero son hechos y cifras», decía él, «nada de tus tonterías; no me des tus opiniones; yo hago el balance de libros el domingo y esa es la manera de pasar el día de reposo. Me atrevo a decir que cuando no tenga más nada que hacer, tendré tiempo para pensar en mi alma». Él era un «caballero inglés fino» y raro; con todo, una noche alzó sus ojos en el infierno y con toda su contabilidad exacta y su balance de cuentas, tuvo que resumir: «No hay ganancias, he ganado riquezas, pero he perdido mi alma». Ay, y si él pudiera regresar, le diría a su hijo: «Hijo mío, mejor empieza los negocios por el lugar correcto, asegura tu alma y luego ocúpate del cuerpo; aférrate a la eternidad y hazlo bien y luego encárgate de las cosas escurridizas del tiempo como mejor puedas en subordinación a aquello». De cualquier manera, deja que el Sr. Mundano Sabio diga lo que quiera, porque Dios, quien sabe más de nosotros que nosotros mismos, dice: «Más bien, busquen primeramente el reino de Dios y su justicia, y todas estas cosas les serán añadidas».

A través de la Biblia en un año: Lucas 19–20

No engañes a nuestra juventud

Desde el principio éste ha sido un asesino, y no se mantiene en la verdad, porque no hay verdad en él. Cuando miente, expresa su propia naturaleza, porque es un mentiroso. ¡Es el padre de la mentira!

JUAN 8:44

«Ah, espera un poco más, nos gustaría que estos jóvenes aprendieran algo de la vida». Pero bueno, mundo vil, ¿qué quieres decir con eso? ¿Qué tienes tú que ver con la vida? Nosotros también queremos que los jóvenes aprendan algo de la vida. Pero, ¿qué es la vida? Porque la verdadera vida solo se encuentra en los seguidores de Cristo quien es la vida. «Bueno», dice el mundo, «pero nosotros queremos decir la *vida*». Yo sé lo que tú quieres decir, quieres decir la muerte. Dices que quieres que los jóvenes aprendan algo de la vida. Te escucho, es la voz de la misma serpiente sibilante que dijo: «llegarán a ser como Dios, conocedores del bien y del mal» y nuestra madre Eva, para conocer el mal así como el bien, ha destruido esta raza. Y muchos jóvenes, al tratar de conocer el bien y el mal, han llegado a conocer aquello que causa dolores de cabeza y palpitaciones al corazón y que los nervios se estremecen con un dolor intenso, ¡aquello que ha llevado al cuerpo frágil a una tumba temprana y condena al alma al infierno más bajo! Oro para que nuestros jóvenes no conozcan la vida de esta manera, sino que conozcan la vida en su verdadero sentido y la busquen donde solo se puede encontrar.

A través de la Biblia en un año: Lucas 21–22

El pecado de la ignorancia

¿Cómo puede el joven llevar una vida íntegra? Viviendo conforme a tu palabra. Yo te busco con todo el corazón; no dejes que me desvíe de tus mandamientos.
SALMOS 119:9-10

Una y otra vez te hemos hablado de la preciosa sangre de Cristo que limpia de todo pecado y de las bendiciones que Jesús te trae cuando se convierte en tu Salvador. Pero también estamos obligados a recordarles a todos ustedes, que profesan haber creído en él y haberse convertido en sus discípulos, que no solo deben tenerlo como su Maestro y Señor sino que deben hacer cualquier cosa que él les ordene. La fe debe obedecer a la voluntad del Salvador así como confiar en su gracia. Desde el momento en que nos convertimos en cristianos, salvados por Cristo, nos convertimos en sus siervos para obedecer todos sus mandamientos. Por lo tanto, nos corresponde escudriñar las Escrituras para conocer cuál es la voluntad de nuestro Maestro. Ahí él la ha escrito en letras claras y es un acto de desobediencia descuidar esta búsqueda. Al rehusarnos conocer cuál es la voluntad del Señor, el pecado de ignorancia se vuelve voluntarioso porque no usamos los medios mediante los cuales pudiéramos recibir instrucción. Cada siervo de Cristo está obligado a saber lo que tiene que hacer y entonces, cuando lo sepa, debe hacerlo de una vez. El primer negocio del hombre cristiano es conocer la voluntad de Cristo y el segundo, hacerla. Una vez aprendido esto, esa voluntad es la ley suprema del cristiano no importa lo que parezca oponérsele.

A través de la Biblia en un año: Lucas 23-24

Esposas como consejeras

¡Estamos condenados a morir! le dijo a su esposa. ¡Hemos visto a Dios! Pero su esposa respondió: Si el Señor hubiera querido matarnos, no nos habría aceptado el holocausto ni la ofrenda de cereales de nuestras manos; tampoco nos habría mostrado todas esas cosas ni anunciado todo esto.

JUECES 13:22-23

Manoa se había casado con una esposa excelente. Ella era la mejor de los dos en cuanto al juicio razonable. Por naturaleza ella era el vaso más frágil pero era la creyente más fuerte y probablemente es por eso que a ella le enviaran el ángel porque a los ángeles les agrada más hablar con aquellos que tienen fe y si ellos pueden escoger su compañía, y la esposa tiene más fe que el esposo, ellos visitarán más pronto a la esposa que a su esposo, porque a ellos les encanta llevar los mensajes de Dios a aquellos que los recibirán con confianza. Evidentemente ella estaba llena de fe, así que cuando su esposo dijo tembloroso: «De seguro moriremos», ella no creyó en una inferencia tan desconfiada. Lo que es más, aunque se dice que las mujeres no pueden razonar, no obstante, he aquí una mujer cuyos argumentos eran lógicos y abrumadores. Es cierto que las percepciones de las mujeres por lo general son mucho más claras que los razonamientos de los hombres: ellas ven la verdad de una vez mientras que nosotros andamos buscando nuestros anteojos. Por lo general sus instintos son tan seguros como nuestros razonamientos y, por tanto, cuando tienen además una mente clara y lógica, son las consejeras más sabias.

A través de la Biblia en un año: Levítico 1–4

Oración sin contestar

La oración de fe sanará al enfermo y el Señor lo levantará. Y si ha pecado, su pecado se le perdonará. Por eso, confiésense unos a otros sus pecados, y oren unos por otros, para que sean sanados. La oración del justo es poderosa y eficaz.
SANTIAGO 5:15-16

Muchas veces podría suceder que la causa de la oración sin contestar yazga en algo que esté relacionado con el pecado. ¿No crees tú que las oraciones sin contestar sean a menudo el escarmiento del Padre por nuestras ofensas? El Salvador, en ese capítulo maravilloso donde expresa su amor por nosotros, dice: «Si obedecen mis mandamientos, permanecerán en mi amor» (Juan 15:10) y luego señala, como un favor especial, si un hombre permanece en su amor y guarda sus mandamientos «lo que quieran pedir se les concederá». Entonces, a mí me parece razonable que si yo no hago la voluntad de Dios, Dios se negará a hacer lo que yo quiero: que si él me pide una cierta responsabilidad y yo me niego a cumplirla, cuando yo le pida cierto privilegio o favor, no es descortés, sino al contrario, muy sabio y cortés que él diga: «No, hijo mío, si no escuchas a mi tierna orden, es cortés que yo niegue tu deseo hasta que te arrepientas y obedezcas». Podría ser también aflicción temporal, pero probablemente esta es una de las formas principales en las que el Maestro inflige los azotes a sus hijos. Ellos son negligentes con sus mandamientos y él dice: «Entonces te demorarás un poco. Todavía no te voy a conceder lo que buscas, sino cuando vengas con una mejor actitud y seas más escrupuloso y blando para cumplir mis mandamientos, entonces tus deseos serán satisfechos».

A través de la Biblia en un año: Levítico 5–8

Ten certeza de la voluntad de Dios

Porque las dádivas de Dios son irrevocables, como lo es también su llamamiento.
ROMANOS 11:29

Tengo el derecho de pedir cualquier cosa que Dios me haya prometido, pero si me voy más allá del rango de las promesas divinas, también me voy más allá del rango de la expectativa confiada y segura. Las promesas son grandes y amplias, pero cuando a uno se le mete una fantasía en la cabeza, no debe suponer que Dios está ahí, en su fantasía. He conocido a algunas personas fanáticas que pensaban que podían vivir por fe. Iban a predicar el evangelio sin tener ningún don para predicar. Iban a ser misioneros en un distrito teniendo el mismo don para ser misioneros que tiene un caballo en un arado. Pero creían que estaban destinados a hacerlo y, por lo tanto, trataban de vivir sus vidas por fe y cuando estaban casi muertos de hambres, entonces se quejaban de Dios y abandonaban la labor. Si Dios realmente los hubiera inspirado y enviado, él los hubiera sostenido y guardado pero si lo hacen por voluntad propia y obstinadamente por su cuenta, entonces es necesario volverlos al punto darse cuenta de su ignorancia de la divina voluntad. Y luego, con frecuencia, oramos de manera que nuestras oraciones no tienen coherencia con la dignidad del Altísimo. A mí me encanta una familiaridad santa con Dios y creo que es encomiable, pero, no obstante, el hombre es hombre mientras que Dios es Dios, y no importa cuánta familiaridad tengamos con él en nuestros corazones, todavía debemos recordar la distancia que existe entre el Altísimo y la más elevada y más amada de todas sus criaturas, y no debemos hablar como si tuviéramos el poder de hacer lo que queremos y lo que nos plazca.

A través de la Biblia en un año: Levítico 9–12

El pecado y sus resultados

Porque la paga del pecado es muerte, mientras que la dádiva de Dios es vida eterna en Cristo Jesús, nuestro Señor.
ROMANOS 6:23

El pecado es ese poder malvado que está en el mundo en rebelión contra el poder bueno y misericordioso de la justicia que está en el trono de Dios. Este poder maligno de impiedad, falsedad, pecado y oposición a la mente de Dios en este momento tiene bajo su dominio a la gran masa de nuestros semejantes. Las raciones con las que este gratifica el valor más desesperado de sus campeones es la muerte.

La muerte es el resultado natural de todo pecado. Cuando un hombre actúa según el orden de Dios, vive; pero cuando quebranta las leyes de su Hacedor, se destruye a sí mismo y hace aquello que causa la muerte. Cuando cualquier hombre comete pecado, muere a la santidad y a la pureza. Mientras más lejos va un hombre en lujuria e iniquidad, más muerto se vuelve a la pureza y a la santidad: pierde el poder para apreciar las bellezas de la virtud o para sentir repulsión con las abominaciones de los vicios. Desde el mismo comienzo nuestra naturaleza ha perdido la delicadeza de la percepción que viene con una vida saludable; y cuando los hombres proceden en fornicación, injusticia o incredulidad o un pecado de cualquier índole, se hunden más y más en esa terrible muerte moral que es el pago seguro del pecado. Tú puedes pecar hasta llegar a una muerte total de la conciencia y ese es el primer pago de tu servicio al pecado.

A través de la Biblia en un año: Levítico 13–16

Casi salvos

Pero la esposa de Lot miró hacia atrás, y se quedó convertida en estatua de sal.
GÉNESIS 19:26

Recuerda a la esposa de Lot y cómo ella iba de camino a salvarse. La señora de Lot creyó tanto en el mensaje que vino a ella acerca de la destrucción de la ciudad que entró en acción. Se levantó temprano al igual que su esposo y se preparó para dejar la casa. Corrió por las calles, pasó la puerta de la ciudad y llegó al valle junto con su esposo.

Esta mujer estaba verdaderamente fuera de Sodoma y casi en Zoar, la ciudad refugio y, no obstante, pereció. Casi llega a salvarse, pero no del todo. Déjame repetir esas palabras, porque estas describen a algunos de ustedes que están aquí en esta hora y estas pudieran ser su epitafio si no se ocupan de lo que hacen: «Casi se salva, pero no del todo». Escapó de la forma más vil de pecado pero no estaba verdaderamente en Cristo, la mente no se destetó de los ídolos, no renunció a la iniquidad en el alma, aunque quizá renunció a ella en una obra externa.

¡Realmente debe ser horrible haber vivido con el pueblo de Dios, haber sido contado con ellos, haber estado unido a ellos por vínculos de sangre y luego, al final, perecer! Haber escuchado el evangelio, haberlo experimentado, en cierta medida, haber corregido la vida de uno debido a esto, haber escapado de la corrupción más sucia del mundo y, sin embargo, no haberse destetado del mundo, no haberse divorciado en limpio del pecado y por consecuencia perecer, la idea es intolerable. Aquella misma salmuera y aquel azufre que cayeron en los habitantes de las cuatro ciudades, alcanzaron a la esposa de Lot. Ella estaba en el borde del aguacero y al caer se saló con fuego; quedó convertida en una columna de sal justo donde estaba parada. ¡Un destino espantoso!

A través de la Biblia en un año: Levítico 17–20

El evangelio completo en un solo versículo

Este mensaje es digno de crédito y merece ser aceptado por todos: que Cristo Jesús vino al mundo a salvar a los pecadores, de los cuales yo soy el primero.

1 Timoteo 1:15

Este texto contiene el evangelio en síntesis y, sin embargo, yo pudiera decir que contiene el evangelio sin quitar nada. Si obtienes las notas condensadas de un sermón o de un discurso, a menudo te pierdes el alma y la médula de este; pero aquí tienes toda la condensación posible, como si todas las grandes verdades del evangelio estuvieran comprimidas con un martillo hidráulico, y, no obstante, no quedara fuera ni una partícula de este.

Jesucristo vino a servir pecadores de todos los tipos. Mientras que puedas caer dentro de la descripción general de «pecadores», no importa la forma que haya tomado tu pecado. Todos los hombres han pecado por igual, y, sin embargo, no todos han pecado de la misma forma. Todos han vagado por el camino descendente y, no obstante, cada uno ha tomado una dirección diferente a los demás. Cristo Jesús vino al mundo a salvar a pecadores respetables y a pecadores de mala reputación. Vino al mundo a salvar a pecadores orgullosos y a pecadores desesperados. Vino al mundo a salvar borrachos, ladrones, mentirosos, proxenetas, adúlteros, asesinos y personas por el estilo. Cualquier tipo de pecado que exista, esta palabra es maravillosamente abarcadora y arrolladora: «Cristo Jesús vino al mundo a salvar a los pecadores». Son un grupo horrible, un lote maléfico, y el infierno es la recompensa que merecen, pero estas son personas que Jesús vino a salvar.

A través de la Biblia en un año: Levítico 21–24

Evidencia de la salvación

Fijemos la mirada en Jesús, el iniciador y perfeccionador de nuestra fe, quien por el gozo que le esperaba, soportó la cruz, menospreciando la vergüenza que ella significaba, y ahora está sentado a la derecha del trono de Dios.

HEBREOS 12:2

Desde el momento que el pecador cree, el hacha queda puesta en la raíz del dominio de Satanás. En cuanto aprende a confiar en el Salvador designado, comienza su cura sin lugar a dudas y en breve será llevado a la perfección. Después de la fe viene la gratitud. El pecador dice: «Yo confío en el Dios encarnado para que me salve. Yo creo que él me ha salvado». Bueno, ¿cuál es el resultado natural? Cómo puede un alma que es agradecida evitar exclamar: «¡Bendito sea Dios por su don inefable!» y «¡Bendito sea su querido Hijo que con tanta libertad dio su vida por mí!» No sería natural, sería algo incluso inferior a lo humano, si el sentido de tal favor no fuera la gratitud. La emoción que le sigue a la gratitud es el amor. ¿Ha hecho él esto por mí? ¿Estoy bajo tal obligación? Entonces amaré su nombre. El pensamiento que le sigue al amor es la obediencia. ¿Qué debo hacer para agradar a mi Redentor? ¿Cómo puedo cumplir con sus mandamientos y dar honor a su nombre? ¿No te das cuenta que el pecador se sana con más rapidez? Su enfermedad era que él estaba completamente fuera de sintonía con Dios y se resistía a la ley divina, pero ¡míralo ahora! Con lágrimas en sus ojos se lamenta de haber ofendido alguna vez, gime y sufre por haber lacerado a un amigo tan querido y causarle tales penas y está pidiendo con amor y ahínco: «¿Qué puedo hacer para mostrarte que me aborrezco por mi pasado y que amo a Jesús para el futuro?»

A través de la Biblia en un año: Levítico 25–27

Confía en las promesas de Dios

Ya no te llamarás Abram, sino que de ahora en adelante
tu nombre será Abraham, porque te he confirmado
como padre de una multitud de naciones.
GÉNESIS 17:5

Yo no sé si Abraham entendió todo el significado espiritual del pacto que se hizo con él; probablemente no, pero él sí entendió que Cristo nacería de él, en quien serían benditas todas las naciones. Aunque para este hombre, viejo, marchito y con una esposa de noventa años, no había probabilidades de convertirse en padre, no obstante, él creyó sin duda alguna que sería el padre de muchas naciones, y eso fue basándose únicamente en que el Dios viviente así se lo había prometido y, por lo tanto, así debía ser.

Pues bien, la fe de cualquier hombre que sea salvo debe tener este carácter. Todo hombre que recibe salvación la recibe mediante una fe como la de Abraham, porque mis hermanos, cuando somos salvos, nosotros también tomamos la promesa de Dios y dependemos de ella. Sí, y al escudriñar la Palabra por fe, tomamos cada promesa que encontramos y decimos: «Esto es verdad» y «Esto es verdad» y así descansamos en todas ellas. ¿No es así con todos ustedes que tienen paz con Dios? ¿No la obtuvieron al descansar en la promesa de Dios según la encontraron en las Escrituras y el Espíritu Santo la abrió ante ustedes? ¿Tienes algún otro fundamento de confianza que no sea la promesa de Dios? La fe que salva al alma cree en la posibilidad de la regeneración y la santificación; no, todavía más, cree en Jesús y obtiene para nosotros poder para convertirnos en hijos de Dios y fortaleza para conquistar el pecado.

A través de la Biblia en un año: Juan 1–2

Fe solo en Cristo

Pues la ley fue dada por medio de Moisés, mientras que la gracia y la verdad nos han llegado por medio de Jesucristo.

JUAN 1:17

Puede que sepas mucho sobre la fe pero la única fe que salva es la creencia en Cristo. «Yo sé en quien he creído». Creer en una doctrina no salvará a un hombre. Tal vez sepas todo el credo y seas ortodoxo, mientras que por otra parte no eres mejor que el diablo; porque yo supongo que el diablo es un teólogo muy atinado. Sin dudas que él conoce la verdad. Él cree y tiembla, pero tú puedes conocerlo y no temblar, y así puedes no llegar a poseer una virtud que hasta el diablo tiene. Una creencia firme en lo que se te predica es bastante bueno, pero creer una doctrina así no te puede salvar.

Algunos tienen fe en su ministro y supongo que eso sea tan halagador para nosotros que difícilmente esperarías que habláramos en contra de esto, pero de todos los vicios este es uno que sin duda debe temerse porque es muy peligroso. Te ordeno ante Dios que siempre sopeses lo que tenemos que decirte y si no está acorde con las Escrituras, échalo a un lado como harías con la basura.

Muchas personas creen a conciencia en sí mismas. La doctrina de la confianza en uno mismo se predica por estos días en muchos lugares. Tu creencia no debe ser que puedes forzar tu entrada al cielo sino que tienes que creer en Cristo porque cualquier otra cosa es una fe que no salva.

Por tanto, ves que tanto el conocimiento que salva como la fe que salva cuelgan de la cruz, ambos miran a las heridas de aquel hombre querido, ese Dios bendito que allí fue la propiciación por nuestros pecados y quien sufrió en nuestro lugar.

A través de la Biblia en un año: Juan 3–4

Amor celestial

Hace mucho tiempo se me apareció el Señor y me dijo: «Con amor eterno te he amado; por eso te sigo con fidelidad.

JEREMÍAS 31:3

Entre el gran corazón del cielo y este pobre palpitante corazón en la tierra se establece el amor, un amor del tipo más querido, verdadero y fiel. De hecho, el amor de una mujer, el amor de una madre, el amor de un cónyuge no es más que agua, pero el amor de Dios es vino; estas son cosas terrenales pero el amor de Dios es celestial. El amor de una madre refleja el amor de Dios, así como una gota de rocío refleja al sol; pero así como la gota de rocío no circunda a ese orbe poderoso, ningún amor que lata en el seno humano podrá jamás circundar, así como ninguna palabra puede expresar la altura, la profanidad, la longitud y la anchura del amor de Dios que es en Cristo Jesús, nuestro Señor. «Te he amado». Acércate entonces, cristiano. Tu Padre, aquel que ayer te castigó, te ama; aquel de quien tan a menudo te olvidas, y a quien ofendes constantemente, aún te ama. Tú sabes lo que es amar. Traduce al amor que sientes por tu amigo más querido, míralo y di: «Dios me ama de manera todavía mejor». Él llevó tus pecados, tus penas, tu muerte, tu tumba, para que tú pudieras recibir el perdón, ser aceptado y recibir el favor divino y así vivir y ser bendecido para siempre.

A través de la Biblia en un año: Juan 5–6

La residencia del corazón

No acumulen para sí tesoros en la tierra, donde la polilla y el óxido destruyen, y donde los ladrones se meten a robar. Más bien, acumulen para sí tesoros en el cielo, donde ni la polilla ni el óxido carcomen, ni los ladrones se meten a robar. Porque donde esté tu tesoro, allí estará también tu corazón.

MATEO 6:19-21

Por otra parte, ¿sientes que día tras día te atraen de la tierra al cielo? ¿Sientes como si allá arriba hubiera un imán que atrae tu corazón de manera que cuando estás trabajando en tu negocio, en tu familia con todos sus cuidados, no puedes evitar lanzar una oración al Altísimo? ¿A veces sientes este impulso inexorable de algo que no entiendes, que te impele a tener comunión con Dios más allá de los cielos? ¡Ay! Si es así, puedes estar seguro que es Cristo quien te atrae. Hay un vínculo entre el cielo y tú, y Cristo está halando ese vínculo y elevando tu alma hacia sí. Si tu corazón está aquí abajo, entonces tu tesoro está aquí; pero si tu corazón está allá arriba, si tus esperanzas más brillantes, tus deseos más tiernos están en los lugares celestiales, tu tesoro claramente está allá y el título de propiedad de ese tesoro se encontrará en el propósito eterno de Dios por el cual él te ordenó para sí mismo para que publiques su alabanza.

A través de la Biblia en un año: Juan 7–8

La necesidad de la vida

Por eso me regocijo en debilidades, insultos, privaciones, persecuciones y dificultades que sufro por Cristo; porque cuando soy débil, entonces soy fuerte.
2 CORINTIOS 12:10

Hay un deber y privilegio elevado y bendecido —diré que ambas cosas— que es para todo cristiano la necesidad de su vida y eso es orar. ¿Sabes orar, mi hermano? Si sabes orar, puedes mover el cielo y la tierra. ¿Sabes orar, mi hermano? Entonces puedes poner a funcionar fuerzas todopoderosas. No sufrirás necesidad porque a la mano que ora le aguardan provisiones eternas: «Pidan y se les dará». No perderás el camino porque te guiará a la respuesta de la oración. Escucharás una voz detrás de ti que dice: «Éste es el camino; síguelo» (Isaías 30:21).

«Ay, señor», dices tú, «yo no puedo orar de modo imperante». Entonces no eres como Jacob, bueno en la lucha. Bueno, déjame presentarte el texto. De esta debilidad en la oración solo puedes hacerte fuerte mediante la fe. Cree en Dios y prevalecerás con Dios. Cree en su promesa e implórala. Cree en su Espíritu y ora por su ayuda. Cree en Jesús, quien intercede, porque mediante él puedes ir arriesgadamente al trono de la gracia. El que sabe orar tiene su mano en una palanca que mueve el universo. Pero no hay oración sin fe. Cree en la oración y orarás con fe. Algunos no creen que la oración implica mucho. ¡Pobre de ellos! ¡Que el Señor los enseñe!

A través de la Biblia en un año: Juan 9–10

Un espíritu de vehemencia e iniciativa

¡Miren que vengo pronto! Traigo conmigo mi recompensa, y le pagaré a cada uno según lo que haya hecho. Yo soy el Alfa y la Omega, el Primero y el Último, el Principio y el Fin.
APOCALIPSIS 22:12-13

Cristo ha comprado este mundo y él lo poseerá desde un extremo al otro de la tierra. Él lo ha redimido y lo reclamará para sí. Puedes descansar tranquilo sabiendo que lo que sea que dice el rollo de la profecía se cumplirá según el determinado consejo y preconocimiento de Dios. Que no te perturben los videntes ni los agoreros. Descansa tranquilo. «Ahora bien, hermanos, ustedes no necesitan que se les escriba acerca de tiempos y fechas, porque ya saben que el día del Señor llegará como ladrón en la noche» (1 Tesalonicenses 5:1-2).

En cuanto a ustedes, su asunto es trabajar para la propagación de su reino, esparcir continuamente la luz que ustedes tienen y orar por más, esperar en Dios más de las lenguas de fuego, más del bautismo del Espíritu Eterno, más poder vital. Cuando toda la iglesia se despierte a un espíritu de vehemencia e iniciativa, la conversión de este mundo se logrará rápidamente, se echarán los ídolos a los topos y los murciélagos, el anticristo se hundirá como una piedra de molino en el torrente y se revelará la gloria del Señor y toda carne le verá, porque la boca del Señor lo ha dicho.

A través de la Biblia en un año: Juan 11–12

Apariencias externas

Porque vino Juan, que no comía ni bebía, y ellos dicen: «Tiene un demonio». Vino el Hijo del hombre, que come y bebe, y dicen: «Éste es un glotón y un borracho, amigo de recaudadores de impuestos y de pecadores». Pero la sabiduría queda demostrada por sus hechos.

MATEO 11:18-19

Otros profetas, cuando vinieron, estaban vestidos con vestiduras raídas y sus costumbres eran austeras y solemnes. Cristo no vino así; vino a ser un hombre entre los hombres, un fiestero con los que festejaban, alguien que comía miel con los que comían miel. No era diferente de nadie y por eso lo llamaban glotón y borracho. ¿Por qué Cristo hizo esto? ¿Por qué se comportó así, como decían los hombres, a pesar de que era en verdad una calumnia? Era porque él quería que sus discípulos no estimaran las carnes ni las bebidas sino que despreciaran esas cosas y vivieran como los demás; porque él les enseñaría que lo que contamina al hombre no es lo que entra en él sino lo que sale. Lo que le hace daño a un hombre no es lo que come con moderación, sino lo que un hombre dice y piensa. No es abstenerse de la carne, no es el mandamiento carnal de «no tomes en tus manos, no pruebes, no toques» lo que constituye los fundamentos de nuestra religión, a pesar de que pudiera ser una buena cláusula añadida a esto. Cristo comió mantequilla y miel, y su pueblo puede comer mantequilla y miel; más aun, cualquier cosa que Dios en su providencia les de, ese será el alimento del hijo de Cristo hijo.

A través de la Biblia en un año: Juan 13–14

Luz para todo el mundo

Una vez más Jesús se dirigió a la gente, y les dijo: «Yo soy la luz del mundo. El que me sigue no andará en tinieblas, sino que tendrá la luz de la vida».

JUAN 8:12

Él dice: «Yo soy la luz del mundo». Él no dice sencillamente: «Yo soy la luz de los judíos» o «Yo soy la luz de los gentiles». Él es ambas cosas. Él es la luz de toda la humanidad. Hay un poquito de luz en el mahometismo. De hecho, teniendo en cuenta la época en que Mahoma vivió, tenía bastante luz; la religión del Corán es inconmensurablemente superior a las religiones de la época en la que el profeta floreció. Él hasta enseñó la unidad de la divinidad de manera muy clara. Sin embargo, la luz del Corán se toma prestada del Antiguo y del Nuevo Testamento. Es una luz prestada. La inteligencia es hurtada.

La luz de los persas, la luz de Zaratustra, la luz de Confucio vino originalmente de los libros sagrados de los judíos. Todas deben haber partido de una fuente, porque toda luz viene del gran Padre de las luces.

Cristo es la luz del mundo, destinado a derramar sus rayos sobre toda la tierra. Viene el día en que toda la humanidad verá esta luz. Los que moran en el desierto se inclinarán ante él y sus enemigos lamerán el polvo. Las islas le rendirán tributo; Sabá y Seba le ofrecerán tributos, sí, todos los reyes caerán delante de él. No puedo evitar creer que el evangelio aun no ha triunfado. Espero la venida de Cristo. Que venga cuando él quiera, nuestros corazones saltarán de gozo al encontrarnos con él.

A través de la Biblia en un año: Juan 15–16

La iglesia

Ustedes antes ni siquiera eran pueblo, pero ahora son pueblo de Dios; antes no habían recibido misericordia, pero ahora ya la han recibido.
1 PEDRO 2:10

La Palabra de Dios nos dice que en medio de la gran masa de hombres se encuentra un pueblo especial, un pueblo que Dios escogió de entre la raza común antes de que las estrellas comenzarán a brillar, un pueblo que el corazón de Dios quería desde antes de la fundación del mundo, un pueblo que fue redimido con la sangre preciosa de Jesús más allá y por encima del resto de toda la humanidad, un pueblo que es propiedad especial de Cristo, el rebaño de su pasto, las ovejas de su mano, un pueblo sobre el cual vela la Providencia, que modela su curso en medio del laberinto intrincado de la vida, un pueblo que será producido al final, cada uno de ellos sin falta delante del trono eterno y apto para el destino exaltado que él revelará en la era venidera.

A través de toda las Escrituras uno lee acerca de este pueblo particular y especial. A veces se les llama «simiente», otras veces «un huerto», otras «un tesoro» y a veces «un rebaño». El nombre común de ellos en el Nuevo Testamento es «la iglesia». Cristo nos dice que la única manera para entrar a la iglesia es a través de él mismo. Él es la puerta, la única puerta. No hay otra manera de entrar a la iglesia que no sea mediante él. Si crees en Cristo, eres miembro de su iglesia. Si tu confianza está puesta en Cristo, quien es la gran vía de salvación de Dios, tienes evidencias de que él te escogió antes de la fundación del mundo; y esa fe tuya te da derecho a todos los privilegios que Cristo ha prometido en su Palabra a los creyentes.

A través de la Biblia en un año: Juan 17–18

La tormenta interior

Hombres de poca fe —les contestó—, ¿por qué tienen tanto miedo? Entonces se levantó y reprendió a los vientos y a las olas, y todo quedó completamente tranquilo.

MATEO 8:26

Los vientos bramaban, las aguas rugían y los discípulos pensaron que de seguro el mar enfurecido se tragaría la pequeña embarcación, así que despertaron a su Maestro del sueño que él tanto necesitaba y le gritaron: «¡Señor, sálvanos, que nos vamos a ahogar!» Al despertarse porque había peligro, él trató primero la causa principal del peligro, ¿cuál era? No los vientos ni las olas sino la incredulidad de los discípulos. Hay más peligro para un cristiano en su propia incredulidad que en las circunstancias más adversas que pudieran rodearle.

Creo que me atrevo a decir, aunque con el Omnipotente todo es posible, que era más fácil para Cristo calmar los vientos y las olas que aquietar la conmoción que surgió a causa de las dudas en las mentes de sus discípulos; él podía traer la calma con más rapidez a la superficie del lago galileo que a los espíritus perturbados de sus apóstoles aterrorizados. Lo mental siempre supera a lo físico; el gobierno de los corazones es mayor que el gobierno de los vientos y las olas. Así que cuando tengamos que batallar con los problemas, empecemos siempre por nosotros mismos: nuestros temores, falta de confianza, egoísmo y voluntad propia, porque el peligro principal reside ahí. Todos los problemas del mundo no pueden hacerte tanto daño como la mitad de un grano de incredulidad. Aquel que por la gracia de Dios es capaz de dominar su propia alma, no necesita dudar que también será dueño de cualquier cosa que se le oponga.

A través de la Biblia en un año: Juan 19–21

Visión divina

Unos hombres le llevaron un paralítico, acostado en una camilla. Al ver Jesús la fe de ellos, le dijo al paralítico: ¡Ánimo, hijo; tus pecados quedan perdonados!

MATEO 9:2

Notarás que nuestro Señor no esperó a que se dijera palabra alguna, sencillamente miró y vio la fe de ellos. Mateo escribe: «Al ver Jesús la fe de ellos». ¿Quién puede ver la fe? Es algo cuyos efectos pueden verse, sus señales e indicios se pueden descubrir y en este caso eran tan eminentes porque romper el techo y bajar al hombre para ponerlo delante de Jesús de una manera tan extraña eran evidencias de su fe en que Jesús lo sanaría. No obstante, los ojos de Cristo no solo vieron las pruebas de su fe sino la fe misma. Allí estaban parados los cuatro hombres, hablando con sus ojos y diciendo: «¡Maestro, mira lo que hemos hecho! Estamos convencidos de que hemos hecho lo correcto y de que tú lo sanarás». Allí estaba el hombre, acostado en su cama, mirando hacia arriba y preguntándose qué haría el Señor, pero evidentemente estaba animado por la creencia de que ahora estaba en una posición de esperanza en la que con toda probabilidad se convertiría en un hombre favorecido más allá de todo el mundo. Cristo no solo vio las miradas de este hombre y de sus portadores, también vio su fe.

Ay, amigos, no podemos ver la fe los unos de los otros; pero podemos ver el fruto de esta. A veces pensamos que podemos discernir la falta de fe, pero para ver la fe en sí se necesita una visión divina; esto necesita la mirada del ojo del Hijo del Hombre. Jesús vio su fe y ahora ese mismo ojo está mirando a todos en este público y él ve tu fe. ¿Tienes alguna que él pueda ver?

A través de la Biblia en un año: Números 1–4

Perdón y obediencia

Pues para que sepan que el Hijo del hombre tiene autoridad en la tierra para perdonar pecados —se dirigió entonces al paralítico—: Levántate, toma tu camilla y vete a tu casa. Y el hombre se levantó y se fue a su casa.
MATEO 9:6-7

Yo creo que la obediencia minuciosa que el Salvador requería era la mejor evidencia de que él había perdonado el pecado del hombre: «Levántate, toma tu camilla y vete a tu casa». De aquí en lo adelante, hacer todo lo que Cristo te ordene, de la manera en que él te ordene hacerlo, porque él te lo ordena, hacerlo de una vez, hacerlo con gozo, hacerlo constantemente, hacerlo con oración, hacerlo con gratitud, debe ser la señal de que en realidad él ha tratado contigo como un Dios perdonador. Me temo que hay algunos que profesan haber sido perdonados ¡que no son tan obedientes a Cristo como debieran serlo! Sé que han descuidado ciertos deberes; una vez hasta conocí a un hombre que no leía ciertas partes de la Palabra de Dios porque le hacían sentir incómodo; pero asegúrate de esto, cuando tú y la Palabra de Dios se pelean, la Palabra de Dios tiene la razón. Hay algo podrido en el estado de Dinamarca si tú no puedes leer un capítulo deseando que no estuviera ahí. Hay algo mal en ti cuando discutes con la Palabra de Dios. Yo digo que la obediencia minuciosa es la evidencia más segura de que el Señor ha perdonado tu pecado. Por ejemplo: «El que crea y sea bautizado será salvo» (Marcos 16:16). No omitas ninguna parte de este precepto, y si Cristo te ordena venir a su mesa y así recordarlo, no vivas descuidando ese mandamiento.

A través de la Biblia en un año: Números 5–8

El toque sanador

«Iré a sanarlo», respondió Jesús.
MATEO 8:7

Durante tres años nuestro Señor anduvo por los hospitales: se pasaba el día entero en una enfermería, en una ocasión a todo su alrededor pusieron a los enfermos en las calles y en todo momento el mal físico cruzaba su camino de una manera u otra. Él extendía su mano o hablaba la palabra y sanaba todo tipo de dolencias, porque era parte del trabajo de toda su vida. «Iré a sanarlo», dijo él, porque era un médico que constantemente estaba ejerciendo y pasaba visitas enseguida para ver al paciente. «Él se ocupaba de hacer el bien» y en todo esto le hacía saber a su pueblo que su intención no era bendecir solo una parte del hombre sino toda nuestra naturaleza, llevando sobre sí no solo nuestros pecados sino también nuestras enfermedades. Jesús quiere bendecir tanto el cuerpo como el alma, y aunque por el tiempo presente él ha dejado nuestro cuerpo en gran parte bajo el control de la enfermedad, porque todavía «el cuerpo está muerto a causa del pecado, pero el Espíritu que está en ustedes es vida a causa de la justicia» (Romanos 8:10), no obstante, cada miembro restaurado, cada ojo abierto y cada herida sanada es una señal de que Jesús se interesa por nuestra carne y nuestros huesos y quiere que el cuerpo comparta los beneficios de su muerte mediante una gloriosa resurrección.

La genialidad del cristianismo es sentir pena por los pecadores y los que sufren. Que la iglesia sea sanadora como su Señor: al menos si no puede desprender sanidad con el borde de su manto ni «decir la palabra» para que la enfermedad huya, que esté entre los más dispuesto a ayudar en todo lo que pueda mitigar el dolor o socorrer en la pobreza.

A través de la Biblia en un año: Números 9–12

Los días de la preparación

El día en que venga para ser glorificado por medio de sus santos
y admirado por todos los que hayan creído, entre los cuales
están ustedes porque creyeron el testimonio que les dimos.
2 TESALONICENSES 1:10

La completa glorificación de Cristo en sus santos será cuando él venga por segunda vez, de acuerdo a la segura palabra de la profecía. Él ahora se glorifica en ellos porque dice: «Todo lo que yo tengo es tuyo, y todo lo que tú tienes es mío; y por medio de ellos he sido glorificado» (Juan 17:10); pero hasta el momento esa gloria es más bien perceptible para sí mismo que para el mundo exterior. Las lámparas se están despabilando y brillarán en breve. Estos son los días de la preparación antes del día de reposo que es un sentido infinito, un día de fiesta. Como se dijo de Ester, que durante muchos meses se preparó con mirra y dulces fragancias antes de entrar al palacio del rey para casarse con él, así mismo ahora nosotros somos purificados y preparados para ese día majestuoso cuando la iglesia perfeccionada se presentará ante Cristo como una novia ante su esposo. Juan dice de ella que estará «preparada como una novia hermosamente vestida para su prometido». Esta es nuestra noche en la que debemos velar, pero mira, viene la mañana, una mañana sin nubes y luego caminaremos en luz porque ha venido nuestro Bien Amado. Esa segunda venida suya será su revelación, aquí estuvo bajo una nube y los hombres no lo percibieron, excepto unos pocos que contemplaron su gloria; pero cuando él venga por segunda vez, todos los velos serán quitados y todo ojo verá la gloria de su rostro. Él aguarda esto y su iglesia le aguarda a él.

A través de la Biblia en un año: Números 13–16

Dios no es mudo

Habla, que tu siervo escucha respondió Samuel.

1 SAMUEL 3:10

El que quiera escuchar a Dios hablar no tiene que esperar mucho porque Dios habla constantemente a los hombres por medio de las Escrituras que nos fueron dadas mediante la inspiración. ¡Qué pena que seamos tan sordos a sus enseñanzas! Se lee tan poco este maravilloso volumen, tan lleno de sabiduría, que muy pocos de nosotros nos podríamos atrever a mirar sus páginas y decir: «Ay, Señor, en este libro he escuchado tu palabra». En otras ocasiones el Señor habla por medio de la providencia. Las providencias tanto nacionales como personales tienen un significado, providencias que afligen y providencias que consuelan, todas tienen una voz. Pero, por desgracia, temo que a menudo la providencia para nosotros es muda porque nosotros somos sordos. Temo que muy pocos de ustedes pueden decir: «Ay, Señor, en la providencia he escuchado tu palabra». El Dios del cielo habla a los hombres por medio de su Espíritu Santo. Él hace esto, a veces, en las funciones comunes del Espíritu sobre los impíos a las que ellos se resisten, como también hicieron sus padres. El Espíritu lucha con hombres; él llama, ellos se niegan; él extiende su mano, pero ellos no lo reconocen. Aunque tenemos oídos para oír, a menudo apagamos al Espíritu, lo entristecemos, hacemos poco caso de sus admoniciones y, no obstante, si no despreciamos sus enseñanzas, muy a menudo las olvidamos y escuchamos las tonterías de la tierra en lugar de la sabiduría de los cielos.

A través de la Biblia en un año: Números 17–20

Atraer la bendición

El justo se ve coronado de bendiciones, pero la boca del malvado encubre violencia.
PROVERBIOS 10:6

Considera. Si reflexionas, verás que Dios es capaz de darle a su iglesia la mayor bendición y de dársela en cualquier momento. Guarda silencio y considera, y verás que él puede dar la bendición a través de ti o de mí; él puede hacer que cualquiera de nosotros, débiles como somos, sea poderoso en Dios para la destrucción de fortalezas; puede hacer que nuestras manos endebles, aunque solo tengamos unas pocas barras de pan y unos peces, sean capaces de alimentar a miles con el pan de vida. Considera esto y pregúntate en la tranquilidad de tu espíritu, ¿qué podemos hacer para obtener la bendición? ¿Lo estamos haciendo? ¿Qué hay en nuestro temperamento, en nuestra oración privada, en nuestras acciones para que Dios nos mande la bendición? ¿Actuamos de manera sincera? ¿Realmente tenemos un deseo de esas cosas que decimos desear? ¿Podríamos renunciar a compromisos mundanos para ocuparnos de la obra de Dios? ¿Podríamos separar tiempo para cuidar la viña del Señor? ¿Estamos dispuestos a hacer la obra del Señor y tiene nuestro corazón la condición para hacerlo de manera eficiente y aceptable? Guarda silencio y considera. Yo sugeriría a cada cristiano que se sentara un rato delante de Dios cuando llegue a casa y adore con el silencio del sobrecogimiento, con el silencio de la vergüenza y con el silencio de pensar cuidadosamente en estas cosas.

A través de la Biblia en un año: Números 21–24

Sentarse a los pies del maestro

Mientras iba de camino con sus discípulos, Jesús entró en una aldea, y una mujer llamada Marta lo recibió en su casa. Tenía ella una hermana llamada María que, sentada a los pies del Señor, escuchaba lo que él decía. Marta, por su parte, se sentía abrumada porque tenía mucho que hacer.

LUCAS 10:38-40

El sonido nos agota, el silencio nos alimenta. Hacer los mandados del Maestro siempre es bueno, pero sentarse a los pies del Maestro es igual de necesario, porque al igual que los ángeles sobresalen en fuerza, nuestro poder para hacer sus mandamientos surge de que agucemos el oído a su Palabra. Si incluso para una controversia humana el silencio es una preparación adecuada, ¿cuánto más no será necesario en las súplicas solemnes con el Eterno? Deja que los manantiales profundos se abran y que las solemnidades de la eternidad ejerzan su poder mientras todavía todo está quieto dentro de nosotros.

Pero, ¿cómo es que ese silencio renueva nuestras fuerzas? Lo hace, primero, al dar espacio para que la Palabra fortalecedora entre a nuestra alma y se sienta realmente la energía del Espíritu Santo. Palabras, palabras, palabras; tenemos tantas palabras y no son más que paja, pero ¿dónde está *el Verbo* que en el principio era Dios y estaba con Dios? Esta Palabra es la semilla viva e incorruptible: «¿Qué tiene que ver la paja con el grano? afirma el Señor» (Jeremías 23:28). Queremos menos de las palabras del hombre y más de él que es la misma Palabra de Dios. Guarda silencio, guarda silencio y deja que Jesús hable.

A través de la Biblia en un año: Números 25–28

Trabajo que no es en vano

Si el hacha pierde su filo, y no se vuelve a afilar, hay que golpear con más fuerza. El éxito radica en la acción sabia y bien ejecutada.
ECLESIASTÉS 10:10

La fuente de nuestra peor debilidad es nuestra fortaleza nacida en casa y la fuente de nuestra peor tontería es nuestra sabiduría personal. Señor, ayúdanos a estar tranquilos hasta que hayamos renunciado a nosotros mismos, hasta que hayamos dicho: «Señor, nuestra manera de trabajar no se compara con la tuya, enséñanos a trabajar. Señor, nuestros juicios son débiles en comparación con tu juicio perfecto; somos tontos; sé nuestro maestro y guíanos en todas las cosas».

Jehová trabaja en todas partes y todas las cosas le sirven. Él obra en la luz, y vemos su gloria, pero igualmente obra en la oscuridad donde no podemos percibirlo. Su sabiduría es demasiado profunda para que hombres mortales puedan entenderla en todo momento. Seamos pacientes y esperemos por su tiempo. Confiemos en el poder de nuestro padre, como confía el niño que está en el pecho de su madre acerca del amor de esta; sin más dudas de las que puede tener de la majestad de Jehová un ángel que está ante el trono, comprometámonos, cada uno según su propia forma, a sufrir y trabajar para la gran causa de Dios, sintiéndonos seguros de que ningún trabajo ni sufrimiento en el Señor puede ser en vano.

A través de la Biblia en un año: Números 29–32

Intercede valientemente

Así que somos embajadores de Cristo, como si Dios los exhortara a ustedes por medio de nosotros.
2 CORINTIOS 5:20

Amado, tú que conoces al Señor, te imploro que te *acerques*. Estás callado, has renovado tu fuerza; ahora disfruta el acceso con valentía. La condición para interceder por otros no es estar alejados de Dios sino muy cerca a él. Hasta Abraham se acercó cuando imploró por Sodoma y Gomorra. Recordemos cuán cerca estamos realmente. Hemos sido lavados de todo pecado en la preciosa sangre de Jesús, en este momento estamos cubiertos de pies a cabeza con la justicia inmaculada de Enmanuel, Dios con nosotros. El Amado nos acepta, sí, en este momento somos uno con Cristo y miembros de su cuerpo. ¿Cómo podríamos estar más cerca? ¿Cuán cerca está Cristo de Dios? ¡Así de cerca estamos nosotros! Entonces, acércate en tus súplicas personales, porque estás cerca a tu Representante del pacto. El Señor Jesús ha llevado a la humanidad en unión con la naturaleza divina y ahora entre Dios y el hombre existe una relación especial y sin paralelo que el universo no puede igualar. Acérquense entonces, hijos de Dios, acérquense porque están cerca. Párense en el lugar que su condición de hijos les da, ahí donde su Representante está parado a vuestro favor.

A través de la Biblia en un año: Números 33–36

Un Dios que escucha la oración

Pero mientras mantenían a Pedro en la cárcel, la iglesia oraba constante y fervientemente a Dios por él.
HECHOS 12:5

Dios le ha concedido a la iglesia misericordias indecibles como respuesta a la intercesión, porque él se complace en bendecir a su pueblo en el propiciatorio. La iglesia de Dios nunca ha ganado una victoria que no sea respuesta a la oración. Toda su historia es para la alabanza de un Dios que escucha la oración. Ven entonces, si antes nos fue tan bien, y si Dios nos invita ahora, sí, si él se deleita en nuestras peticiones, no seamos descuidados y, por el contrario, aumentemos nuestras peticiones delante de él.

Insto encarecidamente a mis hermanos en Cristo a altercar así con el Señor: «Señor, tu verdad no prospera en la tierra, sin embargo, tú has dicho: "Mi palabra no regresará a mí vacía". Señor, cada día eres blasfemado y, no obstante, tú has dicho que toda carne verá tu gloria. Señor, han puesto ídolos, incluso en esta tierra, donde quemaron a tus mártires, están levantando otra vez las imágenes esculpidas. Señor, derrúmbalas por amor a tu nombre, por tu honor te lo imploramos, hazlo. ¿No escuchas el triunfo del enemigo? Dicen que el evangelio está desgastado. Nos dicen que somos reliquias de una raza anticuada, que el progreso moderno ha barrido la fe. ¿Permitirás que así sea, buen Señor? ¿Será el evangelio considerado como un almanaque atrasado y pondrán ellos nuevos evangelios en su lugar? Las almas se pierden. ¡Oh, Dios de misericordia! ¡El infierno se llena, oh Dios de compasión infinita! Jesús solo ve que pocos llegan ante él y se lavan en su preciosa sangre. ¡El tiempo vuela y cada año aumenta el número de los perdidos! ¿Cuánto tiempo, oh Dios, cuánto tiempo? ¿Por qué tardas?» De esta manera, presenta tu caso ante el Señor y él te prestará oído.

A través de la Biblia en un año: Hechos 1–3

Multiplicación espiritual

Y la palabra de Dios se difundía: el número de los discípulos aumentaba considerablemente en Jerusalén, e incluso muchos de los sacerdotes obedecían a la fe.
HECHOS 6:7

La multiplicación es una forma muy antigua de bendición. La bendición que se pronunció sobre el hombre fue de este tipo, porque en el primer capítulo de Génesis leemos en primer lugar: «Los bendijo con estas palabras: "Sean fructíferos y multiplíquense; llenen la tierra"». En un sentido espiritual, esta es la bendición de la iglesia de Dios. Cuando el poder del Espíritu Santo visita la iglesia, esta aumenta en cada aspecto. Cuando una iglesia en medio de una amplia población permanece estática en los números, o incluso se reduce, ningún hombre puede ver en dicha condición la bendición de Dios. Sin dudas, sería una bendición novedosa, porque la primera bendición, la bendición de Pentecostés trajo como resultado que se añadieran tres mil a la iglesia en un día y luego encontramos que «Cada día el Señor añadía al grupo los que iban siendo salvos» (Hechos 2:47). Está claro que la bendición que como iglesia debemos buscar con todo nuestro corazón es ese aumento continuo.

A través de la Biblia en un año: Hechos 4–6

Un buen motivo para orar

Así que acerquémonos confiadamente al trono de la gracia para recibir misericordia y hallar la gracia que nos ayude en el momento que más la necesitemos.
HEBREOS 4:16

Todo verdadero cristiano desea ver que la iglesia crezca; en todo caso yo me compadezco del hombre que se crea cristiano y que no tenga tal deseo. «Que toda la tierra se llene de su gloria» es una aspiración natural de todo hijo de Dios y si algún hombre está convencido de ser un hijo de Dios y, no obstante, no tiene el deseo de ver que la gloria de Dios se manifieste con la conversión de multitudes, yo me compadezco de la condición de su corazón y de su entendimiento. Confío en que todos sintamos el espíritu misionero, todos anhelamos ver el reino del Señor venir y ver que los convertidos en Sión se multipliquen. Pero Dios ha agregado a la concesión de nuestro deseo que debemos orar por este, debemos suplicar y pedir, de lo contrario el crecimiento será retenido.

El Señor sabe cuán beneficioso es para nosotros orar mucho y por tanto él nos facilita acercarnos a él. Él nos da una multitud de razones para acercarnos al propiciatorio y nos da tareas que pueden usarse como argumentos para hacer peticiones frecuentes. Ahora bien, como al Señor le encanta comunicarse con las personas, él se ocupa de darles tareas por las cuales ellos deban venir a él. Nunca debemos temer que se nos interrogue en la puerta de la misericordia y que se nos haga esta dura pregunta: «¿Qué haces aquí?» Porque siempre tenemos alguna razón para orar, de hecho, cada promesa se convierte en una razón para orar porque no se nos concederá la promesa hasta que la hayamos pedido en el propiciatorio.

A través de la Biblia en un año: Hechos 7–9

Nuestro canal de bendición

Por aquellos días Ezequías se enfermó gravemente y estuvo a punto de morir. … Ezequías volvió el rostro hacia la pared y le rogó al Señor: «Recuerda, Señor, que yo me he conducido delante de ti con lealtad y con un corazón íntegro, y que he hecho lo que te agrada.» Y Ezequías lloró amargamente. … «Regresa y dile a Ezequías, gobernante de mi pueblo, que así dice el Señor, Dios de su antepasado David: He escuchado tu oración y he visto tus lágrimas. Voy a sanarte, y en tres días podrás subir al templo del Señor.»

2 Reyes 20:1-5

¿No debiera haber oración en nuestros corazones cuando Dios ha señalado que la oración debe ser el canal de bendición para los pecadores así como para nosotros mismos? Entonces, ¿cómo podemos decir que somos cristianos? Tú podrías decir: «Bueno, yo creo que yo podría ser dispensado», pero debo contestarte que no. «Estoy muy enfermo», dice alguno. Ah, entonces puedes acostarte y orar.

«Soy tan pobre», dice otro. Bueno, no te cobran ni un centavo cada vez que ores a Dios. No importa cuán pobre seas, tus oraciones son iguales de aceptables; solo recuerda, si eres tan pobre, debes orar todavía más porque no puedes dar tu ofrenda en forma de oro. Me gustaría que dijeras como el apóstol: «No tengo plata ni oro pero lo que tengo te doy. Mi Maestro, oraré mucho».

«Ah» dice otro, «pero yo no tengo talentos». Esa es otra razón por la que debes orar más y no por la cual debas dejar de orar porque si no puedes contribuir al servicio público de la iglesia por falta de talento, debes contribuir aun con más fervor a su fortalecimiento mediante el ejercicio privado de la oración y la intercesión y así hacer fuerte a aquellos que son más aptos para ir al frente.

A través de la Biblia en un año: Hechos 10–12

Sin excusa

Oren en el Espíritu en todo momento, con peticiones y ruegos. Manténganse alerta y perseveren en oración por todos los santos.
EFESIOS 6:18

¿Sobre qué base puede alguien ser eximido del deber de orar? Respuesta: Sobre ninguna base. No puedes ser eximido basándote en una simple naturaleza humana porque si Dios salvará a los pecadores en base a la oración y yo no oro, ¿qué soy? Las almas mueren, perecen, se hunden en el infierno mientras que el mecanismo establecido para la salvación es la oración y la predicación de la Palabra y si yo restrinjo la oración, ¿qué soy? Sin duda la bondad humana se ha marchado de mi pecho y he dejado de ser humano, y si es así, no tiene valor hablar de comunión con lo divino. Aquel que no se compadece de un hombre herido y no busca aliviar el hambre de alguien que muere de necesidad es un monstruo. Pero el que no se apiada de las almas que se están hundiendo en un fuego eterno, ¿qué es?

Además, ¿puede encontrarse alguna excusa en el cristianismo para abandonar la oración? Yo respondo, no se encuentra ninguna en el cristianismo más que en la naturaleza humana porque si Cristo nos ha salvado, él nos ha dado de su Espíritu: «si alguno no tiene el Espíritu de Cristo, no es de Cristo» (Romanos 8:9). ¿Y cuál era el Espíritu de Cristo? ¿Miró él a Jerusalén y dijo: «Yo creo que se ha renunciado a la ciudad, está predestinada a la destrucción» y luego siguió tranquilamente su camino? No, no lo hizo. Él creía en la predestinación pero esa verdad nunca enfrió su corazón. Él lloró por Jerusalén y dijo: «¡Jerusalén, Jerusalén, cuántas veces quise reunir a tus hijos, como reúne la gallina a sus pollitos debajo de sus alas, pero no quisiste!»

A través de la Biblia en un año: Hechos 13–16

Compasión por otros

Ríos de lágrimas corren por mis mejillas porque ha sido destruida la capital de mi pueblo. Se inundarán en llanto mis ojos, sin cesar y sin consuelo, hasta que desde el cielo el Señor se digne mirarnos.

LAMENTACIONES 3:48-50

Mientras más nos convirtamos en lo que debemos ser, más dominará la compasión nuestros corazones. ¿Qué dijo el Señor Jesucristo, que es el modelo y el reflejo de la hombría perfecta, con respecto a los pecados y a las aflicciones de Jerusalén? Él sabía que Jerusalén debía perecer, ¿enterró él su pena tras el hecho del decreto divino y endureció su corazón por la idea de la soberanía o la justicia que sería resplandeciente en la destrucción de la ciudad? No, él no, sino que lloró con ojos que borboteaban como una fuente: «¡Jerusalén, Jerusalén, cuántas veces quise reunir a tus hijos, como reúne la gallina a sus pollitos debajo de sus alas, pero no quisiste!» Si vas a ser como Jesús, debes ser tierno y compasivo. Serías el opuesto extremo de él si pudieras sentarte con un contentamiento sombrío y, con una filosofía estoica, convertir en piedra toda la carne que hay en ti. Si es natural, entonces, y por encima de todo, si es natural de la naturaleza dada por la gracia, les imploro, dejen que sus corazones se muevan con piedad; no resistan ver la muerte espiritual de la humanidad. Agoniza cada vez que contemples la ruina de cualquier alma de la simiente de Adán.

Sin duda que los que reciben misericordia deben mostrar misericordia; aquellos que deben todo lo que tienen a la piedad de Dios no deben mostrarse despiadados para con sus hermanos. Encontrarás en todas partes por todo el evangelio que este habla de amor fraternal, de compasiva misericordia y de una piedad que llora. Déjame implorarte que creas que es necesario así como justificable que sientas compasión por los hijos de los hombres.

A través de la Biblia en un año: Hechos 17–19

Un hambre divina

Digo la verdad en Cristo; no miento. Mi conciencia me lo confirma en el Espíritu Santo. Me invade una gran tristeza y me embarga un continuo dolor. Desearía yo mismo ser maldecido y separado de Cristo por el bien de mis hermanos, los de mi propia raza, el pueblo de Israel.

ROMANOS 9:1-4

Pablo se convierte en el salvador de muchos debido al deseo de su corazón y su oración a Dios para que estos se salven. ¡Ay, le imploro a Dios que venga sobre nosotros un hambre divina que no pueda satisfacerse a menos que los hombres se rindan a Jesús!; un deseo intenso y ferviente, un deseo jadeante de que los hombres se sometan al evangelio de Jesús. Esto te enseñará mejor que la mejor preparación que una universidad pueda darte acerca de cómo tratar con los corazones humanos. Esto le dará a la lengua tartamuda la palabra pronta; el corazón ardiente quemará las cuerdas que aprietan firmemente a la lengua. Te convertirás en sabio para ganar almas, aunque quizá nunca exhibas la brillante elocuencia o la fuerza de la lógica. Los hombres se maravillarán ante tu poder, el secreto les será oculto, y el hecho es que el Espíritu Santo te cubrirá y tu corazón te enseñará sabiduría, Dios enseñará a tu corazón. Profundos sentimientos de tu parte hacia otros harán que otros sientan por sí mismo y Dios te bendecirá y eso desde bien temprano.

A través de la Biblia en un año: Hechos 20–22

No te olvides

Si hablo en lenguas humanas y angelicales, pero no tengo amor, no soy más que un metal que resuena o un platillo que hace ruido.
1 CORINTIOS 13:1

En cada uno de nosotros existe la tentación de tratar de olvidar que las almas se están perdiendo. Puedo ir a mi casa por calles respetables y escoger ese camino de modo natural porque así no veo la pobreza de los locales más bajos de la ciudad pero, ¿estoy haciendo lo correcto si trato de olvidar que existen lugares como Bethnal Greens y Kent Streets, y otros lugares semejantes de pobreza? Los patios cerrados, los sótanos, las buhardillas atestadas, las casas de hospedaje, ¿me voy a olvidar de que existen? De seguro que la única manera de que una mente caritativa duerma cómodamente en Londres es olvidar cómo vive la mitad de la población; pero ¿es nuestro objetivo vivir cómodamente? ¿Somos bestias tan brutas que lo único que nos interesa es la comodidad, como los cerdos en su pocilga? No, hermanos, traigamos a la memoria los pecados de nuestra gran ciudad, sus penas y sufrimientos y recordemos también los pecados y las penas del vasto mundo y las decenas de miles de nuestra raza que están marchando constantemente a la eternidad. Más aun, ¡míralos! ¡No cierres los ojos! ¿El horror de la visión hace que te duelan los ojos? Entonces mira hasta que también te duela tu corazón y tu espíritu prorrumpa en agonía delante del Señor.

Mira hacia el infierno un momento; abre bien la puerta; escucha y vuelve a escuchar. Dices que no puedes, que enferma tu alma; deja que se enferme y en su desmayo, déjala caer en los brazos de Cristo el Salvador y exhala un lamento para que él se apure en salvar a los hombres de la ira venidera. No ignores, pido en oración, lo que sí existe.

A través de la Biblia en un año: Hechos 23–25

Amigos de Dios

Yo les he dicho estas cosas para que en mí hallen paz. En este mundo afrontarán aflicciones, pero ¡anímense! Yo he vencido al mundo.
JUAN 16:33

Ismael no recibió burlas, pero Isaac sí porque él nació de la promesa. La posteridad de Esaú nunca sufrió esclavitud en Egipto pero Israel tuvo que prepararse por medio del arduo servicio. La persecución es para el justo; los hombres malvados reciben honra de sus cómplices impíos. La calumnia dispara sus flechas envenenadas no a los depravados, sino a los virtuosos. Los pájaros no picotean las frutas agrias sino que atacan tanto las dulces como las maduras. Los hombres santos deben esperar que se les desvirtúe y a menudo se les difame intencionalmente, mientras que los hipócritas tienen su premio en un homenaje inmerecido. Lleva sobre tus hombros la carga que escojas y nadie se dará cuenta a menos que de hecho ellos obedezcan la vieja regla y «respeten la carga», pero si tomas la cruz de Cristo y valientemente la llevas, muy pocos respetarán la carga o alabarán al que la lleva. Hombres sin gracia le añadirán peso a tu carga porque la ofensa de la cruz aun no ha cesado. La naturaleza de los malvados es odiar al justo así como el lobo se enfurece contra las ovejas. Este mundo no puede ser amigo del amigo de Dios a menos que en verdad Belial pueda tener comunión con Cristo y nosotros sabemos que eso es imposible. De una manera u otra, los egipcios oprimirán a los israelitas hasta el día en que Dios los libere de estos con mano fuerte y brazo extendido. Si hoy la enemistad se restringe en su manifestación es porque la ley de la nación, por la providencia de Dios, no permite la tortura, la hoguera ni la mazmorra.

A través de la Biblia en un año: Hechos 26–28

¿Cómo podemos no amarlo?

Ama al Señor tu Dios con todo tu corazón, con toda tu alma, con toda tu mente y con todas tus fuerzas.
MARCOS 12:30

Dios merece, en todos los aspectos, el amor que exhorta a los santos tener. Piensa en la excelencia del carácter de quien se te pide que ames. Dios es un ser tan perfecto que ahora yo siento que, apartándome por completo de cualquier cosa que él ha hecho por mí, yo lo amo porque él es tan bueno, tan justo, tan santo, tan fiel, tan verdadero. No hay uno solo de sus atributos que no sea exactamente lo que debiera ser. Si miro a su amado Hijo, veo que su carácter está balanceado de una manera tan gloriosa que me pregunto por qué incluso aquellos que niegan su divinidad no adoran un carácter como el de él, porque es absolutamente único. Cuando pienso en el carácter del Espíritu para siempre bendecido, en su paciencia y en su sabiduría, su ternura y su amor para con nosotros, no puedo evitar amarlo. Sí amado, tenemos que amar al Padre, al Hijo y al Espíritu porque nunca los corazones humanos tuvieron tal objeto de amor como la divina Trinidad en unidad.

¿Qué es Dios? «Dios es amor». Esa corta frase lo encierra todo. Él es un Dios maravilloso pero es tan misericordioso como maravilloso. Él está tan lleno de bondad así como el sol está lleno de luz y tan lleno de gracia como el mar está lleno de agua y él se complace en dar a otros todo lo que tiene. Dios, mi Dios, tú eres todo un encanto y el corazón que esté en buena condición tiene que amarte.

A través de la Biblia en un año: Deuteronomio 1-4

La verdad elemental

Por eso Cristo es mediador de un nuevo pacto, para que los llamados reciban la herencia eterna prometida, ahora que él ha muerto para liberarlos de los pecados cometidos bajo el primer pacto.

HEBREOS 9:15

El centro del evangelio es la redención y la esencia de la redención es el sacrificio sustitutivo de Cristo. Aquellos que predican esta verdad, predican el evangelio sin considerar cualquier otro error que pudieran tener, pero los que no predican la expiación, sin considerar lo demás que declaren, han perdido el alma y la esencia del mensaje divino. En estos días me siento obligado a repasar las verdades elementales del evangelio. En la misma iglesia se han levantado hombres que hablan cosas perversas. Hay muchos que nos preocupan con sus filosofías y sus novedosas interpretaciones, por medio de las cuales niegan las doctrinas que profesan enseñar para socavar la fe que han prometido mantener. No tengo deseos de tener fama en nada que no sea predicar el viejo evangelio.

Hermanos míos, por experiencia he encontrado que nada toca el corazón como la cruz de Cristo y cuando la espada de doble filo de la ley toca y hiere el corazón, nada cura sus heridas como el bálsamo que fluye del corazón traspasado de Jesús. Cuando vemos hombres vivificados, convertidos y santificados mediante la doctrina del sacrificio sustitutivo podemos concluir debidamente que esta es la verdadera doctrina de la expiación. No he conocido a hombres que revivan para Dios y la santidad excepto mediante la doctrina de la muerte de Cristo en lugar del hombre.

A través de la Biblia en un año: Deuteronomio 5–8

Ciudadanos del cielo

En cambio, nosotros somos ciudadanos del cielo, de donde anhelamos recibir al Salvador, el Señor Jesucristo.
FILIPENSES 3:20

Mientras estemos aquí tenemos que hacer nuestro mayor esfuerzo por llevar hombres a Cristo, por ganarlos de sus malos caminos, por llevarlos a la vida eterna y por hacerlos, junto con nosotros, ciudadanos de otra tierra mejor.

Al buscar el bien del país como extranjeros, también tenemos que recordar que les corresponde a los extranjeros mantenerse muy tranquilos. ¿Por qué han de conspirar los extranjeros contra el gobierno ni entremeterse en la política de un país del que no tienen ciudadanía? Así que en esta tierra nuestra, donde tú y yo somos extranjeros, debemos ser advenedizos ordenados, que se someten constantemente a aquellos que están en autoridad, llevando vidas ordenadas y pacíficas y, según el mando del Santo Espíritu por medio del apóstol: «Den a todos el debido respeto: amen a los hermanos, teman a Dios, respeten al rey»; «sométanse por causa del Señor a toda autoridad humana». En esta tierra solo estamos de paso y debemos bendecirla al pasar por ella, pero nunca debemos hacer yugo con sus asuntos. Los cristianos, como hombres, aman la libertada y no están dispuestos a perderla ni en el menor sentido, pero espiritualmente sus políticas de gobierno son espirituales y como ciudadanos, velan por el interés de esa república divina a la que pertenecen y aguardan el momento en que, habiendo soportado las leyes de la tierra de su exilio, estarán bajo el dominio bienhechor de aquel que reina en gloria, el Rey de Reyes y Señor de Señores. Si es posible, en cuanto dependa de ustedes, vivan en paz con todos los hombres y sirvan a su tiempo y su generación con tranquilidad, pero no construyan morada para su alma aquí, porque toda esta tierra será destruida con la venida del día terrible.

A través de la Biblia en un año: Deuteronomio 9–12

Discurso celestial

Encarga y enseña estas cosas. Que nadie te menosprecie por ser joven. Al contrario, que los creyentes vean en ti un ejemplo a seguir en la manera de hablar, en la conducta, y en amor, fe y pureza.
1 TIMOTEO 4:11-12

Nuestra manera de hablar debe ser tal que se detecte nuestra ciudadanía. No debemos ser capaces de vivir en una casa mucho tiempo sin que los hombres se enteren quiénes somos. Una vez un amigo mío fue a los Estados Unidos y creo que desembarcó en Boston. No conocía a nadie pero cuando oyó a un hombre decir, porque alguien había dejado caer un barril en el muelle: «Cuidado, o harás de eso un Coggeshall», él dijo: «Usted es de Essex porque ese refrán no se usa en ningún otro lugar que en Essex; déme la mano» y de inmediato se hicieron amigos. Así que nuestra manera de hablar debiera ser tal que cuando un hermano se encuentre con nosotros pueda decir: «Tú eres cristiano, lo sé, porque nadie más habla o actúa así, solo los cristianos». «Seguro que estuviste con Jesús de Nazaret, se te nota por tu acento». Nuestra santidad debiera ser como una especie de francomasonería por medio de la cual sepamos cómo darle la mano al extraño, quién no es un verdadero extraño sino un conciudadano de la familia de la fe.

Oh, queridos amigos, adondequiera que vayamos, nunca debemos olvidar nuestra amada tierra. Hermanos, así como la gente en tierra extranjera ama a su país y siempre se alegra de recibir muchas cartas de su país, espero que tengamos mucha comunicación con la madre patria. Enviamos nuestras oraciones allá como cartas a nuestro Padre y recibimos sus cartas de vuelta en este bendito volumen, su Palabra.

A través de la Biblia en un año: Deuteronomio 13–16

Preparado para ser héroe

Sé lo que es vivir en la pobreza, y lo que es vivir en la abundancia. He aprendido a vivir en todas y cada una de las circunstancias, tanto a quedar saciado como a pasar hambre, a tener de sobra como a sufrir escasez. Todo lo puedo en Cristo que me fortalece.

FILIPENSES 4:12-13

Aquellas personas que solo navegan en un barco pequeño por un lago no tienen historias que contar acerca de aventuras en el mar. Pero el que va a escribir un libro acerca de viajes largos debe viajar muy lejos de la tierra y contemplar el mar en tiempos de tormenta así como de calma. Quizá te convertirás en un cristiano experimentado; darás gran honor a Dios al ser el medio de consuelo para otros que serán probados de manera similar a como tú lo fuiste. Te prepararás para ser un héroe y eso no puede lograrse excepto por medio de penas grandes y amargas que te sobrevengan. Creo que entre nosotros hay algunos a quienes Dios no puede confiarles mucho gozo. La cabeza se marearía si se le pone en un pináculo muy alto y se volvería orgullosa y autosuficiente y por lo tanto se destruiría. Dios no mataría a sus hijos con caramelos como tampoco lo haría con amargura. Cuando lo necesiten tendrán un tónico, pero si el tónico es tan amargo que pareciera que no pueden tomarlo y seguir viviendo, el Señor les quitará el tónico o les dará alguna dulzura deliciosa que quite todo el sabor amargo.

A través de la Biblia en un año: Deuteronomio 17–20

Nuestro todo en todo

Al sentir que se me iba la vida, me acordé del Señor, y mi oración llegó hasta ti, hasta tu santo templo. Los que siguen a ídolos vanos abandonan el amor de Dios. Yo, en cambio, te ofreceré sacrificios y cánticos de gratitud. Cumpliré las promesas que te hice. ¡La salvación viene del Señor!

JONÁS 2:7-9

Desde el principio la dificultad ha sido llegar al final de uno, porque cuando un hombre llega al fin de sí mismo, ha llegado al comienzo de la obra de Dios. Cuando uno está vaciado y no queda nada en lo absoluto, entonces toda la misericordia del pacto de la gracia es suya. Puede que yo tenga dudas en cuanto a si la gracia de Dios se ejercerá en ciertos casos pero no puedo presentar ninguna duda acerca de la liberalidad de la gracia divina para un alma que está vacía, para un alma que está lista para perecer, para un alma que está buscando a Dios y que tiene hambre y sed de justicia. Una vez que tu alma esté tan consciente de tu pecado que toda esperanza de salvación por tus propias obras quede abandonada y sientas que estás completamente condenado, entonces Jesucristo es tuyo porque él vino a llamar, no a justos, sino a pecadores. Así que acéptalo como tuyo, tómalo, recíbelo ahora. Dios ha hecho que Cristo sea la plenitud para llenar nuestro vacío, la justicia para nuestra injusticia, la vida para nuestra muerte, la salvación para nuestra condenación, el todo en todo para nuestra pobreza, nuestra miseria, nuestro pecado.

A través de la Biblia en un año: Deuteronomio 21–24

Una señal esperanzadora

Por lo tanto, le daré un puesto entre los grandes, y repartirá el botín con los fuertes, porque derramó su vida hasta la muerte, y fue contado entre los transgresores. Cargó con el pecado de muchos, e intercedió por los pecadores.

ISAÍAS 53:12

Los movimientos del Espíritu de Dios en las almas de su pueblo son las pisadas de los propósitos eternos de Dios a punto de cumplirse. Para un hombre siempre es una señal esperanzadora que otro ore por él. Es difícil arrastrar a un hombre al infierno a quien un hijo de Dios está halando hacia el cielo mediante la intercesión. A menudo la intercesión de los santos derrota a Satanás en sus tentaciones. Entonces, ten esperanza de que tu sentido personal de compasión por las almas sea un indicio de que Dios las bendecirá. Ismael, de quien Hagar se compadecía, fue un muchacho acerca de quien se hicieron grandes y amplias promesas. Él no podía morir, a Hagar se le había olvidado eso, pero a Dios no. No había sed que pudiera destruirlo porque Dios dijo que haría de Ismael una gran nación. Esperemos que aquellos por quienes tú y yo estamos orando y trabajando estén, de acuerdo con el propósito eterno de Dios, salvaguardados del infierno porque la sangre de Cristo los ha comprado y ellos tienen que pertenecerle al Señor. Nuestras oraciones son insignias de la voluntad de Dios. El Espíritu Santo nos guía a orar por aquellos a quienes él tiene la intención de llamar.

A través de la Biblia en un año: Deuteronomio 25–28

Habla primero con el amo

Entonces comenzó a orar: «Señor, Dios de mi amo Abraham, te ruego que hoy me vaya bien, y que demuestres el amor que le tienes a mi amo. Aquí me tienes, a la espera junto a la fuente, mientras las jóvenes de esta ciudad vienen a sacar agua. Permite que la joven a quien le diga: Por favor, baje usted su cántaro para que tome yo un poco de agua, y que me conteste: Tome usted, y además les daré agua a sus camellos, sea la que tú has elegido para tu siervo Isaac. Así estaré seguro de que tú has demostrado el amor que le tienes a mi amo.»

GÉNESIS 24:12-14

El fiel siervo de Abraham, antes de comenzar, se comunicó con su amo, y esto es una lección para nosotros, los que realizamos tareas de nuestro Señor. Antes de involucrarnos en algún servicio, busquemos el rostro del Amo, hablemos con él y digámosle cualquier dificultad que vislumbremos en nuestra mente. Antes de ponernos a trabajar, sepamos qué debemos hacer y qué respaldo tenemos. Escuchemos de la propia boca de nuestro Señor lo que él espera que hagamos y hasta dónde nos ayudará para hacerlo. Les encargo, mis consiervos, que nunca vayan adelante a suplicarle a los hombres por Dios hasta que no hayan suplicado primero a Dios por los hombres. No intenten presentar un mensaje que no hayan recibido primero que nada del Espíritu Santo. Salgan de la recámara de la comunión con Dios al púlpito del ministerio entre los hombres y habrá un poder y una frescura en ustedes que nadie podrá resistir. El siervo de Abraham habló y actuó como alguien que se sentía obligado a hacer exactamente lo que su amo le ordenó y a decir lo que su amo le dijo; por tanto, su única ansiedad era saber la esencia y la medida de su comisión.

A través de la Biblia en un año: Deuteronomio 29–31

Lluvias de misericordia

Y dijo Manoa a su mujer: Ciertamente moriremos, porque a Dios hemos visto.
JUECES 13:22 (RVR 1960)

Para Manoa y para su mujer fue el mayor gozo posible de la vida, el clímax de su ambición, que serían los padres de un hijo por medio de quien el Señor comenzaría a liberar a Israel. De tan solo pensarlo, el gozo los inundaba, un gozo indecible; pero en el momento en que recibieron la noticia, al menos Manoa se sintió tan cargada en el espíritu que dijo: «Ciertamente moriremos, porque a Dios hemos visto». Tómalo como una regla general: los cielos nublados pronostican una lluvia de misericordia. Cuando experimentes una terrible aflicción, espera un dulce favor. ¿No te acuerdas, con relación a los apóstoles, que sintieron temor cuando entraron en la nube en el monte Tabor? Y, no obstante, fue en esa nube que vieron a su Maestro transfigurado, y tú y yo hemos tenido mucho miedo cuando entramos a la nube, aunque estuvimos ahí para ver más de Cristo y su gloria que nunca antes. La nube que temes es la pared externa de la recámara secreta donde el Señor se revela a sí mismo.

Yo sí creo que cada vez que el Señor está a punto de usarnos en su familia, nos toma como si fuéramos un plato y nos limpia por completo y nos pone en el estante y luego nos baja y pone ahí mismo su propia carne celestial con la cual llenará las almas de otros. Como regla debe haber un vaciamiento, un virar al revés y dejar a un lado, antes de que venga la mayor bendición. Manoa sentía que debía morir y no obstante no podía morir porque él sería el padre de Sansón, el liberador de Israel y el terror de los filisteos.

A través de la Biblia en un año: Deuteronomio 32–34

El remedio divino

Para que por fe Cristo habite en sus corazones. Y pido que, arraigados y cimentados en amor, puedan comprender, junto con todos los santos, cuán ancho y largo, alto y profundo es el amor de Cristo; en fin, que conozcan ese amor que sobrepasa nuestro conocimiento, para que sean llenos de la plenitud de Dios.

EFESIOS 3:17-19

La caída de Adán y la destrucción de la humanidad dieron amplio espacio y margen suficiente para el amor todopoderoso. Entre las ruinas de la humanidad había espacio para mostrar cuánto Jehová amaba a los hijos de los hombres, porque la circunferencia de su amor no era menor que el mundo, y el objeto de este no menos que liberar a los hombres de caer en el foso, y el resultado de este no menos que encontrar un rescate para ellos. El propósito trascendental de ese amor era tanto negativo como positivo: que al creer en Jesús los hombres no perecieran sino que tuvieran vida eterna. La grave enfermedad del hombre dio motivo a la introducción de ese remedio divino que solo Dios pudiera haber ideado y suministrado. Mediante el plan de misericordia y el gran regalo que se necesitaba para llevarlo a cabo, el Señor encontró los medios para mostrar su amor ilimitado a hombres culpables. De no haber caída ni destrucción, Dios nos hubiera mostrado su amor como lo hace a los espíritus puros y perfectos que rodean su trono, pero nunca pudiera habernos presentado su amor en la medida en que lo hace. En el regalo de su Hijo unigénito, Dios nos mostró su amor ya que siendo aun pecadores, en el debido tiempo, Cristo murió por los impíos.

A través de la Biblia en un año: Romanos 1-2

Ama al Señor

Amen al Señor, todos sus fieles.
SALMOS 31:23

Algunas pasiones de nuestra naturaleza pudieran ser exageradas y hacia ciertos objetos, pudieran ir demasiado lejos, pero el corazón, cuando se vuelve a Dios, nunca puede ser demasiado cálido ni estar demasiado emocionado, ni demasiado concentrado en el objeto divino: «Amen al Señor, todos sus fieles».

Pon el énfasis en esa dulce palabra: *amor, amar al Señor como no podrías amar a nadie ni a nada más*. Esposo, ama a tu esposa; padre, ama a tus hijos; hijos, amen a sus padres y todos ustedes amen a sus amigos, y está bien que lo hagan. Sin embargo, deben deletrear todos los otros amores con letras minúsculas pero el AMOR a Dios se deletrea con las mayúsculas más grandes que puedas encontrar. Ámalo intensamente, amen al Señor, todos su fieles, sin ningún límite en su amor.

Además, ámenlo con un principio de amor profundo y duradero. Existe un cierto tipo de amor humano que arde rápidamente como la maleza ý luego se apaga. Así hay también algunos cristianos que parecen amar al Señor de manera irregular y rápida, cuando se emocionan o en ciertas épocas especiales; pero les pido, amados, que dejen que su amor sea un fuego profundamente arraigado y duradero. ¿Y si lo comparo con la combustión en el mismo centro de un volcán? Es posible que no siempre esté en erupción pero siempre tiene dentro un calor intenso y cuando sí arde, ay, ¡qué tremenda marea, qué bullir, qué hervidero, qué llamas y que torrentes de lava a todo alrededor! Siempre debe haber fuego en le corazón aunque este sea un tanto callado y tranquilo.

A través de la Biblia en un año: Romanos 3–4

Anticipar el conflicto

El traidor les había dado esta contraseña: «Al que le dé un beso, ése es; arréstenlo y llévenselo bien asegurado.» Tan pronto como llegó, Judas se acercó a Jesús. —¡Rabí! —le dijo, y lo besó. Entonces los hombres prendieron a Jesús.
MARCOS 14:44-46

Nuestro Señor les dijo a los discípulos: «En este mundo afrontarán aflicciones» (Juan 16:33), y explicó que esto quería decir que los hombres los expulsarían de las sinagogas; sí, que llegaría el momento en que aquellos que los mataran pensarían que estaban sirviendo a Dios. «Así mismo serán perseguidos todos los que quieran llevar una vida piadosa en Cristo Jesús» (2 Timoteo 3:12).

La oposición del mundo no está confinada a la persecución sino que a veces toma la forma aun más peligrosa de la adulación, se ofrecen anzuelos agradables y se utilizan encantos para alejar al creyente de su Señor. El mundo ha herido a muchos penosamente cuando los ha saludado con el beso de Judas en sus labios y un puñal en la mano derecha con el cual matar el alma. Pobre de aquellos que ignoran las artimañas del mundo. Este es un problema lastimoso bajo el sol: que los hombres son falsos; sus palabras más suaves que la mantequilla pero por dentro son espadas desenvainadas. Esto a menudo sorprende a los cristianos jóvenes. Ellos imaginaron que ya que los piadosos estaban fascinados con sus encantos, todos los demás estarían igualmente complacidos, tropiezan cuando descubren que se habla mal de su bondad. ¿Hay algún recluta primerizo entre mis oyentes? Dejen que aprenda que ser un soldado de la cruz significa una verdadera guerra y no una pelea falsa. Él está en territorio enemigo y llegará el momento en que, como veterano de guerra, se sorprenderá si pasa un día sin conflicto o es capaz de envainar su espada durante una hora.

A través de la Biblia en un año: Romanos 5-6

Los compasivos

Mientras lo apedreaban, Esteban oraba. —Señor Jesús —decía—, recibe mi espíritu. Luego cayó de rodillas y gritó: —¡Señor, no les tomes en cuenta este pecado! Cuando hubo dicho esto, murió.
HECHOS 7:59-60

Algunos corazones tiernos no solo se sorprenden sino que se quedan consternados y se afligen ante la oposición del mundo. Espíritus tiernos y gentiles que no se enfrentarían a nadie si pudieran evitarlo, que sienten agudamente los ataques injustificados de aquellos que preferirían agradar en lugar de provocar. La sensibilidad del amor hace que los caracteres más delicados sean los más susceptibles al dolor bajo la cruel oposición, especialmente cuando viene de un pariente querido. Para aquellos que aman a Dios y al hombre, a veces es una agonía verse obligados a parecer como la causa de la contienda, incluso por amor a Cristo.

El que más ama es quien más se parece a Dios, y aquel cuyo corazón está más lleno de compasión es quien más se acerca a la imagen de Cristo. En el reino de Dios los espíritus más fuertes resultan ser más bien enanos y no gigantes. Debemos tener fuerza de carácter y estar preparados para luchar tenazmente por la fe; no obstante, mientras más amor mostremos, mejor y, por lo tanto, más dolor nos costará estar continuamente en guerra con los espíritus fríos. Esta es una parte de la tribulación que debemos soportar, y mientras más valentía mostremos al enfrentarla, más a fondo ganaremos las batallas de la paz y la pureza.

A través de la Biblia en un año: Romanos 7–8

El abanderado

Pues los sufrimientos ligeros y efímeros que ahora padecemos producen una gloria eterna que vale muchísimo más que todo sufrimiento.
2 CORINTIOS 4:17

Pensamos demasiado en nosotros mismos y hablamos de la vida como si fuera un conflicto demasiado duro debido a la carga de nuestros cuidados y responsabilidades; pero, ¿qué comparación existe entre nuestra carga y la de Jesús? Un pastor con un gran rebaño no carece de ansiedades a cada hora; pero, ¿qué son esas antes los cuidados del pastor Jefe? Él veló por la gran multitud que ningún hombre puede contar, quienes le fueron encargados por el padre, y él llevó los dolores de todos ellos. Esta es una carga que tú y yo, mi querido amigo, ni tan siquiera podemos imaginar y, no obstante, sin dejar a un lado el peso, él luchó contra el mundo y lo venció.

Cuando toda la multitud marcha a la batalla, cada uno de nosotros toma un lugar en las filas y la guerra continúa contra todos nosotros; pero, ¿adónde crees tú que las flechas volaron en mayor cantidad? ¿Adónde fueron arrojadas las jabalinas una tras otra, gruesas como pedriscos? «El abanderado entre los diez miles» era el blanco principal. A mí me parece que el príncipe de las tinieblas le dijo a sus ejércitos: «No luchen ni con pequeños ni con grandes, excepto con el Rey de Israel», porque él fue tentado en todo al igual que nosotros. Tú y yo encontramos algunas tentaciones pero él las soporta todas. Yo tengo las mías y tú tienes las tuyas, pero él tuvo las mías y las tuyas y aquellas que son comunes a todos sus santos; no obstante, estando en el centro de la refriega, él permaneció ileso y clamó: «yo he vencido al mundo». La gracia, por lo tanto, también nos puede vestir de triunfo porque ninguna carga suprema de huestes sobre huestes será jamás dirigida en contra nuestra.

A través de la Biblia en un año: Romanos 9–10

Nuestra guía

Todo esto lo digo ahora que estoy con ustedes. Pero el Consolador, el Espíritu Santo, a quien el Padre enviará en mi nombre, les enseñará todas las cosas y les hará recordar todo lo que les he dicho.

JUAN 14:25-26

El Espíritu Santo dentro de nosotros es para servirnos de guía. Él nos revela una verdad tras otra mediante su luz y su guía y sí «aprendemos del Señor». Él es también nuestra guía práctica al cielo, nos ayuda y nos dirige en el viaje hacia arriba. Ojalá que los cristianos, para su vida diaria, averiguaran más a menudo en cuanto a la guía del Espíritu Santo. ¿No sabes tú que el Espíritu de Dios mora dentro de ti? No necesitas andar siempre corriendo de un amigo a otro en busca de dirección: espera en el Señor en silencio, siéntate tranquilo delante del oráculo de Dios. Usa el discernimiento que Dios te ha dado, pero cuando eso no sea suficiente, recurre a aquel a quien el señor Bunyan llama «el Secretario Supremo», quien vive dentro, que es infinitamente sabio y quien puede guiarte al hacerte escuchar la voz detrás de ti que dice: «este es el camino, ve por él». El Espíritu Santo te guiará en la vida, te guiará en la muerte y te guiará a la gloria. Te protegerá del error moderno y también del error antiguo. Te guiará de manera que no sabes y en la oscuridad te guiará de manera que no has visto: él hará estas cosas en ti y no te abandonará.

A través de la Biblia en un año: Romanos 11–12

El consolador

Alabado sea el Dios y Padre de nuestro Señor Jesucristo, Padre misericordioso y Dios de toda consolación, quien nos consuela en todas nuestras tribulaciones para que con el mismo consuelo que de Dios hemos recibido, también nosotros podamos consolar a todos los que sufren.

2 CORINTIOS 1:3-4

Nuestro Dios no quiere que sus hijos sean infelices y por lo tanto, él mismo, en la tercera persona de la bendita Trinidad, ha asumido el cargo de Consolador. ¿Por qué lleva tu rostro colores tan lúgubres? Dios puede consolarte. Tú que estás bajo la carga del pecado, es verdad que ningún hombre puede ayudarte para darte paz, pero el Espíritu Santo sí puede. ¡Oh, Dios, a todo el que busca y no ha logrado encontrar reposo, concédele tu Santo Espíritu! Pon tu Espíritu dentro de él y él descansará en Jesús. Y tú, querido pueblo de Dios, que estás preocupado, recuerda que la preocupación y el Espíritu Santo se contradicen entre sí. «Pondré mi Espíritu en ustedes» quiere decir que te convertirás en alguien apacible, tranquilo, resignado y conforme con la voluntad divina. Entonces tendrás fe en Dios de que todo está bien. ¿Puedes tú decir: «Dios mío, Díos mío»? ¿Quieres algo más? ¿Puedes concebir algo más allá de tu Dios? ¡Omnipotente para hacerlo todo eternamente! ¡Infinito para dar! ¡Fiel para recordar! Él es todo lo que es bueno. Él solo es la luz: «En él no hay oscuridad». El Espíritu Santo nos hace entender esto cuando está dentro de nosotros. En él nuestra felicidad a veces se eleva a grandes olas de regocijo, como si saltara a la gloria.

A través de la Biblia en un año: Romanos 13–14

El poder sustentador de Dios

¡Alabado sea Dios, Padre de nuestro Señor Jesucristo! Por su gran misericordia, nos ha hecho nacer de nuevo mediante la resurrección de Jesucristo, para que tengamos una esperanza viva y recibamos una herencia indestructible, incontaminada e inmarchitable. Tal herencia está reservada en el cielo para ustedes.

1 PEDRO 1:3-4

«Reservada en el cielo para ustedes, a quienes el poder de Dios protege mediante la fe hasta que llegue la salvación» (1 Pedro 1:4-5). Quizá este sea uno de los mejores elíxires para un cristiano con pesadumbre: que no está protegido por su propio poder y que no ha quedado a merced de su propia protección sino que lo protege el Altísimo. «Podrán desfallecer mi cuerpo y mi espíritu, pero Dios fortalece mi corazón; él es mi herencia eterna» (Salmos 73:26). «Porque sé en quién he creído, y estoy seguro de que tiene poder para guardar hasta aquel día lo que he dejado a su cuidado» (2 Timoteo 1:12). Pero si quitara esa doctrina de que el Salvador guarda a su pueblo, ¿dónde quedaría mi esperanza? ¿Qué tiene el evangelio que merezca mi predicación o que merezca que tú la recibas? Yo sé que él ha dicho: «Yo les doy vida eterna, y nunca perecerán, ni nadie podrá arrebatármelas de la mano» (Juan 10:28). Pero, Señor, ¿qué si desmayan, si comienzan a murmurar en su aflicción? ¿No perecerán entonces? No, nunca perecerán. Pero imagínate que el dolor se haga tan intenso que su fe flaquee. ¿No perecerán entonces? No. «Nunca perecerán ni ningún hombre los arrebatará de mi mano». ¡Ah! Esta es la doctrina, la seguridad que da ánimo: «Esto es para ustedes motivo de gran alegría, a pesar de que hasta ahora han tenido que sufrir diversas pruebas por un tiempo» (1 Pedro 1:6).

A través de la Biblia en un año: Romanos 15–16

Adoración por medio de la ofrenda

Cada uno debe dar según lo que haya decidido en su corazón, no de mala gana ni por obligación, porque Dios ama al que da con alegría.

2 Corintios 9:7

Observa también, una vez más —en lo referente a las acciones misericordiosas que la mayoría de la humanidad poco estima— que sabemos que Dios acepta nuestra adoración en las cosas pequeñas. Él permitió que su pueblo llevara sus novillos, a otros que llevaran sus carneros y se los ofrecieran a él, aunque estas eran personas que tenían suficientes riquezas como para ser capaces de ofrecerle un tributo de sus rebaños y manadas. Pero también le permitió a lo pobres ofrecer un par de tórtolas o dos pichones de palomas, y nunca he encontrado en la Palabra de Dios que él diera menos importancia a la ofrenda de las tórtolas que al sacrificio de los novillos. También sé que nuestro Señor siempre bendito, cuando estuvo aquí, amó la alabanza de los niños pequeños. Ellos no traían ni oro ni plata como los sabios del Oriente, pero clamaban: «Hosanna» y el Señor no se disgustó con sus Hosannas sino que aceptó su alabanza juvenil. Y recordamos que una viuda echó en la ofrenda dos moneditas, que solo era un cuarto de un penique, pero ya que era todo lo que tenía, él no rechazó el regalo sino que más bien tomó nota de este en su honor. Ahora estamos bastante familiarizados con el incidente, pero con todo y eso, es maravilloso. ¡Dos moneditas que son un cuarto de penique dadas al Dios infinito! ¡Un cuarto de penique aceptado por el Rey de Reyes! Por lo tanto, no midas las acciones pequeñas con las escalas y medidas humanas, sino estímalas como lo hace Dios, porque el Señor siente respeto por el corazón de su pueblo; él no da tanta importancia a sus obras en sí mismas sino a los motivos por los que se dan en servicio.

A través de la Biblia en un año: Josué 1–4

Cada uno ha sido llamado de manera especial

Pasando Jesús de allí, vio a un hombre llamado Mateo, que estaba sentado al banco de los tributos públicos, y le dijo: Sígueme. Y se levantó y le siguió.

MATEO 9:9 (RVR 1960)

El llamamiento del hombre llamado Mateo pareció accidental e improbable. «Pasando Jesús de allí», cuando estaba a punto de ir a realizar otra cosa, alejándose de Capernaúm, o sencillamente andando por una de sus calles, fue «pasando de allí» que esto sucedió.

En ese momento también había muchas otras personas en Capernaúm, sin embargo, Cristo no los llamó. Él los vio, pero no de la misma manera en que vio al hombre llamado Mateo. Y de manera similar, en ese día de misericordia en que recibiste la bendición de la salvación, quizá había una congregación muy concurrida, pero hasta donde sabes, la bendición no llegó a más nadie, solo a ti. ¿Por qué, entonces, vino a ti? Tú no sabes, a menos que hayas aprendido a mirar más allá de las cortinas en el Lugar Santo y a ver por la luz de la lámpara en el velo. Si has mirado allí, sabes que cuando Jesucristo pasa, lo que los hombres consideran accidentes es intencional, las miradas de sus ojos han sido ordenadas desde la eternidad; y cuando él mira a alguien, lo hace de acuerdo al propósito eterno y al preconocimiento de Dios. Hacía mucho tiempo que el Señor había considerado a ese hombre llamado Mateo, así que cuando el tiempo se cumplió, Jesucristo pasó por ese camino y miró con amor y misericordia a aquel hombre llamado Mateo. Él lo vio en ese momento porque, mucho antes, lo había vislumbrado.

A través de la Biblia en un año: Josué 5–8

Cuando el Señor pregunta

Cuando el día comenzó a refrescar, oyeron el hombre y la mujer que Dios andaba recorriendo el jardín; entonces corrieron a esconderse entre los árboles, para que Dios no los viera. Pero Dios el Señor llamó al hombre y le dijo: ¿Dónde estás?

GÉNESIS 3:8–9

Una de las cosas más terribles con relación a este encuentro de Dios con Adán fue que Adán tuvo que responder a las preguntas del Señor. El Señor le dijo: «¿Acaso has comido del fruto del árbol que yo te prohibí comer?» (Génesis 3:11). En nuestros tribunales de justicia no requerimos que los hombres responden a preguntas que los incriminaría, pero Dios lo hace; y en el gran día final, los impíos serán condenados por su propia confesión de culpa. Mientras están en este mundo, ponen un rostro cínico y declaran que no le han hecho daño a nadie, ni tan siquiera a Dios: pagan lo que les corresponde, son tan buenos como sus vecinos y mejores que la mayoría de ellos; pero todo su alarde y valentía desaparecerá el día del juicio. O se parará en silencio delante de Dios —y su silencio reconocerá la culpa ante los ojos de Dios— o si hablan, sus vanas excusas y disculpas no harán otra cosa que condenarlos. Ellos se condenarán a sí mismo con su propia boca, como aquel siervo malvado y perezoso que fue lanzado a las tinieblas de afuera donde está el lloro y el crujir de dientes. ¡Quiera Dios que nunca conozcamos por experiencia personal y triste lo que significan esas expresiones!

A través de la Biblia en un año: Josué 9–12

El estado natural de la tierra

Padre —dijo Jesús—, perdónalos, porque no saben lo que hacen. Mientras tanto, echaban suertes para repartirse entre sí la ropa de Jesús.
LUCAS 23:34

Cuando un hombre es ignorante y no sabe lo que debe hacer, ¿qué debe hacer? Bueno, no debe hacer nada hasta que sepa. Pero he ahí el problema, aunque no sabíamos, escogimos hacer lo incorrecto. Si no sabíamos, ¿por qué no escogimos hacer lo correcto? Pero al estar en la oscuridad, nunca nos volvemos a lo bueno sino que siempre damos bandazos a la izquierda, de pecado en pecado. ¿No nos demuestra esto cuán depravados son nuestros corazones? Aunque buscamos estar en lo correcto, cuando nos dejan solos, nos vamos a hacer lo malo. Deja a un niño solo, a un hombre solo, a una tribu sola sin enseñanza e instrucción, y ¿cuál es el resultado? Pues el mismo que cuando uno deja solo un campo. Nunca produce, ni por casualidad, trigo o cebada. Déjalo solo y aparecen hileras de malas hierbas, espinas y zarzas, lo que demuestra que el estado natural de la tierra se inclina a producir aquello que no vale nada.

Necesitabas luz pero cerraste tus ojos al sol. Tuviste sed pero no tomaste del manantial de agua viva de modo que tu ignorancia, aunque estaba allí, era una ignorancia criminal que debías confesar ante el Señor. ¡Oh, ven a la cruz, tú que ya has estado allí y has perdido allí tu carga! Ven y confiesa tu culpa una vez más y abraza de nuevo esa cruz y mira a aquel que derramó en ella su sangre y alaba su querido nombre, aquel que una vez oró por ti: «Padre —dijo Jesús—, perdónalos, porque no saben lo que hacen».

A través de la Biblia en un año: Josué 13–16

Imita a Cristo

Por eso, dispónganse para actuar con inteligencia; tengan dominio propio; pongan su esperanza completamente en la gracia que se les dará cuando se revele Jesucristo. Como hijos obedientes, no se amolden a los malos deseos que tenían antes, cuando vivían en la ignorancia.

1 PEDRO 1:13-14

La ignorancia de Cristo y de las cosas eternas debiera ser detestable para nosotros. Si por medio de la ignorancia hemos pecado, debiéramos terminar con esa ignorancia. Seremos estudiantes de su Palabra. Estudiaremos la obra maestra de todas las ciencias, el conocimiento de Cristo crucificado. Pediremos al Espíritu Santo que aleje de nosotros la ignorancia que genera el pecado. Que Dios permita que no volvamos a caer en los pecados de la ignorancia, sino que seamos capaces de decir: «Sé en quien he creído y por lo tanto, buscaré más conocimiento hasta que comprenda, junto con todos los santos, cuán ancho y largo, alto y profundo es el amor de Cristo; en fin, que conozcan ese amor que sobrepasa nuestro conocimiento».

Voy a incluir aquí algo práctico. Si te regocijas por estar perdonado, muestra tu gratitud imitando a Cristo. Nunca antes hubo una súplica como esta: «Padre, perdónalos, porque no saben lo que hacen». Suplica así por otros. ¿Alguien te ha hecho daño? ¿Hay personas que te calumnian? Ora esta noche: «Padre, perdónalos, porque no saben lo que hacen». Demos siempre bien por mal, bendición por maldición y cuando se nos llame a sufrir las maldades de otros, creamos que no actuarían como lo hacen si no fuera por su ignorancia. Oremos por ellos y hagamos que su ignorancia sea la súplica por su perdón: «Padre, perdónalos, porque no saben lo que hacen».

A través de la Biblia en un año: Josué 17–20

El camino a la misericordia

Pero en ti se halla perdón, y por eso debes ser temido.
SALMOS 130:4

¿Has observado el versículo que viene antes de este texto? Dice así: «Si tú, Señor, tomaras en cuenta los pecados, ¿quién, Señor, sería declarado inocente? (Salmos 130:3). Eso es una confesión. Ahora bien, la confesión siempre debe preceder al perdón. «Si confesamos nuestros pecados, Dios, que es fiel y justo, nos los perdonará y nos limpiará de toda maldad» (1 Juan 1:9). Si tratamos de encubrir nuestro pecado, «si afirmamos que no tenemos pecado, nos engañamos a nosotros mismos y no tenemos la verdad» (1 Juan 1:8), y no puede venir ningún perdón de parte de Dios para nosotros. Por lo tanto, declárate culpable, declárate culpable. Debes hacerlo porque eres culpable. Descubrirás que es lo más sabio que puedes hacer, porque esta es la única manera de obtener misericordia. Entrégate a la misericordia de tu Juez y encontrarás misericordia, pero primero reconoce que necesitas misericordia. Sé honesto con tu conciencia y honesto con tu Dios, y confiesa tu iniquidad y acongójate ante la justicia que no has alcanzado.

A través de la Biblia en un año: Josué 21–24

¿Cuestionar a Dios?

¿Te has puesto a pensar en mi siervo Job? —volvió a preguntarle el Señor—. No hay en la tierra nadie como él; es un hombre recto e intachable, que me honra y vive apartado del mal. Y aunque tú me incitaste contra él para arruinarlo sin motivo, ¡todavía mantiene firme su integridad!

JOB 2:3

El Señor nos envía lo malo así como lo bueno de esta vida mortal, de él son el sol que alegra y la escarcha que hiela; de él son la calma profunda y el tornado feroz. Hacer hincapié en segundas razones es a menudo frívolo, carente de validez. Los hombres dicen de cada aflicción: «Podría haberse evitado si tal y tal cosa hubiera ocurrido». Quizá si se hubiera llamado a otro médico, la vida de este niño querido se hubiera salvado. Es posible que si me hubiera movido en tal dirección en los negocios, no hubiera sido un perdedor. ¿Quién puede juzgar lo que podría haber sido? Nos perdemos en conjeturas interminables y somos crueles con nosotros mismos, recopilamos material para dolores innecesarios. Las cosas no sucedieron así, entonces, ¿por qué hacer conjeturas de cómo habría sido si las cosas hubieran sido diferentes? Es una tontería. Nos indignamos con la causa más inmediata de nuestro dolor y por tanto no nos sometemos a Dios. Siempre y cuando yo busque el origen de mi aflicción en el error, mi pérdida en la equivocación de otro, mi dolencia en un enemigo y demás, yo soy de la tierra, terrenal, pero cuando me elevo a mi Dios y veo su mano obrando, obtengo calma. No tengo una palabra de queja. «He guardado silencio; no he abierto la boca, pues tú eres quien actúa» (Salmos 39:9). «Hecha sobre Jehová tu carga» es un precepto que será fácil practicar cuando veas que la carga tuvo su origen en Dios.

A través de la Biblia en un año: 1 Corintios 1 –2

La causa está distante

¿Por qué me rechazas, Señor? ¿Por qué escondes de mí tu rostro?
SALMOS 88:14

No me pregunto por qué sufren algunos cristianos, pero si no sufrieran entonces sí debo cuestionarme. Los he visto, por ejemplo, descuidar la oración familiar y otros deberes hogareños y sus hijos han llegado a deshonrarlos. Si claman: «¡Qué aflicción!», no nos gusta decir: «Ah, pero debieras haberla esperado, tú fuiste la causa», pero decir eso sería la verdad. Cuando los hijos se marchan del hogar paterno y se entregan al pecado, no nos sorprende que el padre haya tenido un temperamento áspero, amargado y malhumorado. No esperaríamos recoger higos de espinos ni uvas de cardos. Hemos visto hombres que su único pensamiento era: «conseguir dinero, conseguir dinero» y, no obstante, profesan ser cristianos. Tales personas han sido preocupadas e infelices, pero no nos hemos asombrado. No, si se alejan tercamente de Cristo, él se alejará de ellos.

Pero a veces la causa del castigo está más allá. Todo cirujano te dirá que en el comienzo de la vida o en la vejez existen enfermedades que se vuelven problemáticas y que pudieron tener su causa en la juventud debido a alguna maldad o por accidente, y el mal puede haber estado latente todos esos años. Así mismo los pecados de nuestra juventud pueden traernos las penas de nuestros años más maduros, y las faltas y las omisiones de hace veinte años pueden azotarnos hoy. Yo sé que es así. Si la falta fuera de una época tan grande, debiera llevarnos a una búsqueda más completa y a una oración más frecuente.

A través de la Biblia en un año: 1 Corintios 3–4

Agitar las aguas

Quita la escoria de la plata, y de allí saldrá material para el orfebre.
PROVERBIOS 25:4

Dios visitará las transgresiones de sus hijos. Él dejará con frecuencia que los pecadores comunes vayan por la vida sin increpaciones, pero no así con sus hijos. Si fuera hoy a tu casa y en el camino vieras a varios muchachos lanzando piedras y rompiendo ventanas, puede que no interfirieras, pero si vieras a tu hijo entre ellos, estoy seguro de que lo llamarías y harías que se arrepintiera de eso.

Quizá se envíe el castigo por causa de un pecado que todavía no se ha desarrollado, cierta propensión latente a hacer el mal. Puede que el dolor tenga la intención de descubrir el pecado, para que tú lo busques. ¿Tienes idea de cuán malo eres por naturaleza? Ninguno de nosotros sabe de lo que seríamos capaces si no fuera por la gracia. ¡Creemos que tenemos un temperamento dulce, una disposición amigable! ¡Esto lo veremos! Andamos con una compañía irritante, estamos fastidiados e insultados, y nos tocan con tanta destreza en lugares sensibles que nos enloquecemos con la ira y nuestro espíritu bueno y amigable se desvanece como el humo, y esto no sucederá sin dejar atrás las manchas negras. ¿No es algo temible estar tan agitados? Sí, lo es, pero si nuestros corazones fueran puros, ningún tipo de agitación los contaminaría. Agita el agua pura tanto tiempo como quieras y no aparecerá ningún fango. El mal es malo cuando se ve pero es igual de malo cuando no se ve. Sería de gran provecho para un hombre saber qué pecado hay en él porque entonces se humillará a sí mismo delante de su Dios y comenzará a luchar contra su propensión. A veces, por tanto, puede que se nos envíe la prueba para que podamos discernir el pecado que mora en nosotros y busquemos su destrucción.

A través de la Biblia en un año: 1 Corintios 5–6

El fruto viene más adelante

Toda rama que en mí no da fruto, la corta; pero toda rama que da fruto la poda para que dé más fruto todavía.*
JUAN 15:2

Cuando tengamos problemas, no esperemos percibir algún beneficio inmediato como resultado de este. Yo mismo he tratado de ver, estando en un profundo dolor, si me he resignado un poco más o si me he vuelto más fervoroso en la oración, o más absorto en la comunión con Dios, y confieso que en dichos momentos nunca he sido capaz de ver ni la más ligera huella de mejoría porque el dolor distrae y dispersa los pensamientos. Recuerda la palabra: «sin embargo, después produce una cosecha de justicia y paz» (Hebreos 12:11). El jardinero toma su cuchillo y poda los árboles frutales para que estos den más fruto; su hijito viene caminando detrás pisándole los talones y grita: «Padre, yo no veo que el fruto salga en los árboles después que los has cortado». No, hijo querido, no es probable que lo veas, pero regresa en unos pocos meses cuando llegue la época de dar frutos y verás las manzanas doradas que agradecen el cuchillo. El fruto del Espíritu que tiene la intención de perdurar, requiere un tiempo para producirse y no se madura en una noche.

En un verdadero creyente los problemas graves tienen el efecto de aflojar las raíces de su alma hacia la tierra y de apretar el firme anclaje de su corazón hacia el cielo. Todo marinero del mar de la vida sabe que cuando soplan las brisas suaves, los hombres tientan al mar abierto con velas desplegadas, pero cuando viene la tormenta negra, aullando desde su guarida, se apresuran al puerto con toda velocidad.

A través de la Biblia en un año: 1 Corintios 7–8

El poder de condolerse

Tú dijiste: '¡Ay de mí! ¡El Señor añade angustia a mi dolor! Estoy agotado de tanto gemir, y no encuentro descanso.
JEREMÍAS 45:3

La aflicción nos da, por medio de la gracia, el inestimable privilegio de conformidad al Señor Jesús. Oramos para ser semejantes a Cristo pero, ¿cómo podemos serlo si no somos gente de dolores en lo absoluto y nunca nos convertimos en amigos de la aflicción? Semejantes a Cristo y, sin embargo, ¡nunca atravesamos el valle de las lágrimas! Semejantes a Cristo y no obstante, tenemos todo lo que el corazón pudiera desear, y nunca soportamos la contradicción de pecadores en contra nuestra, y nunca decimos: «¡Mi alma sobrepasa el dolor, hasta la muerte!» No sabes lo que estás pidiendo. ¿Has dicho: «¿Déjame sentarme a tu derecha en tu reino?» Esto no se te puede conceder a menos que estés dispuesto también a beber de su copa y ser bautizado con su bautismo. La participación de su pena debe preceder la participación de su gloria.

Una vez más, nuestros sufrimientos son muy útiles para nosotros cuando Dios los bendice, porque nos ayudan a ser útiles a otros. Debe ser algo terrible nunca haber sufrido el dolor físico. Tú dirás: «Me gustaría ser ese hombre». Ah, a menos que tuvieras una gracia extraordinaria, te volverías duro y frío; llegarías a ser una especie de hombre de hierro fundido, que rompe a la gente con su toque. No, que mi corazón sea tierno, hasta suave, aunque para ablandarlo necesite el dolor, porque anhelo saber cómo sujetar las heridas de mi hermano. Que mi ojo tenga lista una lágrima por las penas de mi hermano incluso si para hacerlo, tuviera que derramar miles por mí mismo. Escapar del sufrimiento sería escapar del poder de condolerme y eso, entre todas las cosas, se debe despreciar.

A través de la Biblia en un año: 1 Corintios 9–10

El perdón

De modo que se toleren unos a otros y se perdonen si alguno tiene queja contra otro. Así como el Señor los perdonó, perdonen también ustedes.
COLOSENSES 3:13

Ve al Antiguo Testamento y verás que este revela sacrificios: de ovejas, novillos y cabras. ¿Qué significaban todos ellos? Significaban que había una vía de perdón por medio del derramamiento de sangre, le enseñaban esto a los hombres: Que Dios aceptaría ciertos sacrificios a favor de ellos. Luego ve al Nuevo Testamento y verás que este revela más claramente que Dios aceptó un sacrificio, el sacrificio que él mismo dio, porque «no escatimó ni a su propio Hijo, sino que lo entregó por todos nosotros» (Romanos 8:32). En este Libro lees cómo «Dios es justo y, a la vez, el que justifica a los que tienen fe en Jesús» (Romanos 3:26); cómo puede ser él un Dios justo y a la vez un Salvador; cómo puede perdonar y, no obstante, ser tan justo como si castigara y no mostrara misericordia. Esto, en realidad, es la revelación del evangelio; fue para enseñar esto que se escribió este libro, para decirte que «en Cristo, Dios estaba reconciliando al mundo consigo mismo, no tomándole en cuenta sus pecados» (2 Corintios 5:19). Por lo tanto, venimos a ti, no solo con un susurro esperanzado, sino con una seguridad completa, clara, enfática e incuestionable: «Hay perdón. Hay perdón».

A través de la Biblia en un año: 1 Corintios 11–12

¡Gracias a Dios que es así!

Y todo el que invoque el nombre del Señor será salvo.
HECHOS 2:21

Aquí hay una palabra amplia, una palabra muy amplia: «*todo* el que invoque el nombre del Señor será salvo». «*Todo*». Yo he escuchado que cuando una persona está haciendo su testamento, si desea dejar todo lo que tiene a una persona, digamos, a su esposa, si simplemente lo dice, es lo mejor que puede hacer, que más le vale no entrar en detalles y empezar a hacer una lista de lo que deja porque probablemente deje algo fuera. Ahora bien, Dios hace este testamento muy claro, él no entra en detalles, solo dice: «todo». Eso significa el hombre negro, el rojo, el amarillo y el blanco. Significa el hombre rico y el hombre pobre. Significa todo el mundo de todo tipo y los que no son de ningún tipo o todos los tipos juntos. «Todo». Eso me incluye a mí, estoy seguro, pero estoy igualmente seguro de que te incluye a ti, tú que eres un extranjero y peregrino, quienquiera que seas. Es mucho mejor decirlo así, sin entrar en detalles, porque de otra manera, alguien podría quedarse fuera.

A través de la Biblia en un año: 1 Corintios 13–14

¿Escuchas la llamada?

Ahora bien, ¿cómo invocarán a aquel en quien no han creído? ¿Y cómo creerán en aquel de quien no han oído? ¿Y cómo oirán si no hay quien les predique? ¿Y quién predicará sin ser enviado? Así está escrito: «¡Qué hermoso es recibir al mensajero que trae buenas nuevas!»

ROMANOS 10:14-15

¿Entonces quién debe predicar? Todo el que pueda predicar debe hacerlo. El don de la predicación es la responsabilidad de predicar. Hay muchas personas que debieran predicar el evangelio pero que no lo hacen. Para esta obra no se requiere un alto grado de dones. No dice: «¿Cómo oirán sin un doctor en divinidad?» No dice: «¿Cómo oirán sin un predicador popular?» ¡Ay, querido! Algunos de nosotros estuviéramos perdidos si la salvación dependiera de escuchar a un hombre de grandes habilidades. Yo aprendí mi teología, de la cual nunca me he desviado, de una anciana que era la cocinera en la casa donde yo era un ujier. Ella podía hablar sobre las cosas profundas de Dios y mientras yo me sentaba y escuchaba lo que, como una cristiana madura, tenía que decir sobre lo que el Señor había hecho por ella, aprendí más de su enseñanza que de nadie que haya conocido desde entonces. No es necesario tener instrucción universitaria para ser capaz de hablar de Cristo; algunos de los mejores trabajadores de esta iglesia tienen muy poca educación pero traen muchos a Cristo.

A través de la Biblia en un año: 1 Corintios 15–16

Mira hacia arriba

Al día siguiente Juan vio a Jesús que se acercaba a él, y dijo: «¡Aquí tienen al Cordero de Dios, que quita el pecado del mundo!»
JUAN 1:29

Conozco a muchas personas cuyas conciencias están realmente despiertas y se ven como pecadores ante los ojos de Dios, pero en lugar de mirar al Cordero de Dios, se miran continuamente a sí mismos. No creo que tengan ninguna confianza en su propia justicia pero temen no sentir su culpa tanto como debieran. Creen que todavía no están lo suficientemente despiertos, lo suficientemente humillados, lo suficientemente penitentes, etc., y así fijan sus ojos en sí mismos con la esperanza de obtener paz con Dios. Imagina que ayer o antes de ayer, hayas sentido mucho frío y por tanto saliste fuera de tu casa y fijaste tu mirada en el hielo y en la nieve. ¿Crees que ese cuadro te habría calentado? No, sabes que habrías sentido más frío a cada instante. Imagina que eres muy pobre y con esmero fijas tus ojos en tu bolsillo vacío. ¿Crees que eso te enriquecerá? O imagina que tuviste un accidente y que uno de tus huesos se fracturó. Si piensas seriamente en ese hueso fracturado, ¿crees que tu consideración lo enmendaría? Sin embargo, algunos pecadores parecen imaginar que la salvación viene a ellos por medio de la consideración de su condición perdida y arruinada. Mis queridos oyentes no convertidos, están perdidos lo sepan o no. Den eso por sentado. Si van a ser salvos, no se miren a sí mismos, sino miren «al cordero de Dios».

A través de la Biblia en un año: Jueces 1–4

Nuestra luz verdadera

En el principio ya existía el Verbo, y el Verbo estaba con Dios, y el Verbo era Dios. Él estaba con Dios en el principio. Por medio de él todas las cosas fueron creadas; sin él, nada de lo creado llegó a existir. En él estaba la vida, y la vida era la luz de la humanidad. Esta luz resplandece en las tinieblas, y las tinieblas no han podido extinguirla.

JUAN 1:1-5

Jesucristo fue la Luz verdadera en oposición al lino humeante de la tradición. ¡Escuchen a esos rabinos! Se creen que son la luz del mundo. Su sofisma es una contienda interminable de palabras; su investigación no merita tu estudio; su conocimiento no merita a los entendidos. Ellos pueden decirte exactamente cuál es el versículo que está en el medio de la Biblia y cuál es la letra central en la palabra central. Discutían sus paradojas hasta volverse tontos. Refinaban sus sutilezas hasta que la doctrina acababa en la duda; la verdad simple se degradaba a una tonta charla sin sentido; sus traducciones de las Escrituras eran una parodia y sus comentarios un insulto al sentido común. Pero Cristo, la Luz verdadera y celestial, apaga todas tus luminarias terrenales. El rabino judío, el filósofo griego, el padre eclesiástico y el pensador teológico moderno son meteoritos que se disuelven en la bruma. Mediante sus tradiciones o conjeturas anulan la Palabra de Dios. Cree lo que dijo Jesús y lo que pensaban sus apóstoles y lo que te revela su propia Palabra: Cristo es la Luz verdadera.

A través de la Biblia en un año: Jueces 5–7

Dar la gloria a Dios

Ustedes son la luz del mundo. Una ciudad en lo alto de una colina no puede esconderse. Ni se enciende una lámpara para cubrirla con un cajón. Por el contrario, se pone en la repisa para que alumbre a todos los que están en la casa. Hagan brillar su luz delante de todos, para que ellos puedan ver las buenas obras de ustedes y alaben al Padre que está en el cielo.

MATEO 5:14-16

Si has recibido la luz de Dios, deja que tu luz brille tanto delante de los hombres que la vean y le den la gloria a Dios por ello. Me temo que esta observación perturbará a muchos cristianos practicantes. Dicen que han visto al Señor. No tengo razones para dudar la verdad de lo que dicen, pero si lo han visto, ¿por qué no testifican? Juan escribe: «Yo lo he visto y por eso testifico» (Juan 1:34); pero en muchos casos en estos tiempo, pudiera escribirse: «Lo hemos visto y no testificamos», porque algunos de los que profesan haber visto a Cristo por fe ni tan siquiera dan el paso al frente para confesarlo en el bautismo, según lo que dice su Palabra; y muchos no se unen a la iglesia visible y no se ocupan en la Escuela Dominical ni en ninguna otra forma de servicio cristiano. ¿Qué será de ustedes que, teniendo un talento, no lo ponen en acción? ¡Ay, perezosos!, que han envuelto su talento en una servilleta, ¿cómo responderán por esto el día en que el Maestro llame a sus siervos para hacerles el juicio?

A través de la Biblia en un año: Jueces 8–10

Trofeos de Cristo

Escrito está: «Creí, y por eso hablé». Con ese mismo espíritu de fe también nosotros creemos, y por eso hablamos. Pues sabemos que aquel que resucitó al Señor Jesús nos resucitará también a nosotros con él y nos llevará junto con ustedes a su presencia. Todo esto es por el bien de ustedes, para que la gracia que está alcanzando a más y más personas haga abundar la acción de gracias para la gloria de Dios.

2 CORINTIOS 4:13-1 5

Puedo hablar sobre asuntos que me confirman el poder de mi Señor y Maestro porque he visto los triunfos de Cristo. He visto hombres que solían vivir en pecado y borracheras y se han hecho honestos y sobrios; y he visto mujeres caídas llegar a los pies de Jesús como penitentes. Desde el principio, lo que ha llegado a ser un largo ministerio, la carroza del evangelio en la que he montado, ha tenido cautivos para honrar los triunfos de Cristo. Desde el principio, las multitudes han decidido dejar el pecado y se han vuelto al Dios viviente, y tengo que creer en el poder de la gracia divina, no puedo dudarlo. No hay duda alguna, la prueba de lo que el árbol es se encuentra en el fruto y el fruto es muy abundante. Pregúntales a los misioneros lo que Cristo ha hecho en los mares del sur, y te hablarán de islas que una vez estuvieron habitadas por caníbales desnudos, donde ahora los hombres están vestidos y en sus cabales, sentados a los pies de Jesús. El mundo entero pulula de trofeos de Cristo y aun pululará más. «Y nosotros hemos visto y declaramos que el Padre envió a su Hijo para ser el Salvador del mundo» (1 Juan 4:14) y predicamos con la completa convicción de que «rebosará la tierra con el conocimiento del Señor como rebosa el mar con las aguas» (Isaías 11:9).

A través de la Biblia en un año: Jueces 11–13

Ora por el poder

Una vez, mientras comía con ellos, les ordenó: —No se alejen de Jerusalén, sino esperen la promesa del Padre, de la cual les he hablado: Juan bautizó con agua, pero dentro de pocos días ustedes serán bautizados con el Espíritu Santo.

HECHOS 1:4-5

Si sientes la necesidad de clamar a Dios para que te dé el poder de predicar, el poder espiritual, el poder del Espíritu Santo; si sientes la necesidad de enseñar en la Escuela Dominical —y no vale la pena que lo hagas a menos que sientas la necesidad de hacerlo y te han enviado a hacerlo—, entonces ora pidiendo el poder para ganar las almas de esos queridos hijos para Cristo. Si mañana sientes el llamado a escribir una carta a un amigo o amiga acerca de su alma, hazlo porque sientes el llamado a hacerlo, pero ora a Dios para que te muestre cómo hacerlo. Ora para que él le dé poder a las palabras que pronuncies, para que puedas decir las palabras correctas e incluso dar el tono correcto a esas palabras. Hasta el tono de un predicador tiene mucha importancia. «¿Y quién predicará sin ser enviado?» (Romanos 10:15). Deben estar revestidos de poder divino, pero el Señor puede vestir hasta a un niño con ese poder, lo ha hecho con frecuencia. Él puede revestir a una humilde mujer cristiana, que nunca ha hablado en público, con el poder de ganar almas, con frecuencia lo ha hecho. Primero aguarda en Jerusalén hasta que seas investido con poder de lo alto, y luego sal como testigo de Cristo, porque ¿cómo predicarás excepto si te envían?

A través de la Biblia en un año: Jueces 14-17

Nuestro servicio razonable

Hermanos míos, ¿de qué le sirve a uno alegar que tiene fe, si no tiene obras? ¿Acaso podrá salvarlo esa fe? Supongamos que un hermano o una hermana no tienen con qué vestirse y carecen del alimento diario, y uno de ustedes les dice: "Que les vaya bien; abríguense y coman hasta saciarse", pero no les da lo necesario para el cuerpo. ¿De qué servirá eso? Así también la fe por sí sola, si no tiene obras, está muerta.

SANTIAGO 2:14-17

Hay algunos que parecen estar dispuestos a aceptar a Cristo como su Salvador que no lo recibirían como Señor. Ellos no lo dirían así claramente, pero como las acciones dicen más que las palabras, eso es lo que prácticamente dicen sus acciones. Qué triste es que algunos hablen de su fe en Cristo y no obstante, ¡sus obras no dan pruebas de su fe! Algunos hasta hablan como si entendieran lo que queremos decir con el pacto de la gracia, sin embargo, no hay ninguna buena evidencia de la gracia en sus vidas sino que abunda una prueba muy clara del pecado (no de la gracia). No puedo concebir que sea posible que alguien reciba a Cristo como Salvador y, no obstante, no lo reciba como Señor. Uno de los primeros instintos de un alma redimida es caer a los pies del Salvador y con gratitud y adoración clamar: «Bendito Maestro, reconozco que, al comprarme con tu sangre preciosa, soy tuyo, solo tuyo, completamente, para siempre. Señor, ¿qué quieres que haga?» Un hombre que realmente ha sido salvado por gracia no necesita que se le diga que está bajo obligación solemne de servir a Cristo, la nueva vida que hay dentro de él se lo dice. En lugar de considerarlo una carga, gustosamente se rinde en alma, cuerpo y espíritu al Señor que lo ha redimido, y considera que este es su servicio razonable.

A través de la Biblia en un año: Jueces 18–21

Gracia completa y gratuita

Mis queridos hijos, les escribo estas cosas para que no pequen. Pero si alguno peca, tenemos ante el Padre a un intercesor, a Jesucristo, el Justo.

1 JUAN 2:1

El apóstol Juan nos presenta un testimonio muy claro y enfático de la doctrina del perdón completo y gratuito del pecado. Él declara que la sangre de Jesucristo, el amado Hijo de Dios, nos limpia de todo pecado y que si algún hombre peca, tenemos un abogado. Es evidente que no teme cometer alguna travesura al declarar esta verdad tan ampliamente Por el contrario, él hace esta afirmación con la idea de promover la santidad de sus «queridos hijos». El objetivo de esta valiente declaración sobre el amor del Padre para con sus hijos pecadores es «para que no pequen». Esta es una respuesta triunfante a esa objeción terriblemente incierta que tan a menudo incita a los adversarios del evangelio contra las doctrinas de la gracia gratuita: que estas llevan a los hombres al libertinaje. No parece que el apóstol Juan pensara de esta manera porque para que estos «queridos hijos» no pecaran, él en realidad les declara la misma doctrina que nuestros adversarios llaman licenciosa. Aquellos hombres que creen que predicar la gracia de Dios completa, honesta y claramente, llevará a los hombres al pecado, no saben lo que dicen ni lo que afirman. Los hombres no tienen un argumento para pecar ni en la naturaleza ni en la gracia de la bondad de Dios.

A través de la Biblia en un año: 2 Corintios 1–3

Armados con valor santo

Cuando los setenta y dos regresaron, dijeron contentos: «Señor, hasta los demonios se nos someten en tu nombre». «Yo veía a Satanás caer del cielo como un rayo», respondió él. «Sí, les he dado autoridad a ustedes para pisotear serpientes y escorpiones y vencer todo el poder del enemigo; nada les podrá hacer daño. Sin embargo, no se alegren de que puedan someter a los espíritus, sino alégrense de que sus nombres están escritos en el cielo».

LUCAS 10:17-20

En presencia del hombre, Satanás es grande, fuerte y astuto, pero en presencia del Cristo de Dios, él se reduce en completa intrascendencia. Él sabe que no puede resistir siquiera una palabra de los labios de Cristo ni una mirada de sus ojos, así que dice: «¿Por qué te entrometes, Jesús, Hijo del Dios Altísimo?» (Marcos 5:7). La pregunta es como si Satanás le suplicara a Cristo que no expusiera su poder, que no lo tocara sino que lo dejara en paz, como si fuera demasiado insignificante para que lo notaran. Así son las artimañas de Satanás, él lloriquea como un perro azotado y se agacha a los pies del gran Maestro y mira a su rostro y le pide que lo deje solo porque él conoce bien el poder del Hijo de Dios. Sí, el nombre de Jesús tiene un poder maravilloso sobre todas las huestes del infierno; así que no nos desconcertemos ni desmayemos ante todos los ejércitos de Satanás, por contrario, debemos luchar con valor santo, contra todos los poderes del mal, porque seremos más que vencedores sobre estas por medio de nuestro Señor Jesucristo.

A través de la Biblia en un año: 2 Corintios 4–6

Sirve con gozo

Y los discípulos quedaron llenos de alegría y del Espíritu Santo.
HECHOS 13:52

Muchas personas parecen creer que ser cristiano es algo muy pesaroso, que los creyentes en Cristo son un grupo miserable e infeliz que nunca se alegra. Bueno, debo admitir que sí conozco algunas pequeñas comunidades de personas que se consideran lo mejor de los cristianos y que se reúnen los domingos para tener juntos un quejido común; pero no considero que la mayoría de nosotros, que adoramos en este lugar, somos culpados de algo así. Servimos a un Dios feliz, y creemos en un evangelio gozoso, y el amor de Cristo en nuestros corazones nos ha hecho anticipar muchos de los gozos del cielo aunque estamos aquí en la tierra.

«La paz de Dios, que sobrepasa todo entendimiento», cuida nuestros corazones y pensamientos en Cristo Jesús y «el gozo del Señor es nuestra fortaleza». Quizá, si dejáramos que los impíos supieran de este gozo y de esta paz, bajarían las armas de su rebelión y dirían: «no sabíamos que la religión de Jesucristo era así tan bendecida. No sabíamos que había una música así en la gran casa del Padre. No sabíamos que había un becerro gordo esperando a que lo maten por nosotros y que toda la familia se alegraría por nosotros. Ahora que sabemos el gozo que hay ahí, entraremos y nunca más saldremos».

A través de la Biblia en un año: 2 Corintios 7–8

Atrapados en la gran red

También se parece el reino de los cielos a una red echada al lago, que recoge peces de toda clase. Cuando se llena, los pescadores la sacan a la orilla, se sientan y recogen en canastas los peces buenos, y desechan los malos.

MATEO 13:47-48

Recuerdas que el Señor Jesucristo dijo, con respecto a esa ciudad en las que sus obras poderosas se llevaron a cabo, que sería más tolerable el día del juicio para Sodoma y Gomorra que para Capernaúm y Betsaida donde él había estado tan a menudo. Cristo ha estado cerca de ti y tú has escuchado su evangelio, el que muchos pobres paganos no han escuchado. Ahora que has escuchado el evangelio, el evangelio del sacrificio expiatorio de Cristo, su sangre clamará en tu contra, así como la sangre de Abel clamó en contra de Caín, si no se aplica a ti para limpiarte de pecado. No puedes escapar del Señor Jesucristo. Estás atrapado en la malla de la gran red que él ha lanzado sobre todos aquellos que han escuchado el evangelio. «El que cree en él no es condenado, pero el que no cree ya está condenado por no haber creído en el nombre del Hijo unigénito de Dios. Ésta es la causa de la condenación: que la luz vino al mundo, pero la humanidad prefirió las tinieblas a la luz, porque sus hechos eran perversos» (Juan 3:18-19). Si no crees en el Señor Jesucristo, decides que él no te salve y quedarte en la condición en la que ya estás, es decir «condenado».

A través de la Biblia en un año: 2 Corintios 9–10

Remedios

Jesús continuó: "Seguramente ustedes me van a citar el proverbio: '¡Médico, cúrate a ti mismo!'"
LUCAS 4:23

Viaja tan rápido como puedas por una dirección equivocada y no llegarás al lugar que buscas. Vanas son todas las cosas fuera de Jesús, nuestro Señor.

¿Has visitado al doctor Ceremonia? Él es, en este momento, el doctor de moda. ¿Te ha dicho que debes cuidar de formas y reglas? ¿Te ha recetado tantas oraciones y tantos cultos? ¡Ah! Muchos van a él y perseveran en un ciclo de ceremonias religiosas pero, estas no traen alivio duradero a la conciencia. ¿Has probado con el doctor Moralidad? Él tiene una amplia clientela y es un buen médico judío viejo. «Sé bueno en el carácter exterior», dice él, «y esto trabajará en el interior y limpiará el corazón». Se supone que él y su asistente, el doctor Educación —quien es casi tan inteligente como su maestro— hayan curado a muchas personas, pero tengo buena evidencia de que ninguno de los dos, ni juntos ni separados, podrían tratar alguna vez con una enfermedad interior. Hagas lo que hagas, tus propios esfuerzos no detendrán la herida de un corazón sangrante. El doctor Mortificación también tiene una clientela selecta, pero los hombres no se salvan negándose a sí mismos hasta que antes nieguen su propia justicia. El doctor Emoción tiene muchos pacientes, pero sus curas rara vez sobreviven a la puesta del sol. Los espíritus tiernos buscan mucho al doctor Sentimiento, estos tratan de sentir pena y remordimiento, pero, de hecho, la manera de curarse no está en ese distrito. Hágase todo lo que se pueda hacer fuera de nuestro bendito Señor Jesucristo y el alma enferma no mejorará en nada. Puedes probar remedios humanos durante toda una vida pero el pecado seguirá teniendo el poder, la culpa seguirá aferrada a la conciencia y el corazón permanecerá tan duro como siempre.

A través de la Biblia en un año: 2 Corintios 11–13

A los pies de Jesús

Uno de ellos, al verse ya sano, regresó alabando a Dios a grandes voces. Cayó rostro en tierra a los pies de Jesús y le dio las gracias, no obstante que era samaritano.

LUCAS 17:15-16

Este hombre cayó a los pies de Jesús, él no se sentía bien en su lugar hasta que cayó allí. «No soy nadie, Señor», pareció decir y por tanto, cayó con el rostro en tierra. Pero el lugar en que se postró fue «a los pies de Jesús». ¡Yo prefiero no ser nadie a los pies de Jesús que ser cualquier cosa en algún otro lugar! No hay lugar tan honorable como a los pies de Jesús. Ah, ¡yacer ahí siempre y solo amarlo por completo y dejar que el yo muera! ¡Ay, tener a Cristo parado sobre uno, como la única figura que eclipsa tu vida de ahora en adelante y para siempre! El verdadero agradecimiento se postra delante del Señor.

Añadido a esto estaba la adoración. Él cayó a los pies de Jesús glorificando a Dios y dándole gracias. Adoremos a nuestro Salvador. Que otros piensen de Jesús como les plazca, pero nosotros pondremos nuestro dedo en la marca de los clavos y diremos: «¡Mi Señor y mi Dios!» Si hay un Dios, él es Dios en Cristo Jesús para nosotros. No debemos dejar de adorar nunca a aquel que ha demostrado su divinidad al librarnos de la lepra del pecado. ¡Toda adoración sea a su suprema majestad!

A través de la Biblia en un año: Rut 1–2

La línea de demarcación

Cierto día Josué, que acampaba cerca de Jericó, levantó la vista y vio a un hombre de pie frente a él, espada en mano. Josué se le acercó y le preguntó: ¿Es usted de los nuestros, o del enemigo? ¡De ninguno! respondió. Me presente ante ti como comandante del ejército del Señor. Entonces Josué se postró rostro en tierra.

JOSUÉ 5:13-14

Una línea roja se extiende entre los justos y los malvados, la línea del sacrificio expiatorio; la fe cruza esa línea, pero nada más lo puede hacer. Fe en la preciosa sangre es la gran distinción en el fundamento y todas esas gracias que brotan de la fe hacen que el justo se separe más y más del mundo impío que, al no tener raíz, no tienen el fruto. ¿Tú crees en Jesucristo? ¿De qué lado estás? ¿Estás con nosotros o con nuestros enemigos? ¿Te unes al grito de la cruz? ¿Te atrae la bandera alzada del amor de un Salvador que esta a punto de morir? Si no, entonces sigues estando fuera de Dios, fuera de Cristo, un extranjero del estado de Israel y tendrás tu porción entre los enemigos del Salvador.

Hay una aguada línea divisoria entre los justos y los malvados, tan clara como esa que divide la muerte de la vida. Un hombre no puede estar entre la vida y la muerte, está vivo o está muerto. Existe una clara línea de demarcación entre la vida y la muerte, Dios ha fijado una división similar entre los justos y los malvados. No hay *estados intermedios*, no hay moradores anfibios en la gracia y fuera de la gracia; no hay indefinidos monstruosos que no son ni santos ni pecadores. Hoy estás vivo por las influencias vigorizantes del Espíritu Santo o estás muerto en tus transgresiones y pecados.

A través de la Biblia en un año: Rut 3–4

¿Calcular la omnipotencia?

¿Puedes hacer que las constelaciones salgan a tiempo? ¿Puedes guiar a la Osa Mayor y a la Menor? ¿Conoces las leyes que rigen los cielos? ¿Puedes establecer mi dominio sobre la tierra? ¿Puedes elevar tu voz hasta las nubes para que te cubran aguas torrenciales? ¿Eres tú quien señala el curso de los rayos? ¿Acaso te responden: Estamos a tus órdenes? ¿Quién infundió sabiduría en el ibis, o dio al gallo entendimiento?¿Quién tiene sabiduría para contar las nubes?

JOB 38:32-37

Con demasiada frecuencia queremos ver cómo el Señor llevará a cabo su Palabra. Comenzamos a calcular, como los discípulos, que doscientos denarios de pan no serán suficientes para la multitud, y en cuanto a unos pocos peces, no podemos creer que sirvan de algo entre tantos. Por supuesto, si tenemos que diseñar de acuerdo a las leyes de la mecánica, tenemos que calcular nuestras fuerzas y medios de demanda en proporción a los resultados que se quieren producir; pero ¿por qué aplicar la línea delgada de la mecánica al Dios omnipotente? No, creo que hacemos algo peor, porque no realizamos nuestros cálculos de manera correcta con respecto a la obra del Señor, si lo hiciéramos, calcularíamos que dada la omnipotencia, ya no existen las dificultades y las imposibilidades han desaparecido. Si en realidad el Señor es todopoderoso, entonces, ¿cómo nos atrevemos a cuestionar las formas y los medios? Las formas y los medios son asunto suyo y no nuestro y con él nunca debieran surgir preguntas así.

A través de la Biblia en un año: Gálatas 1–2

¡No pongas a Dios en una caja!

¿Quién eres tú para juzgar al siervo de otro? Que se mantenga en pie, o que caiga, es asunto de su propio señor. Y se mantendrá en pie, porque el Señor tiene poder para sostenerlo.
ROMANOS 14:4

Dios tiene mil maneras de lograr sus propósitos. De haberlo querido, habría convertido en pan cada piedra de Samaria y habría hecho harina del polvo de sus calles. Si mandó alimento al desierto sin cosecha, y agua al desierto sin viento y sin lluvia, él podría hacer lo que quisiera y realizar su obra a su manera. No nos permitamos el pensar en limitar al Santo de Israel a un modo especial de actuar. Cuando escuchamos de hombres a quienes están llevando a manifestarse con nuevas formas de hacer la obra, no sintamos que «esto tiene que estar mal», más bien esperemos que sea muy probable que esté bien porque necesitamos escapar de estas rutinas horribles y convencionalismos miserables que son más bien impedimentos que ayudas. Algunos hermanos muy estereotipados consideran que es un crimen que un evangelista cante el evangelio; y en cuanto a ese órgano americano, ¡espantoso! Uno de estos días otro grupo de almas conservadoras difícilmente soportará un servicio sin cosas así, porque el horror de los tiempos pasados es el ídolo de los siguientes. Cada hombre en su propio orden, y Dios los usa a todos; y si hay alguna peculiaridad, idiosincrasia, mucho mejor. Dios no hace a sus siervos de la misma manera que los hombres echan el hierro en los moldes, él tiene una obra separada para cada uno y deja que cada hombre haga su obra a su forma y que Dios lo bendiga.

A través de la Biblia en un año: Gálatas 3–4

Pon las cosas en claro con Dios

Vengan, pongamos las cosas en claro dice el Señor. ¿Son sus pecados como escarlata? ¡Quedarán blancos como la nieve! ¿Son rojos como la púrpura? ¡Quedarán como la lana! ¿Están ustedes dispuestos a obedecer? ¡Comerán lo mejor de la tierra! ¿Se niegan y se rebelan? ¡Serán devorados por la espada! El Señor mismo lo ha dicho.

ISAÍAS 1:18-20

Creo que sería sabio de nuestra parte, criaturas pecadoras que somos, aceptar la conferencia que Dios propone. De todos modos, no perdemos nada con ello. Si el Señor dice: «Vengan, pongamos las cosas en claro», él debe tener algún propósito de amor con eso; por lo tanto, vayamos a nuestro Dios y razonemos con él. Yo invitaría a cualquier hombre aquí que esté todo deseoso de estar bien con Dios, a que empiece a pensar en su Dios y en sus propios caminos. De seguro que para algunos de ustedes llegó la hora de volverse a él, a quien han provocado durante tanto tiempo. Por ejemplo, ahí está su Libro, ¿lo lees tú? ¿No testifica en tu contra el polvo que tiene encima? No crees que valga la pena saber lo que Dios ha revelado en su Palabra. Tratas a tu Hacedor y Amigo como si sus cartas no merecieran siquiera una hora de lectura; y las dejas completamente olvidadas. ¿Es así como debiera ser? Si quieres estar bien con Dios, ¿el primer paso no sería obedecer su mandamiento «Así dice ahora el Señor Todopoderoso: "Reflexionen sobre su proceder!"» (Hageo 1:5)? ¿Y el próximo paso no debiera ser obedecer esa otra palabra: «Sométete a Dios; ponte en paz con él, y volverá a ti la prosperidad» (Job 22:21)?

A través de la Biblia en un año: Gálatas 5–6

No por obras

Porque por gracia ustedes han sido salvados mediante la fe; esto no procede de ustedes, sino que es el regalo de Dios, no por obras, para que nadie se jacte. Porque somos hechura de Dios, creados en Cristo Jesús para buenas obras, las cuales Dios dispuso de antemano a fin de que las pongamos en práctica.

EFESIOS 2:8-10

Tenemos necesidad de seguir repudiando esta vieja mentira de Satanás de que los hombres se salvan por sus obras. Esas hojas de higuera que Adán cosió para cubrir su desnudez todavía están a favor de sus descendientes. No toman el manto de justicia de Cristo sino que más bien prefieren salvarse a sí mismos. Una o dos palabras para ti, mi amigo. ¿Dices que irás al cielo por guardar la ley? Ah, has escuchado el viejo refrán de cerrar el establo cuando el caballo no está, ¡me temo que esto te aplicaría muy bien a ti también! ¿Así que ahora vas a dejar cerrado el establo y estás seguro de que el caballo nunca saldrá? Si amablemente vas y miras, ¡descubrirás que se fue! Pero, ¿cómo puedes guardar una ley que ya se quebrantó? Si vas a ser salvo, la ley de Dios es como un vaso de puro alabastro que debe presentarse a Dios sin grietas ni manchas. ¿No te das cuenta de que ya has roto el vaso? Mira, allí hay una grieta. «¡Ah!», dices tú, «eso fue hace mucho tiempo». Sí, yo lo sé, pero es una grieta; y ahí mismo está la marca negra de tu dedo pulgar. Hombre, el vaso ya está roto y no puedes ir al cielo mediante tus buenas obras cuando no tienes ninguna.

A través de la Biblia en un año: 1 Samuel 1–4

Pareció bueno a sus ojos

¿Pueden dos caminar juntos sin antes ponerse de acuerdo?
AMÓS 3:3

El diablo le teme a todo contacto con Cristo y lo hace porque, en primer lugar, la naturaleza de Cristo es muy contraria a la suya. Y estos dos, en lugar de estar de acuerdo, se oponen entre sí en todo sentido. Hay una guerra muy antigua entre ambos, una guerra que, en lo que concierne a este mundo, se proclamó en el huerto del Edén cuando Dios le dijo a la serpiente: «pondré enemistad entre tú y la mujer, y entre tu simiente y la de ella; su simiente te aplastará la cabeza, pero tú le morderás el talón» (Génesis 3:15). Cristo ama la luz, Satanás ama las tinieblas. Cristo obra vida, Satanás obra muerte. Cristo es amor, Satanás es odio. Cristo es bondad, Satanás es maldad. Cristo es verdad, Satanás es falsedad.

Además, Satanás está muy consciente de que la misión de nuestro Señor Jesucristo en este mundo no es para su bien. Él no tiene parte en la encarnación de Cristo ni en su sacrificio expiatorio. Este es uno de los resultados maravillosos de la elección de la gracia. Esas personas que tropiezan en la elección de algunos hombres en lugar de otros, también debieran tropezar ante el hecho de que Cristo no redimió a los ángeles caídos, solo a hombres caídos. ¿Quién de nosotros puede decir por qué Dios escogió salvar a los hombres y no a los ángeles? La única respuesta que conozco para esa pregunta es: «Sí, Padre, porque esa fue tu buena voluntad» (Mateo 11:26). Se obvió a los ángeles poderosos y a nosotros, que no somos más que gusanos de la tierra, se nos miró con ojos de misericordia y amor; y Satanás, al saber esto y estar celoso del amor que ilumina a los hombres, no puede soportar la presencia de Cristo.

A través de la Biblia en un año: 1 Samuel 5–8

¿Bronce con oro?

Nadie puede servir a dos señores, pues menospreciará a uno y amará al otro, o querrá mucho a uno y despreciará al otro. No se puede servir a la vez a Dios y a las riquezas.
MATEO 6:24

Que cada creyente considere la vida de Dios dentro de él como su posesión más preciosa, mucho más valiosa que la vida natural. ¿No es el espíritu infinitamente más precioso que el cuerpo? Hermanos, si vamos a padecer hambre, que padezca hambre nuestro cuerpo y no nuestro espíritu. Si algo no debe crecer, que sea la naturaleza más vil. No vivamos ansiosamente por este mundo y lánguidamente por el mundo que vendrá. Al tener la vida divina dentro de nosotros, no descuidemos alimentarla y suplir sus necesidades. Tenemos al hombre que renuncia a asistir a servicios religiosos durante la semana porque tiene hambre de aumentar su negocio: compra bronce con oro. Otro abandona el lugar donde disfruta el ministerio del evangelio para ir en busca de un salario mayor a un lugar donde su alma morirá de hambre: cambia harina fina por cáscara. Otro se une a todo tipo de malas compañías, donde él sabe que su carácter sufre y su alma corre peligro, y su excusa es para bien. Ay, señores, ¿será que esta vida eterna que ustedes dicen poseer tiene tan poco valor ante sus ojos? Entonces, protesto ante ustedes los que no la tienen en lo absoluto. ¿Cómo entonces podrían ser tontos si el Señor los ha hecho sabios para salvación? «Echen mano de la vida eterna» porque este es el bien principal, por amor a esta pueden dejar cosas inferiores. «Busquen primeramente el reino de Dios y su justicia, y todas estas cosas les serán añadidas».

A través de la Biblia en un año: 1 Samuel 9–12

Vive para la vida eterna

«Todo está permitido», pero no todo es provechoso. «Todo está permitido», pero no todo es constructivo. Que nadie busque sus propios intereses sino los del prójimo.
1 CORINTIOS 10:23-24

Ojalá que todos los hombres en este tiempo abundaran en dar limosnas, pero especialmente aquellos que son seguidores del amoroso Jesús. Considera tus transacciones desde el punto de vista de la eternidad. Mide lo que haces, no como si fueran a considerarlos los hombres del mundo, sino como si tú mismo lo fueras a juzgar cuando contemples en el país celestial el rostro de aquel a quien amas. No quiero que cuando vayas a morir tengas que decir: «Tuve muchas posesiones, pero he sido un mal mayordomo. Tuve habilidad pero malgasté las mercancías de mi Amo. Lo único que hice con mi riqueza fue habilitar bien mi casa, quizá comprar cuadros costosos y darme lujos que me hicieron más daño que bien». Espero, por el contrario, que puedas decir: «Solo por gracia soy salvo, pero esa gracia me permitió consagrar mis bienes y darles el mejor uso. Puedo presentar mi mayordomía sin temor. No viví para la vida fugaz que ahora ha terminado, sino para la vida eterna». Hermanos, algunos hombres gastan tanto en sí mismo y tan poco en el Señor que para mí es como si se comieran la manzana y le dieran a Cristo las cáscaras: acumulan la harina y le dan al Señor un poquito del salvado. No vivas como los insectos que mueren en un día, sino como hombres que viven para siempre.

A través de la Biblia en un año: 1 Samuel 13-16

Examínense a sí mismos

Examínense para ver si están en la fe; pruébense a sí mismos. ¿No se dan cuenta de que Cristo Jesús está en ustedes? ¡A menos que fracasen en la prueba! Espero que reconozcan que nosotros no hemos fracasado.
2 CORINTIOS 13:5-6

He conocido a muchos creyentes verdaderos que se preocupan porque temen ser hipócritas, mientras que muchos hipócritas nunca se han hecho esa pregunta. Miles de los que han ido con toda seguridad al cielo se detuvieron muchas veces en el camino, pusieron sus dedos en las cejas y se preguntaron: «¿Soy un creyente verdadero? ¡Qué raras confusiones surgen! ¿Realmente he pasado de muerte a vida o es una fantasía y un sueño?» Y, no obstante, te digo que el hipócrita ha ido cantando por su mundo, seguro, creía él, de pasar por la puerta de perla hasta que al final se encontró a sí mismo arrastrado hasta el hoyo en la montaña que es la puerta secreta del infierno. Muchos que parecían justos han estado podridos hasta la médula, un fruto que el Rey no puede aceptar en su mesa. Ay, ustedes que nunca se preguntan si son cristianos, comiencen a hacerse la pregunta, examínense a sí mismos si están en la fe, no dejen que ninguna presunción los atrape con su abrazo mortífero.

A través de la Biblia en un año: 1 Samuel 17–20

Protéjanse de la vanagloria

Por lo tanto, si alguien piensa que está firme, tenga cuidado de no caer.
1 CORINTIOS 10:12

Ahora intentaré describir el peligro que quiero advertirte. Un hombre cristiano se pasa mucho tiempo sin ningún problema sobresaliente: tiene a sus hijos con él, su hogar es feliz, el negocio es extremadamente próspero, de hecho tiene todo lo que el corazón pudiera desear: cuando mira a su alrededor puede decir como David: «Bellos lugares me han tocado en suerte; ¡preciosa herencia me ha correspondido!» (Salmos 16:6). Ahora, el peligro está en que él piense demasiado en estas cosas secundarias y se diga a sí mismo: «Mi montaña está firme, jamás seré conmovido». Y luego, aunque el hombre nunca se atrevió a decirlo con palabras, un sentimiento indistinto avanza lentamente dentro de él, que no hay necesidad de que él vele tanto como otras personas; estaría seguro de no caer si fuera tentado. De hecho, se pregunta cómo algunos de sus hermanos pueden vivir de la manera en que viven, él está seguro de que no podría hacerlo. Siente que podría luchar con cualquier tentación y salir más que vencedor. Se ha vuelto tan fuerte que se siente como si fuera un Sansón. Ahora sabe mucho más de lo que sabía antes y cree que ya está viejo como para caer como le hubiera sucedido algunos años atrás. «¡Ah!», piensa él, «soy un cristiano modelo». Él no lo dice así pero eso acecha en su mente. Su corazón está entorpecido con las cosas terrenales y su mente inflada con la vanagloria.

A través de la Biblia en un año: 1 Samuel 21–24

Aflojarse gradualmente

¿Quién puede afirmar: «Tengo puro el corazón; estoy limpio de pecado»?
PROVERBIOS 20:9

Qué noticias tan desgarradoras nos llegan a veces a nosotros, los que velamos por la iglesia cristiana. Fulano de tal, alguien que conocíamos como un gran practicante que se sentaba con nosotros a la mesa de la comunión y quien parecía estar muy avanzado en las cosas espirituales, ha caído en cierta clase de vicio que es absolutamente repulsivo, del cual el alma se rebela y este es el mismo hombre de quien recibimos consejos y con quien íbamos a la casa de Dios. Si pudiera rastrearse la historia de estos tremendos criminales, sería en gran medida así: empezaron bien, pero se fueron aflojando gradualmente, hasta que al final estuvieron maduros para el pecado inmundo. ¡Ah! No sabemos en lo que podemos caer cuando comenzamos a ir cuesta abajo, muy abajo, adonde terminará. Debemos orar a Dios que mejor nos fuera morirnos pronto que vivir para caer en los terrores de ese descenso. ¿Quién habría pensado que David, el hombre conforme al corazón de Dios, llegaría a ser el asesino de su amigo Urías con la intensión de robarle a su esposa? Oh, David, ¿estás tan cerca del cielo y a la vez tan cerca del infierno? En cada uno de nuestros corazones hay un David, y si comenzamos a resbalarnos de Dios, no sabemos hasta dónde podamos llegar. El peligro secreto que sale de todo esto es que cuando un hombre llega al estado de la seguridad carnal, está listo para cualquier mal.

A través de la Biblia en un año: 1 Samuel 25–28

¿Qué regalos traes tú?

Tome Su Majestad y presente como ofrenda lo que mejor le parezca...Pero el rey le respondió a Arauna: Eso no puede ser. No voy a ofrecer al Señor mi Dios holocaustos que nada me cuesten.
2 SAMUEL 24:22, 24

Hay cientos de practicantes que nunca le dieron a Dios nada que les costara la auto negación; no, no tanto como quedarse sin un plato en la mesa, sin un cuadro en la pared o sin un anillo en el dedo. Hay varios cristianos practicantes que gastan mucho más en las suelas de sus botas que en Cristo, y muchas mujeres que gastan más en las plumas y las flores que adornan sus sombreros que en su Salvador. Sí, he oído de hombres que decían que eran perfectos y, no obstante, ¡tenían medio millón y estaban acumulando más! Los pecadores mueren y son condenados y los misioneros no tienen apoyo y, sin embargo, estos hombres absolutamente perfectos están apilando el oro y dejando que la causa de Cristo se detenga por falta de medios. Esa no es mi teoría de la perfección; no, no me parece a mí que corresponda con la idea de un cristiano común que dice que no es dueño de sí. Si realmente eres salvo, hermano, ni un cabello de tu cabeza te pertenece; la sangre de Cristo o te ha comprado o no, y si lo ha hecho, entonces eres todo de Cristo, cada parte de ti y no puedes comer, ni beber ni dormir sino para Cristo. «En conclusión, ya sea que coman o beban o hagan cualquier otra cosa, háganlo todo para la gloria de Dios» (1 Corintios 10:31). ¿Comprendes eso?

A través de la Biblia en un año: 1 Samuel 29–31

Servicio de primera clase

Ahora, hermanos, queremos que se enteren de la gracia que Dios ha dado a las iglesias de Macedonia. En medio de las pruebas más difíciles, su desbordante alegría y su extrema pobreza abundaron en rica generosidad. Soy testigo de que dieron espontáneamente tanto como podían, y aún más de lo que podían, rogándonos con insistencia que les concediéramos el privilegio de tomar parte en esta ayuda para los santos.

2 CORINTIOS 8:1-4

Hermanos, sean tan apasionados para honrar a Cristo como lo fueron una vez para deshonrarlo. Así como le han dado al diablo servicio de primera clase, dejen que Cristo reciba lo mismo. Recuerden que en los días de su pecado, algunos de ustedes se dedicaron a esto por completo, que ningún gasto los detenía, ¿verdad? Oh, no, si querían placer en el pecado, allá iban las cinco y las cien libras esterlinas. Cuán a menudo me encuentro hombres, particularmente aquellos dados a la bebida, que tienen libras en sus bolsillos y nunca saben adónde van, pero no se detienen hasta que todo se gasta, sea poco o mucho. Pobres tontos, pobres tontos. Sin embargo, quisiera que pudiéramos servir a Cristo con igual generosidad. No debiera considerarse ningún gasto siempre y cuando podamos honrar a Dios y bendecir su nombre. Trae la caja de alabastro, rómpela, no importan los pedazos, derrama el aceite y deja que todo sea para Jesús. Fue así como serví a Satanás y será así como serviré a Cristo.

A través de la Biblia en un año: Efesios 1–2

Soldados consagrados

No es que esté dándoles órdenes, sino que quiero probar la sinceridad de su amor en comparación con la dedicación de los demás. Ya conocen la gracia de nuestro Señor Jesucristo, que aunque era rico, por causa de ustedes se hizo pobre, para que mediante su pobreza ustedes llegaran a ser ricos.
2 Corintios 8:8-9

Oh, ¿quién será el siervo de mi Amo? ¡Ahí viene! ¿No lo ves? No lleva sobre su cabeza una diadema sino una corona de espinas, bajo sus mejillas ves los escupitajos corriendo, sus pies todavía están enrojecidos por las heridas y sus manos todavía están adornadas con las marcas de los clavos. Este es tu Amo, y estas son las insignias de su amor por ti. ¿Qué servicio le darás? ¿El de un simple practicante que pronuncia su nombre pero que no le ama? ¿El de un frío religioso que ofrece un servicio mal dispuesto por causa del temor? Oro para que no lo deshonres así. Yo elevo el estandarte para reclutar bajo la bandera de Cristo a aquellos que de ahora en adelante sean hombres de Cristo de pies a cabeza; y la iglesia debe ser feliz y feliz debe ser todo el Israel de Dios si un número escogido se recluta y permanece fiel a sus colores. No necesitamos más cristianos nominales, ni cristianos tibios, a quienes mi Amo escupirá de su boca. Necesitamos hombres que ardan de amor, totalmente consagrados, intensamente dedicados, quienes, por la esclavitud de la que han escapado y la libertad en la que han entrado, están bajo promesa para gastarse y ser gastados por el nombre de Jesús hasta que hayan llenado la tierra de su gloria y hayan hecho que todo el cielo repique con su alabanza.

A través de la Biblia en un año: Efesios 3–4

Sellados continuamente

En él también ustedes, cuando oyeron el mensaje de la verdad, el evangelio que les trajo la salvación, y lo creyeron, fueron marcados con el sello que es el Espíritu Santo prometido. Éste garantiza nuestra herencia hasta que llegue la redención final del pueblo adquirido por Dios, para alabanza de su gloria.

EFESIOS 1:13-14

Algunos han imaginado que existe un acto separado del Espíritu de Dios en el que este sella a los creyentes. Pudiera ser así, no voy a cuestionar eso, pero sentiría mucho si cualquier hombre aquí, viviendo en pecado, pudiera con todo y eso mirar atrás a una especie de entusiasmo religioso o regocijo y decir: «Estoy a salvo porque en aquella ocasión yo fui sellado» y sentiría mucho que cualquier hermano considerara alguna experiencia extraordinaria, que vivió en un día determinado hace mucho tiempo, la razón verdadera por la cual es salvo. Un sello es para el presente y no es un mero recuerdo, sino un objeto palpable *ahora,* y delante de los ojos. Me temo que muchos han sido engañados al caer en la despreocupación por la noción de un sello que recibieron hace mucho tiempo. Busquemos la verdad. Según el texto, hasta donde puedo leerlo, he aquí un hombre que creyó en Jesús y desea un sello de que Dios lo ama: Dios le da el Espíritu y eso es todo lo que él puede desear o esperar. No se desea nada más; nada más sería tan bueno. El mismo hecho de que el Espíritu de Dios obra en ti tanto el querer como el hacer para que se cumpla la buena voluntad de Dios, es tu sello, no necesitas nada más. No digo que cualquier acción del Espíritu Santo deba considerarse como el sello, sino que todas estas juntas constituyen ese sello, ya que demuestran que él está en nosotros.

A través de la Biblia en un año: Efesios 5-6

Cristo debe causar la conmoción

Cuando vio a Jesús desde lejos, corrió y se postró delante de él.
—¿Por qué te entrometes, Jesús, Hijo del Dios Altísimo? —gritó con fuerza—. ¡Te ruego por Dios que no me atormentes!
MARCOS 5:6-7

Adondequiera que Jesús llega, hay conmoción. No había acabado de poner los pies en las costas de Gadara cuando de una vez lo atacan los poderes de las tinieblas, y no había pasado mucho tiempo cuando toda la población del distrito quedó afectada con su presencia. No importa cuán poco influyentes sean las demás personas, nunca es así con Jesús. Él siempre es o el «olor de muerte que los lleva a la muerte» o el «olor de vida que los lleva a la vida» (2 Corintios 2:16). Él nunca es un Cristo insípido. De él siempre sale virtud y la virtud agita la oposición de los malhechores de manera que, inmediatamente, salen a luchar contra él.

Recuerda que cuando Pablo y Silas predicaron en Tesalónica, los judíos incrédulos gritaban: «¡Estos que han trastornado el mundo entero han venido también acá!» (Hechos 17:6). ¿Era eso algo maravilloso? No, ¿no era más bien exactamente lo que el Señor Jesucristo había profetizado cuando dijo: «No vine a traer paz sino espada (Mateo 10:34)? Él dijo que por su causa habría división incluso en las familias, de manera que un hombre estaría en desacuerdo con su padre, y una hija con su madre y los enemigos de un hombre serían los de su propia familia. Cristo debe causar conmoción adondequiera que vaya y su evangelio debe causar conmoción dondequiera que se predique. El estancamiento es incoherente con la vida. Un sueño sepulcral es la condición de aquellos que están muertos en el pecado, pero estar despiertos en acción es la consecuencia segura de cuando el evangelio viene a alguien con poder.

A través de la Biblia en un año: 2 Samuel 1–4

En construcción

Él mismo constituyó a unos, apóstoles; a otros, profetas; a otros, evangelistas; y a otros, pastores y maestros, a fin de capacitar al pueblo de Dios para la obra de servicio, para edificar el cuerpo de Cristo. De este modo, todos llegaremos a la unidad de la fe y del conocimiento del Hijo de Dios, a una humanidad perfecta que se conforme a la plena estatura de Cristo.

EFESIOS 4:11 13

¿No están ustedes conscientes, creyentes, de estar edificados conforme a un glorioso modelo elevado y noble? Todavía no parece lo que seremos, pero deben estar conscientes de que cada hilada de piedras preciosas se edifica sobre el fundamento de la fe en Cristo. Ya que ustedes han conocido al Señor, han hecho un notable avance. Por momentos tienes temor de solo crecer hacia abajo, pero has crecido; hay algo en ti ahora que no tenías hace diez años. Yo estoy claramente consciente, de alguna manera, de que hace veinte años no estaba donde estoy ahora. Quiero que la vida que hay en mí se desarrolle y sea libre. ¿Nunca te sientes así? ¿No has sentido como si tú mismo fueras grande con una naturaleza muchos más gloriosa y has deseado la liberación de la carne y la debilidad? Estos gemidos, aspiraciones, esperanzas y deseos son todos sellos de salvación; tú nunca encontrarás a los impíos así conmovidos. Estos dolores son característicos de la vida. Tú no eres una estructura terminada, sino una casa en proceso de construcción y puedes estar seguro de que uno de estos días se pondrá la última piedra con gritos de «Gracia, gracia para con ella».

A través de la Biblia en un año: 2 Samuel 5–8

Lazos de gracia

En esto conocemos lo que es el amor: en que Jesucristo entregó su vida por nosotros. Así también nosotros debemos entregar la vida por nuestros hermanos. Si alguien que posee bienes materiales ve que su hermano está pasando necesidad, y no tiene compasión de él, ¿cómo se puede decir que el amor de Dios habita en él? Queridos hijos, no amemos de palabra ni de labios para afuera, sino con hechos y de verdad.

1 JUAN 3:16-18

Nosotros debiéramos reconocer los lazos de sangre más de lo que lo hacemos. Somos demasiado propensos a olvidar que Dios «de un solo hombre hizo todas las naciones para que habitaran toda la tierra» (Hechos 17:26), de manera que mediante el común vínculo de sangre, todos somos hermanos. Pero amados, los lazos de gracia son mucho más fuertes que los lazos de sangre. Si realmente nacieron de Dios, son hermanos por medio de una hermandad que es más fuerte que la hermandad natural que te permitió acostarte en la misma cuna y prenderte al mismo pecho porque los hermanos según la carne pudieran estar separados eternamente. La mano derecha del Rey podría ser la posición conferida a uno y su izquierda, la posición conferida al otro, pero los hermanos que realmente nacieron de Dios comparten una hermandad que debe durar para siempre.

Si somos del mundo, el mundo amará a los suyos, lo mismo sucede si somos del Espíritu, el Espíritu amará a los suyos. Toda la familia redimida de Cristo está firmemente ligada. Nosotros mismos, habiendo nacido de Dios, seguimos buscando para ver a aquellos que han «nacido de nuevo, no de simiente perecedera, sino de simiente imperecedera» (1 Pedro 1:23), y cuando los vemos, no podemos evitar amarlos. De una vez se produce entre nosotros un lazo de unión.

A través de la Biblia en un año: 2 Samuel 9–12

Aférrense los unos a los otros

Tengan cuidado de sí mismos y de todo el rebaño sobre el cual el Espíritu Santo los ha puesto como obispos para pastorear la iglesia de Dios, que él adquirió con su propia sangre. Sé que después de mi partida entrarán en medio de ustedes lobos feroces que procurarán acabar con el rebaño.
HECHOS 20:28–29

Los cristianos deben amarse unos a otros porque son súbditos de un Rey quien es también su Salvador. Somos una pequeña pandilla de hermanos en medio de una vasta multitud de enemigos. Cristo dijo a sus discípulos: «Los envío como ovejas en medio de lobos» (Mateo 10:16). Si son verdaderos cristianos, no tendrán el amor de la gente de este mundo, no es posible. Ellos se asegurarán de ridiculizarte y llamarte tonto o hipócrita o algo igual de menospreciativo. Bueno, entonces, aférrense más los unos a los otros. Somos como una compañía pequeña de solados en un país enemigo, fuertemente acuartelados por los enormes batallones del enemigo, tenemos que unirnos, tenemos que ser como un solo hombre, agrupados en la comunión más íntima, tal y como nos ordena nuestro gran Capitán. Quiera Dios que el hecho de encontrarnos en un país enemigo dé como resultado que seamos más unidos de lo que hemos sido antes. Cuando escucho a un hombre cristiano encontrarle defectos a su ministro, siempre deseo que el diablo hubiera encontrado a alguna otra persona para hacer su sucia obra. Espero que ninguno de ustedes sea hallado jamás quejándose de los siervos de Dios que están dando lo mejor de sí para ayudar en la causa de su Señor. Hay muchos que están listos para encontrarles defectos y sería mucho mejor que sus faltas, si las tienen, fueran señaladas por un enemigo que por ustedes que pertenecen a la misma familia que ellos.

A través de la Biblia en un año: 2 Samuel 13–16

Nuestro apuntador santo

Cuando los hagan comparecer ante las sinagogas, los gobernantes y las autoridades, no se preocupen de cómo van a defenderse o de qué van a decir, porque en ese momento el Espíritu Santo les enseñará lo que deben responder.

LUCAS 12:11-12

El Espíritu Santo actúa para con su pueblo como una especie de apuntador de un declamador. Un hombre tiene que presentar una parte de la obra que se ha aprendido, pero su memoria es traicionera y, por lo tanto, en algún lugar fuera del alcance de la vista hay un apuntador de manera que cuando el orador no sepa qué decir y pudiera utilizar una palabra equivocada, se escucha un murmullo que sugiere la palabra correcta. Cuando el orador prácticamente ha perdido el hilo de su discurso, él inclina su oído y el apuntador le da la palabra clave que lo ayudará con su memoria. Si se me permite el símil, yo diría que esto representa en parte la obra del Espíritu de Dios en nosotros, sugiriéndonos el deseo correcto y trayendo a nuestra memoria lo que sea que Cristo nos ha dicho. A menudo en la oración llegamos a un punto muerto, pero él incita, sugiere e inspira y así seguimos adelante. Puede que nos cansemos en la oración, pero el Consolador nos alienta y nos refresca con pensamientos que dan ánimo. Cuando de hecho, en nuestro desconcierto, casi nos sentimos impulsados a abandonar la oración, el murmullo de su amor deja caer un carbón encendido desde el altar a nuestra alma y nuestros corazones resplandecen con mayor ardor que antes. Considera al Espíritu Santo como tu apuntador y deja que tu oído esté abierto a su voz.

A través de la Biblia en un año: 2 Samuel 17–20

Apartados

De este evangelio he sido yo designado heraldo, apóstol y maestro. Por ese motivo padezco estos sufrimientos. Pero no me avergüenzo, porque sé en quién he creído, y estoy seguro de que tiene poder para guardar hasta aquel día lo que he dejado a su cuidado. Con fe y amor en Cristo Jesús, sigue el ejemplo de la sana doctrina que de mí aprendiste. Con el poder del Espíritu Santo que vive en nosotros, cuida la preciosa enseñanza que se te ha confiado.

2 TIMOTEO 1:11-14

Todo hombre es llamado a hacer tanto bien como pueda, pero algunos hombres son apartados para trabajar en departamentos específicos de la obra cristiana y deben ser doblemente cuidadosos de hacerlo todo en nombre de su Maestro. Si un barco estuviera encallado y rompiéndose, y la tripulación estuviera a punto de perecer, estamos todos autorizados para hacer tanto como podamos para salvar la nave naufragada, pero los hombres que pertenecen a la tripulación designada para el bote salvavidas, tienen el derecho de ir a la vanguardia, tomar los remos y hacerse a la mar. Están autorizados para ir a la cabeza con valentía ante el peligro. Entonces, hermanos míos, aquellos de ustedes que han sentido dentro de sí el llamamiento divino, el impulso sagrado que los obliga a dedicar sus vidas a la salvación de quienes los rodean, pueden hacerlo valientemente y sin excusas. Vuestra autoridad viene de Cristo porque el Espíritu Santo los ha apartado para la obra. Que ningún hombre les ponga obstáculos ni los desanime. Avancen a las filas delanteras negándose a sí mismos.

A través de la Biblia en un año: 2 Samuel 21–24

Permanecer siempre

Permanezcan en mí, y yo permaneceré en ustedes. Así como ninguna rama puede dar fruto por sí misma, sino que tiene que permanecer en la vid, así tampoco ustedes pueden dar fruto si no permanecen en mí.

JUAN 15:4

«Separados de mí no pueden ustedes hacer nada», dijo nuestro Señor (Juan 15:5) y nosotros hemos conocido la verdad de esa frase al ver los intentos desacertados que han terminado en fracasos funestos; pero en el futuro recordemos esta verdad de manera práctica. Nunca comencemos una obra sin buscar poder de lo alto. A menudo realizamos el servicio cristiano como si nos sintiéramos a la altura del mismo; oramos sin pedirle a Dios que nos prepare el corazón; cantamos —ay hermanos, y cómo sucede esto a nivel mundial— sin suplicarle al Espíritu Santo en lo absoluto que reanime nuestras alabanzas; y temo que algunos de nosotros debemos confesar con pesar que en ocasiones predicamos como si la predicación fuera obra nuestra y no obra del Espíritu Santo que está dentro de nosotros.

Hazlo todo con la fortaleza del Maestro y ¡qué distinto será todo! Reconoce siempre que estés trabajando que tu fortaleza solo proviene del Señor. Nunca permitas que te pase por la mente que como un cristiano experimentado tienes una habilidad para el trabajo que es particularmente tuya, de manera que puedes prescindir de las oraciones pidiendo ayuda divina, algo tan necesario para los jóvenes. Nunca imagines que porque durante muchos años has realizado un servicio con aceptación, puedes, por lo tanto, hacerlo ahora sin una ayuda renovada. Esta es la manera en la que el poder de Dios y la vitalidad de la piedad resultan tan raras en las iglesias. Si no nos sentimos consciente día tras día de la debilidad que mora en nosotros y por consiguiente la necesidad de fortaleza fresca del Altísimo, pronto dejaremos de estar llenos de gracia.

A través de la Biblia en un año: Filipenses 1–2

Talento enterrado

Y ahora tengan en cuenta que voy a Jerusalén obligado por el Espíritu, sin saber lo que allí me espera. Lo único que sé es que en todas las ciudades el Espíritu Santo me asegura que me esperan prisiones y sufrimientos. Sin embargo, considero que mi vida carece de valor para mí mismo, con tal de que termine mi carrera y lleve a cabo el servicio que me ha encomendado el Señor Jesús, que es el de dar testimonio del evangelio de la gracia de Dios.

HECHOS 20:22–24

Ya hemos visto qué es hacerlo todo en el nombre del Señor Jesús. Detengámonos un momento para recordarte que este pasaje imparte una grave reprensión a muchos que profesan ser cristianos. Hay demasiados miembros de iglesias que no hacen nada en nombre de Jesús. Desde el día en que los bautizaron en el nombre del Padre, del Hijo y del Espíritu Santo, no han hecho nada más en ese nombre. ¡Ah, hipócritas! ¡Dios tenga misericordia de ustedes! Qué pena, ¡cuántos más hacen tan poco en el nombre de Cristo! Observé este comentario en una carta que escribió cierto pastor, que no creo que es dado a hablar duramente, él creía que en su propia iglesia uno de cada tres miembros no estaba haciendo algo por Cristo. Yo no podría hablar con tanta tristeza de ustedes pero sí temo que una gran parte de las fuerzas de esta iglesia no se están utilizando para el Señor. Creo que aquí prácticamente se utiliza más que en cualquier otra iglesia, pero no obstante se malgasta mucho vapor, hay muchos talentos enterrados y por tanto Jesús está defraudado.

A través de la Biblia en un año: Filipenses 3–4

Un milagro de la gracia

¿No saben que los malvados no heredarán el reino de Dios? ¡No se dejen engañar! Ni los fornicarios, ni los idólatras, ni los adúlteros, ni los sodomitas, ni los pervertidos sexuales, ni los ladrones, ni los avaros, ni los borrachos, ni los calumniadores, ni los estafadores heredarán el reino de Dios. Y eso eran algunos de ustedes. Pero ya han sido lavados, ya han sido santificados, ya han sido justificados en el nombre del Señor Jesucristo y por el Espíritu de nuestro Dios.

1 Corintios 6:9-11

¿Ven a ese hombre que una vez tenía el hábito de entrar y salir de las tabernas? Su hablar en aquellos tiempos era sucio, inmundo, abominable; su pobre esposa estaba amoratada y golpeada debido a su crueldad; sus hijos se morían de hambre y no tenían zapatos. Ahora él está con nosotros en esta casa de oración y es miembro del cuerpo místico de Cristo. Si fuéramos a pedirle que se pusiera en pie y nos contara del gran cambio que se ha producido en él, todos nos regocijaríamos al oírle testificar que el Señor lo ha perdonado, lo ha lavado, lo ha limpiado y ha renovado su corazón. ¿Pensó ese hombre alguna vez en su estado no regenerado que la vida de Cristo estaría en él despertando su cuerpo mortal y cambiando toda su naturaleza? Algo así nunca se le ocurrió. ¿Acaso no es él un milagro de la gracia? Pues yo creo ciertamente que si el diablo se convirtiera y se convirtiera otra vez en un ángel santo, no sería más maravilloso que la conversión de algunos que están aquí presentes. El Señor ha hecho por ellos cosas extrañas, cosas maravillosas, de lo cual se alegra nuestro corazón al pensar en lo que él ha hecho.

A través de la Biblia en un año: 1 Reyes 1–4

Él satisface nuestra necesidad

Pero como Jesús permanece para siempre, su sacerdocio es imperecedero. Por eso también puede salvar por completo a los que por medio de él se acercan a Dios, ya que vive siempre para interceder por ellos. Nos convenía tener un sumo sacerdote así: santo, irreprochable, puro, apartado de los pecadores y exaltado sobre los cielos.

HEBREOS 7:24-26

¿No es esta una asociación maravillosa, que Cristo llevara en sí mismo todo aquello que nos correspondía a nosotros, hasta la tristeza y el desconsuelo y al final, hasta la misma muerte? Ese cuerpo bendito, aunque no vio corrupción, no obstante, estuvo tan muerto como cualquiera otra persona que haya muerto jamás. Cristo tomó todo lo que nos pertenecía en esa maravillosa asociación.

Ahora mira el resultado de esa unión que hace posible que Cristo satisfaga todas nuestras necesidades. Por ejemplo, yo traigo mi pecado pero ante eso, él presenta su redención. Yo le traigo muerte, pero él presenta su resurrección. Yo le llevo debilidad, y él la satisface con su fortaleza. Yo traigo mi maldad, y Dios hace de Cristo mi justicia. Yo le presento mi naturaleza maligna y Dios hace de él mi santificación. Cualquier cosa mala que yo tenga para presentar como contribución a la asociación, él lo cubre con un esplendor de bondad que lo borra y enriquece mi alma mucho más que antes. Oh, qué maravilloso es entrar en asociación con su Hijo, ¡Jesucristo nuestro Señor!

A través de la Biblia en un año: 1 Reyes 5–8

Codicia el trabajo humilde

El más importante entre ustedes será siervo de los demás. Porque el que a sí mismo se enaltece será humillado, y el que se humilla será enaltecido.
MATEO 23:11-12

Si hay algún puesto en la iglesia en el que el obrero tendrá que trabajar duro y no recibir agradecimiento, tómalo y confórmate. Si puedes realizar un servicio que muy pocos tratan de hacer o de apreciar cuando otros lo realizan, realízalo, con santo deleite. Codicia el trabajo humilde y cuando lo obtengas, alégrate de poder seguir haciéndolo. No hay mucho arrebato en cuanto a los lugares más humildes; no les vas a robar a nadie al buscarlos. Para el primer lugar tenemos que hacer elecciones y encuestar a toda la comunidad, pero para los lugares más humildes no hay gran ambición; por lo tanto, selecciona un lugar así y mientras escapas a la envidia, también obtienes una conciencia tranquila. Si fuéramos más de Cristo, debiéramos empujarnos más hacia los lugares de sacrificio con alegría y de manera voluntaria, considerando que nuestro honor principal es servir a Dios y a la iglesia de maneras que sean oscuras y desdeñadas porque al hacerlo, nos libraremos del espíritu farisaico que anhela la alabanza de parte del hombre.

A través de la Biblia en un año: 1 Reyes 9–12

El día todavía está por llegar

Después vi un cielo nuevo y una tierra nueva, porque el primer cielo y la primera tierra habían dejado de existir, lo mismo que el mar.

APOCALIPSIS 21:1

«El Hijo de Dios fue enviado precisamente para destruir las obras del diablo» (1 Juan 3:8). ¡Qué obra tan horrible ya ha realizado el diablo en el mundo! Mira ahora cómo el huerto del Edén está mustio y arruinado, convertido en un desierto. La tierra fértil está produciendo espinas y cardos; y mira al hombre, quien fue hecho a la imagen de Dios, reducido a la posición de un pecador que tiene que trabajar arduamente, que se gana el pan con el sudor de su frente. Mira la guerra, el hambre y la pestilencia y todo tipo de males y dolor esparcidos densamente por toda la tierra y recuerda que todo esto fue el resultado de una desobediencia a la cual el hombre fue llevado por la tentación del diablo. Pero el diablo tiene muy poco para gloriarse por causa del daño que ha causado porque Cristo vino para deshacerlo. En la persona del segundo Adán, el Señor del cielo, el hombre se levantó de todo el pecado en que cayó por medio del primer Adán y en cuanto a este pobre mundo, tan infestado de pecado como está, ya sufre dolores de parto anticipando el nuevo nacimiento que aún le aguarda y llegará el día en que los cielos nuevos y la nueva tierra demostrarán cómo Cristo ha cancelado por completo la maldición y ha hecho que la tierra esté fragante con la bendición. Es por esta razón que Satanás odia la presencia de Cristo, porque Cristo va a destruir su obra maligna y por tanto teme que Cristo se le acerque.

A través de la Biblia en un año: 1 Reyes 13–16

La gracia combate los «si»

Mis queridos hijos, les escribo estas cosas para que no pequen. Pero si alguno peca, tenemos ante el Padre a un intercesor, a Jesucristo, el Justo.

1 Juan 2:1

El apóstol dice: «si alguno peca». El «si» podría escribirse en letras tan pequeñas como quisieras porque la suposición es una cuestión de certeza. «¿Si alguno peca?» La mano gentil del discípulo amado usa términos muy tiernos y suaves, poniéndolo como una suposición, como si fuera algo asombroso que pecásemos luego de tanto amor, misericordia y bondad. Sin embargo, Juan sabía muy bien que todos los santos pecan porque él mismo ha declarado que si algún hombre dice que no peca, es un mentiroso y no hay verdad en él. Los santos todavía son, sin excepción, pecadores. Fue la gracia quien produjo un cambio tan grande, no habría gracia en lo absoluto de no haber sido así. Es bueno advertir este cambio. El cristiano ya no ama el pecado, este es el objeto de su más severo horror; él ya no lo considera como algo insignificante, ni juega con él ni habla de este con despreocupación. Lo mira como a una serpiente venenosa, cuya misma sombra debe evitarse. Ya no se aventurará más de manera voluntaria a llevar la copa a sus labios como el hombre que una vez casi perdió su vida al beber veneno. El corazón del cristiano no da ánimo al pecado aunque este no se expulse. El pecado puede entrar al corazón y luchar por el dominio, pero no puede ocupar el trono.

A través de la Biblia en un año: 1 Reyes 17–19

Tristes y molestos

Si afirmamos que no tenemos pecado, nos engañamos a nosotros mismos y no tenemos la verdad. Si confesamos nuestros pecados, Dios, que es fiel y justo, nos los perdonará y nos limpiará de toda maldad. Si afirmamos que no hemos pecado, lo hacemos pasar por mentiroso y su palabra no habita en nosotros.

1 JUAN 1:8-10

El cristiano nunca peca con ese alarde tan grande del cual son culpables los no regenerados. Otros se revuelcan en las transgresiones y hacen de su vergüenza, su gloria; pero cuando el creyente cae, él guarda silencio, se entristece y se enoja. Los pecadores van a sus pecados como niños al huerto de su propio padre pero los creyentes se escabullen como ladrones que han estado robando el fruto prohibido. En un cristiano la vergüenza y el pecado siempre van de la mano. Si se emborracha de pecado, se avergonzará de sí mismo e irá a la cama como un perro sin raza azotado. Él no puede proclamar sus transgresiones como hacen algunos en medio de una multitud obscena, alardeando de sus hazañas malignas. Su corazón está destrozado en su interior, y cuando él ha pecado, pasa muchos, muchos días con los huesos doloridos.

Ni tampoco gana él con la plenitud de la deliberación que pertenece a otros hombres. El pecador puede sentarse durante todo un mes y pensar en la iniquidad que intenta perpetrar hasta que tiene los planes bien organizados y ha madurado su proyecto, pero el cristiano no puede hacer eso. Puede que ponga el pecado en su boca y se lo trague en un instante, pero no puede seguir dándole vueltas. Aquel que puede organizar y tramar una transgresión sigue siendo un hijo verdadero de la vieja serpiente.

A través de la Biblia en un año: 1 Reyes 20–22

Fuertes en amor

Jesús se volvió hacia ellas y les dijo: «Hijas de Jerusalén, no lloren por mí; lloren más bien por ustedes y por sus hijos».

LUCAS 23:28

Hay demasiadas personas tan absortas en su propio dolor que no tienen lugar en sus almas para la simpatía. ¿No las conoces? Lo primero que hacen cuando se levantan en la mañana es contar la terrible historia de la noche que pasaron. ¡Ay, querido! Y no han acabado todavía de comer un desayuno saludable antes de que su usual dolor aparezca por algún lugar. Necesitan el cuidado especial y la piedad de toda la familia. Durante todo el día la gran misión es mantener a todo el mundo consciente de cuánto está soportando el enfermo. Esta persona tiene el derecho patente de monopolizar toda la simpatía que el mercado pueda ofrecer y luego no quedará ninguna para el resto de los afligidos. Si estás demasiado ocupado contigo mismo, no queda mucho de ti para dar a nadie más. Qué diferente es esto a nuestro Señor que nunca gritó: «¡Tengan compasión de mí! ¡Tengan compasión de mí, amigos míos!» A él se le describe «soportando la cruz, despreciando la vergüenza». Tan fuerte era su amor que aunque salvó a otros, no se salvó a sí mismo, aunque consoló a los afligidos, nadie lo consoló a él.

A través de la Biblia en un año: Colosenses 1–2

Nuestras órdenes de marcha

Jesús se acercó entonces a ellos y les dijo: «Se me ha dado toda autoridad en el cielo y en la tierra. Por tanto, vayan y hagan discípulos de todas las naciones, bautizándolos en el nombre del Padre y del Hijo y del Espíritu Santo, enseñándoles a obedecer todo lo que les he mandado a ustedes. Y les aseguro que estaré con ustedes siempre, hasta el fin del mundo».

MATEO 28:18-20

Mientras meditaba a solas sobre este pasaje, sentí que su poder me arrastraba. Me sentí completamente incapaz de considerar con calma sus términos o de investigar sus razones. El mandato con el cual concluye el texto se repetía una y otra vez en mis oídos, hasta que me resultó imposible estudiarlo porque mis pensamientos corrían de aquí para allá, haciendo miles de preguntas y todas con la intención de ayudarme a responder por mí mismo la solemne pregunta: «¿Cómo voy a ir yo y enseñar a todas las naciones, bautizándolas en el nombre del Padre, del Hijo y del Espíritu Santo?»

¡Oh! Quisiera que la iglesia pudiera escuchar al Salvador dirigiéndole ahora estas palabras; porque las palabras de Cristo son palabras vivas que no solo tuvieron poder ayer, sino que tienen poder hoy. Los mandatos del Salvador son perpetuos en cuanto a su deber; no solo obligaban a los apóstoles sino que también nos obligan a nosotros y este yugo cae sobre todo cristiano. Hoy no estamos exentos del servicio que hacían los primeros seguidores del Cordero, nuestras órdenes de marchar son las mismas que ellos tuvieron y nuestro Capitán requiere de nosotros obediencia tan pronta y perfecta como la requirió de ellos.

A través de la Biblia en un año: Colosenses 3–4

Demuestra la promesa de Dios

Les dijo: «Vayan por todo el mundo y anuncien las buenas nuevas a toda criatura. El que crea y sea bautizado será salvo, pero el que no crea será condenado».
MARCOS 16:15-16

Hermanos, los paganos están pereciendo, ¿los dejaremos perecer? *Su* nombre es blasfemado, ¿guardaremos silencio y nos quedaremos tranquilos? El honor de Cristo se echa por tierra y sus enemigos profieren injurias contra su persona y se resisten a su trono; ¿sufriremos esto nosotros sus soldados y no buscarán nuestras manos el puño de nuestra espada, la espada del Espíritu, que es la Palabra de Dios? Nuestro Señor demora su venida, ¿empezaremos a dormir o a comer o a emborracharnos? ¿No debiéramos más bien ceñir los lomos de nuestra mente y clamar a él: «Ven pronto, Señor Jesús»? Los escépticos burlones de estos últimos tiempos han dicho que la conquista del mundo para Cristo no es más que un sueño o un pensamiento ambicioso que pasó por la mente de nuestro líder pero que nunca se logrará. Algunos sostienen que las supersticiones de los paganos son demasiado fuertes como para derribarlas con nuestras enseñanzas y que las fortalezas de Satanás son completamente inexpugnables contra nuestros ataques. ¿Será así? ¿Nos contentaremos neciamente con quedarnos tranquilos? No, más bien solucionemos el problema, demostremos que la promesa de Dios es verdad, demostremos que las palabras de Jesús son palabras sobrias, mostremos la eficacia de su sangre y la invencibilidad de su Espíritu al salir en espíritu de fe, enseñando a todas las naciones y ganándolas para la obediencia de Cristo nuestro Señor.

A través de la Biblia en un año: 2 Reyes 1–4

¿Irás tú?

Por tanto, mi servicio a Dios es para mí motivo de orgullo en Cristo Jesús. No me atreveré a hablar de nada sino de lo que Cristo ha hecho por medio de mí para que los gentiles lleguen a obedecer a Dios. Lo ha hecho con palabras y obras, mediante poderosas señales y milagros, por el poder del Espíritu de Dios. Así que, habiendo comenzado en Jerusalén, he completado la proclamación del evangelio de Cristo por todas partes, hasta la región de Iliria. En efecto, mi propósito ha sido predicar el evangelio donde Cristo no sea conocido, para no edificar sobre fundamento ajeno.

ROMANOS 15:17-20

A veces mi alma anhela y suspira por la libertad de predicar a Cristo donde nunca antes se ha predicado; no por construir sobre el fundamento que otro hombre ha puesto sino por ir a alguna tierra inexplorada, alguna tierra salvaje donde el ministro de Cristo nunca ha puesto un pie, que allí «se alegrarán el desierto y el sequedal; se regocijará el desierto y florecerá como el azafrán» (Isaías 35:1). Me he preguntado seriamente si yo no testificaría la gracia de Jesús en China o en India y ante Dios he respondido esa pregunta. Siento solemnemente que mi posición en Inglaterra no me permitiría dejar la esfera en la que estoy ahora, de lo contrario mañana me ofrecería como misionero. Tú estás libre del trabajo tan grande que yo tengo sobre mí, tienes talentos que todavía no se han dedicado a ningún fin especial y poderes que aún no se han consagrado a ningún propósito dado ni limitado a ninguna esfera; ¿no escuchas a mi Maestro diciendo, en tonos de pena lastimera, mezclados con una autoridad que no puede negarse: «vayan y hagan discípulos de todas las naciones, bautizándolos en el nombre del Padre y del Hijo y del Espíritu Santo» (Mateo 28:19)?

A través de la Biblia en un año: 2 Reyes 5–8

Desata el poder

En las manos del Señor el corazón del rey es como un río: sigue el curso que el Señor le ha trazado.
PROVERBIOS 21:1

Todo poder le ha sido dado a Cristo: poder sobre las voluntades de los hombres así como sobre las olas del mar. Pero los acontecimientos políticos te impiden llegar a un país determinado; debido a los tratados o a la falta de estos, no hay lugar para el misionero en un imperio así. *Ora,* y las puertas se abrirán; *suplica,* y las barras de bronce serán cortadas en dos. Cristo tiene poder sobre las políticas. Él puede cambiar el corazón de los príncipes y presidir en los concilios de los senados; él puede hacer que las naciones que durante mucho tiempo han estado cerradas, se abran a la verdad.

Verdaderamente Dios ha abierto el mundo y lo ha puesto en el umbral de nuestra puerta; si no ha hecho un mundo más pequeño, al menos lo ha puesto más al alcance de nuestras manos. Los países que una vez no podían alcanzarse, ahora se han abierto a nosotros. Y hay otras tierras y lugares que en un tiempo parecían rodeados de montañas infranqueables y, sin embargo, ahora tenemos una carretera. Oh, ¡qué no haya la disposición de arrojarse a ese camino montando los caballos blancos de la salvación! Oh, ¡ojalá que tuviéramos el corazón, el espíritu y el alma para aprovechar la excelente oportunidad y predicar a Cristo donde nunca antes se haya predicado! Entonces, como podemos ver claramente, todo poder ha sido dado a Cristo sobre todas las cosas en este mundo y se ha utilizado para la propagación de su verdad.

A través de la Biblia en un año: 2 Reyes 9–12

Envía lo mejor

Cuando llegaron a la casa, vieron al niño con María, su madre; y postrándose lo adoraron. Abrieron sus cofres y le presentaron como regalos oro, incienso y mirra.

MATEO 2:11

Ahora bien, yo quisiera que el llamamiento divino llegara a algunos hombres dotados. Tú, que quizá tienes alguna riqueza propia, ¿qué mejor objetivo en la vida que dedicarte tú y tu riqueza a la causa del Redentor? Ustedes, hombres jóvenes, que tienen delante posibilidades brillantes pero que todavía no tienen las ansiedades de mantener a una familia, ¿no sería algo noble rendir tus brillantes posibilidades para convertirte en un humilde predicador de Cristo? Mientras mayor sea el sacrificio, más honor para ti y más aceptable para él.

Yo anhelo que podamos ver a los hombres jóvenes saliendo de las universidades y a los estudiantes de nuestras escuelas secundarias, que podamos ver a nuestros médicos, abogados, hombres de negocios y mecánicos instruidos dejando todo lo que tienen, cuando Dios toque sus corazones, para enseñar y predicar a Cristo. No vale la pena enviar a los paganos hombres que en casa no sirven para nada. No podemos enviar hombres con habilidades de tercera y décima clase; tenemos que enviar a los mejores. Los hombres más valientes deben guiar a la vanguardia. Oh, Dios, unge a tus siervos, te lo imploramos; pon en sus corazones el fuego que nunca se apaga; haz que arda tanto dentro de ellos que tengan que morir o predicar, que tengan que acostarse con los corazones destrozados o de lo contrario ser libres para predicar donde nunca se ha escuchado de Cristo.

A través de la Biblia en un año: 2 Reyes 13–15

Señor de verdad

Mi reino no es de este mundo —contestó Jesús—. Si lo fuera, mis propios guardias pelearían para impedir que los judíos me arrestaran. Pero mi reino no es de este mundo.
—¡Así que eres rey! —le dijo Pilato.
—Eres tú quien dice que soy rey. Yo para esto nací, y para esto vine al mundo: para dar testimonio de la verdad. Todo el que está de parte de la verdad escucha mi voz.

JUAN 18:36-37

Recuerdas que Napoleón dijo: «He fundado un imperio por la fuerza y se ha derretido; Jesucristo estableció su reino por amor y hasta el día de hoy se mantiene y se mantendrá». A ese reino se refiere la Palabra de nuestro Señor, el reino de la verdad espiritual en el que Jesús reina como Señor sobre aquellos que son de la verdad. Él proclamó ser rey y la verdad que él reveló, y de la cual él era la personificación, es por tanto, el cetro de su imperio. Mediante la fuerza de la verdad él reina sobre aquellos corazones que sienten el poder de la injusticia y la verdad y, por consiguiente, se rinden voluntariamente a su dirección, creen en su Palabra y los gobierna su voluntad. Es como Señor espiritual que Cristo proclama su soberanía entre los hombres; él es Rey sobre mentes que lo aman, confían en él y lo obedecen porque ven en él la verdad por la que desfallecen sus almas. Otros reyes reinan en nuestros cuerpos, pero Cristo reina sobre nuestras almas; aquellos gobiernan por la fuerza pero él lo hace por el atractivo de la justicia; la realeza de ellos es, en gran medida, una realeza ficticia, pero la de él es verdadera y tiene su fuerza en la verdad.

A través de la Biblia en un año: 2 Reyes 16–18

Ser testigos de la verdad

Por lo tanto, pónganse toda la armadura de Dios, para que cuando llegue el día malo puedan resistir hasta el fin con firmeza. Manténganse firmes, ceñidos con el cinturón de la verdad, protegidos por la coraza de justicia, y calzados con la disposición de proclamar el evangelio de la paz.

EFESIOS 6:13-15

Si amas al Señor, sé un testigo de la verdad. Debes hacerlo de manera personal y también debes hacerlo en colectivo. Nunca te unas a una iglesia cuyo credo no creas entera y genuinamente, porque si lo haces, estás fingiendo y además te haces partícipe del error del testimonio de otros hombres. Yo ni por un momento diría algo que retrasara la unidad cristiana, pero hay algo antes de la unidad y eso es «la verdad en las partes interiores» y la honestidad delante de Dios. Yo no me atrevo a ser miembro de una iglesia cuya enseñanza yo sepa que es falsa en unos aspectos vitales. Preferiría irme al cielo solo que contradecir a mi conciencia con tal de tener compañía.

¿Estás dispuesto a andar en la verdad por el fango y por el lodazal? ¿Tienes el valor de profesar una verdad pasada de moda? ¿Estás dispuesto a creer la verdad contra la que la mal llamada ciencia ha descargado su ira? ¿Estás dispuesto a aceptar la verdad aunque se dice que solo los pobres y los ignorantes la recibirán? ¿Estás dispuesto a ser el discípulo del galileo cuyos apóstoles eran pescadores? De cierto, de cierto te digo que aquel día, cuando la verdad en la persona de Cristo venga en toda su gloria, les irá mal y también a aquellos que tuvieron vergüenza de reconocerla y de reconocer a su Amo.

A través de la Biblia en un año: 2 Reyes 19–21

Ofendidos por Cristo

Así que les dijo: «Un hombre de la nobleza se fue a un país lejano para ser coronado rey y luego regresar. Llamó a diez de sus siervos y entregó a cada cual una buena cantidad de dinero. Les instruyó: «Hagan negocio con este dinero hasta que yo vuelva». Pero sus súbditos lo odiaban y mandaron tras él una delegación a decir: «No queremos a éste por rey».

LUCAS 19:12-14

Recuerdas que el autor del segundo salmo dice: «Los reyes de la tierra se rebelan; los gobernantes se confabulan contra el Señor y contra su ungido. Y dicen: "¡Hagamos pedazos sus cadenas! ¡Librémonos de su yugo!"» (Salmos 2:2-3). La decisión de la naturaleza humana, hasta que se renueva, siempre es esta: «No dejaremos que este Hombre reine sobre nosotros». Los hombres pueden estar dispuestos a que Cristo los salve pero no a que él reine sobre ellos. Leyes como: «Amarás a tu prójimo como a ti mismo» «Debes perdonar hasta setenta veces siete», la ley del amor, la ley de la gentileza, la ley de la bondad; el hombre dice que las admira pero cuando estas leyes le llegan a casa y toman las riendas de su ambición, restringen su codicia y condenan su justicia falsa, enseguida él se ofende y cuando Cristo dice: «El cielo y la tierra pasarán, pero mis palabras no pasarán»; cuando comienza a enseñar la necesidad de pureza absoluta y a decir que incluso una mirada lasciva es un pecado, los hombres responden: «Su gobierno no nos conviene», y lo cuelgan para morir porque no se van a someter a su autoridad.

A través de la Biblia en un año: 2 Reyes 22–25

Así somos

Este mensaje es digno de crédito y merece ser aceptado por todos: que Cristo Jesús vino al mundo a salvar a los pecadores, de los cuales yo soy el primero. Pero precisamente por eso Dios fue misericordioso conmigo, a fin de que en mí, el peor de los pecadores, pudiera Cristo Jesús mostrar su infinita bondad. Así vengo a ser ejemplo para los que, creyendo en él, recibirán la vida eterna.

1 TIMOTEO 1:15-16

Sí, amados, cuando les rogamos que se reconcilien con Dios, no nos damos ningún aire, como si fuéramos superiores a ustedes por naturaleza o hubiéramos sido superiores en nuestra pasada manera de vivir antes de la conversión. No, más bien somos huesos de sus huesos y carne de su carne. ¿Ustedes son pecadores? También lo fuimos. ¿Están rebeldes para con Dios? Nosotros también lo fuimos. ¿Están endurecidos sus corazones? Así lo estaban los nuestros. No los miramos desde una elevada plataforma de dignidad fingida, porque reconocemos nuestra propia naturaleza en la de ustedes; por lo tanto, venimos a ustedes como compañeros en el pecado y a pesar de que es algo triste haber pecado alguna vez, nos alegra pensar que podemos hablarles de un mal que nos ha asediado, el poder que hemos sentido dolorosamente y que hemos sufrido con arrepentimiento, como aún deben hacer ustedes. Esperamos que nuestra condición anterior como pecadores e incrédulos nos haga hablarles con más ternura y nos permita llegar mejor todavía a sus corazones. Dios pudiera haberles enviado ángeles y quizá ustedes, al principio, se sintieran impresionados por su gloria, pero sus sermones habrían sido fríos y poco compasivos en comparación con los nuestros porque ellos no pueden conocer tu miseria y degradación como la conocemos nosotros.

A través de la Biblia en un año: 1 Tesalonicenses 1–2

La marca del discipulado

Arrepiéntanse y bautícese cada uno de ustedes en el nombre de Jesucristo para perdón de sus pecados —les contestó Pedro—, y recibirán el don del Espíritu Santo. En efecto, la promesa es para ustedes, para sus hijos y para todos los extranjeros, es decir, para todos aquellos a quienes el Señor nuestro Dios quiera llamar.

HECHOS 2:38-39

«El que crea y sea bautizado será salvo, pero el que no crea será condenado» (Marcos 16:16). Es decir, si un hombre participa en la salvación generosa que Cristo ha realizado, debe creer en Cristo, debe confiar en Cristo, debe creer que Cristo es el Salvador que Dios designó y que es capaz de salvarlo. Debe actuar de acuerdo a esa creencia y ponerse en manos de Jesús, y si lo hace, será salvo.

Además, el texto dice que *se debe bautizar.* No es que haya algún tipo de virtud en el bautismo, pero es una pequeña cosa que Cristo espera que el hombre que confía en que él lo salve, deba confesar y mostrar su afecto por él. Aquel que desea tener a Cristo como su Salvador, debe estar preparado para reconocer abiertamente que está del lado de Cristo. Por ende, el bautismo se convierte en la marca del discipulado, la señal exterior de la fe interior mediante la cual un hombre le dice a todo el que observa: «Me confieso muerto para el mundo; confieso que estoy enterrado con Cristo; me declaro resucitado a una nueva vida en él; hagan con eso lo que quiera y ríanse tanto como quieran; no obstante, con la fe en Cristo como mi Señor me abandono de todo lo demás para seguirlo».

A través de la Biblia en un año: 1 Tesalonicenses 3–5

Vínculos de amor

Esposos, amen a sus esposas, así como Cristo amó a la iglesia y se entregó por ella para hacerla santa. Él la purificó, lavándola con agua mediante la palabra, para presentársela a sí mismo como una iglesia radiante, sin mancha ni arruga ni ninguna otra imperfección, sino santa e intachable.

TITO 1:9

Una unión misteriosa se ha establecido entre Cristo y su iglesia, la cual se compara constantemente con el matrimonio: «Porque el esposo es cabeza de su esposa, así como Cristo es cabeza y salvador de la iglesia, la cual es su cuerpo» (Efesios 5:23). Jesús es el novio y la iglesia es su novia. Están desposados el uno con el otro, están unidos para siempre con vínculos de amor y esperan con igual sagrada expectativa el día del matrimonio cuando se cumplirá el propósito eterno de Dios y el deseo del Redentor. De igual manera que el esposo ejerce un liderazgo en su casa, que no es para nada tiránico ni autoritario (cuando la relación se lleva de manera correcta), sino un gobierno fundado en las reglas de la naturaleza y aprobado por el consentimiento del amor, así también gobierna Cristo a su iglesia, no como un señor déspota que coacciona y obliga a su novia a someterse en contra de su voluntad, sino como un esposo bien amado que obtiene obediencia voluntaria del corazón de la amada, siendo tan admirado en todas las cosas y tenido en tan alta estima como para ganar la preeminencia indisputable.

El reino de Jesucristo no es una tiranía, su cetro no está hecho de hierro, él no gobierna con golpes, maldiciones ni amenazas sino que su cetro es de plata y su gobierno es el amor. Las únicas cadenas que usa son las cadenas de su gracia que constriñe, su dominio es espiritual y se extiende a los corazones dispuestos que se deleitan en inclinarse delante de él y en darle el honor debido a su nombre.

A través de la Biblia en un año: 1 Crónicas 1–4

Cristo es la cabeza

Él es la cabeza del cuerpo, que es la iglesia. Él es el principio, el primogénito de la resurrección, para ser en todo el primero.
COLOSENSES 1:18

Ya que Cristo es la cabeza de su cuerpo, la iglesia, solo él puede decidir las doctrinas de esta. Nada debe recibirse como aprobado por la deidad a menos que venga con su sello. Para el siervo fiel de Jesucristo no importa que algo le llegue con la antigüedad gris de las edades para que sea venerable. Como hombre sensible, el cristiano respeta la antigüedad, pero como súbdito leal del rey, no se inclina ante la antigüedad como para dejar que esta se convierta en la gobernadora de Sión en lugar del Cristo vivo. Puede que una multitud de hombres buenos se reúna y puede que, en su juicio, ellos propongan un dogma y afirmen que es esencial e indudable, y quizá incluso amenacen con muchos peligros a aquellos que no reciban su veredicto, pero si no se autorizó el dogma mucho antes de que lo decidieran, si no estaba escrito en el Libro, la decisión del concilio erudito no significa nada. Todos los padres, doctores, eclesiásticos y confesores juntos no pueden añadir una palabra a la fe que una vez se les dio a los santos. Sí, me atrevo a decir que el consenso unánime de todos los santos en el cielo y en la tierra no sería suficiente para hacer una sola doctrina que obligue a la conciencia a menos que Jesús así lo haya determinado.

A través de la Biblia en un año: 1 Crónicas 5–8

La autoridad de Cristo

Retenedor de la palabra fiel tal como ha sido enseñada, para que también pueda exhortar con sana enseñanza y convencer a los que contradicen.
TITO 1:9

La autoridad exclusiva de Cristo debe mantenerse de manera rigurosa en todo aspecto, pero las iglesias son muy dadas a dejarse guiar por algo más. Algunos quisieran que nos dejemos guiar por los resultados. Hemos escuchado una discusión sobre el asunto de si debemos o no continuar con operaciones misioneras, ¡ya que hay tan pocos convertidos! ¿Cómo puede siquiera surgir la pregunta cuando el mandato del Maestro dice así: «Id por todo el mundo y predicad el evangelio a toda criatura» (Marcos 16:15)? Ese mandato, pronunciado en boca de Jesús, nuestro soberano, sigue vigente y los resultados de las misiones no pueden tener efecto, de una manera u otra, sobre las mentes leales en cuanto a su manera de proceder. Si a partir de este día y durante los próximos diez mil años ni una sola alma se convierte a Dios mediante las misiones extranjeras, si todavía quedara una iglesia de Cristo, sería su deber enviar con creciente vigor a sus hijos al campo misionero porque su deber no se mide por los resultados sino por la autoridad imperial de Cristo.

Pero se nos dice que los descubrimientos de la ciencia han afectado la creencia y por lo tanto, debemos cambiar nuestra forma según cambie la filosofía. Todavía tenemos el mismo rey, las mismas leyes, las mismas enseñanzas de la Palabra y debemos presentar su enseñanza de la misma manera y en el mismo espíritu. Si hacemos esto, si cualquier iglesia hace esto, es decir, tomar su verdad de los labios de Jesús y vivir acorde a su Palabra y salir en su nombre, tal iglesia no puede fracasar de ninguna manera, porque el fracaso de tal iglesia sería el fracaso de la misma autoridad del Maestro.

A través de la Biblia en un año: 1 Crónicas 9–12

Ningún gozo lo sobrepasa

El fruto del justo es árbol de vida; Y el que gana almas es sabio.
PROVERBIOS 11:30 (RVR 1960)

Hermanos y hermanas, oro pidiendo que prediquen el evangelio de Jesucristo, por su propio bien, si no hubiera alguna otra razón. Dependan de esto, su propio vigor espiritual mejorará mucho mediante sus obras de amor y su fervor por el servicio de Cristo. Yo lo considero como un termómetro invariable con el cual medir la espiritualidad del corazón de un hombre. Si él está haciendo o no algo para Cristo, esto hablará de su vida y de su conversación. ¿Alguna vez sentiste el gozo de ganar un alma para Cristo? Si es así, no necesitarás ningún otro argumento para intentar divulgar el conocimiento de su nombre a toda criatura. Te digo algo, no hay gozo fuera del cielo que lo sobrepase: sentir que alguien te agarra de la mano y te dice: «Por medio tuyo fui sacado de las tinieblas a la luz, rescatado de las borracheras o reclamado quizá de los peores vicios, para amar y servir a mi Salvador». Ver a tus hijos espirituales a tu alrededor y decir: «Aquí estoy y también estos a quienes me has dado».

A través de la Biblia en un año: 1 Crónica 13–16

Realizar la voluntad del Amo

Su señor le respondió: «¡Hiciste bien, siervo bueno y fiel! En lo poco has sido fiel; te pondré a cargo de mucho más. ¡Ven a compartir la felicidad de tu señor!»
MATEO 25:21

El poder de la iglesia es doble. Es un poder para testificar de lo que Cristo ha revelado. Ella es un testigo y como tal debe actuar. Tiene, además, un poder ministerial mediante el cual realiza la voluntad de Cristo y cumple con su mandato como sierva y ministra fiel de Cristo. Algunos siervos se reúnen en el salón de los siervos, tienen órdenes de realizar ciertas tareas y además les han dado órdenes en cuanto a cómo realizarla. Luego consultan entre sí los detalles menores, cómo pueden cumplir mejor con las reglas del amo y hacer lo que él ordena. Hacen muy bien al comportarse así. Pero imagina que comenzaran a consultar si los objetivos propuestos por el amo son buenos o si las reglas que él ha puesto pudieran alterarse. De inmediato se convertirían en rebeldes y estarían en peligro de ser despedidos. De la misma manera, una iglesia que se reúne para consultar cómo realizar la voluntad del Amo, y cómo hacer cumplir sus leyes, hace bien; pero una iglesia que se reúne para crear nuevas leyes o una iglesia que se reúne para gobernar según su juicio y opinión, imaginando que su decisión tendrá peso, comete un error y se coloca en una posición falsa. La única doctrina que he tratado de presentar es esta: que solo aquel que compró la iglesia y la salvó, puede gobernar la iglesia y sin duda alguna, nuestros corazones, sin excepción, se inclinan antes esto.

A través de la Biblia en un año: 1 Crónicas 17-19

¡Su amor es mayor!

¿Quién acusará a los que Dios ha escogido? Dios es el que justifica. ¿Quién condenará? Cristo Jesús es el que murió, e incluso resucitó, y está a la derecha de Dios e intercede por nosotros. ¿Quién nos apartará del amor de Cristo? ¿La tribulación, o la angustia, la persecución, el hambre, la indigencia, el peligro, o la violencia?

ROMANOS 8:33-35

¿Hemos caído durante la última semana en un estado notable de total incredulidad? ¿Hemos tenido pensamientos duros con respecto a Dios? ¿Algún pecado ha suspendido nuestra comunión con nuestro Salvador? ¿Tenemos ahora frío el corazón y estamos vacíos de emoción espiritual? ¿Nos sentimos bastante indignos de acercarnos a aquel que nos amó con tan grande amor? No te desanimes. El Dios de toda paciencia no te abandonará. El amor que nuestro Señor Jesucristo siente por su pueblo es tan grande que él pasa por alto las transgresiones, iniquidades y pecados. No, no hay ira de su parte que te separe de tu Señor. Ya que él viene a ti de manera tan misericordiosa, ¿no vendrás tú a él gustosamente? No creas ni por un momento que él fruncirá el ceño o que te rechazará. Él no te recordará tus oraciones frías, tu lugar de oración descuidado, tu Biblia sin leer ni te regañará por perder oportunidades de comunión sino que te recibirá con misericordia, te amará libremente y te concederá justo lo que necesitas en este momento.

A través de la Biblia en un año: 1 Crónicas 20–23

Aprendices lentos

Por tanto, si sienten algún estímulo en su unión con Cristo, algún consuelo en su amor, algún compañerismo en el Espíritu, algún afecto entrañable, llénenme de alegría teniendo un mismo parecer, un mismo amor, unidos en alma y pensamiento.

FILIPENSES 2:1-2

Tú y yo no somos ni el alfa ni la omega para la ley, porque la hemos quebrantado por completo. Ni tan siquiera hemos aprendido su primera letra: «Ama al Señor tu Dios con todo tu corazón» y estoy seguro de que sabemos muy poco de la segunda: «Ama a tu prójimo como a ti mismo». A pesar de estar renovados por gracia, somos muy lentos para aprender la santidad y la espiritualidad de la ley; estamos tan impactados por la letra que a menudo perdemos su espíritu por completo. Pero, amado, si quieres ver la ley cumplida, mira la persona de nuestro bendito Señor y Amo. ¡Qué amor a Dios hay ahí!

Jesús amó de manera tal que todo el amor que jamás haya brillado en el pecho humano, si pudiera reunirse, no sería más que una chispa, mientras que su gran amor para con el hombre sería como un horno ardiente calentado siete veces más de lo que la imaginación humana pudiera concebir. No permitan, amados amigos, si están en Cristo Jesús, que los temores legales los aflijan con los recuerdos de sus fracasos en cuanto a la obediencia, como si fueran a destruir su alma. Busquen la santidad pero nunca pongan su confianza en la santidad. Busquen la virtud, esfuércense por ella, pero no se desanimen cuando vean sus propias imperfecciones. La justicia que les salva es la justicia de Cristo, aquella en la que Dios te acepta es la perfecta obediencia de Cristo; y decimos de eso otra vez, con las palabras del texto, Jesucristo es «el Alfa y la Omega, el Primero y el Último, el Principio y el Fin» (Apocalipsis 22:13).

A través de la Biblia en un año: 1 Crónicas 24–26

El hombre piadoso

Sepan que el Señor honra al que le es fiel.
SALMO 4:3

No todos los hombres son piadosos. De hecho, los impíos conforman la mayor parte de la raza humana. Y los hombres que son piadosos, no lo son todos al mismo nivel. El hombre que teme a Dios y desea en verdad conocerlo tiene cierto grado de piedad. El hombre que ha comenzado a confiar en el Salvador que Dios envió como propiciación por el pecado tiene una medida bendecida de piedad. El hombre que tiene una constante comunión con Dios, que viene al Padre con sus oraciones más profundas y sus lágrimas de arrepentimiento y que anhela tener un conocimiento más profundo y completo de Dios, es un hombre piadoso en un sentido incluso más elevado. Y aquel que por medio de la comunión continúa con Dios, se asemeja a él y refleja la imagen de Cristo como una fotografía porque lo ha observado durante un largo tiempo y se ha regocijado en él con intensidad, este sí es *un* hombre piadoso. El hombre que encuentra a su Dios en todas partes, que lo ve en todas las obras de sus manos, el hombre que ve el origen de todo en Dios, tanto lo que es motivo de alegría como de tristeza, el hombre que va a Dios para todo, que lleva cada asunto ante el trono de la gracia y cada petición ante el Dios de la misericordia; el hombre que no puede vivir sin su Dios, para quien Dios es el motivo de mayor gozo, su ayuda y su consuelo; el hombre que habita en Dios, ese es el hombre piadoso. Este es el hombre que morará para siempre con Dios, porque le teme y le es fiel y en el buen tiempo del Señor, lo llamará a aquel lugar bendito donde verá a Dios y se regocijará en él por los siglos de los siglos.

A través de la Biblia en un año: 1 Crónicas 27–29

La vida de oración

Oren en el Espíritu en todo momento, con peticiones y ruegos. Manténganse alerta y perseveren en oración por todos los santos.
Efesios 6:18

Algunas oraciones toman la forma de acciones, y una obra puede ser un acto de oración. Amar a nuestros semejantes y desear su bien es un tipo de oración práctica consolidada. Dar limosnas puede ser una oración, o predicar el evangelio, o tratar de ganar a un extraviado, o cargar un niño en tus rodillas y hablarle del Salvador. Tales actos son, con frecuencia, las oraciones más aceptables. Pero para actuar así, también debes derramar con palabras tu corazón ante el Señor. Y cuando no puedes hacer esto, es igual de dulce si tan solo lo miras, y como los lirios derraman su fragancia ante aquel que los creó, así mismo tú, incluso sin hablar, adoras a Dios con esa profunda adoración que es demasiado elocuente para expresarse con palabras; esa cercanía santa que, al ser tan íntima, no necesita de los sonidos, no vaya a ser que estos rompan el encanto del silencio divino que se establece. Las pocas palabras pero el abundante fluir del espíritu es una buena combinación en la oración. Una oración bendecida es postrarte ante Dios en silencio, o suspirar y llorar, o gemir según el Espíritu te guíe. Todo esto es oración, cualquiera que sea la forma que asuma, y es la señal y la marca de la vida de un verdadero creyente.

A través de la Biblia en un año: 2 Tesalonicenses 1–3

El cielo en la tierra

Nada me produce más alegría que oír que mis hijos practican la verdad.
3 Juan 4

He tenido días muy felices en mi vida, pero mis momentos más felices han sido como uno que tuve la semana pasada. Saludé a alrededor de cien personas que se dirigían a mí como su padre espiritual. Daba la impresión que para ellos era algo grandioso tocar mi mano, mientras yo, con lágrimas en mis ojos al ver a cada uno de ellos, me sentía como si estuviera en el cielo, porque nunca antes había visto a esas personas. Quizá algunos de ellos estuvieron en esta casa en algún momento, o tal vez yo fui de pueblo en pueblo y los encontré a las puertas de sus casas donde me detenían para decirme «de cuánta bendición ha sido ese sermón para mí» y «mi padre leyó sus sermones y murió en paz luego de haberlos leído» también: «Bien pudiera haber muerto de dicha porque esta es la felicidad más grande que podemos tener en la tierra». Busca a los pecadores, mi hermano, busca su conversión con toda tu alma y corazón. Si ustedes son de los hombres y mujeres felices que cantan la canción más dulce que puede cantarse en esta tierra, «que sea una alabanza a nuestro Dios», no tan solo a tu Dios, sino también al Dios de aquellos que, en su infinita misericordia, él te permita traer a los pies de tu mismo amado Salvador.

A través de la Biblia en un año: 2 Crónicas 1–4

Mientras aún hablamos

Tan pronto como empezaste a orar, Dios contestó tu oración.
He venido a decírtelo porque tú eres muy apreciado.
DANIEL 9:23

¿Tiene el Espíritu de Dios alguna limitación? ¿Por qué no puede el ministro más débil convertirse en el medio para la salvación de miles de personas? ¿Se ha acortado el brazo de Dios? Cuando yo les pido que ustedes oren para que Dios haga que el ministerio sea vivo y potente como una espada de dos filos para la salvación de los pecadores, no les estoy pidiendo una tarea difícil y mucho menos imposible. Para obtener lo que queremos solo tenemos que pedir. Antes que llamemos, Dios responderá, y mientras aún hablamos, él habrá oído; solo él puede saber los resultados que tendrá este sermón, si escoge bendecirlo. A partir de este momento puede que te decidas a orar más; a partir de este momento Dios puede bendecir más el ministerio. A partir de ahora más púlpitos que nunca antes pueden llenarse de vitalidad y vigor. A partir de este momento la Palabra de Dios puede comenzar a fluir y a correr y obtener una asombrosa e ilimitada victoria. Solo tienen que luchar en oración, reúnanse en sus casas, vayan a sus cuartos, persistan, pidan con insistencia a tiempo y fuera de tiempo, agonicen por las almas. Olvidarás todo lo que has escuchado y lo que otros te han dicho será como nada, comparado con lo que oirás con tus oídos y lo que verás con tus ojos a tu alrededor.

A través de la Biblia en un año: 2 Crónicas 5–8

Un espíritu quebrantado

El sacrificio que te agrada es un espíritu quebrantado; tú, oh Dios, no desprecias al corazón quebrantado y arrepentido.

SALMO 51:17

Si tú y yo tenemos un espíritu quebrantado, *desaparecerá toda idea de nuestra propia importancia.* ¿Cuál es la utilidad de un corazón quebrantado? ¡Lo mismo que una vasija o una botella rota! Los hombres la lanzan a la basura. Sin embargo, David dice: «Tú, oh Dios, no desprecias al corazón quebrantado y arrepentido» (Salmo 51:17), como si supiera que todos los demás lo iban a rechazar. Ahora bien, ¿sientes que no vales nada? A pesar de que sabes que eres un hijo de Dios, ¿sientes que no darías ni un centavo por ti mismo? No deseas reclamar el primer lugar, el último te sienta mejor, de hecho, te cuestionas si estarás en algún lugar del ejército de Dios. Ay, hermanos, creo que mientras más nos usa Dios, menos debemos pensar acerca de nosotros mismos; y mientras más nos llena con su Espíritu, ¡más se sobrecogerá nuestro espíritu dentro de nosotros en un absoluto asombro de que él haya podido usar vasos rotos como nosotros! Bien, ahora cultiva ese sentimiento de subestimación e insignificancia, considéralo como tu condición y actúa según ella, considérate como menor que el menor de tus hermanos; humíllate ante el asombro de que Dios haya permitido que tu nombre esté en la lista de sus elegidos. Admira la gracia que Dios tuvo contigo y maravíllate de ella en una profunda humillación de espíritu. Eso es parte del sacrificio que Dios no despreciará.

A través de la Biblia en un año: 2 Crónicas 9–12

No finjas

El Señor está cerca de los quebrantados de corazón, y salva a los de espíritu abatido.
SALMO 34:18

Si tú y yo tenemos un corazón quebrantado y arrepentido, significa que ya nuestra frivolidad y superficialidad se nos ha ido. *Ya no somos frívolos y superficiales.* Hay personas que juegan con las cosas espirituales, pero cuando hay quebrantamiento de corazón, la persona termína con esta actitud. Un corazón quebrantado es serio, solemne y reflexivo. Un corazón quebrantado nunca juega con Dios ni repasa los textos bíblicos como si la Biblia existiera para probar cuán listos somos. Un espíritu quebrantado es tierno, serio y está cargado con consideraciones serias. Disfruta de aquel espíritu ahora, sé solemne delante de Dios, aférrate a las cosa eternas, suelta las sombras; ¿de qué valen? Pero fija tu alma en las cosas divinas y eternas. Persigue esta modo de pensar y de esta manera trae a Dios un espíritu quebrantado y contrito.

Además, un espíritu quebrantado no es hipócrita. Ese vaso, lleno y sellado, puede contener la más preciosa esencia de las rosas o la más horrible pudrición. Yo no sé lo que hay en él. Pero rómpelo y pronto averiguarás. No hay hipocresía en un corazón quebrantado. ¡Oh, hermanos y hermanas, sean ante los hombres lo que son ante Dios! Sean lo que parecen ser, sin pretensiones. Temo que en cierta medida todos somos hipócritas; con mucha frecuencia oramos y predicamos más allá de nuestra propia experiencia y quizá pensamos que tenemos más fe de lo que en realidad tenemos, y más amor del que jamás hemos conocido. ¡Que el Señor permita que tengamos un corazón quebrantado que se revele debido a este mismo quebrantamiento!

A través de la Biblia en un año: 2 Crónicas 13–16

El gozo de un corazón quebrantado

En Betania, mientras estaba él sentado a la mesa en casa de Simón llamado el leproso, llegó una mujer con un frasco de alabastro lleno de un perfume muy costoso, hecho de nardo puro. Rompió el frasco y derramó el perfume sobre la cabeza de Jesús.

MARCOS 14:3

Un espíritu quebrantado implica que todos los secretos y las esencias del espíritu han salido a relucir. Seguramente recuerdas lo que sucedió cuando aquella santa mujer rompió el frasco de alabastro; leemos que «la casa se llenó de la fragancia del perfume» (Juan 12:3). Un corazón quebrantado no puede tener secretos. Ahora todo está al descubierto, ahora su esencia fluye. Demasiadas veces nuestras oraciones y nuestra adoración son como cajas cerradas, no puedes decir lo que hay en ellas. Pero no sucede esto con los corazones quebrantados. Cuando los corazones quebrantados cantan, lo hacen en verdad. Cuando los corazones quebrantados suplican, en realidad lo hacen. Los corazones quebrantados nunca juegan a arrepentirse o a creer. En la actualidad hay mucho de la religión que es bastante superficial, todo queda en la superficie, una pequeña cantidad de pintura del evangelio, con solo un barniz de profesión, se extiende rápido y parece muy hermoso. Pero los corazones quebrantados no son así, en ellos un himno es un verdadero himno, una oración es una verdadera oración, la atención a los sermones es una ocupación seria y la predicación de estos es la ocupación más seria de todas. ¡Oh, cuán bueno sería que algunos de ustedes fueran rotos en pedazos! ¡Oh, adorar a Dios en espíritu y en verdad! Bien ha dicho alguien: «Nadie adoró jamás a Dios con todo su corazón a menos que lo haya adorado con un corazón quebrantado, y nunca hubo un corazón en verdad quebrantado que no se transformara entonces en un corazón entero».

A través de la Biblia en un año: 2 Crónicas 17–20

Nuestra brújula

El portero le abre la puerta, y las ovejas oyen su voz. Llama por nombre a las ovejas y las saca del redil. Cuando ya ha sacado a todas las que son suyas, va delante de ellas, y las ovejas lo siguen porque reconocen su voz.

JUAN 10:3-4

Cientos de años atrás, cuando los hombres comenzaban a aventurarse en el mar, mantenían siempre sus botes a la vista de la orilla. Podía ser que aquel marinero griego o romano fuera un gran maestro de su galeón, pero no podía perder de vista la tierra que conocía porque no tenía brújula y sabía muy poco o nada de observaciones astronómicas. Aquí y allá podían colocarse varios faros, pero estos se consideraban como una maravilla. Sin embargo, en la actualidad un barco puede permanecer un mes sin ver tierra, e incluso así su posición en el mapa será tan certera como la posición de tu asiento. Las observaciones de los cuerpos celestes, el mapa y la brújula, controlarán por completo la posición de la embarcación y al término de los treinta días llegará a un punto que nunca estuvo a la vista, y lo alcanzará con tanta exactitud como si hubiera transitado por una autopista en vez de haber estado navegando por el inmenso océano. Su viaje ha sido como si hubiera recorrido una línea de ferrocarril de puerto a puerto. Así es la vida cristiana, la vida de fe. No vemos las cosas espirituales, sin embargo, nos dirigimos hacia ellas con absoluta certeza. Nos dirige la Palabra de Dios, que es nuestro mapa, y nuestra brújula es el testimonio del Espíritu dentro de nosotros. Vemos a aquel que es invisible y vamos en busca de un cielo lleno de «cosas que ojo no ha visto». Para la gloria de Dios alcanzaremos ese puerto con tanta certeza como la bala alcanza su blanco.

A través de la Biblia en un año: 2 Crónicas 21–24

Un camino peligroso

Los que quieren enriquecerse caen en la tentación y se vuelven esclavos de sus muchos deseos. Estos afanes insensatos y dañinos hunden a la gente en la ruina y en la destrucción. Porque el amor al dinero es la raíz de toda clase de males. Por codiciarlo, algunos se han desviado de la fe y se han causado muchísimos sinsabores.

1 TIMOTEO 6:9-10

Oh, cristiano, si te mantienes en el camino del Rey estarás seguro, pero hay callejones y curvas que no debes tomar, si lo haces, tú serás el responsable. Hay cientos y temo que hasta miles de miembros de iglesias que dicen que son el pueblo de Dios y, sin embargo, parecen vivir por completo dentro del mundo. Su objetivo principal es hacer dinero y lograr su realización personal, tal como sucede con todos los hombres impíos. El reino de Cristo, las necesidades de su iglesia, los sufrimientos de las almas que perecen, ocupan un lugar muy pequeño en sus corazones; viven por completo para sí mismos, solo que intentan esconderlo bajo el pretexto de que tienen que proveer para sus familias. «Busquen primeramente el reino de Dios y su justicia, y todas estas cosas les serán añadidas» es un texto acerca del cual necesitamos predicar a los que profesan ser cristianos en Londres y en todo el mundo.

Muchos toman el camino del orgullo. Ser grandes, famosos, estimados, tener una elevada reputación, para eso es que viven. Creo que en este mundo no existe ningún estado de vida superior que el que Dios ha dado a todo aquel que cree en el Señor Jesucristo.

A través de la Biblia en un año: 2 Crónicas 25–28

Caminos seguros

Necio es el que confía en sí mismo; el que actúa con sabiduría se pone a salvo.
PROVERBIOS 28:26

Haz lo que Dios te dice, como Dios te diga y porque Dios te lo dice, y no sufrirás daño alguno. El Señor le ordenó a Moisés que agarrara la serpiente de la que él huyó, él lo hizo así y esta no lo mordió. Por el contrario, la serpiente se convirtió en una vara que obró maravillas. Obedece al Señor en todas las cosas. Ten en cuenta las jotas y las tildes, porque aquel que «infrinja uno solo de estos mandamientos, y enseñe a otros a hacer lo mismo, será considerado el más pequeño en el reino de los cielos; pero el que los practique y enseñe será considerado grande en el reino de los cielos» (Mateo 5:19).

También existe la opción de confiar en la providencia divina con la confianza de un niño. Dichoso el hombre que siempre espera en Dios hasta saber lo que debe hacer, que siempre le pide al Señor que lo guíe y que no confía en su propio entendimiento. Busca la dirección providencial del Señor y espera la guía divina. Es mucho mejor permanecer parado que correr por el camino equivocado. Espera un poco y busca la dirección de Dios, y no te muevas hasta que escuches la voz detrás de ti que diga: «Este es el camino; síguelo» (Isaías 30:21).

Y estoy seguro que el camino del servicio consagrado para la gloria de Dios es uno de esos caminos seguros. Es bueno cuando un hombre dice: «Elijo mi camino según esta norma: ¿Cómo puedo servir mejor a Dios?» «¿En cuál camino puedo glorificar mejor a Dios?» Ese es tu camino al cielo, cristiano, el camino en el que el Señor se glorifica mejor en ti. Si caminas por ese sendero, de seguro estarás protegido por su poder soberano.

A través de la Biblia en un año: 2 Crónicas 29–32

Fiel a tus convicciones

«Tenemos una ciudad fuerte. Como un muro, como un baluarte, Dios ha interpuesto su salvación. Abran las puertas, para que entre la nación justa que se mantiene fiel. Al de carácter firme lo guardarás en perfecta paz, porque en ti confía».

ISAÍAS 26:1-3

Determina que si otros hacen lo que mejor les parece, no serás responsable por sus acciones; pero tú harás lo que creas que sea correcto. Si eres cristiano, compórtate como tal, sé un seguidor de Cristo en todo, según te guíen la Palabra de Dios y tu propia conciencia. Descubrí que el hábito de pensar por mí mismo y actuar según mis convicciones me era muy útil, y me ha sido útil hasta el día de hoy. En este instante soy capaz de esperar en la presencia de Dios, sin confiar en este o en aquel hombre, sino solo en el brazo eterno que sostendrá a todo el que delante de Dios determine seguir la verdad, adondequiera que esta lo pueda guiar.

Ahora bien, ruego que cada cristiano en este lugar —en especial los que comienzan su vida— analice bien este asunto, porque el gozo, la paz y la tranquilidad interior de la vida, dependerán en gran medida de la fidelidad a las convicciones de cada aspecto que mantengan con la ayuda de Dios. Esta noche, el mismo gran Rey parece estar diciendo: «Pondré mis ojos en los fieles de la tierra, para que habiten conmigo; solo estarán a mi servicio los de conducta intachable» (Salmo 101:6). Él es el hombre que escogeré para que me sirva.

A través de la Biblia en un año: 2 Crónicas 33–36

Un dios de carne

El Señor no se deleita en los bríos del caballo, ni se complace en la agilidad del hombre, sino que se complace en los que le temen, en los que confían en su gran amor.
SALMO 147:10-11

Es bueno ser sabio y estudioso, y mientras más puedas cultivar tu mente, mejor: pero recuerda las palabras del apóstol: «No muchos de ustedes son sabios, según criterios meramente humanos; ni son muchos los poderosos ni muchos los de noble cuna» (1 Corintios 1:26). Con frecuencia, la sabiduría que proviene solo de la mente natural puede convertirse en escamas para el ojo espiritual, al esconder del alma la visión bendita que es la única que la puede salvar. Es cierto, tanto en el aspecto mental como en el físico, que el Señor no se complace en ninguna de las facultades que el hombre posee si está destituido de la guía de Dios.

Otra cosa en la que el Señor no se complace es la llamada *auto suficiencia*, de la que tanto se habla en la actualidad. Esta es solo otra forma de «los bríos del caballo» y de «la agilidad del hombre». Algunos hombres se sienten orgullosos de decir que se formaron a sí mismos, ¡y por lo general observo que adoran a su creador! Al creer que se han formado a sí mismos, son devotos de sí mismos; pero un hombre que se formó a sí mismo está mal formado. Aquello que proviene del hombre no es más que una corriente contaminada de una fuente impura; de la maldad nace la maldad, y una naturaleza depravada da lugar a la depravación. Es solo cuando Dios nos hace nuevas criaturas en Cristo Jesús que nos sentimos felices de ser criaturas, y a él debemos dar toda la gloria. Es necio adorar a un dios de madera o de piedra; del mismo modo es necio adorar a un dios de carne y es aun más necio cuando ese dios eres tú mismo.

A través de la Biblia en un año: 1 Timoteo 1–2

La complacencia de Dios en ti

El Señor se complace en los que le temen, en los que confían en su gran amor.
SALMO 147:11

Cuando Dios se complace en algún hombre, podemos comparar el resultado de su favor con el placer que experimentamos con nuestros hijos. Ahora, sin extenderme demasiado en este tema, te digo que si temes al Señor y esperas en su misericordia, Dios se complace tanto en ti como tú lo haces con tu hijo querido, y mucho más, porque Dios tiene una mente infinita y de ella proviene un deleite infinito, de modo que él te ve con infinita complacencia.

¿Puedes creer esto? Tú no te ves a ti mismo de esa manera, al menos espero que no, pero Dios te ve a través de Jesucristo. Dios te ve como serás algún día. Ve en ti lo que te hará crecer hasta convertirte en un ser celestial y, por lo tanto, se complace en ti. No importa lo que otros piensen de ti. Quiero que vayas a tu casa y pienses: «Si mi Padre celestial se complace en mí, en realidad no me interesa si mis semejantes no me entienden o no me aprecian». Si tú y yo buscamos complacernos con las buenas opiniones de otras personas, corremos el riesgo de que nos hieran las malas opiniones. Vive de manera que agrades a Dios, y si no agradas a tus semejantes, bueno, entonces no hay nada que hacer. El único objetivo de tu vida debe ser el poder decir: «Siempre hago las cosas que son agradables a él». Camina con Dios por fe, como lo hizo Enoc, para que puedas tener un testimonio como el suyo: «Él agradó a Dios». Y si tú has agradado a Dios, ¿qué importa aquel al que no has agradado?

A través de la Biblia en un año: 1 Timoteo 3–4

La belleza de la humildad

Dichosos los humildes, porque recibirán la tierra como herencia.
MATEO 5:5

En las Escrituras encontrarás que las personas más hermosas eran las humildes. Recuerdo solo tres personas de quienes las Escrituras dicen que sus rostros resplandecieron, ¿las recuerdas, verdad? Primero el Señor Jesucristo, cuyo rostro resplandeció tanto cuando bajó del Monte de la Transfiguración, que las personas vinieron corriendo hacia él. ¡Cuán humilde y sencillo de corazón fue él! Otro hombre cuyo rostro resplandeció fue Moisés, cuando bajó del monte de la comunión con Dios, y de quien leemos: «Moisés era muy humilde» (Números 12:3). La tercera persona cuyo rostro resplandeció fue Esteban, cuando estuvo delante del concilio y de la manera más humilde habló de su Señor y Maestro. Si quieres que tu rostro resplandezca alguna vez, debes deshacerte del espíritu altanero y orgulloso, tienes que ser humilde, ya que el resplandor de la luz divina nunca reposará en una frente donde esté presente la ira. Sé gentil, apacible, paciente como tu Señor y entonces él te hará hermoso. El Señor otorga gran belleza a sus hijos que son tranquilos y sumisos. Si puedes soportar y callar, si puedes evitar el pronunciar una palabra dura, esa misma humildad en ti se convierte en belleza.

Además, Dios hermosea a las personas humildes con paz. Ellas no tienen necesidad de ir y pedir perdón o arreglar disputas porque no participan en disputas. Durante la noche no tienen que pensar: «En realidad dijimos lo que no debimos», porque no lo dijeron. Hay una gran belleza en la paz que produce la humildad.

A través de la Biblia en un año: 1 Timoteo 5–6

La belleza en la humildad

Refrena tu enojo, abandona la ira; no te irrites pues esto conduce al mal. Porque los impíos serán exterminados, pero los que esperan en el Señor heredarán la tierra. Dentro de poco los malvados dejarán de existir; por más que los busques, no los encontrarás. Pero los desposeídos heredarán la tierra y disfrutarán de gran bienestar.

SALMO 37:8-11

Otra belleza que Dios otorga a los humildes es el contentamiento. Aquellos que tienen un espíritu afable y apacible por medio de la gracia de Dios están satisfechos con lo que tienen. Le dan gracias a Dios por lo poco; piensan como aquella mujer piadosa que comió un pedazo de pan y bebió un poco de agua y dijo: «¡Qué! ¡Todo esto y además, Jesucristo!» Hay un gran encanto en el contentamiento, mientras que la envidia y la avaricia son cosas feas a los ojos de aquellos que tienen un mínimo de percepción espiritual. Así que la humildad, al producir contentamiento, nos embellece.

La humildad también produce santidad y, ¿quién no ha escuchado acerca de «la belleza de la santidad»? Cuando alguien se propone controlar su temperamento y someter su voluntad y su mente a Jesús de la forma más dulce, la consecuencia será la obediencia a Dios, y la vida entera se vuelve hermosa. Alabemos al Señor que tuvo a bien poner algo de belleza en nosotros y bendigamos a Dios por la santidad de su pueblo siempre que la veamos manifestarse. Es una lástima que esto sea tan escaso pero, ¡qué consuelo es saber que el Señor tiene algunos dentro de su pueblo que son de espíritu humilde y apacible, a quienes hermosea con la salvación!

A través de la Biblia en un año: Esdras 1–3

El hombre consagrado

A los ricos de este mundo, mándales que no sean arrogantes ni pongan su esperanza en las riquezas, que son tan inseguras, sino en Dios, que nos provee de todo en abundancia para que lo disfrutemos. Mándales que hagan el bien, que sean ricos en buenas obras, y generosos, dispuestos a compartir lo que tienen.

1 Timoteo 6: 17-18

Cada hijo de Dios es un hombre consagrado. Su consagración no se identifica con ningún símbolo externo; no se nos ordena que nos dejemos crecer el pelo, o que nos abstengamos de determinadas comidas o bebidas. El cristiano es un hombre consagrado, pero sus semejantes no ven su consagración, excepto en los hechos que son el resultado que produce.

«Sin embargo», dice alguien, «¿podemos consagrarnos a Cristo? Yo pensaba que eso era tan solo para los ministros». Oh, no, mis hermanos, todos los hijos de Dios deben ser hombres consagrados. ¿A qué te dedicas? ¿Estás involucrado en el mundo de los negocios? Si eres lo que profesas ser, tu negocio tiene que estar consagrado a Dios. Quizá no tienes familia, estás involucrado en el comercio y cada año ahorras una suma considerable. Pero déjame contarte el ejemplo de alguien completamente consagrado a Dios. En Bristol vive un hombre cuyas ganancias son grandes y, ¿qué hace con ellas? Trabaja continuamente en los negocios para obtener ganancias pero anualmente dedica todas esas ganancias a la causa del Señor, excepto aquello que requiere para cubrir las necesidades de la vida. Hace que sus necesidades sean tan pocas como sea posible, de modo que tenga más para poder dar. Él es un hombre de Dios en su negocio. Hermanos, ustedes en su negocio deben ser hombres tan consagrados a Dios como lo es el ministro en su púlpito; pueden hacer de sus transacciones diarias un solemne servicio a Dios.

A través de la Biblia en un año: Esdras 4–7

La vida apartada

No se dejen engañar: «Las malas conversaciones corrompen las buenas costumbres».

1 Corintios 15:33

Puede suceder que alguno de ustedes que profesa ser cristiano haya estado viviendo distanciado de Dios. No has llevado una vida apartada, has tratado de ser amigo del mundo y de Cristo a la vez, y tus hijos no están creciendo como desearías que lo hicieran. Dices que tus hijos no han salido buenos y que tus hijas solo piensan en las cosas superficiales y mundanas. ¿Te admiras de que esto haya sucedido? Dices: «¡Ay!, siempre he tratado de complacerlos, pensando que al hacerlo así podía ganarlos para Cristo». ¡Ah! Nunca ganarás un alma para el bien mediante un compromiso con el mal. Una decisión por Cristo y su verdad es lo que tiene el mayor poder en la familia y en el mundo también.

Nadie duda que las malas compañías puedan hacer malo a un hombre, y del mismo modo es seguro que las buenas compañías tienen la tendencia de inclinar a los hombres hacia aquello que es bueno. Es algo provechoso tener a alguien a tu lado cuyo corazón esté lleno de amor hacia Dios. Es una gran bendición tener como madre a una verdadera santa o como hermano o hermana a alguien que teme a Dios, y es un privilegio especial estar unido de por vida, con los más estrechos lazos, a alguien cuyas oraciones puedan elevarse junto con las nuestras y cuyas alabanzas también se mezclen con las nuestras. Hay algo en el compañerismo cristiano que nos impacta hacia la dirección correcta, a menos que el corazón esté del todo inclinado a la maldad.

A través de la Biblia en un año: Esdras 8–10

El verdadero Dios

Me asombra que tan pronto estén dejando ustedes a quien los llamó por la gracia de Cristo, para pasarse a otro evangelio. No es que haya otro evangelio, sino que ciertos individuos están sembrando confusión entre ustedes y quieren tergiversar el evangelio de Cristo.

GÁLATAS 6:1-7

Me temo que en la actualidad nueve de cada diez personas no creen en el Dios que nos revela la Biblia. Puedo citar ejemplos de periódicos, revistas, folletos y también de púlpitos, en los que se manifiesta que se adora a un nuevo dios, no al Dios del Antiguo Testamento, pues se considera demasiado severo, demasiado estricto, demasiado rígido para nuestros maestros modernos. Se encogen ante la sola mención del Dios de los puritanos. Si Jonathan Edwards resucitara, no lo escucharían ni un minuto; dirían que tienen un nuevo dios que no es como el de su tiempo. Pero, hermanos, yo creo en el Dios de Abraham, de Isaac y de Jacob, ese Dios es mi Dios. Sí, el Dios que en el Mar Rojo ahogó a Faraón y a sus soldados y que mientras lo hacía, inspiró a su pueblo a cantar ¡Aleluya!; el Dios que hizo que la tierra se abriera y se tragara a Corán, Datán, Abiram y toda su compañía. Un Dios terrible es el Dios que yo adoro; es el Dios y el Padre de nuestro Señor y Salvador Jesucristo, lleno de misericordia, gracia y compasión, tierno y amable, pero a la vez justo y temible en su santidad, y terrible fuera de sus lugares santos. Ese es el Dios que adoramos y todo aquel que se acerca a él por medio de Jesucristo y confía en él como su maestro, aprenderá bien todo lo que necesita saber.

A través de la Biblia en un año: 2 Timoteo 1–2

La iglesia imperfecta

Por tanto, imiten a Dios, como hijos muy amados, y lleven una vida de amor, así como Cristo nos amó y se entregó por nosotros como ofrenda y sacrificio fragante para Dios.

EFESIOS 5:1-2

He escuchado personas que encuentran faltas en los miembros de las iglesias y dicen que no pueden reunirse con ellos, porque son de un tipo inferior. Bueno, yo conozco muchos tipos diferentes de personas y, a pesar de todo, me alegro de ser parte del pueblo de Dios, incluso en su iglesia visible, y no de cualquier otro grupo de personas en el mundo entero. Considero que el denigrante pueblo de Dios es la mejor compañía que haya tenido.

«Oh», dice alguien, «me uniré a la iglesia cuando encuentre una perfecta». Entonces nunca te unirás a ninguna. «Ah», dice, «pero quizá lo haga». Bueno, pero no seguirá siendo una iglesia perfecta luego que te unas a ella, porque a partir del momento en que te reciban dentro de sus miembros, dejará de serlo. Creo que si Cristo puede amar a una iglesia, yo también puedo hacerlo; y si es una que Cristo considera como su iglesia, puedo sentirme agradecido de ser miembro de ella. Cristo «amó a la iglesia y se entregó por ella» (Efesios 5:25); entonces, ¿no debo yo considerar un honor que se me permita entregarme a ella? ¡Qué vergüenza es que algunos se unan a la iglesia pensando en lo que podrán obtener de ella! Sin embargo, para algunas personas los panes y los peces siempre son una carnada.

A través de la Biblia en un año: 2 Timoteo 3–4

Interésate en los nuevos convertidos

Los fuertes en la fe debemos apoyar a los débiles, en vez de hacer lo que nos agrada. Cada uno debe agradar al prójimo para su bien, con el fin de edificarlo.
ROMANOS 15:1-2

A ustedes que han sido creyentes en Cristo Jesús durante mucho tiempo, que tienen mucha experiencia, que conocen el amor y la fidelidad de nuestro Dios de los pactos y que son fuertes en el Señor y en el poder de su fuerza, quiero pedirles que busquen a los nuevos convertidos y le hablen palabras buenas y adecuadas, que puedan animarlos y fortalecerlos. ¿Por qué somos tan reticentes cuando una palabra pudiera hacer que nuestro hermano más débil se regocijara? Por lo tanto, les ruego a todos ustedes, a los que Dios ha bendecido en gran manera, que velen por aquellos que tienen un bajo nivel en las cosas espirituales y traten de alegrarlos y animarlos. Mientras lo hacen, Dios, a cambio, los bendecirá, pero si descuidan ese hermoso deber, pudiera suceder que ustedes mismos lleguen a sentirse desesperados y necesiten un amigo que los anime.

Con toda certeza veríamos un crecimiento más rápido en la gracia entre los nuevos convertidos si los cuidáramos y los alimentáramos mejor. Algunos de nosotros les debemos mucho a los cristianos más viejos y experimentados que conocimos en nuestros comienzos. Yo soy un ejemplo. Busquemos que se diga de nosotros, cuando también envejezcamos, que ayudamos a aquellos que eran niños cuando nosotros éramos jóvenes a convertirse en personas útiles en sus años maduros.

A través de la Biblia en un año: Nehemías 1–3

La mayor recompensa

El Señor mismo descenderá del cielo con voz de mando, con voz de arcángel y con trompeta de Dios, y los muertos en Cristo resucitarán primero. Luego los que estemos vivos, los que hayamos quedado, seremos arrebatados junto con ellos en las nubes para encontrarnos con el Señor en el aire. Y así estaremos con el Señor para siempre. Por lo tanto, anímense unos a otros con estas palabras.

1 TESALONICENSES 4:16-18

¿Cuál es la mayor recompensa de aquellos que se refugian bajo las alas de Dios? Yo respondo que obtendremos la mayor recompensa el día que dejemos estos cuerpos de carne y hueso, para que duerman en Jesús, mientras que nuestro espíritu deje el cuerpo para estar presente ante el Señor. En este estado incorpóreo disfrutaremos una perfecta armonía de espíritu, pero recibiremos una recompensa aún mayor cuando el Señor venga por segunda vez y nuestros cuerpos se levanten de entre los muertos para formar parte del glorioso reino del Rey que ha descendido. Entonces, en nuestra humanidad perfecta, veremos el rostro de aquel que amamos y seremos como él. Entonces vendrá la adopción, cuando nuestro cuerpo será redimido para estar en cuerpo, alma y espíritu, la trinidad en unidad, para siempre con el Padre, el Hijo y el Espíritu Santo, nuestro Dios trino. Esta bendición inimaginable es la plena recompensa por confiar bajo las alas de Jehová.

A través de la Biblia en un año: Nehemías 4–7

La vida de gozo

En resumidas cuentas, ¿cuál es nuestra esperanza, alegría o motivo de orgullo delante de nuestro Señor Jesús para cuando él venga? ¿Quién más sino ustedes? Sí, ustedes son nuestro orgullo y alegría.

1 Tesalonicenses 2:19-20

Los que confían en Dios y lo siguen tienen otra gran recompensa, la bendición de hacer el bien. ¿Puede alguna otra cosa hacernos más felices? Este gozo es un diamante de la mejor calidad. Iguala, si puedes, el gozo que produce ayudar al huérfano o la viuda. ¡Busca algo que produzca tanto gozo como el salvar un alma de la muerte y cubrir multitud de pecados! Valdría la pena tener fe en Dios, incluso si viviéramos aquí para siempre, si nuestra vida estuviera dedicada a hacer el bien al pobre y al necesitado, y a rescatar a los equivocados y a los caídos. Si deseas probar el gozo más puro que fluye de las fuentes del paraíso, prueba la bendición inagotable de salvar un alma perdida. Cuando la fe en Dios te enseña a negarte a ti mismo y vivir por completo para glorificar a Dios y beneficiar a tus semejantes, te colocas en el camino del Señor y de sus ángeles, y al seguirlo, reinarás en él.

Pienso, hermanos, que nuestra suerte es mucho mejor que la del más rico emperador, si este no conoce al Salvador. ¡Ay, pobres reyes, pobres príncipes, pobres nobles, pobres ricos que no conocen a Cristo! ¡Pero dichosos los pobres que lo conocen! ¡Felices los esclavos que lo aman! ¡Felices los hombres y mujeres moribundos que se regocijan en él! Ellos tienen un gozo perpetuo y un continuo placer porque Dios es el todo de su vida.

A través de la Biblia en un año: Nehemías 8–10

Aliméntate de la Palabra de Dios

¡Cuánto amo yo tu ley! Todo el día medito en ella. Tus mandamientos me hacen más sabio que mis enemigos porque me pertenecen para siempre. Tengo más discernimiento que todos mis maestros porque medito en tus estatutos.
SALMOS 119:97-99

Nada puede nutrir mejor el alma del creyente que el alimentarse de la Palabra y digerirla por medio de la meditación frecuente en ella. No es de extrañarse que algunos crezcan tan poco si meditan tan poco. Debemos tomar la verdad y repasarla una y otra vez en las partes más recónditas de nuestro espíritu y así sacaremos de ella la esencia divina que nos alimenta. Para ti, ¿no es la meditación tu tierra de Gosén? Si los hombres una vez dijeron: «Hay grano en la tierra de Egipto», ¿por qué no pueden siempre decir que lo mejor del trigo se encuentra en la oración secreta? La devoción privada es una tierra que fluye leche y miel, un paraíso que tiene toda clase de frutas, una casa de banquetes con vinos a elección. ¿Dónde podemos alimentarnos y descansar en verdes pastos de una forma tan dulce como lo hacemos cuando meditamos en la Palabra? La meditación destila la quintaesencia de las Escrituras y llena nuestra boca de una dulzura que excede la de la miel virgen que destila el panal. Tus tiempos de retiro y de oración deben ser tus pasatiempos reales o, al menos, tiempos de renovación en los que, al igual que los cosecheros al mediodía, te sientes con Booz y comas de la provisión generosa de tu Maestro.

A través de la Biblia en un año: Nehemías 11-13

La fe que salva

Sin embargo, alguien dirá: «Tú tienes fe, y yo tengo obras». Pues bien, muéstrame tu fe sin las obras, y yo te mostraré la fe por mis obras. ¿Tú crees que hay un solo Dios? ¡Magnífico! También los demonios lo creen, y tiemblan.
SANTIAGO 2: 18-19

Si yo digo que creo en Dios pero continúo viviendo en pecado de una manera voluntaria y consciente, entonces mi fe es inferior a la de los demonios, porque ellos «creen, y tiemblan». Hay algunos hombres que profesan creer en Dios pero no tiemblan ante él sino que se comportan de forma indebida y presuntuosa. Ese no es el tipo de fe que salva el alma. La fe que salva es la que produce buenas obras, la que lleva al arrepentimiento o la que viene acompañada de esas buenas obras y la que conduce al amor a Dios, a la santidad y a un deseo de ser hechos como el Salvador. Las buenas obras no son la raíz de la fe, pero son su fruto. Una casa no descansa en las tejas de su techo, sin embargo, no puedes vivir en ella si no tiene techo. Del mismo modo nuestra fe no descansa en las buenas obras pero sería una fe pobre e inútil si no tuviera algo del fruto del Espíritu para probar que proviene de Dios. Jesucristo nos dice cómo un hombre puede llegar a ser santo como Dios es santo y, a pesar de eso, nunca hablar acerca de su santidad ni soñar en confiarse de esta. Debemos vivir como si fuéramos a ser salvos por medio de nuestras buenas obras pero sin tener confianza alguna en ellas, sino considerarlas como basura, para ganar a Cristo y permanecer en él, no por nuestra propia justicia, que es la de la ley, sino por aquella que proviene de la fe en Jesucristo, la justicia que es de Dios por fe.

A través de la Biblia en un año: Tito 1-3

¿Puede Dios olvidar?

Antes de recibir esa circuncisión, ustedes estaban muertos en sus pecados. Sin embargo, Dios nos dio vida en unión con Cristo, al perdonarnos todos los pecados y anular la deuda que teníamos pendiente por los requisitos de la ley. Él anuló esa deuda que nos era adversa, clavándola en la cruz.

COLOSENSES 2:13-14

¿Cómo es que Dios no puede ver ningún pecado en los creyentes, si él ve todas las cosas? Esto es un dilema que muchos no comprenden. Dios está en todas partes y todas las cosas están ante sus ojos que todo lo ven, sin embargo, dice: «En aquellos días se buscará la iniquidad de Israel, pero ya no se encontrará. En aquel tiempo se buscarán los pecados de Judá, pero ya no se hallarán» (Jeremías 50:20). Me arriesgo a decir que ni siquiera Dios puede ver lo que ya no existe, ni siquiera sus ojos pueden ver algo que no está y eso es lo que sucede con el pecado de aquellos que han creído en Jesús: ha dejado de ser. Dios mismo ha declarado: «No me acordaré más de su pecado». Pero, ¿puede Dios olvidar? Por supuesto que sí, pues dice que lo hará. Daniel recibió la descripción de la obra del Mesías con estas memorables palabras: «poner fin a sus transgresiones y pecados, pedir perdón por su maldad, establecer para siempre la justicia» (Daniel 9:24). Bueno, entonces *hay* un final para el pecado, según esta otra declaración divina, llena de gracia: «He disipado tus transgresiones como el rocío, y tus pecados como la bruma de la mañana» (Isaías 44:22). Así que se han ido, han dejado de ser, Cristo los ha cancelado y, por tanto, Dios ya no los ve. ¡Qué gran esplendor el del perdón que Dios ha otorgado a los creyentes, al barrer todos sus pecados para siempre!

A través de la Biblia en un año: Ester 1–3

Deja que Dios te guíe

Los gabaonitas, al darse cuenta de cómo Josué había tratado a las ciudades de Jericó y de Hai, maquinaron un plan. Enviaron unos mensajeros, cuyos asnos llevaban costales viejos y odres para el vino, rotos y remendados.

JOSUÉ 9:3-4

Pienso que nuestras pruebas provienen, con frecuencia, por asuntos que no hemos llevado ante el Señor e incluso más, estoy seguro que cometemos los mayores errores en aquellos asuntos que consideramos más simples y que no llevamos al Señor, que en los que sí llevamos a él. Los gabaonitas engañaron a los hombres de Israel porque llevaban costales viejos y odres rotos y remendados, y los israelitas dijeron: «Está claro que estos hombres tienen que haber venido desde muy lejos para tener sus cosas así», de modo que hicieron un pacto con ellos sin buscar la voluntad del Señor. De no haberles parecido todo tan claro, habrían ido al Señor en busca de dirección, y él los habría guiado de forma correcta. Te equivocas cuando piensas que puedes ver tu camino, pero cuando no puedes ver tu camino y confías en que Dios te guiará por una senda que no conoces, irás bien. Estoy persuadido de que el asunto más simple y trivial que no llevamos a Cristo se convertirá en un problema, mientras que el más intrincado laberinto, bajo la dirección de Jesucristo, será un camino seguro para los pies de todos los que confían en la sabiduría infalible de su Señor y Salvador.

A través de la Biblia en un año: Ester 4–7

Pídele y cuéntale

No me escogieron ustedes a mí, sino que yo los escogí a ustedes y los comisioné para que vayan y den fruto, un fruto que perdure. Así el Padre les dará todo lo que le pidan en mi nombre.

JUAN 15:16

Si no vienes a Jesús y le cuentas todo lo que hay en tu corazón, perderás su consejo y ayuda, y el consuelo que estos producen. Me imagino que ninguno de nosotros sabe lo que ha perdido en el camino, y que mucho menos podemos calcular los bienes espirituales que pudiéramos haber tenido y que hemos perdido. Hay muchos hijos de Dios que pudieran estar enriquecidos con bendiciones y, sin embargo, permanecen tan pobres como el mendigo Lázaro. Solo tienen migajas de consuelo y están llenos de dudas y temores cuando podían sentirse seguros desde hace mucho tiempo. Hay muchos herederos del cielo que están viviendo nada más de la cáscara del alimento del evangelio cuando podían estar participando de los manjares del que habla Moisés: «con natas y leche de la manada y del rebaño, y con cebados corderos y cabritos; con toros selectos de Basán y las mejores espigas del trigo» (Deuteronomio 32:14). Amados, con mucha frecuencia no tienen porque no piden, o porque no creen, o porque no confían en Jesús y no le cuentan. ¡Cuán fuerte pudiera ser el débil si acudiera a Jesús con más frecuencia! ¡Cuán rica pudiera ser el alma pobre si tomara en todo tiempo del inagotable tesoro de Cristo! Si fuéramos y habláramos con Jesús y le contáramos todo lo que está en nuestro corazón, ¿no estaríamos viviendo en los suburbios del cielo, cerca de las puertas de perlas?

A través de la Biblia en un año: Ester 8–10

La providencia divina

Todo tiene su momento oportuno; hay un tiempo para todo lo que se hace bajo el cielo.
ECLESIASTÉS 3:1

Ahora bien, hermanos, todas las fuerzas del mal luchan contra la causa de Dios y contra la verdad y me atrevo a decir que eso está ocurriendo en este momento, porque ni el diablo ni sus demonios ni los ateos permanecen quietos, pero de esto estamos seguros: el Señor lo sabe, y tiene listos a su Ester y a su Mardoqueo para frustrar sus designios.

Cada hijo de Dios está donde él lo ha colocado con algún propósito y la aplicación práctica de este primer punto es guiarte a buscar el propósito por el que Dios te ha colocado donde estás ahora. Habías deseado otra posición donde pudieras hacer algo por Jesús: no desees nada de esto, sino sírvele donde estás. Si estás sentado a las puertas del palacio del rey, hay algo que debes hacer ahí, si ocupas el trono de la reina, hay algo para que hagas allí; no busques ser el portero o la reina, sirve a Dios desde donde estés.

Ester lo hizo bien porque actuó según le correspondía y Mardoqueo también lo hizo bien porque actuó según su condición. Me gusta pensar, mientras los observo, que a cada uno de ustedes Dios los colocó en el lugar correcto, así como un buen capitán organiza su ejército, y a pesar de que no conocemos el plan de batalla, durante el conflicto veremos que él ha colocado a cada soldado en el lugar donde debía estar. Entonces, no olvides el hecho de que Dios en su providencia coloca a sus siervos en posiciones donde los pueda utilizar.

A través de la Biblia en un año: Filemón

Destino y elección

En amor nos predestinó para ser adoptados como hijos suyos por medio de Jesucristo, según el buen propósito de su voluntad, para alabanza de su gloriosa gracia, que nos concedió en su Amado.
EFESIOS 1:4-6

Está claro que la voluntad divina se cumplirá y, a la vez, los hombres tienen libre albedrío. «No entiendo eso», dice alguien. Mi querido amigo, yo debo decir lo mismo: tampoco lo entiendo. He conocido a muchos que pensaban que lo entendían todo, pero creo que tenían una opinión de sí mismos más elevada de lo que la verdad aconsejaba. Algunos de mis hermanos niegan el libre albedrío y así terminan con el asunto; otros afirman que no hay predestinación y resuelven el problema. Ya que yo no deseo terminar con el problema y no deseo obviar alguna parte de la verdad creo que ambos, la predestinación y el libre albedrío, son hechos. Cómo pueden ellos concordar, no lo sé ni me interesa, estoy satisfecho con saber lo que Dios ha escogido revelarme y, de la misma forma, contento con lo que no me revela. Ahí va: el hombre tiene libre albedrío en lo que hace, es responsable de sus acciones, y culpable cuando hace lo malo; también será castigado con justicia y si se pierde, la culpa será solo de él. Pero hay Uno que rige sobre todo y que, sin hacerse cómplice del pecado, hace posible que incluso las acciones de los hombres malvados sirvan a sus propósitos justos y santos. Cree estas dos verdades y verás cómo concuerdan en la vida diaria, aunque no seas capaz de diseñar una teoría en un papel para mostrar cómo armonizan.

A través de la Biblia en un año: Job 1–4

Peligro

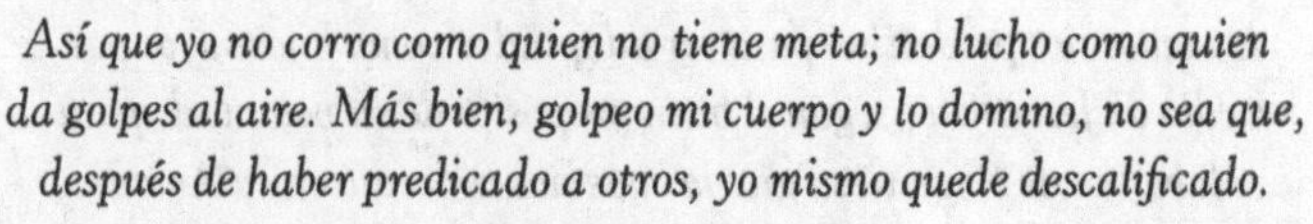

Así que yo no corro como quien no tiene meta; no lucho como quien da golpes al aire. Más bien, golpeo mi cuerpo y lo domino, no sea que, después de haber predicado a otros, yo mismo quede descalificado.

1 CORINTIOS 9:26-27

Siento que es mi responsabilidad ir, domingo tras domingo, y todos los días de la semana a decirte cosas muy preciosas acerca de Cristo, y a veces yo mismo las disfruto. Incluso si nadie más es bendecido por ellas, yo lo soy, y voy a casa y alabo al Señor por eso. Pero mi diario temor es que enseñe los textos y predique cosas buenas a otros y, sin embargo, mi propio corazón no se beneficie. Mi oración es que el Señor Jesús me muestre donde él alimenta a su pueblo y me deje alimentarme con él, de modo que yo pueda conducirte a los pastos donde él está y estar yo mismo allí, al mismo tiempo que te traigo a ti. A ustedes, maestros de la Escuela Dominical, evangelistas y otros, queridos, amados colegas, por quienes agradezco a Dios siempre, creo que el punto principal por el cual tienen que velar es no perder su propia espiritualidad mientras tratan de hacer a otros espirituales. Acudan al Bienamado y pídanle que les deje alimentar su rebaño donde él alimenta a su pueblo, y que les permita sentarse a sus pies así como María, incluso cuando están trabajando en la casa, como Marta. No hagas menos, más bien haz más, pero pide hacerlo en tal comunión con él que tu trabajo se mezcle con el suyo, y que lo que hagas no sea más que él trabajando por medio de ti, y tu regocijo sea derramar sobre otros lo que él ha derramado sobre tu propia alma.

A través de la Biblia en un año: Job 5–8

¿Mecánico?

Hazme justicia, Señor, pues he llevado una vida intachable; ¡en el Señor confío sin titubear! Examíname, Señor; ¡ponme a prueba! purifica mis entrañas y mi corazón. Tu gran amor lo tengo presente, y siempre ando en tu verdad.

SALMO 26:1-3

Me asusta la tendencia de hacer la obra de Dios con un espíritu mecánico y frío, pero más allá de eso, tiemblo al pensar que pueda sentir pasión por la obra de Cristo pero permanecer frío ante el mismo Señor. Temo que tal condición del corazón es posible, que podemos encender un gran fuego en las calles para que el público se caliente y tener tan solo un leño medio encendido en nuestro corazón donde Jesús pueda calentar sus manos. Cuando nos reunimos en la iglesia, la buena compañía nos ayuda a calentar nuestros corazones, y cuando trabajamos para el Señor con otros, ellos nos estimulan y hacen posible que renovemos toda nuestra energía y fuerza, y entonces pensamos: «De seguro mi corazón tiene una posición saludable ante Dios». Pero, amados, dicha emoción puede ser un pobre indicio de nuestro estado real. Amo ese fuego apacible, santo, que crece en lo más íntimo de mi cuarto cuando estoy solo, y ese es el punto que más me concierne, tanto por mí como por ti, no sea que estemos haciendo la obra de Cristo sin Cristo, al tener mucho que hacer pero sin pensar mucho en *él;* ocupados en el mucho servicio pero olvidados de él. ¿Por qué? Porque muy pronto eso nos conducirá a hacer un Cristo de nuestro propio servicio, un anticristo de nuestra propia labor. Ama tu trabajo, pero ama más a tu Maestro; ama tu rebaño, pero aun más ama al Gran Pastor, y permanece cerca de él, porque no hacerlo será una señal de infidelidad.

A través de la Biblia en un año: Job 9–12

El alma feliz

A los que son amados por Dios el Padre, guardados por Jesucristo y llamados a la salvación: Que reciban misericordia, paz y amor en abundancia.
JUDAS 1:1-2

Las almas piadosas nunca se sienten del todo bien a no ser que estén en un estado de cercanía a Cristo; y, obsérvalo bien, cuando no están cerca de Cristo, pierden la paz. Mientras más cerca están de Jesús, más cerca están de la paz celestial; y mientras más se alejan de Jesús, más cerca están de ese mar agitado que es la continua zozobra de la maldad. No hay paz en el hombre que no habita de forma permanente a la sombra de la cruz; porque Jesús es nuestra paz y si él está ausente, nuestra paz también lo está. Sé que al ser justificados, tenemos paz con Dios pero esto es «a través de nuestro Señor Jesucristo», así que el hombre justificado por sí mismo no puede producir el fruto de la justificación a no ser que permanezca en Jesucristo, quien es el Señor y el dador de la paz. El cristiano sin comunión con Cristo pierde toda su vida y energía, es como algo muerto. No tiene vitalidad, sí, es como un ser inanimado hasta que Cristo venga. Pero cuando con ternura el Señor derrama su amor en nuestros corazones, entonces su amor enciende el nuestro y nuestra sangre salta de gozo en nuestras venas, como Juan el Bautista en el vientre de Elisabet. Cuando el corazón está cerca de Cristo late fuerte y, ya que Jesucristo está en ese corazón, está lleno de vida, de vigor y de fuerza.

Amados, para nosotros todos los placeres de la vida son como nada; los hemos probado y considerado como basura. Si frente a todas las cosas mortales estamos en un estado de insatisfacción, entonces hemos aprendido a través de la gracia divina que nadie como Jesús puede hacer felices nuestras almas.

A través de la Biblia en un año: Job 13–16

El estándar de Dios

Estaba él de pie junto a un muro construido a plomo, y tenía una cuerda de plomada en la mano.

AMÓS 7:7

Todo lo que Dios construye está construido con precisión, recto, cuadrado y justo. En la naturaleza ves el cumplimiento de esa regla; en ella no hay nada fuera de proporción. Los que entienden de estas cosas y las estudian te dirán que incluso la forma y el tamaño de la tierra tienen relación con el brote de una flor o la presencia de una gota de rocío en el borde de una hoja, y que si el sol fuera más grande o más pequeño, o si el material que conforma la tierra fuera más denso o diferente en algún sentido, entonces todo, lo más mayúsculo y lo más diminuto, se desestabilizaría.

En los asuntos espirituales es manifiesto que siempre que Dios trata con las almas, usa la plomada. Al comenzar con nosotros, se da cuenta que el propio cimiento de nuestra naturaleza está fuera de la línea perpendicular y, por lo tanto, no intenta construir sobre él sino que comienza su operación quitándolo. La primera obra de la gracia divina en el alma es derribar todo aquello que la naturaleza ha construido. El hombre ha hecho grandes esfuerzos para construirlo, pero todo tiene que derribarse, hasta que quede un gran hueco. A la vista de Dios el hombre debe sentirse vacío, derribado y humillado, porque si Dios va a ser el todo en él, entonces él mismo tiene que ser nada; y si Cristo va a ser su Salvador, tiene que ser un Salvador completo, de principio a fin. Así que Dios tiene que derribar y eliminar el cimiento del mérito humano porque no puede construir bien sobre él.

A través de la Biblia en un año: Job 17–20

Confiado hasta en la hora de la muerte

Yo, por mi parte, ya estoy a punto de ser ofrecido como un sacrificio, y el tiempo de mi partida ha llegado. He peleado la buena batalla, he terminado la carrera, me he mantenido en la fe. Por lo demás me espera la corona de justicia.

2 Timoteo 4:6-8

¡Con cuánta confianza Pablo contempla la perspectiva de la muerte! No se atemoriza ante ella. Con la calma y la serenidad que otorgan, no solo la resignación y la sumisión sino la seguridad y el valor, se muestra gozoso y feliz e incluso encantado con la esperanza de que su cuerpo mortal se desintegre y sea revestido con el nuevo cuerpo que Dios ha preparado para sus santos. Aquel que puede hablar de la tumba y de lo que viene después con tan sabia anticipación, fe y ferviente deseo como lo hizo Pablo, es digno de envidia. Los príncipes bien pueden entregar sus coronas ante tan certera y segura esperanza de inmortalidad. Si son capaces de decir con él: «Así que nos mantenemos confiados, y preferiríamos ausentarnos de este cuerpo y vivir junto al Señor» (2 Corintios 5:8), bien pudieran cambiar su rango terrenal por tal recompensa.

De este lado del cielo, ¿qué puede ser más celestial que prepararnos bien para pasar el río de la muerte? Por otra parte, ¡qué estado mental tan temible y espantoso el de las personas que, con nada ante ellos que no sea la muerte, no tienen esperanza y no encuentran salida, la mortaja es su último vestido, la tumba y el cementerio su destino! Sin la esperanza de volverse a levantar en un futuro mejor, sin la perspectiva de ver a Dios cara a cara con gozo, con razón cualquier referencia a la muerte disgusta a estos hombres.

A través de la Biblia en un año: Job 21–24

El tiempo de Dios

Mi ardiente anhelo y esperanza es que en nada seré avergonzado, sino que con toda libertad, ya sea que yo viva o muera, ahora como siempre, Cristo será exaltado en mi cuerpo. Porque para mí el vivir es Cristo y el morir es ganancia.

FILIPENSES 1:20-21

Dios, de manera inalterable, ha fijado el tiempo de nuestra partida, aunque nosotros no lo conocemos. Él lo ha establecido y preparado de un modo tan correcto, sabio y amoroso que ningún subterfugio o azar puede romper los designios del destino. En el cuidado de su provisión se comprueba la sabiduría del amor divino.

Job sufrió grandes calamidades cuando perdió a sus hijos, a sus siervos, sus manadas y sus rebaños. Sin embargo, no concedió mucha importancia a la forma en que vinieron sus problemas, si fue por un ataque de los sabeanos o por una reyerta con los caldeos; si el fuego cayó del cielo o el viento sopló de la selva, eso no importaba mucho. Cualesquiera que fueran los extraños hechos que escuchó, un solo pensamiento penetraba su corazón y una expresión salía de sus labios. «El Señor ha dado, el Señor ha quitado. ¡Bendito sea el nombre del Señor!» (Job 1:21). De la misma forma, amado, cuando llegue el tiempo de tu partida, ya sea por enfermedad o desgaste, por accidente o asalto, cuando tu alma abandone su morada presente, descansa confiado en que «tus tiempos están en sus manos», y ten la completa seguridad que «todos sus santos están en sus manos». Hay un tiempo para la partida y el tiempo que Dios tenga determinado para llamarme es mi tiempo para partir.

A través de la Biblia en un año: Job 25–28

Cierra tus ojos al pecado

¿No se dan cuenta de que un poco de levadura hace fermentar toda la masa?
1 CORINTIOS 5:6

¡Ay, si nuestra madre Eva hubiera cerrado los ojos cuando la serpiente señaló aquella hermosa manzana en el árbol! ¡Ay, si hubiera cerrado los ojos ante ella! Ay, si hubiera dicho: «No, ni siquiera la voy a mirar». El mirar lleva a desear, y el deseo conduce al pecado. Dices: «No puede haber daño alguno en mirar, en ver por uno mismo, ¿no se nos ha dicho que probemos todas las cosas?» «Solo ven aquí, joven», dice el tentador, «no sabes lo que es la vida; una noche será suficiente para mostrarte un poco de alegría. Solo ven por una o dos horas y mira». «Oh, no», dice el hombre cuyos ojos ven al Rey en su hermosura, «el árbol del conocimiento del bien y del mal nunca trajo al hombre ningún bien, así que por favor, déjame solo. Cierro mis ojos para no verlo. No quiero participar, ni siquiera como espectador».

Recuerda que no puedes tener solo la mitad de Cristo. No lo puedes tener como tu redentor si no lo tienes como tu gobernador. Tienes que recibirlo tal y como es. Él es un Salvador, pero él salva a su pueblo de sus pecados. Ahora bien, si alguna vez recibiste a Cristo como tu Salvador, encontraste belleza en él. Él es precioso a tus ojos, porque lo más precioso que existe en el mundo para un pecador es su Salvador. Si es así, cerrarás tus ojos para no ver, tus oídos para no oír, tus manos para que no toquen cualquier iniquidad, y retirarás tu pie de ella para vivir la vida que vives en la carne por la fe en el Hijo de Dios, para su gloria y honor.

A través de la Biblia en un año: Job 29–32

La herencia del creyente

Por su gran misericordia nos ha hecho nacer de nuevo mediante la resurrección de Jesucristo, para que tengamos una esperanza viva y recibamos una herencia indestructible, incontaminada e inmarchitable. Tal herencia está reservada en el cielo para ustedes.

1 PEDRO 1:3-4

Ahora bien, una herencia no es algo que se compre con dinero, ni se gane con alguna obra, ni se conquiste. Si un hombre tiene una herencia, en el sentido recto de la palabra, la tiene desde su nacimiento. No fue por ningún mérito especial que este tuviera, sino que sencillamente recibió la propiedad que ahora posee por ser el hijo de su padre. Así sucede con el cielo. El hombre que reciba esta herencia gloriosa no la obtendrá por las obras de la ley, ni por los esfuerzos de la carne, se le dará como un derecho que recibe por gracia porque ha «nacido de nuevo mediante la resurrección de Jesucristo, para que tengamos una esperanza viva» (1 Pedro 1:3) y así se ha convertido en un heredero del cielo tanto por sangre como por nacimiento.

Los que van a la gloria son los hijos, pues ¿no está escrito, que el autor de nuestra salvación «llevará a muchos hijos a la gloria» (Hebreos 2:10)? No van allí como siervos, ningún siervo tiene derecho a recibir la herencia de su señor. No importa cuán fiel sea, no es el heredero de su amo. Pero debido a que ustedes son hijos —hijos por la adopción de Dios, hijos por la regeneración del Espíritu— ya que gracias a una energía sobrenatural han nacido de nuevo, se convierten en herederos de la vida eterna y entran en las mansiones que tiene nuestro Padre celestial en los cielos. Entonces, cuando pensemos en el cielo, pensemos en él como un lugar que es nuestro y un estado que disfrutaremos como resultado del nacimiento, no de las obras.

A través de la Biblia en un año: Job 33–36

El placer del trabajo

Por eso, están delante del trono de Dios, y
día y noche le sirven en su templo.
APOCALIPSIS 7:15

Una idea correcta del cielo es que es un lugar de servicio ininterrumpido. Es una tierra cuyos habitantes sirven a Dios día y noche en su templo, sin conocer el cansancio ni decaer nunca. ¿Conoces el placer del trabajo? Aunque me quejo cuando las personas esperan cosas imposibles de mí, la alegría más grande de mi vida es estar ocupado en las cosas de Dios. El día en que no predico no soy feliz, pero el día de mi mayor y más profundo gozo es el día que tengo el privilegio de predicar el evangelio y trabajar para Dios. El servicio es un placer. Alabar a Dios es un placer. Trabajar para él es la mayor bendición que un mortal pueda conocer. ¡Oh, cuán dulce debe ser cantar sus alabanzas sin que nuestra garganta se quede seca! ¡Oh, qué bendición estar siempre agitando las alas y nunca cansarse! ¡Oh, qué dulce será disfrutar el volar en círculos alrededor del trono de Dios en el cielo mientras dure la eternidad sin tener que poner la cabeza en la almohada, ni nunca sentir el peso de la fatiga ni los síntomas que nos advierten que debemos descansar, sino continuar por siempre en la eternidad como un río ancho que fluye con las perpetuas corrientes del servicio! ¡Oh, ese debe ser un tremendo disfrute! ¡Eso tiene que ser el cielo, servir a Dios día y noche en su templo! Muchos de ustedes han servido a Dios en la tierra y han probado algo de esa bendición.

A través de la Biblia en un año: Job 37–39

Permanece en el camino.

Timoteo, ¡cuida bien lo que se te ha confiado! Evita las discusiones profanas e inútiles, y los argumentos de la falsa ciencia. Algunos, por abrazarla, se han desviado de la fe. Que la gracia sea con ustedes.

1 Timoteo 6:20-21

No hay mal tan lamentable dentro de nuestras comunidades cristianas como el de los miembros que se apartan. El mismo diablo no es un enemigo tan sutil como lo fue Judas cuando, luego de la cena, Satanás entró en él. Judas era amigo de Jesús. Jesús se dirigía a él como tal. Y Judas dijo: «Salve, Maestro», y lo besó. Pero Judas fue quien lo traicionó. Esa imagen pudiera consternarte, es un peligro que tú también puedes estar corriendo. En todas nuestras iglesias, de todos los que se reciben como miembros, hay algunos desertores. Continúan durante un tiempo y luego regresan al mundo. La razón principal por la que se retraen es una incongruencia obvia. «Aunque salieron de entre nosotros, en realidad no eran de los nuestros; si lo hubieran sido, se habrían quedado con nosotros» (1 Juan 2:19).

Aquellos que se apartan, ¿qué sucede con ellos? Bueno, si son hijos de Dios, te diré lo que sucede con ellos porque lo he visto muchas veces. Aunque se apartan, no son felices. No pueden descansar, porque se sienten miserables aunque traten de aparentar estar alegres. Luego de un tiempo comienzan a recordar su primer estado, porque en aquel entonces les iba mejor que ahora. Regresan, pero hay más y más cicatrices, sin hablar de la vergüenza que tienen que llevar con ellos a la tumba; nunca serán los hombres que antes fueron.

A través de la Biblia en un año: Job 40–42

La apostasía

Esfuérzate por presentarte a Dios aprobado, como obrero que no tiene de qué avergonzarse y que interpreta rectamente la palabra de verdad.

2 TIMOTEO 2:15

Observemos en detalle las variadas causas o excusas para la deserción. ¿Por qué renuncian a la profesión de fe que una vez hicieron? La razón fundamental es una falta de gracia, una ausencia de fe verdadera, de santidad vital. Sin embargo, quiero con ansiedad referirme a las razones externas que muestran la apostasía interna del corazón. Hay algunos en la actualidad, como existían también en los tiempos de Jesús, que se apartaron de Cristo porque no podían soportar su doctrina. Hay muchos aspectos en los que el evangelio resulta ofensivo a la naturaleza humana y el orgullo de la criatura se rebela.

Las doctrinas erradas conducen a muchos a la apostasía. Empiezan leyendo artículos con el objetivo de responder al escepticismo científico o intelectual. Leen un poco más y avanzan un poco más profundo en esa corriente turbia, porque se sienten capaces de lidiar con esas corrientes insidiosas. Continúan, hasta que al final quedan atrapados. No acuden a aquellos que pudieran ayudarlos en su lucha, sino que continúan hasta que ya no dan pie, y el que dijo que era un creyente termina siendo un ateo empedernido, dudando incluso acerca de la existencia de Dios. ¡Ay, si aquellos que son bien enseñados estuvieran contentos con la enseñanza que reciben! ¿Por qué coquetear con las herejías? ¿Qué pueden hacer ellas, sino contaminar sus mentes? Insiste en el estudio de la Palabra de Dios. Si te toca enfrentarte con estos males, hazlo con valentía, orando a Dios para que te ayude. Pero si no es necesario, ¿qué tienes que hacer tú probando un material tan nocivo como ese?

A través de la Biblia en un año: Hebreos 1–2

El hombre que es cuidadoso

Dichoso el hombre que no sigue el consejo de los malvados, ni se detiene en la senda de los pecadores ni cultiva la amistad de los blasfemos.
SALMO 1:1

No es bueno que te vean parado, mucho menos sentado con hombres que tienen actitudes perversas y conversaciones corruptas. Puede que hayas escuchado la historia, aunque es tan buena que vale la pena repetirla, de la señora que puso un anuncio en busca de un cochero y esperó hasta tener tres candidatos. Al primero le dijo lo siguiente: «Quiero un buen cochero que sea capaz de montar mis dos caballos y, por lo tanto, te pregunto: ¿cuán cerca del peligro puedes guiar el coche y sentirte seguro?» Él le contestó: «Bueno, yo pudiera guiarlo hasta muy cerca; pudiera llegar hasta un paso del precipicio sin temor de sufrir un accidente siempre y cuando sostenga las riendas». La señora lo despidió con la seguridad de que no serviría. Al segundo que vino le hizo la misma pregunta: «¿Cuán cerca del peligro podrías guiar el coche?» Con la determinación de obtener el puesto, dijo: «Pudiera manejar a la distancia del grosor de un cabello y no sufrir ningún percance». «Usted no llena los requisitos», dijo ella. Vino el tercero, pero su manera de pensar era diferente, así que cuando le hicieron la pregunta: «¿Cuán cerca del peligro podrías manejar?», este contestó: «Señora, nunca lo he intentado. Siempre he tenido como regla manejar tan lejos del peligro como me sea posible». La señora lo contrató al instante. De la misma manera, creo que el hombre más confiable de todos es el que tiene cuidado de no correr riesgos, al tener el temor de Dios en su corazón, y de limitarse de cualquier conducta equivocada.

A través de la Biblia en un año: Hebreos 3–4

La comunión bendecida

Se mantenían firmes en la enseñanza de los apóstoles, en la comunión, en el partimiento del pan y en la oración.

Hechos 2:42

Temo que si no te has convertido, todo lo que encuentras en este mundo es una compañía bastante agitada; no tienes muchos amigos que te ayuden, te bendigan y te proporcionen paz mental. Pero si te hubieras unido al Señor Jesucristo te habrías dado cuenta que hay muchas delicias en esta vida que se encuentran bajo las alas del Altísimo. Aquel que viene a Cristo encuentra padre y madre, hermanos y hermanas; encuentra muchos amigos amables y queridos que están conectados con Cristo y, por lo tanto, aman a los que están unidos a él. Entre las dichas más grandes de mi vida sin duda se encuentra la comunión cristiana, y pienso que muchos que han venido del campo a Londres han extrañado durante mucho tiempo esta comunión, hasta que se encontraron con personas cristianas y se sienten felices otra vez. Ay, pecador solitario, que entras y sales de aquí y de allá y dices: «Parece que a nadie le importo», si vinieras a Cristo y te unieras a la iglesia que está protegida bajo sus alas, ¡pronto encontrarías una feliz comunión! Recuerdo que en la época de la persecución uno de los santos dijo que había perdido a su padre y a su madre al ser desterrado de su país, pero dijo: «He encontrado cientos de padres y de madres, porque en cualquier hogar cristiano que he visitado, me han atendido con tanta amabilidad al recibirme como un extranjero lejos de su tierra, como si fueran mi padre o mi madre».

A través de la Biblia en un año: Hebreos 5–6

El último gran día

Cuando lo corruptible se vista de lo incorruptible, y lo mortal, de inmortalidad, entonces se cumplirá lo que está escrito: «La muerte ha sido devorada por la victoria». «¿Dónde está, oh muerte, tu victoria? ¿Dónde está, oh muerte, tu aguijón?»

1 CORINTIOS 15:54-55

Habrá una muerte segunda, pero esta no tendrá poder sobre nosotros. ¿Comprendes la belleza de esa imagen? Es como si camináramos entre las llamas del infierno y estas no tuvieran poder para devorarnos, igual que aquellos hijos santos caminaron entre los carbones encendidos del horno de Nabucodonosor, siete veces calentado. Puede que la muerte tense su arco y coloque la flecha en su lugar. Pero, ¡ay, muerte, nos reímos de ti! ¡Y a ti, infierno, te desafiamos! Pues por encima de ustedes dos, enemigos del hombre, seremos más que vencedores por medio de aquel que nos amó. Permaneceremos invulnerables e invencibles, desafiantes y sonrientes en la cara de nuestro enemigo. Y todo esto porque Dios ha lavado nuestro pecado y nos ha cubierto con su justicia perfecta.

Cuando nos levantemos otra vez, estaremos libres de toda corrupción: ya no tendremos ninguna tendencia al mal. «Y limpiaré la sangre de los que no había limpiado; y Jehová morará en Sion» (Joel 3:21, RVR 1960). «Sin mancha ni arruga ni ninguna otra imperfección» (Efesios 5:27), sin siquiera una sombra de una mancha que el ojo omnisciente pueda descubrir, seremos tan puros como Adán antes de la caída, tan santos como la humanidad inmaculada cuando la mano divina la creó por primera vez. Seremos mejores que Adán, porque Adán podía llegar a pecar, pero nosotros estaremos tan arraigados en la bondad, la verdad y la justicia que no experimentaremos nunca más la tentación, y mucho menos tendremos temor de caer. En ese último gran día apareceremos sin mancha y sin arruga.

A través de la Biblia en un año: Hebreos 7–9

Cristo y su perfección

Se han acercado a Dios, el juez de todos; a los espíritus de los justos que han llegado a la perfección.
HEBREOS 12:23

Quizá el punto principal por el que Cristo recibirá la gloria será la absoluta perfección de todos los santos. Ellos estarán «sin mancha ni arruga ni ninguna otra imperfección» (Efesios 5:27). Todavía no hemos experimentado qué es la perfección y, por tanto, casi no la podemos concebir; consideramos nuestros pensamientos demasiado pecaminosos como para que nos puedan ofrecer una idea completa de lo que debe ser la perfección absoluta. Pero no tendremos pecado en nosotros, porque nos presentaremos «intachables» ante el trono de Dios (Apocalipsis 14:5), y nunca más nos sentiremos propensos a pecar. La voluntad no estará inclinada a la maldad, sino que estará para siempre centrada en lo que es bueno. Los sentimientos nunca más serán egoístas; estarán sometidos a Cristo. Nunca se equivocarán. No habrá dulce o amargo, serán «perfectos, así como su Padre celestial es perfecto» (Mateo 5:48), y en verdad, hermanos, el que hace estas cosas en nosotros nos parecerá maravilloso. Adoraremos y admiraremos a Cristo por sus grandiosos resultados. ¡Oh, Maestro todopoderoso, con qué extraña mezcla trabajaste para convertir este hombre inclinado a la morosidad en una gran masa de amor! ¿Cómo trabajaste con este monstruo de codicia, solo interesado en su propio beneficio, para que pasara a encontrar todo su beneficio en ti? ¿Cómo venciste ese espíritu orgulloso, ese espíritu inconstante, ese espíritu perezoso, ese espíritu lujurioso, cómo te las arreglaste para eliminar todo eso? ¿Cómo extirpaste de tu redimido la raíz principal del pecado, y cada pequeña raíz de pecado que quedó, de modo que ni siquiera quedara una pequeña fibra?

A través de la Biblia en un año: Hebreos 10–11

Las joyas en su corona

En resumidas cuentas, ¿cuál es nuestra esperanza, alegría o motivo de orgullo delante de nuestro Señor Jesús para cuando él venga? ¿Quién más sino ustedes? Sí, ustedes son nuestro orgullo y alegría.

1 TESALONICENSES 2:19-20

Los tesalonicenses estaban hundidos en el pecado, y este pobre fabricante de tiendas vino y les habló de Jesús y de su evangelio. Creyeron a su testimonio y esa creencia cambió las vidas de los que lo escucharon y los hizo santos, y al ser renovados se convirtieron en santos perfectos, y allí los encontramos, y Cristo se glorificó en ellos. ¿No sería algo delicioso que en la eternidad pudieras contemplar que aquella tarde cuando fuiste a tu clase en la Escuela Dominical y, con un poco de miedo de no poder decir mucho, hablaste de Jesucristo con lágrimas en los ojos y una preciosa niña creyó en su poderoso nombre gracias a tu testimonio? En los años que vendrán esa niña estará entre los que brillan para la gloria de Cristo por siempre. O quizá visites un asilo y le hables a algunos de los pobres vagabundos que están allí, o a alguna mujer que haya pecado, acerca de la historia del amor de tu Señor que derramó su sangre, y uno de esos corazones rotos entienda la preciosa palabra y venga a Jesús, y entonces el carácter celestial comenzará a formarse en él, y habrás asegurado otra joya para la diadema del Redentor. Pienso que admirarás su corona todavía más porque al ver algunos brillantes que resplandecen en ella, dirás: «Bendito sea su nombre para siempre, pues me ayudó a sumergirme en el mar y buscar esa perla preciosa para él», y ahora adorna su sagrada corona. ¡Ahora, todos ustedes, hagan lo mismo!

A través de la Biblia en un año: Hebreos 12–13

Aquí no

Si el mundo los aborrece, tengan presente que antes que a ustedes, me aborreció a mí. Si fueran del mundo, el mundo los querría como a los suyos. Pero ustedes no son del mundo, sino que yo los he escogido de entre el mundo. Por eso el mundo los aborrece.

JUAN 15:18-19

Sería inútil tratar de enseñarle astronomía a un caballo como también es una necedad de la misma clase enseñarle las experiencias espirituales a un hombre inconverso. Pudiera pararme a predicar de mi Señor hasta la medianoche ante un grupo de hombres inconversos que al escuchar lo que tengo que decir, dirán: «Pudiera ser cierto». Pero ellos no son capaces de discernirlo pues es algo que va más allá del aprecio de los sentidos. Así es la vida espiritual. Amado, puedes reinar sobre el pecado, pero el pecador no te ve como un rey. Puedes oficiar como sacerdote ante Dios, pero el hombre impío no percibe tu sacerdocio ni tu adoración. No esperes que lo haga; perderás tu tiempo si tratas de enseñarle estos misterios, excepto si entra por la misma puerta por la que tú mismo entraste.

¿Qué hizo el mundo con Jesucristo enseguida que lo vio? ¿Colocarlo en el trono e inclinarse para adorar su absoluta perfección? No, no lo hicieron así: «Despreciado y rechazado por los hombres, varón de dolores, hecho para el sufrimiento» (Isaías 53:3). Su lugar estaba fuera del campamento, llevar la cruz fue su ocupación, no un solo día, sino todos los días. Así debes esperar que sea la suerte de la parte de tu vida que es espiritual y que los hombres verán; en cuanto vean que es una vida espiritual la tratarán como trataron al Salvador. La despreciarán.

A través de la Biblia en un año: Salmos 1-4

Fiel a tu Maestro

Tengan cuidado con la gente; los entregarán a los tribunales y los azotarán en las sinagogas. Por mi causa los llevarán ante gobernadores y reyes para dar testimonio a ellos y a los gentiles.

MATEO 10:17-18

Sueñas que los hombres te admirarán, que mientras más santo seas y más te parezcas a Cristo, más pacíficas se mostrarán las personas contigo. No sabes lo que te espera. «Basta con que el discípulo sea como su maestro, y el siervo como su amo. Si al jefe de la casa lo han llamado Belcebú, ¡cuánto más a los de su familia!» (Mateo 10:25). Pienso que si fuéramos más como Cristo, debíamos ser más amados por los amigos de Cristo y más odiados por sus enemigos. No creo que el mundo se mostraría tan condescendiente con la iglesia actual si no fuera porque la iglesia se ha acomodado al mundo. Cuando cualquiera de nosotros habla con denuedo, se nos imputan motivos mercenarios, nuestras palabras se tergiversan y los hombres nos aborrecen. Temo que somos bien tratados, hermanos, porque somos como los profetas que profetizaban paz, paz, paz, cuando no había paz. Seamos fieles a nuestro Maestro, que nuestra posición sea como la suya, y recibiremos el mismo trato que él recibió.

A través de la Biblia en un año: Salmos 5–8

El sustentador de la fe

Cuando entró en la casa, se le acercaron los ciegos, y él les preguntó: «¿Creen que puedo sanarlos?» «Sí, Señor» le respondieron. Entonces les tocó sus ojos y les dijo: «Se hará con ustedes conforme a su fe». Y recobraron la vista. Jesús les advirtió con firmeza: «Asegúrense de que nadie se entere de esto.

MATEO 9:28-30

Si tienes fe es porque el Señor ha tratado contigo; esa es la marca de su mano en ti. En la tierra no existe ni siquiera un grano de fe que él mismo no haya creado. Por la fe te ha sacado de tu estado de muerte en el pecado y de la oscuridad natural de tu mente. «Su fe te ha salvado», porque es el candelabro que sostiene la luz que alumbra lo más profundo de tu corazón. Tu Dios y Salvador ha puesto esa fe en ti. Nuestro Señor es también el sustentador de la fe, ya que la fe nunca es independiente de aquel que la produce. El mejor creyente dejaría de creer en este mismo instante sino fuera por el fluir constante de la gracia que mantiene la llama ardiendo. Si has tenido alguna experiencia de la vida interior, quiero que sepas que el que te dio la vida te sustentará, o de lo contrario volverás a tu estado de muerte natural. Ya que la fe se alimenta de día en día a la mesa de Jesús, él sabe dónde está presente. Es algo bueno saber que el sustentador de la fe, quien la creó y la mantiene, también sabe discernirla.

A través de la Biblia en un año: Salmos 9–12

Una fe que se lanza

Ciertamente les aseguro que el que cree en mí las obras que yo hago también él las hará, y aún las hará mayores, porque yo vuelvo al Padre.
JUAN 14:12

¡Oh, que no nos gloriemos en algo más que no sea la cruz! Por mi parte, estoy contento de ser un tonto, si el Antiguo Testamento se considera una tontería. Lo que es más, estoy contento de perderme si el sacrificio de Jesús no trae la salvación. Estoy tan seguro de lo que creo que si me quedara solo en el mundo como el único creyente en la doctrina de la gracia, no pensaría en abandonarla, ni en transformarla un poco para ganar a otra persona.

«Cuándo venga el Hijo del hombre, ¿encontrará fe en la tierra?» (Lucas 18:8), la clase de fe que la merece de nosotros. ¿Creemos en Jesús de forma práctica, con un estilo que se centra en los hechos? ¿Es nuestra fe hecho y no ficción? Si hemos conocido la verdad de la fe, ¿tenemos el grado de fe que debemos tener? Solo piensa en esto: «Les aseguro que si tienen fe tan pequeña como un grano de mostaza, podrán decirle a esta montaña: "trasládate de aquí para allá» (Mateo 17:20). ¿Qué quiere decir esto? Hermanos, ¿no nos hemos salido de la vía? ¿Sabemos, por lo menos, qué significa tener fe? A veces me cuestiono si creemos de verdad. ¿Qué señales siguen a nuestra creencia? Cuando pensamos en los prodigios que pudiera hacer la fe, cuando consideramos las maravillas que nuestro Señor pudiera haber hecho entre nosotros si no hubiera sido por nuestra incredulidad, ¿no nos sentimos humillados? ¿Nos hemos lanzado alguna vez a las profundidades confiando por completo en el Dios eterno? ¿Nos hemos aferrado a las promesas de Dios y descansado solo en el brazo del Omnipotente, el cual es más que suficiente para hacer cumplir cada promesa?

A través de la Biblia en un año: Salmos 13–16

La plena influencia de lo invisible

Por tanto, no nos desanimamos. Al contrario, aunque por fuera nos vamos desgastando, por dentro nos vamos renovando día tras día. Pues los sufrimientos ligeros y efímeros que ahora padecemos producen una gloria eterna que vale muchísimo más que todo sufrimiento. Así que no nos fijamos en lo visible sino en lo invisible, ya que lo que se ve es pasajero, mientras que lo que no se ve es eterno.

2 Corintios 4:16-18

Pablo es contado entre los más valientes de los valientes. También notamos con admiración cómo el héroe de tantos peligros y conflictos podía hervir con fervor y, sin embargo, tenía uno de los espíritus más calmados y apacibles. Había aprendido a vivir más allá de aquellas circunstancias que preocupan y perturban, había transitado entre las sombras del tiempo y entrado a poseer las realidades de la eternidad. No ponía su confianza en las cosas que se ven, sino que confiaba por completo en aquellas que no se ven; y, como consecuencia, entró en una paz profunda y hermosa que lo hizo fuerte, resuelto, firme, inconmovible. Le pido a Dios que todos podamos adquirir el arte de Pablo de estar «siempre confiado», su hábito de renovar el hombre interior de día en día. ¿No estamos demasiado aptos para vivir en el presente inmediato que se revela por medio de los sentidos? Los proyectos de un buey no cambian de día en día: beber del arroyo o permanecer en los verdes pastos es su todo en todo. Así sucede con la mayoría de los hombres; sus almas están atadas a sus cuerpos, presas en las circunstancias diarias. Si pudiéramos liberarnos por completo de la carga de las cosas que vemos y sentimos y pudiéramos sentir la influencia de lo invisible y lo eterno, ¡cuánto del cielo disfrutaríamos incluso antes de alcanzar la ribera celestial!

A través de la Biblia en un año: Salmos 17–20

Como nuestro Señor

¡Fíjense qué gran amor nos ha dado el Padre, que se nos llame hijos de Dios!
1 JUAN 3:1

Cuando recién naciste como cristiano, naciste de la misma forma que nació Cristo, porque naciste del Espíritu Santo. ¿Qué pasó después de eso? El diablo intentó destruir la nueva vida en ti, tal como Herodes trató de matar a tu Señor; tú estás en peligro inminente e inmediato, igual que Cristo estuvo en peligro. Creciste en estatura y en gracia, y cuando aún la gracia era joven, asombrabas a aquellos que te rodeaban con las cosas que decías, hacías y sentías, porque no te podían entender; igual que Jesús cuando fue al templo que asombró a los doctores de la ley que se reunían a su alrededor. El Espíritu de Dios vino a morar en ti, no en la misma medida, pero aún así descendió sobre ti, como lo hizo sobre el Señor. Tú has estado con él en el río Jordán y has recibido el conocimiento divino de que eres el hijo de Dios. Tu Señor fue llevado al desierto para ser tentado y tú también has sido tentado por el maligno. Has estado con el Señor todo el tiempo, desde el primer día hasta ahora. Si has sido capacitado, por medio de la gracia, para vivir como debes, has transitado los senderos apartados de este mundo con Jesús; has estado en este mundo pero no has sido de él, santo, sin mancha, sin arruga y separado de los pecadores. Por lo tanto, has sido despreciado. Has tenido que asumir tu parte de pasar desconocido y sin alguien que te represente, porque eres como fue él en este mundo.

A través de la Biblia en un año: Salmos 21–24

Somos suyos

«Ningún ojo ha visto, ningún oído ha escuchado, ninguna mente humana ha concebido lo que Dios ha preparado para quienes lo aman».

1 Corintios 2:9

¡Oh, qué gozo el de ser herederos junto con Cristo de todo lo que él posee! ¿Qué es el cielo? Es el lugar que su amor ideó, que su ingenio inventó, que su abundancia proveyó, que su realeza adornó, que su sabiduría preparó, que él mismo glorifica; en ese cielo estarás con él para siempre. Habitarás en el mismo palacio del Rey, las puertas de perlas y las calles de oro no serán demasiado buenas para ti. Ustedes los que lo aman a él habitarán para siempre con él, no cerca de él en un lugar secundario, como vive un siervo a las puertas de la mansión de su señor, sino que vivirás con él en el mismo palacio de la metrópolis del universo. En resumen, los creyentes serán identificados con Cristo. ¿Buscan al Pastor? No podrán verlo en toda su perfección a menos que esté rodeado de su rebaño. ¿Será ilustre el Rey? ¿Cómo puede ser esto si sus servidores se pierden? ¿Buscan al Novio? No pueden imaginarlo en todo el esplendor de su gloria sin su novia. ¿Será bendita la Cabeza? Eso no podría suceder si estuviera separada de los miembros. ¿Será Cristo para siempre glorificado? ¿Cómo puede serlo si pierde sus joyas? Él es un cimiento y, ¿qué sería si todo su pueblo no estuviera construido sobre él como se construye un palacio? Oh, hermanos, no habrá Cristo sin cristianos; no habrá un Salvador sin salvados; no habrá un Hermano Mayor sin hermanos menores; no habrá Redentor sin sus redimidos.

A través de la Biblia en un año: Salmos 25–28

La iglesia que todo lo conquista

De Sión se dirá, en efecto: «Este y aquel nacieron en ella. El Altísimo mismo la ha establecido».

SALMO 87:5

En los primeros tiempos la iglesia era como el monte de Sión, solo una pequeña colina. ¿Qué observaron las naciones de la tierra? Vieron a un humilde Hombre con doce discípulos. Pero esa pequeña colina creció, y varios miles se bautizaron en el nombre de Jesús, continuó creciendo y se hizo poderosa. La piedra que sin manos humanas fue arrancada de la colina comenzó a quebrar los reinos en pedazos, y en la actualidad, la pequeña colina que fue Sión se ha convertido en un enorme monte. Pero comparada con los sistemas colosales de idolatría, todavía es pequeño. Los hindúes y los chinos miran nuestra religión y dicen: «Es un bebé que nació ayer; la nuestra es una religión de muchos siglos». El mundo oriental compara el cristianismo con una neblina que cubre las tierras bajas, pero imaginan que sus sistemas son como los Alpes, más altos que los cielos. Ah, pero a eso nosotros respondemos: «Tu montaña se derrumba y tu colina se disuelve, pero nuestro monte de Sión continúa creciendo y, aunque parezca algo extraño, tiene vida en sus entrañas y seguirá creciendo, tendrá que seguir creciendo hasta que todos los sistemas de idolatría sean menos que nada ante él, hasta que se derrumben los dioses falsos y se derroten los poderosos sistemas de idolatrías, entonces esta montaña se levantará sobre todos ellos y esta religión cristiana seguirá creciendo hasta que al nutrirse de aquellos antiguos seguidores de herejías e idolatrías humanas, alcance el cielo, y Dios en Cristo sea el todo en todo». Ese es el destino de nuestra iglesia, es una iglesia que todo lo conquista, que sobrepasa cualquier competidor.

A través de la Biblia en un año: Salmos 29–32

Por Jesús

Entonces dirá el Rey a los que estén a su derecha: «Vengan ustedes, a quienes mi Padre ha bendecido; reciban su herencia, el reino preparado para ustedes desde la fundación del mundo».
MATEO 25:34

Fíjate que es como si Cristo nos dijera que las acciones que se mencionarán el día del juicio, como prueba de que somos los bendecidos por el Señor, provinieran de la gracia de Dios, porque dice: «Ustedes, a quienes mi Padre ha bendecido; reciban su herencia, el reino preparado para ustedes desde la fundación del mundo». Ellos dieron de comer al hambriento, pero primero la gracia soberana los alimentó a ellos. Cubrieron al desnudo, pero primero el infinito amor los cubrió a ellos. Fueron a las cárceles, pero primero la gracia liberadora los libertó de una cárcel aún peor. Visitaron a los enfermos, pero el Buen Médico, en su infinita misericordia, vino primero y los visitó a ellos. Es evidente que no pensaban que había algo de meritorio en lo que hacían, nunca pensaron que los recompensarían por ello. Cuando comparezcan ante el trono del juicio, la sola idea de que pueda haber alguna excelencia en lo que han hecho será nueva para los santos, porque tienen una idea muy pobre de sus propios actos, y lo que han hecho les parece demasiado imperfecto como para que se hable de ello. Los santos dieron de comer al hambriento y cubrieron al desnudo porque hallaban placer al hacerlo. Lo hicieron porque no pudieron evitarlo, su nueva naturaleza los movía. Lo hicieron porque su delicia era hacer el bien y era su hábitat, tanto como el agua es el hábitat del pez y el aire, del ave. Hicieron bien por amor a Cristo, porque lo más dulce que pueda existir en este mundo no se iguala a hacer algo por Jesús.

A través de la Biblia en un año: Salmos 33–36

¿Has buscado con un propósito?

Los profetas, que anunciaron la gracia reservada para ustedes, estudiaron y observaron esta salvación. Querían descubrir a qué tiempo y a cuáles circunstancias se refería el Espíritu de Cristo, que estaba en ellos, cuando testificó de antemano acerca de los sufrimientos de Cristo y de la gloria que vendría después de estos. A ellos se les reveló que no se estaban sirviendo a sí mismos, sino que les servían a ustedes. Hablaban de las cosas que ahora les han anunciado los que les predicaron el evangelio por medio del Espíritu Santo enviado del cielo. Aun los mismos ángeles anhelan contemplar esas cosas.

1 PEDRO 1:10-12

Debemos adorar a Dios con devoción y debemos esforzarnos para adorarlo de la forma que él demanda. ¿Cuántas personas tienen un tipo de —cómo llamarlo— religión siempre feliz y a la suerte? Creen lo mismo que creyeron su mamá y su papá. Muchos de ustedes asisten a ciertos lugares de adoración, no porque hayan averiguado si la secta a la que pertenecen es verdadera o no, sino porque siguieron la corriente y allí permanecen. Cuán pocos toman la Biblia para investigarla por ellos mismos; sin embargo, ningún hombre obedece a Dios como él demanda si no hace esto. Si yo no pudiera decir con honestidad: «Soy miembro de esta denominación porque he analizado las verdades que creen mis hermanos y creo que están de acuerdo con el Libro de Dios», no podría sentir que he actuado con rectitud ante el Altísimo.

A través de la Biblia en un año: Salmos 37–40

Negociar con la conciencia

Sé fuerte y valiente, porque tú harás que este pueblo herede la tierra que les prometí a sus antepasados. Solo te pido que tengas mucho valor y firmeza para obedecer toda la ley que mi siervo Moisés te mandó. No te apartes de ella para nada; solo así tendrás éxito dondequiera que vayas. Recita siempre el libro de la ley y medita en él de día y de noche; cumple con cuidado todo lo que en él está escrito. Así prosperarás y tendrás éxito.

JOSUÉ 1:6-8

La idea de que hay personas buenas en todas las sectas es muy buena, pero muchos la han pervertido y la usan como excusa para no averiguar cuáles son las verdades y las ordenanzas de Dios. Puedes estar seguro que todo aquel que tergiverse uno de los más pequeños mandamientos de Jesús y así lo enseñe a los hombres, se considerará muy pequeño en el reino de los cielos. Toda verdad es importante. Jugar con la conciencia es el pecado de la época actual. Hay hombres que hasta han ocupado el púlpito de alguna iglesia en cuyas doctrinas fundamentales no creen. Incluso, les hemos escuchado reclamar su derecho de seguir en el púlpito luego de haber negado las doctrinas de la denominación a la que pertenecen. Dios nos libre a cada uno de nosotros de tener cualquier habilidad de creer en una conciencia así. Sé justo, incluso en las cosas pequeñas. Sé preciso, pues sirves a un Dios preciso. El amor hacia los demás es una cosa, ser flojos con ustedes mismos es otra bien diferente.

A través de la Biblia en un año: Salmos 41–44

Espacios de tiempo

Lo que quiero decir, hermanos, es que nos queda poco tiempo.
1 CORINTIOS 7:29

¿Me sería posible dirigirme a cada uno de ustedes y tomarlos del brazo, y con el mayor afecto —incluso con lágrimas— rogarles en nombre de aquel a quien le deben su alma, que despierten y le rindan su servicio personal al Amado de sus corazones? No pongan excusas, porque no habrá ninguna excusa válida para quien los compró a tan alto precio. Me dirás que tu negocio requiere mucho de tu tiempo, y yo sé que es así, entonces usa tu negocio de modo que sirvas a Dios en él. Todavía quedarían algunos espacios de tiempo que podrías dedicarle a su servicio santo; habría algunas oportunidades para hacer obra de evangelismo. Algunos de ustedes no tendrían la excusa de los «negocios», ya que tienen tiempo libre. ¡Oh, les ruego que no dediquen ese tiempo libre a frivolidades, a conversaciones intrascendentes, a dormir y a autocomplacerse! El tiempo corre y los hombres perecen. Con tan horrible situación no podemos darnos el lujo de hacer concesiones. ¡Oh, si tuviera el poder de conmover el alma y el corazón de mis compañeros cristianos mediante una descripción de esta enorme ciudad que se ahoga en la iniquidad! De seguro el pecado, la tumba y el infierno son temas que crean inquietud incluso en el corazón más frío. ¡Oh, si pudiera lograr que tuvieran siempre presente al Redentor que murió en una cruz por aquellas almas que se están perdiendo! ¡Oh, si pudiera dibujar el cielo que los pecadores se están perdiendo, y su remordimiento al ver que han sido autoexcluidos!

A través de la Biblia en un año: Salmos 45–48

Un arma muy valiosa

Pues aunque vivimos en el mundo, no libramos batallas como lo hace el mundo. Las armas con que luchamos no son del mundo, sino que tiene el poder divino para derribar fortalezas.
2 CORINTIOS 10:3-4

Intercede por tus amigos. Ruega a Cristo por ellos, menciona sus nombres en tus constantes oraciones, establece tiempos especiales para rogar a Dios por ellos. Deja que el caso de tu querida hermana llegue a los oídos del Mediador, una y otra vez repite el nombre de tu querido hijo en tus intercesiones. Como Abraham rogó por Ismael, así deja que tu ruego se levante por aquellos que te rodean, de modo que el Maestro los visite en su misericordia. La intercesión es traer las almas a Cristo, y esto lo podrás hacer incluso cuando quizá ya no puedas hacer otras cosas. Aquí hay un arma muy valiosa para aquellos que no pueden predicar o enseñar: pueden empuñar la espada de dos filos que es la oración. Cuando los corazones son demasiado duros para responder a los sermones y rechazan los buenos consejos, que todavía permanezca el amor que nos mueva a rogar a Dios por ellos. Las lágrimas y los lamentos prevalecen ante el trono de misericordia y, si perseveramos allí, el Señor manifestará su gracia eterna en los espíritus más endurecidos.

A través de la Biblia en un año: Salmos 49–52

Tu nicho

El ojo no puede decirle a la mano: «No te necesito». Ni puede la cabeza decirle a los pies: «No los necesito». Al contrario, los miembros del cuerpo que parecen más débiles son indispensables, y a los que nos parecen menos honrosos los tratamos con honra especial.

1 Corintios 12:21-23

Ahora tú, joven, si te vuelves diligente en la distribución de tratados, en la asistencia a la Escuela Dominical, es posible que puedas llegar a ser un ministro; pero si te detienes y no haces nada hasta que no lo puedas hacer todo, permanecerás inservible, serás un impedimento para la iglesia en vez de una ayuda para ella. Queridas hermanas en Jesucristo, ninguna de ustedes debe pensar que está en una posición en la cual no pueden hacer nada. Eso es un enorme error que Dios nunca cometería. Debes tener algún talento y algo que hacer que nadie más puede hacer. En toda esa estructura que es el cuerpo humano cada pequeño músculo y cada pequeña célula tiene sus propias características y su función; y aunque algunos médicos han dicho que podemos prescindir de este o de aquel órgano, pienso que ni una fibra de todo el diseño de la naturaleza humana se puede desechar, se requiere todo el material. Así sucede con el cuerpo místico, la iglesia, hasta el miembro más pequeño es necesario; el miembro más insignificante de la iglesia cristiana es necesario para su crecimiento. Pídele a Dios que te diga lo que hay en tu nicho y permanece en él, ocupando tu lugar hasta que Jesucristo venga y te dé tu recompensa.

A través de la Biblia en un año: Salmos 53-56

Dios bendecirá

En cuanto a los que eran reconocidos como personas importantes – aunque no me interesa lo que fueran, porque Dios no juzga por las apariencias --, no me impusieron nada nuevo. Al contrario, reconocieron que a mí se me había encomendado predicar el evangelio a los gentiles, de la misma manera que a Pedro predicarlo a los judíos. El mismo Dios que facultó a Pedro como apóstol de los judíos me facultó también a mí como apóstol de los gentiles. En efecto, Jacobo, Pedro y Juan, que eran considerados columnas, al reconocer la gracia que yo había recibido, nos dieron la mano a Bernabé y a mí en señal de compañerismo, de modo que nosotros fuéramos a los gentiles y ellos a los judíos.

GÁLATAS 2:6-9

¡Oh, qué gran misericordia es que las imperfecciones de nuestro ministerio no nos impidan que Dios nos use para salvar a las almas! Si así no fuera, ¡qué poco bien se haría en el mundo! El Sr. Juan Wesley predicó con gran énfasis un punto de vista del evangelio, y Guillermo Huntingdon predicó otro punto de vista diferente. Estos dos hombres habrían sentido un horror santo el uno hacia el otro y se habrían censurado el uno al otro muy concienzudamente, sin embargo, ningún hombre racional se atrevería a decir que las almas no se salvaron bajo el ministerio de Juan Wesley o bajo el de Guillermo Huntingdon, ya que Dios los bendijo a los dos. Ambos ministerios eran imperfectos pero ambos eran sinceros y fueron útiles. Así sucede con nuestros testimonios. Todos son imperfectos, llenos de exageraciones de una verdad y comprensiones erróneas de otra, pero siempre que prediquemos del verdadero Cristo que Moisés y los profetas anunciaron, nuestros errores serán perdonados y Dios bendecirá nuestro ministerio, a pesar de cada desperfecto.

A través de la Biblia en un año: Salmos 57–60

Reunámonos

Mantengamos firme la esperanza que profesamos, porque fiel es el que hizo la promesa. Preocupémonos los unos por los otros, a fin de estimularnos al amor y a las buenas obras. No dejemos de congregarnos, como acostumbran hacerlo algunos, sino animémonos unos a otros, y con mayor razón ahora que vemos que aquel día se acerca.

HEBREOS 10:23-25

El primer día de la semana, cuando los apóstoles se reunieron después que el Señor resucitó, Tomás fue el único ausente de los once discípulos. Tomás estaba allí el segundo día del Señor, y de los once él era el único que dudaba. No soy capaz de decir cuánto influyó el hecho de haber estado ausente en la primera reunión para que ahora dudara, pero parece bastante probable que de haber estado allí el primer día, habría disfrutado la misma experiencia que los otros diez y habría podido decir como ellos: «Hemos visto al Señor». No dejemos de congregarnos, como acostumbran hacerlo algunos, porque no podemos imaginar cuántas cosas nos perderíamos si no lo hiciéramos. Aunque nuestro Señor se puede revelar a individuos en la soledad como lo hizo con María Magdalena, por lo general se revela a dos o tres; más que todo, se complace en estar en la reunión de sus siervos. El Señor se siente más en casa cuando de pie en medio de su pueblo dice: «Paz a ustedes». No dejemos de reunirnos con nuestros hermanos en la fe. Por mi parte, las reuniones del pueblo de Dios me son muy queridas. Donde Jesús hace sus visitas, allí estaré yo.

A través de la Biblia en un año: Salmos 61–64

Hasta Tomás se convenció

Tomás, al que apodaban el Gemelo, y que era uno de los doce, no estaba con los discípulos cuando llegó Jesús. Así que los otros discípulos le dijeron:
—¡Hemos visto al Señor!
—Mientras no vea yo la marca de los clavos en sus manos, y meta mi dedo en las marcas y mi mano en su costado, no lo creeré —repuso Tomás.
JUAN 20:24-25

Si me dijeras que la resurrección del Señor la presenciaron hombres que estaban preparados para creerla, te diría que estás completamente equivocado. Ni uno de los discípulos se dio cuenta del significado de la profecía del Señor donde explicaba que se levantaría de entre los muertos. Era difícil que alguno captara la idea. En Tomás vemos a un hombre que era bastante difícil de convencer, un hombre tan obstinado que era capaz de pensar que sus diez amigos, con quienes había estado durante años, podían engañarlo. Ahora bien, si tuviera que atestiguar la veracidad de algún hecho, me gustaría llamar al estrado a alguien que fuera reconocido por ser desconfiado y escéptico. Me sentiría feliz al dar con alguien que dudara y desconfiara, pero que a la larga se sintiera abrumado por las evidencias que lo llevaron a creer. Estoy seguro que tal hombre expondría su testimonio con toda convicción, como lo hizo Tomás cuando exclamó: «Mi Señor y mi Dios». No podemos tener un mejor testigo del hecho de la resurrección del Señor que este frío, cauteloso, prudente y reflexivo Tomás, quien llegó a tener una certeza absoluta.

A través de la Biblia en un año: Salmos 65-68

Visitaciones divinas

Olviden las cosas de antaño; ya no vivan el pasado. ¡Voy a hacer algo nuevo! Ya está sucediendo, ¿no se dan cuenta? Estoy abriendo un camino en el desierto, y ríos en lugares desolados.
ISAÍAS 43:18-19

Es muy posible que, además de cultivar un deseo vehemente de que la religión se revitalice, podamos haber estado imaginando una concepción de la forma que debe tomar la visitación divina. Quizá estés imaginando que Dios va a levantar a un predicador extraordinario cuyo ministerio atraiga multitudes, y que mientras esté predicando, Dios Espíritu Santo, confirmará la palabra de modo que cientos se conviertan en cada mensaje. Se levantarán otros evangelistas con el mismo espíritu, y de punta a cabo esta isla escuchará la verdad y experimentará su poder.

Ahora bien, pudiera suceder que Dios nos visitara de esa forma. Pudiera ser que viéramos otra vez las señales y maravillas como las que suelen acompañar los avivamientos. Su Espíritu Santo se puede revelar como un río poderoso que arrastre las multitudes con su corriente majestuosa, pero si él lo desea, bien puede revelar su poder con la suavidad del rocío el cual, sin percibirlo apenas, refresca toda la tierra. Nos puede suceder como a Elías, cuando el fuego y el viento pasaron ante él pero el Señor no estaba en ninguno de esos dos poderosos elementos y prefirió entrar en comunión con su siervo en un susurro suave y apacible. Quizá ese susurro suave y apacible sea la voz de Dios en esta congregación. Entonces sería inútil que tratáramos de trazar el camino del Dios eterno. Dios nos libre de estar rechazando todo el bien que él quiera darnos tan solo porque no venga en la forma que imaginamos debe ser la correcta.

A través de la Biblia en un año: Salmos 69–72

La morada de Dios

¿Acaso no saben que su cuerpo es templo del Espíritu Santo, quien está en ustedes y al que han recibido de parte de Dios?
1 Corintios 6:19

¿Está tu casa preparada para que Jesús entre y habite en ella? Conozco algunas casas donde mi Señor no podría quedarse ni siquiera una sola noche, pues las conversaciones y todo su ambiente no congeniarían con él. Entonces, ¿estás tu preparado para eliminar todo lo que le desagrade y limpiar tu casa de toda esa maldad? No puedes esperar que el Señor Jesús venga a tu casa si también invitas al diablo a venir. Cristo no podía permanecer en el mismo cielo con el diablo; enseguida que Satanás pecó, Cristo lo echó del lugar santo. Cristo no podía soportar tener allí un espíritu pecaminoso, un espíritu de maldad, y él no vendrá a vivir en tu casa si estás proveyendo para la lujuria de la carne, la lujuria de los ojos, para la vanidad de la vida y para todas esas cosas malvadas que él detesta. ¿Estás preparado, por medio de su gracia, para limpiar tu casa de todas estas cosas?

Además, tenemos que asegurarnos que nadie moleste a nuestro Invitado. Es difícil hospedarse con algunas personas porque sus hijos son muy malcriados. A mi Señor no le gusta morar en hogares donde Elí es la cabeza de la familia y donde los hijos y los jóvenes viven como mejor les parece; pero si viene a tu casa, querrá que tú seas como Abraham, de quien dijo: «Yo lo he elegido para que instruya a sus hijos y a su familia, a fin de que se mantengan en el camino del Señor y pongan en práctica lo que es justo y recto» (Génesis 18:19). ¿Acaso no deseas que diga eso de tu casa? ¿Acaso no lo deseas con fervor? Estoy seguro que así es.

A través de la Biblia en un año: Salmos 73–76

Honrar a Dios

Seis días antes de la Pascua llegó Jesús a Betania, donde vivía Lázaro, a quien Jesús había resucitado. Allí se dio una cena en honor de Jesús.

JUAN 12:1-2

Con frecuencia solía ir a los campos para predicar, allí me quedaba en una granja cuyo dueño, un amable señor ya mayor, me servía en su mesa por lo menos cien libras de carne para comer conmigo. Año tras año continuaba haciendo lo mismo, por lo que un día le dije: «Usted debe tener una idea muy particular de mi apetito, es imposible que yo pueda comerme todas esas masas de carne que sirve en su mesa». «Oh», dijo, «nosotros sabemos qué hacer con las que sobran luego que usted se marcha, ya que hay muchas personas pobres y muchos campesinos en los alrededores, y ellos se las comen». «Pero», pregunté, «¿Por qué tiene tanta comida cuando yo vengo?» «Dios lo bendiga, Señor», respondió, «yo le daría un pedazo del tamaño de mi casa si pudiera conseguirlo, puede estar seguro que lo haría, solo para mostrarle cuán bienvenido es en mi casa». Entendí lo que quería decir y aprecié su gentileza y los exhorto para que, en un sentido mucho más elevado, hagamos nosotros todo lo que podamos para mostrarle al Señor Jesús cuán bienvenido es en nuestra casa y en nuestro corazón.

¡Cuán bienvenido debe ser nuestro bendito Salvador que viene para borrar nuestros pecados, cambiar nuestra naturaleza y honrarnos con su compañía real, para preservarnos firmes hasta el final, de modo que pueda llevarnos, a nosotros y a nuestros hijos, a vivir con él para siempre! ¡Oh, debemos atender muy bien a un Invitado como él!

A través de la Biblia en un año: Salmos 77–80

El corazón humano

Este se acercó a Jesús para besarlo, pero Jesús le preguntó: «Judas, ¿con un beso traicionas al Hijo del hombre?»
LUCAS 22:47-48

Una razón por la cual programar la traición fue que Dios ordenó que el pecado del hombre alcanzara su punto culminante con la muerte de Jesús. Dios, el gran dueño del viñedo, mandó a muchos siervos y los labradores maltrataron a unos y apedrearon a otros. Por último dijo: «Enviaré a mi Hijo; seguro que a él lo respetarán». Cuando ellos mataron al heredero para obtener su herencia, la rebelión de los labradores había alcanzado la máxima expresión. El asesinato de nuestro bendito Señor fue la mayor culpa de la humanidad porque dio rienda suelta al odio hacia Dios que se esconde en el corazón del hombre. Cuando el hombre se convirtió en un asesino del ser divino, el pecado alcanzó su mayor grado. Y ese grado se puso de manifiesto en el horrible hecho que cometió el hombre que traicionó a Jesús. Si no hubiera sido por Judas, no hubiéramos sabido cuán oscura y baja puede llegar a ser la naturaleza humana. Rechazo a los hombres que tratan de disculpar la traición de este hijo de perdición, este malvado apóstata. Mis hermanos, debemos detestar a este maestro de la infamia; él está en el lugar que le pertenece y el anatema de David, parte del cual citó Pedro, cayó sobre él: «Que resulte culpable al ser juzgado, y que sus propias oraciones lo condenen. Que se acorten sus días, y que otro se haga cargo de su oficio» (Salmo 109:7-8). Con toda seguridad, al igual que al diablo una vez se le permitió atormentar los cuerpos de los hombres, también tomó posesión de Judas como casi nunca lo ha hecho con otros hombres, para que nosotros podamos ver cuán inicuo y cuán desesperadamente malvado es el corazón humano.

A través de la Biblia en un año: Salmos 81–84

Un terreno peligroso

El amor al dinero es la raíz de toda clase de males. Por codiciarlo, algunos se han desviado de la fe y se han causado muchísimos sinsabores.
1 TIMOTEO 6:10

Yo creo solemnemente que de todos los hipócritas, los peores son aquellos cuyo dios es el dinero. Tal vez pienses que un borracho es peor, pero gracias a Dios hemos visto muchos de ellos que, luego de volver a su vicio en la condición de cristianos caídos, han abandonado su vicio por segunda vez y han regresado. Sin embargo, me temo que han sido muy pocas las veces que hemos visto a hombres avaros alcanzar la salvación, tan pocas veces que pudiéramos escribirlo en la uña de un dedo. Este es un pecado que el mundo no condena, el ministro más fiel escasamente pudiera golpearlo en la frente. Dios es testigo de la dureza con que he tratado a hombres cuya riqueza está en este mundo y que, sin embargo, pretenden ser seguidores de Cristo, pero ellos siempre dicen: «Eso no es conmigo». Lo que yo llamo avaricia ellos lo llaman prudencia, discreción, economía, etc.; y harán acciones que me harían escupir, mientras que ellos piensan que sus manos están limpias luego de llevarlas a cabo, y que pertenecen al pueblo de Dios, y escuchan lo que escucha el pueblo de Dios, y piensan que luego de haber vendido a Cristo por una ganancia irrisoria, todavía irán al cielo. ¡Ay, almas, almas, almas, manténganse alertas, más que todo, de la avaricia! La raíz de toda clase de males no es el dinero, ni la falta de él, sino *el amor* al dinero. No es el hecho de ganarlo, ni siquiera de ahorrarlo. Es el hecho de amarlo, de convertirlo en tu dios, de considerarlo como lo mejor, y no considerar la causa de Cristo, ni la verdad de Cristo, ni la santidad de Cristo, sino que sacrificas todo lo que posees por obtener ganancias.

A través de la Biblia en un año: Salmos 85–88

Lo que Dios revela

Toda la Escritura es inspirada por Dios y útil para enseñar, para reprender, para corregir y para instruir en la justicia, a fin de que el siervo de Dios esté enteramente capacitado para toda buena obra.

2 TIMOTEO 3:16-17

He escuchado decir que hay algunas verdades en la Palabra de Dios de las cuales es mejor no predicar. Admiten que son verdades, pero dicen que no son edificantes. No estoy de acuerdo con nada de eso; es como volver atrás, al método que usaron los romanos. Todo lo que la sabiduría de Dios consideró bueno revelar, los siervos de Dios deben considerar sabio proclamar. ¿Quiénes somos nosotros para juzgar entre esta y aquella verdad y para decir que sobre esto debemos predicar y sobre aquello no? Este sistema nos convertiría, después de todo, en jueces de lo que debe ser el evangelio de Cristo. No debe suceder eso con nosotros; sería asumir una responsabilidad que somos incapaces de llevar.

Mi hermano, lo que el Señor te haya enseñado por medio de su Espíritu, díselo a otros. Según tengas oportunidad, revélales lo que Dios te ha revelado a ti; recuerda lo que el mismo Jesús encargó a sus discípulos: «Lo que les digo en la oscuridad, díganlo ustedes a plena luz; lo que se les susurra al oído, proclámenlo desde las azoteas» (Mateo 10:27). Debes predicar todas las verdades en su debida proporción; hay un tiempo para una y un tiempo para la otra, y no debes omitir ninguna. Al final de nuestro ministerio, debemos ser capaces de decir: «No me he callado nada de lo que Dios me ha enseñado, sino que lo he enseñado a otros, así que mi ministerio ha sido veraz».

A través de la Biblia en un año: Salmos 89–90

¿Llevarás su cruz?

Cuando se lo llevaban, echaron mano de un tal Simón de Cirene, que volvía del campo, y le cargaron la cruz para que la llevara detrás de Jesús.
LUCAS 23:26

En lo que concierne a la reconciliación del hombre con Dios, el Señor pisó el lagar a solas, sin nadie a su lado; pero en lo referente a la conversión del mundo y su rescate del poder del error y la maldad, Cristo no está solo. Nosotros somos obreros junto con Jesús. Estamos en las manos de Dios para compartir los dolores y el trabajo por medio de los cuales él libera a los hombres de las ataduras del pecado y Satanás, y los trae a la libertad de la verdad y la justicia. Por lo tanto, es importante el hecho de que para llevar la cruz, aunque no para morir en ella, fuera necesaria la presencia de uno que estuviera cerca de Jesús. Llevar la cruz detrás de Jesús es la ocupación de la persona fiel. Simón de Cirene representa a toda la iglesia de Dios y a cada creyente en particular. Con frecuencia, Jesús había dicho: «El que no toma mi cruz y me sigue, no puede ser mi discípulo», y ahora por fin se materializa ese sermón en una persona. El discípulo debe ser como su Maestro: aquel que está dispuesto a seguir al Crucificado, debe estar dispuesto a llevar él mismo la cruz. Esto lo vemos de forma práctica en Simón de Cirene, quien llevó la cruz de Jesús sobre sus hombros.

¿Debe Simón llevar la cruz solo,
y todos los demás quedarse libres?
No; hay una cruz para cada uno,
y también hay una cruz para mí.

A través de la Biblia en un año: Salmos 91–94

Una carga bendita

Fijemos la mirada en Jesús, el iniciador y perfeccionador de nuestra fe, quien por el gozo que le esperaba soportó la cruz, menospreciando la vergüenza que ella significaba, y ahora está sentado a la derecha del trono de Dios.

HEBREOS 12:2

Por supuesto que el camino más fácil es convertirse en monje y vivir una tranquila vida en un claustro y servir a Dios sin hacer nada; o hacerse monja, vivir en un convento y pretender ganar las luchas de la vida huyendo de ellas. ¿No es esto absurdo? Ustedes, las mujeres y los hombres cristianos, deben permanecer firmes y vivir para Jesús en el lugar donde la providencia de Dios los haya puesto. Si tu llamado no es un llamado a pecar, y tus alrededores no representan una tentación demasiado grande para ti, mantente firme y nunca pienses en rendirte. Si tu carga es pesada, considérala como la cruz de Cristo para ti e inclina tu espalda para cargarla. Puede ser que al principio te duela el hombro, pero con el tiempo te harás más fuerte, porque como tus días serán tus fuerzas: «Bueno es que el hombre aprenda a llevar el yugo desde su juventud» (Lamentaciones 3:27), pero es bueno para el hombre llevar su cruz tanto en la edad madura como en su juventud, de hecho, nunca debemos rechazar tan bendita carga. Como las alas para el ave y las velas para el barco, así es la cruz para el espíritu del hombre cuando acepta llevarla como la preciosa carga de su vida. Ahora bien, Simón, ¿dónde estás tú? ¡Hombre, carga la cruz en el nombre de Dios!

A través de la Biblia en un año: Salmos 95–98

Completa consagración

Ahora escuchen esto, ustedes que dicen: «Hoy o mañana iremos a tal o cual ciudad, pasaremos allí un año, haremos negocios y ganaremos dinero». ¡Y eso que ni siquiera saben qué sucederá mañana! ¿Qué es su vida? Ustedes son como la niebla, que aparece por un momento y luego se desvanece.

SANTIAGO 4:13-14

¿Cuál es el valor de la vida de un hombre que se involucra en los negocios, gana dinero, se hace rico y muere? Esta clase de vida termina con un párrafo que publica el periódico de Londres declarando el valor del difunto: «Este miserable no tenía ningún valor, sus posesiones tenían valor pero él no tenía ninguno. Si hubiera valido algo, habría empleado su dinero para hacer bien a la humanidad, pero como mayordomo infiel acumuló los bienes de su Maestro en montones que se pudren». La mayoría de los hombres buscan su propio bien. Pero una vida entregada a Jesús, a pesar de que tiene que llevar su cruz, es noble, heroica y sublime. La verdadera vida es la que se consagra por completo a Cristo y a su cruz y se asemeja a la vida de los ángeles. De hecho, es incluso más elevada pues es la vida de Dios dentro del alma del hombre. Tú que aspiras a vivir con nobleza, proponte vivir una vida que valga la pena vivirla, recordarla y convertirla en el comienzo de la eternidad ante el trono de Dios.

Algunos de ustedes pueden estar comenzando a sentir el peso de la cruz sobre sus hombros cuando piensan en las necesidades de aquellos que los rodean. Ellos mueren, perecen por falta de conocimiento, tanto los ricos como los pobres, al obviar a Jesús, quedan muchos de ellos atrapados en una justicia de apariencias nada más. Están pereciendo. Y tú, ¿no tienes compasión? ¿Está tu corazón tan duro como el acero? Estoy seguro que no puedes negar que los tiempos actuales demandan de ti una vida consagrada y esforzada.

A través de la Biblia en un año: Salmos 99–102

El ladrón que creyó

Luego dijo: «Jesús, acuérdate de mí cuando vengas en tu reino».
LUCAS 23:42

Nota que este hombre creyó en Jesucristo cuando literalmente lo vio sufriendo la muerte de un malhechor bajo las circunstancias más vergonzosas posibles. Tú nunca te has dado cuenta lo que significa ser crucificado. Eso va más allá de nuestra experiencia. Este hombre lo vio con sus propios ojos y llamar «Señor» a quien estaba colgando de un madero, fue un gran triunfo de fe. Decirle que lo recordara cuando viniera en su reino, a pesar de verlo desangrándose y a punto de morir, fue un significativo acto de confianza, un noble acto de fe.

Recuerda también que en ese momento, cuando el ladrón confió en Jesús, todos sus discípulos lo habían abandonado y habían huido. Puede ser que Juan estuviera observando a una cierta distancia y que algunas santas mujeres estuvieran un poco más lejos, pero ninguno estuvo presente para ver morir a Jesús. Judas lo vendió, Pedro lo negó y el resto lo abandonó. Fue entonces que el ladrón moribundo llamándolo «Señor» le dijo: «Jesús, acuérdate de mí cuando vengas en tu reino». A eso yo llamo una fe gloriosa. Algunos de ustedes no creen, a pesar de estar rodeados de amigos cristianos, a pesar de que pueden ver el testimonio de aquellos que están a su lado. Sin embargo, aquel hombre que estaba solo, ¡le implora a Jesús y lo llama su Señor! Después que Jesús muriera el centurión creyó, pero antes, este ladrón fue el único que confesó la fe y se aferró al Salvador cuando no había nadie más que dijera «Amén» a lo que había dicho.

A través de la Biblia en un año: Salmos 103–106

¿Por qué estamos aquí todavía?

Uno de los criminales allí colgados empezó a insultarlo: «¿No eres tú el Cristo? ¡Sálvate a ti mismo y a nosotros!» Pero el otro criminal lo reprendió.
LUCAS 23:39-40

¿Por qué nuestro Señor no nos llevó a todos de una vez para el paraíso? Porque tenemos algo que hacer en la tierra. *¿Lo estás haciendo?* Hay algunas personas buenas que todavía están en la tierra pero, ¿por qué? ¿Cuál es su utilidad? No puedo entenderlo. Si de verdad forman el pueblo de Dios, ¿qué están haciendo aquí todavía? Se levantan en las mañanas, desayunan y en el transcurso del día almuerzan, comen y se acuestan a dormir. A la mañana siguiente se levantan a una hora determinada y hacen lo mismo que el día anterior. ¿Es esto vivir para Jesús? ¿Es esto vida? No parece suficiente. ¿Es esta la vida de Dios en un hombre? ¡Ay, hermano cristiano, justifica el hecho de que tu Señor todavía te tenga aquí esperando! ¿De qué otra forma lo puedes justificar, que no sea sirviéndolo con todas tus fuerzas? ¡Que el Señor te ayude a hacerlo así! ¿Por qué? Porque le debes tanto al Señor como aquel ladrón moribundo. ¡Qué gran deuda tienen ustedes, jóvenes cristianos, con el Señor! Y si ese pobre ladrón transformó su vida en unos minutos para servir de testimonio a la posteridad, ¿acaso no debemos nosotros, que hemos tenido el privilegio de vivir muchos años luego de nuestra conversión, dedicarnos a servir con excelencia al Señor? ¡Vamos, es hora de levantarse, si es que hemos estado durmiendo! Empecemos a vivir con plenitud, como si hasta ahora hubiéramos estado medio muertos. ¡Dejemos que el Espíritu de Dios pueda hacer algo en nosotros de modo que podamos ser obreros útiles en la viña para el gozo del paraíso!

A través de la Biblia en un año: Salmos 107–110

Inmersos en su servicio

Mientras lo apedreaban, Esteban oraba. «Señor Jesús» decía, «recibe mi espíritu». Luego cayó de rodillas y gritó: «¡Señor, no les tomes en cuenta este pecado!» Cuando hubo dicho esto, murió.

HECHOS 7:59-60

Observemos la muerte de Esteban y notemos su carácter general. Nos sorprende que sucediera en el mejor momento de su servicio. Lo habían designado oficial de la iglesia en Jerusalén para velar que las ofrendas se distribuyeran de forma correcta entre los pobres, en especial, las viudas griegas. Desempeñó su labor para la satisfacción de toda la iglesia y llevó a cabo un servicio excelente, de modo que los apóstoles pudieron dedicarse de lleno a su verdadero trabajo, es decir, la predicación y la oración, y no es algo insignificante asumir la carga de otro si eso libera a aquel para que pueda dedicarse a un servicio más eminente que el que nosotros mismos pudiéramos desempeñar. Pero Esteban no se conformó con ser un diácono, sino que comenzó a ministrar en las cosas santas como un defensor de la Palabra, lo que hizo con gran poder, ya que estaba lleno de fe y del poder del Espíritu Santo. Esteban sobresale en la lista de los héroes de la historia de la iglesia como un líder, tanto que los enemigos del evangelio reconocieron la utilidad de su prominencia y lo hicieron objeto de su más fiera oposición, pues por lo general se encolerizan más contra aquellos que hacen el mayor bien. Esteban permaneció en la vanguardia del ejército del Señor; sin embargo, lo mataron. «Un misterio», dicen algunos. «Un gran privilegio», digo yo. ¿Quién desea que Dios lo lleve en algún otro tiempo? ¿Acaso no es mejor morir con el yugo puesto, cuando todavía eres útil? ¿Quién desea vivir hasta ser una carga, en vez de una ayuda?

A través de la Biblia en un año: Salmos 111-114

Una calma como la del cielo

Al oír esto, rechinando los dientes montaron en cólera contra él. Pero Esteban, lleno del Espíritu Santo, fijó la mirada en el cielo y vio la gloria de Dios, y a Jesús de pie a la derecha de Dios.

HECHOS 7:54-55

Los últimos momentos de Esteban estuvieron llenos de calma, paz, confianza y gozo. Nunca se retractó ante aquella furiosa audiencia. Les dijo la verdad completa, con tanto denuedo como si hubiera estado pronunciando un discurso agradable a sus oídos. Cuando ellos se encolerizaron, no les tuvo miedo; sus labios no temblaron, no se retractó ni suavizó una sola de sus expresiones, sino que las punzó hasta el corazón con mayor fidelidad. Con la valentía de un hombre de Dios, puso su rostro como un pedernal. Consciente de que estaba predicando su último sermón, empuñó la espada de dos filos que es la Palabra de Dios, clavándola en sus mismas almas. No le importaba cuánto fruncían el ceño, o cómo crujían sus dientes. Estaba tan calmado como el cielo que se abría encima de él y a pesar de que lo habían echado de la ciudad, continuó haciendo su trabajo. Cuando lo sacaron fuera de las puertas y le quitaron su ropa para ejecutarlo, no pronunció una sola expresión de temor ni un grito de miedo; permaneció firme y encomendó su alma a Dios con toda calma, y cuando las primeras piedras asesinas lo derribaron a tierra, cayó sobre sus rodillas, no para pedir misericordia ni para lanzar un gemido, sino para pedirle al Señor que tuviera misericordia de los que lo asesinaban. Luego cerró sus ojos como un niño cansado de jugar en un día de verano que se queda dormido en el regazo de su madre: y «durmió». Cristiano, cree entonces que si permaneces en Jesús, eso mismo sucederá contigo.

A través de la Biblia en un año: Salmos 115-118

Amor y servicio

Pero la gracia del Señor se derramó sobre mí con abundancia, junto con la fe y el amor que hay en Cristo Jesús.
1 Timoteo 1:14

La gracia de Dios, que es capaz de salvar al mayor de los pecadores, puede de seguro salvar a aquellos que han pecado en menor grado. Si el puente de la gracia puede soportar el peso de un elefante, de seguro puede soportar el del ratón. Si la misericordia de Dios fue suficiente para redimir al peor de los pecadores, puede tener paciencia contigo. Si una puerta es bastante grande como para que pase por ella un gigante, cualquier mortal de tamaño normal tendrá espacio suficiente. Ningún hombre puede decir que es un pecador demasiado malvado como para ser salvo, porque hace mil ochocientos años que el mayor de los pecadores fue salvado. Así que, ¿por qué no puedes serlo tú? Después que Pablo recibió la salvación, se convirtió en el más destacado de los santos. El Señor no le designó un lugar de segunda clase en la iglesia. Había sido el principal de los pecadores, pero el Señor no dijo: «Te he salvado, pero siempre recordaré tu maldad como una desventaja para ti». No fue así: lo consideró fiel, colocándolo en el ministerio y en el apostolado, de modo que no fue menor que cualquiera de los apóstoles. No hay ninguna razón por la que, a pesar de que tu pecado haya sido enorme, tú no puedas ser igual de útil para el Señor. Por el contrario, hay una razón por la que debes ser todavía más útil, porque aquel a quien mucho se le perdona, mucho ama, y el amor abundante lleva al servicio abundante.

A través de la Biblia en un año: Salmos 119

De pura gracia

En el viaje sucedió que, al acercarse a Damasco, una luz del cielo relampagueó de repente a su alrededor. Él cayó al suelo y oyó una voz que le decía: «Saulo, Saulo, ¿por qué me persigues?» «¿Quién eres, Señor?» preguntó. «Yo soy Jesús, a quien tú persigues».

HECHOS 9:3-5

La conversión de Pablo pudiera servir como una descripción de la conversión de cualquiera de nosotros. ¿Cómo tuvo lugar su salvación? Bien, está claro que no había nada en Pablo que lo hiciera merecedor de la salvación. Podrías haberlo analizado hasta lo sumo y no habrías encontrado algo en él que te diera una esperanza de que tal vez pudiera creer en Jesús. Su procedencia, su preparación, lo que le rodeaba y los logros de su vida, todo lo inclinaba a ser un devoto del judaísmo y lo alejaba del cristianismo. El primero de los ancianos de la iglesia que habló con él sobre las cosas divinas casi no podía creer en su conversión. «Señor», le dijo, «he oído hablar mucho de ese hombre y de todo el mal que ha causado a tus santos en Jerusalén» (Hechos 9:13). Le costaba trabajo creer que aquel lobo hambriento se hubiera convertido en una oveja. No había nada en Saulo que favoreciera la fe en Jesús; el terreno de su corazón era pedregoso, el pico no podía atravesarlo, y la buena semilla no podía encontrar raíz. Sin embargo, el Señor convirtió a Saulo y puede hacer lo mismo con otros pecadores pero tiene que ser una obra de pura gracia y del poder divino ya que en la naturaleza caída del hombre no hay ni siquiera un lugar santo del tamaño de la punta de un alfiler sobre el cual pudiera descender la gracia. La gracia transformadora no encuentra su hábitat natural en nuestros corazones, tiene que crear su propio suelo. Y, bendito sea Dios, es capaz de hacerlo, porque para Dios todas las cosas son posibles.

A través de la Biblia en un año: Salmos 120–123

El antídoto más efectivo

Al partir para Macedonia, te encargué que permanecieras en Éfeso y les ordenaras a algunos supuestos maestros que dejen de enseñar doctrinas falsas y de prestar atención a leyendas y genealogías interminables. Esas cosas provocan controversias en vez de llevar adelante la obra de Dios que es por la fe.

1 TIMOTEO 1:3-4

¡Con cuánta exactitud se repiten los acontecimientos! Cuando vienen los mismos males, debemos aplicar los mismos remedios. Cuando aparece una enfermedad que causó grandes estragos en épocas pasadas, los médicos investigan los medicamentos que fueron efectivos en aquel entonces. Tenemos que hacer lo mismo con las cosas espirituales. Tenemos que ver lo que Pablo hizo en su época cuando la malaria de la falsa doctrina estaba en el aire. La efectividad de esa regla tan sencilla es asombrosa. Cuando se hace un descubrimiento científico o tecnológico, parece complicado al principio por la misma razón por la cual es imperfecto; pero todas las mejoras se llevan a cabo con vistas a simplificar las cosas. Lo mismo sucede con las enseñanzas espirituales. Cuando vemos la realidad dejamos de ser superfluos. No nos dediquemos a inventar sabios métodos para resolver la tensión actual en el mundo espiritual, en su lugar usemos el método que fue tan efectivo en los días de Pablo. Él mismo le enseñó el evangelio a Timoteo: no solo le hacía escuchar su doctrina, sino también ver su práctica. No podemos forzar a los hombres a aceptar la verdad pero podemos hacer que nuestras enseñanzas sean claras y precisas, y vivir de acuerdo con ellas. La verdad y la santidad son los antídotos más efectivos contra el error y la injusticia. El apóstol le dijo a Timoteo: «Permanece firme en lo que has aprendido y de lo cual estás convencido, pues sabes de quiénes lo aprendiste» (2 Timoteo 3:14).

A través de la Biblia en un año: Salmos 124–127

Encargados de preservar

¡Pero tengan cuidado! Presten atención y no olviden las cosas que han visto sus ojos, ni las aparten de su corazón mientras vivan. Cuéntenselas a sus hijos y a sus nietos.

DEUTERONOMIO 4:9

Con vistas a estar preparado para el conflicto que se aproxima, solo tenemos que predicar y vivir el evangelio, y no dejar de enseñarles a los niños la Palabra de Dios. Debemos tener muy en cuenta esto último, porque es de la boca de los niños y de los que maman que se perfecciona la alabanza. Concéntrate en los planes apostólicos y espera con toda seguridad sus mismos triunfos. Predica a Cristo, predica la Palabra a tiempo y fuera de tiempo e instruye a los niños. Uno de los métodos de Dios para preservar los campos de las malas hierbas es sembrar trigo en ellos cuando aún son suelos jóvenes.

La obra de la gracia de Dios en Timoteo comenzó con la instrucción temprana. «Desde tu niñez conoces las Sagradas Escrituras» (2 Timoteo 3:15). Nota el tiempo para la instrucción. La expresión «desde tu niñez» puede comprenderse mejor si decimos: «desde que eras muy pequeño», o como lo dice la Biblia en Lenguaje Sencillo: «desde niño». No significa un adolescente o un joven, sino un niño que recién está saliendo de su infancia. Desde muy pequeño Timoteo había conocido los escritos sagrados. Esta expresión, sin lugar a dudas, se utiliza para mostrar que nunca es demasiado temprano para comenzar a llenar la mente de nuestros hijos con el conocimiento de las Escrituras. Los bebés aprenden mucho antes de lo que suponemos. Durante los primeros meses de vida de un niño, este aprende más de lo que nosotros imaginamos. Muy pronto aprende que su madre lo ama y que depende de ella y, si la madre es una mujer sabia, aprende el significado de la obediencia y la necesidad de someter su voluntad a una voluntad superior. Esto puede ser clave para toda su vida en el futuro.

A través de la Biblia en un año: Salmos 128–131

Guía a los pequeños

Instruye al niño en el camino correcto, y aun en su vejez no lo abandonará.
PROVERBIOS 22:6

Los niños deben leer las Sagradas Escrituras tan pronto como aprenden a leer. Es muy notable que muchos maestros hayan dicho que han visto a los niños aprender a leer mejor cuando lo hacen utilizando la Biblia. No estoy seguro por qué sucede esto, tal vez sea por la sencillez del lenguaje, pero yo creo que es cierto. Con frecuencia, los niños recuerdan un suceso que aparece en la Biblia pero olvidan otros hechos de la historia secular. En la Biblia hay una adaptación para los seres humanos de todas las edades y, por lo tanto, se adapta muy bien a los niños. Cometemos un error al pensar que debemos comenzar con otro tipo de lectura y luego pasar a las Escrituras. La Biblia es el libro ideal para los niños. La mente de los niños no puede comprender algunas partes de ella, porque ni siquiera el más sabio de entre nosotros puede hacerlo. Hay profundidades en las que el leviatán puede nadar, pero también hay arroyos de los que pueden beber las ovejas. Los maestros sabios saben cómo guiar a los pequeños a los pastos delicados junto a aguas de reposo.

A través de la Biblia en un año: Salmos 132–135

Una verdad sagrada

Hijo mío, no te olvides de mis enseñanzas; más bien, guarda en tu corazón mis mandamientos. Porque prolongarán tu vida muchos años y te traerán prosperidad. Que nunca te abandonen el amor y la verdad: llévalos siempre alrededor de tu cuello y escríbelos en el libro de tu corazón. Contarás con el favor de Dios y tendrás buena fama entre la gente.

PROVERBIOS 3:1-4

¡Ay, queridas madres, Dios les ha dado a ustedes una sagrada encomienda! En efecto, les ha dicho: «Llévate a este niño y críamelo. Yo te pagaré por hacerlo». Tu llamado es equipar al futuro hombre de Dios, de modo que pueda estar capacitado para toda buena obra. Aquellos que piensan que las madres que permanecen en casa cuidando de su pequeña familia no están haciendo nada, piensan lo opuesto a la verdad. A una madre piadosa casi nunca le es posible dejar su hogar para ir a la iglesia. Pero no piensen que no están haciendo nada por la iglesia; por el contrario, están llevando a cabo el mejor servicio para el Señor. Madre, la crianza de tus hijos en el temor de Dios es tu primer y más importante deber.

A través de la Biblia en un año: Salmos 136–139

Un servicio santo

Todo el que infrinja uno solo de estos mandamientos, por pequeño que sea, y enseñe a otros a hacer lo mismo, será considerado el más pequeño en el reino de los cielos; pero el que los practique y enseñe será considerado grande en el reino de los cielos.
MATEO 5:19

En la actualidad, ya que existen tan pocas madres y abuelas cristianas, la iglesia ha considerado que es sabio suplementar la enseñanza hogareña a los niños bajo sus alas. Esta recibe bajo su cuidado maternal a aquellos niños cuyos padres no son cristianos. Considero esa una tarea bendita. Me siento muy agradecido por los muchos hermanos y hermanas que se dedican a enseñar en la Escuela Dominical y también durante algunas noches de la semana, a los niños de otros, quienes, con el tiempo, serán como sus propios hijos. Dichos maestros asumen los deberes de padre y madre, por amor al Señor, para con aquellos niños que están descuidados en su propio hogar. Los padres cristianos no pueden pensar que el objetivo de la Escuela Dominical es liberarlos de sus responsabilidades como padres. Lo primero y lo más natural que deben hacer los padres cristianos es instruir a sus hijos en el camino y el temor del Señor. No obstante, es un trabajo meritorio asumir el deber de enseñar a los niños de otros, cuando los responsables naturales no lo han asumido. El Señor Jesús mira con placer a quienes alimentan sus corderitos y nutren a sus bebés, porque no es su voluntad que ninguno de estos se pierda. Adelante, hombres y mujeres temerosos de Dios, santifíquense en este gozoso acto de servicio.

A través de la Biblia en un año: Salmos 140–143

La enseñanza temprana

Desde tu niñez conoces las Sagradas Escrituras, que pueden darte la sabiduría necesaria para la salvación mediante la fe en Cristo Jesús.
2 TIMOTEO 3:15

Nota que a Timoteo lo enseñaron, no solo a reverenciar las cosas santas en general sino, en especial, a conocer *las Escrituras*. Las enseñanzas de su madre y su abuela eran las enseñanzas de las Sagradas Escrituras. Imagínate que reunamos a los niños el Día del Señor con el objetivo de divertirlos y proporcionarles unas horas felices; o para instruirlos, como hacemos durante el resto de la semana, en los principios de la educación moral, ¿qué hemos hecho? No hemos hecho nada que sea digno de ese día o de la iglesia de Dios. Imagínate que tenemos especial cuidado en enseñar a los niños las reglas y regulaciones de nuestra propia iglesia y no los llevamos a las Escrituras; imagínate que les presentemos un libro que contenga las normas de nuestra iglesia pero que no pasemos tiempo con la Biblia, ¿qué hemos hecho? Dichas normas pueden ser correctas o no y, por tanto, podemos haber enseñado a nuestros niños cosas verdaderas o erróneas, pero si nos centramos en las Sagradas Escrituras, no vamos a cometer errores. Con tal norma, sabemos que haremos lo correcto. Este Libro es la Palabra de Dios y si lo enseñamos, enseñamos aquello que el Señor aceptará y bendecirá. ¡Oh, queridos maestros, y aquí me estoy hablando a mí también, que nuestras enseñanzas se basen cada vez más en las Escrituras! No teman si nuestros alumnos olvidan lo que les enseñamos, sino oren para que recuerden lo que el Señor les enseña. ¡Que las verdades divinas acerca del pecado, la justicia y el juicio queden grabadas en sus corazones! ¡Que nunca olviden las verdades reveladas acerca del amor de Dios, la gracia de nuestro Señor Jesucristo y la obra del Espíritu Santo!

A través de la Biblia en un año: Salmos 144–147

Dios está en control

Señor, yo sé que el hombre no es dueño de su destino, que no le es dado al caminante dirigir sus propios pasos.

Jeremías 10:23

¿Tienes algún hijo que haya abandonado el hogar? ¿Quizá un joven voluntarioso y obstinado que se fue porque no pudo aceptar las restricciones de una familia cristiana? Es triste que esto suceda, muy triste en verdad, pero no te desesperes ni te angusties por él. No sabes dónde está, pero Dios sí lo sabe; no puedes ir tras él, pero el Espíritu Santo sí puede hacerlo. ¿Se fue en un viaje a Shangai? Ah, puede ser que haya un Pablo en Shangai a quien Dios use como un medio para su salvación, y ya que ese Pablo no está aquí en Londres, tuvo que ir a Shangai a encontrarlo. ¿Se va a Australia? Quizá allí alguien le diga una palabra de bendición a tu hijo que sea la única que llegue a su corazón. Yo no puedo decirla, nadie en Londres puede; pero el hombre que encuentre allí lo hará y, por tanto, Dios permite que se vaya lejos con toda su obstinación y necedad para que la gracia pueda alcanzarlo y efectuar su salvación. Lo peor que puede pasarle a un joven es, a veces, lo mejor que le pudo suceder.

A través de la Biblia en un año: Salmos 148–150

Una fe preciosa

Cuando venga el Hijo del hombre, ¿encontrará fe en la tierra?
LUCAS 18:8

A nuestro Señor que ha de venir no le importarán los tesoros de los ricos ni los honores de los grandes. No mirará las habilidades que hemos desarrollado, ni las influencias que tenemos, sino que mirará nuestra fe. Su gloria es «ser creído en el mundo» y eso será lo que tendrá en cuenta. Este mercadero celestial considera la fe como una perla de gran precio, la fe es tan preciosa para Jesús como lo es para nosotros. En el último día tendrá lugar un minucioso escrutinio que buscará una cosa fundamental, dónde hay fe y dónde no la hay. Aquel que cree será salvo; aquel que no cree será condenado. La búsqueda se llevará a cabo en nuestros hogares y en nuestros corazones, y la pregunta será: ¿Dónde está tu fe? ¿Honraste a Cristo, confiando en su Palabra y en su sangre, o no lo hiciste? ¿Glorificaste a Dios al creer en su revelación y depender de sus promesas, o no? El hecho de que nuestro Señor en su venida buscará la fe nos debe llevar a considerarla como algo muy valioso. No es un mero acto del intelecto, es una gracia del Espíritu Santo que glorifica a Dios y produce obediencia en el corazón. Jesús la busca porque él es el objeto de ella, y es por medio de ella que en su primera venida se lleva a cabo su propósito. Nuestro Salvador está buscando la fe. «Atentamente observa al ser humano; con sus propios ojos lo examina» (Salmo 11:4). Este es el oro que él está buscando en la cantera de nuestra humanidad. Este es el objetivo de su búsqueda real: ¿crees en el Señor Jesucristo?

A través de la Biblia en un año: Santiago 1–2

La fe

Así que los que viven por la fe son bendecidos
junto con Abraham, el hombre de fe.
GÁLATAS 3:9

¿Dónde está la predicación o la enseñanza que se lleva a cabo con fe absoluta en lo que se predica o enseña? Es inútil forzar a otros a escuchar y aceptar lo que decimos. Mis hermanos y hermanas, ¿dónde está nuestra fe? En la iglesia parecía algo casi sobrenatural cuando se dijo que el Sr. Jorge Mueller caminó en fe con respecto a las cosas temporales. Educar a los niños en la fe era criarlos en la convicción de un temor reverente. Nos encontramos en una época en la que las personas no confían a Dios las cosas rutinarias de la vida, ¿no es cierto? Día a día Abraham caminó con Dios, pero si ahora te encuentras con un hombre que camina con Dios en su negocio y que con fe lleva a Dios cada detalle y cada asunto de su vida hogareña, las personas lo miran con asombro y cierto grado de reticencia. Piensan que tiene gracia en su corazón pero también sospechan que le falta un tornillo o no actuaría de esa manera. Oh, sí, decimos que tenemos fe, pero cuando se trata de las cotidianas realidades de la vida, ¿dónde está nuestra fe?

Mis hermanos, ¿por qué están tan afanados? ¿Por qué están tan ansiosos, si tienen fe en Dios? ¿Por qué muestran tanta desconfianza con respecto a las cosas de este mundo, como lo hacen los hombres mundanos? ¿Por qué ese temor? ¿Esa murmuración? ¿Esa preocupación? Oh, mi Salvador, si vinieras ahora no hallaríamos excusa para nuestra desconfianza, nuestros necios temores, nuestra falta de dulce descanso en ti. No confiamos en ti como debemos hacerlo, y si ese es el caso de aquellos que son deudores a tu fidelidad amorosa, ¿dónde encontrarás fe en la tierra?

A través de la Biblia en un año: Santiago 3–5

¿Por qué tengo temor?

Sobre este monte rasgará el velo que cubre a todos los pueblos, el manto que envuelve a todas las naciones. Devorará a la muerte para siempre; el señor omnipotente enjugará las lágrimas de todo rostro, y quitará de toda la tierra el oprobio de su pueblo. El Señor mismo lo ha dicho.

ISAÍAS 25:7-8

Bien, hermanos, tan cierto como que el Señor resucitó, así resucitarán todos los santos a una vida gloriosa de sus cuerpos, mientras que la vida de sus almas no ha dejado de ser ni siquiera un instante. En este sentido él conquistó la muerte y desde aquella victoria memorable Cristo cada día vence la muerte, pues les da su Espíritu a los santos, y al tener dicho Espíritu dentro de ellos, enfrentan a su último enemigo sin temor alguno; con frecuencia lo enfrentan con canciones; quizá con aún mayor frecuencia lo enfrentan con un rostro calmado y duermen en paz. Muerte, no te temeré; ¿por qué habría de hacerlo? Pareces un dragón pero ya no tienes aguijón. Tus dientes están rotos, león viejo; ¿por qué habría de temerte? Sé que ya no eres capaz de destruirme, sino que te han enviado como mensajero para conducirme a las puertas de oro por donde entraré y cara a cara veré para siempre a mi Salvador. Algunos santos antes de morir han dicho que su lecho de muerte ha sido el mejor que tuvieron en sus vidas. Muchos de ellos han preguntado: «Dime, alma mía, ¿esto es la muerte?» Morir ha sido algo tan diferente de lo que esperaban, tan tranquilo y gozoso; se sienten tan libres de toda carga, se sienten tan aliviados en vez de sentirse abrumados, que se han cuestionado si ese es el monstruo que han temido durante toda su vida. ¡Amados, nuestro Señor exaltado ha vencido la muerte en todos estos sentidos!

A través de la Biblia en un año: Proverbios 1–3

Vencedores

El último enemigo que será destruido es la muerte.
1 CORINTIOS 15:26

Nota que la muerte es el último enemigo de cada cristiano y el último que será destruido. Ahora bien, si la Palabra de Dios dice que es el último, quiero recordarte algo de la sabiduría práctica: deja que sea el último. Hermano, no pretendas alterar el orden, sino deja que lo último sea lo último. Conocí a un hermano que quería vencer la muerte mucho antes de que esta llegara. Pero, hermano, no recibirás la gracia para los últimos momentos de tu vida hasta que estos no lleguen. ¿Qué beneficio tendría recibir la gracia para la hora de la muerte mientras todavía vives? Solo necesitas un bote cuando llegas a un río. Pide la gracia para vivir y así glorifica a Cristo mediante ella, y entonces tendrás la gracia para la hora de la muerte cuando esta llegue. Tu enemigo será destruido, pero no hoy. Hay una gran cantidad de enemigos que enfrentar hoy, así que confórmate con dejar tranquila a la muerte por un rato. Este enemigo será destruido, pero desconocemos el tiempo en que esto sucederá; lo que tenemos que saber es que somos llamados a ser buenos soldados de Jesucristo, según lo requiera el deber de cada día. ¡Mi hermano, enfrenta tus pruebas a medida que vengan! En el tiempo propicio Dios te ayudará a vencer a tu último enemigo, pero mientras tanto ocúpate de vencer al mundo, la carne y el diablo. Si vives bien, morirás bien.

A través de la Biblia en un año: Proverbios 4–6

El riesgo que corremos es limitado

De hecho, sabemos que si esta tienda de campaña en que vivimos se deshace, tenemos de Dios un edificio, una casa eterna en el cielo, no construida por manos humanas.

2 CORINTIOS 5:1

La confianza que Pablo tenía en que si su cuerpo se deshacía no perdería nada, le impidió desmayar. Él sabía qué era lo peor y se preparó para ello. Afuera se desencadenaban grandes tormentas pero el apóstol conocía el límite de su posible pérdida, así que estaba listo. Todo lo que podemos perder es la frágil tienda de campaña en la que vivimos. No existe ninguna posibilidad de que perdamos más que eso. Cuando el hombre sabe que el riesgo que corre es limitado, esto calma su mente. Las cosas indescifrables e inescrutables son los peores ingredientes del pánico y el temor: cuando puedes controlar tus temores, los has vencido. El apóstol sabía que estaba en este mundo con el noble propósito de glorificar a Dios, ganar almas y edificar a los santos, y estaba resuelto a cumplir el ministerio que se le había encomendado. Se dijo a sí mismo que su peor curso sería desmayar en la vida de servicio, ya que el mayor riesgo que podía implicar la perseverancia en su llamado era la muerte, y eso él lo consideraba como perder una tienda de campaña y ganar una mansión. El emperador romano podía cortarle la cabeza, o podían apedrearlo hasta morir, o crucificarlo como a su Maestro, ¡pero no temía tales destinos! Para él eso era solo la destrucción de su vieja tienda de campaña; no afectaba su espíritu inmortal; podía sonreír y cantar: «Pues los sufrimientos ligeros y efímeros que ahora padecemos producen una gloria eterna que vale muchísimo más que todo sufrimiento» (2 Corintios 4:17).

A través de la Biblia en un año: Proverbios 7–9

Nuestra navaja

Ciertamente, la Palabra de Dios es viva y ponderosa, y más cortante que cualquier espada de dos filos. Penetra hasta lo más profundo del alma y del espíritu, hasta la médula de los huesos, y juzga los pensamientos y las intenciones del corazón.

HEBREOS 4:12

La promulgación de un credo frío y la exposición de algunas doctrinas y su aplicación lógica, sin lidiar con la conciencia de los oyentes, sin presentarles su pecado, sin decirles el peligro que están corriendo, sin rogarles con lágrimas y súplicas que vengan al Salvador, ¡es un trabajo sin ningún poder! Buscamos obreros, no charlatanes. Ahora bien, fíjate lo que lleva un obrero en sus manos. Es una hoz. Su filo, con el que corta el grano, es agudo y cortante. El obrero corta con exactitud, atraviesa el grano y lo echa a la tierra. El hombre que Dios busca para que trabaje en su cosecha no puede venir con palabras suaves y delicadas y doctrinas halagadoras que se refieran a la dignidad de la naturaleza humana y a la excelencia de la auto ayuda y de los esfuerzos propios para rectificar nuestra condición caída y cosas por el estilo. Dios maldecirá a esa boca acaramelada, ya que esa es la maldición de esta generación. El predicador honesto llama pecado al pecado y al pan, pan y al vino, vino, y le dice a los hombres: «Se están arruinando ustedes mismos, cuando rechazan a Cristo se colocan al borde del infierno y allí se perderán para toda la eternidad. No hay alternativas, tienen que escapar de la ira que vendrá mediante la fe en Jesús, o serán echados para siempre de la presencia de Dios y perderán todo posible gozo». El predicador debe lograr que sus sermones sean cortantes. El propósito de nuestra hoz es cortar. El evangelio tiene que herir la conciencia y atravesar el corazón, con el objetivo de separar el alma del pecado y del yo, tal como se separa el grano del suelo.

A través de la Biblia en un año: Proverbios 10–12

Se necesitan habilidades divinas

Pasando por la orilla del mar de Galilea, Jesús vio a Simón y a su hermano Andrés que echaban la red al lago, pues eran pescadores. «Vengan, síganme» les dijo Jesús, «y los haré pescadores de hombres». Al momento dejaron las redes y lo siguieron.

Marcos 1:16-18

Para pescar las almas de los hombres necesitas tener tanto juicio como cuando estás pescando en el mar, porque los hombres son peces curiosos y con frecuencia las sombras los asustarán. Lanzar de la forma correcta tu cordel es un arte que no se aprende con facilidad. Algunos nunca aprenden y, por tanto, no son capaces de atraer a las almas, mientras que otros poseen los instintos sagrados que les ayudan a atrapar el corazón de los hombres y apoderarse de ellos. Tenemos que ser sabios para ganar almas; los necios no ganan almas. Tenemos que lograr una empatía con los hombres, conocer incluso sus debilidades, y debemos relacionarnos con ellos, aceptarlos como son y presentarles la verdad de forma que puedan entenderla y aceptarla. Si eres un testigo de Cristo, pídele al Espíritu de sabiduría que te guíe. Ora en busca de dirección para que tu ocupación de ganar almas no se convierta en un discurso poco juicioso. Que tu celo sea con prudencia.

A través de la Biblia en un año: Proverbios 13–15

Por medio del Espíritu

«No será por la fuerza ni por ningún poder, sino por mi Espíritu», dice el Señor Todopoderoso.
ZACARÍAS 4:6

Existe un poder sutil y secreto, un *poder espiritual*, por medio del cual, en el mundo *espiritual*, un hombre se transforma en un príncipe para reinar con Dios y compartir con él su poder; y al aprender a prevalecer ante Dios por los hombres, adquiere el arte de prevalecer en llevar a los hombres a Dios. Primero es un luchador solo al lado del río Jaboc y luego se convierte en un luchador en medio de una multitud de pecadores, conquistándolos para Cristo, llevándolos *cautivos* en el nombre del Altísimo. El poder de la oración es el mayor poder que existe. La comunión con Dios es poder, y la santidad, por encima de todas las cosas, es un gran poder entre los hijos de los hombres.

Este poder espiritual hace a un hombre influyente en un sentido muy diferente al que el mundo usa la palabra *influyente,* un pobre uso de la palabra. Queremos hombres que sean influyentes en el sentido espiritual, hombres que, de uno u otro modo, impacten a sus semejantes. En su presencia los hombres no pueden hacer lo que suelen hacer de modo habitual en otras partes. Cuando tales hombres están en cualquier compañía, refrenan el pecado sin decir una palabra; incitan la justicia sin apenas decir una sola frase. Triunfan, no por la fuerza ni por ningún poder, sino por el Espíritu del Señor que habita en ellos.

A través de la Biblia en un año: Proverbios 16–18

Vidas transformadas

¿No saben que los malvados no heredarán el reino de Dios? ¡No se dejen engañar! Ni los fornicarios, ni los idólatras, ni los adúlteros, ni los sodomitas, ni los pervertidos sexuales, ni los ladrones, ni los avaros, ni los borrachos, ni los calumniadores, ni los estafadores heredarán el reino de Dios. Y eso eran algunos de ustedes. Pero ya han sido lavados, ya han sido santificados, ya han sido justificados en el nombre del Señor Jesucristo y por el Espíritu de nuestro Dios.

1 CORINTIOS 6:9-11

Nuestro Señor es un gran transformador del carácter. No me gusta hablar de mí mismo, pero voy a hablar de alguien que conozco muy bien. Entró a este tabernáculo siendo un borracho, un blasfema, un amante de las cosas impuras, y mientras se predicaba la Palabra, el Señor lo quebrantó y derritió su corazón. Ahora odia lo que un día amó, y las cosas que antes le parecían aburridas —tanto que maldecía y blasfemaba ante su sola mención, o se burlaba de aquellos que las amaban— ahora él también las ama y se maravilla de estar donde ahora se encuentra. Pregúntale a su esposa si ha habido algún cambio en él, pregúntale a sus hijos si ha habido algún cambio en él; pregúntale a sus compañeros de trabajo, a su jefe, pregúntale a cualquiera y todos te dirán: «No es el mismo hombre». ¡Oh, si hay alguien que quiere probar el camino de la justicia y abandonar el pecado, que escuche mi testimonio, el cual sale de labios sin engaño! «Digo la verdad y no miento» (1 Timoteo 2:7). El Señor es capaz de transformar el carácter de una forma maravillosa, lo ha hecho en muchos de nosotros y, si puedes creer en él, también lo hará por ti.

A través de la Biblia en un año: Proverbios 19–21

Un nuevo tipo de evidencia

La noticia de estos sucesos llegó a oídos de la iglesia de Jerusalén, y mandaron a Bernabé a Antioquía. Cuando él llegó y vio las evidencias de la gracia de Dios, se alegró y animó a todos a hacerse el firme propósito de permanecer fieles al Señor.

HECHOS 11:22-23

El Espíritu de Dios que Cristo nos da mueve a los hombres a tener pensamientos elevados y nobles. El egoísmo no domina nunca más al hombre que cree en Cristo; este ama a sus semejantes, desea su bien, puede perdonarlos si lo acosan, puede entregar su vida por ellos. ¿Acaso no hemos tenido a muchos que han salido para ir a los paganos y dar sus vidas por la causa de Cristo? Estuve hablando con un hermano del Congo, le hablé de las muchas muertes que sucedían allí y me dijo: «Sí, parece algo muy triste que tantos misioneros deban morir, pero señor», añadió, «esa es la primera cosa que hemos hecho en África que brinda alguna esperanza. Con frecuencia he oído que los nativos me dicen: "Estos hombres deben tener una religión verdadera, porque de no ser así no hubieran venido aquí a morir por nosotros, los pobres hombres negros". Los hombres comienzan a creer en este nuevo tipo de evidencia. La sangre del misionero se convierte en la semilla de la iglesia». No dudo que así sea. Y amado, si tú y yo somos capaces de comenzar a vivir por completo para Cristo, si podemos vivir con nobleza, si podemos deshacernos de nuestro yo, si somos capaces de elevarnos por encima de las cosas materiales y probar que creemos en todo lo que decimos, convenceremos a nuestros semejantes de la verdad de nuestra religión.

A través de la Biblia en un año: Proverbios 22–24

El arrepentimiento

Y en su nombre se predicarán el arrepentimiento y el perdón de pecados a todas las naciones, comenzando por Jerusalén.

LUCAS 24:47

Me siento feliz de ver en este versículo la antigua virtud llamada arrepentimiento. Solía predicarse acerca de esta, pero ya ha pasado de moda. Dicen que hemos malinterpretado su significado y que esto solo significa un «cambio en la forma de pensar» y nada más. Me gustaría que los que se consideran tan sabios en su dominio del griego conocieran un poco más de ese idioma, para que no estuvieran tan prestos a formular sus aseveraciones infalibles. El arrepentimiento del evangelio es un cambio muy radical de la manera de pensar, uno que no se realiza en ningún hombre si no es por la intervención del Espíritu de Dios.

También debemos predicar los motivos del arrepentimiento, para que los hombres no se arrepientan solo por el temor al infierno, sino por la misma naturaleza del pecado. Cuando se ven encarcelados, todos los ladrones lamentan lo que hicieron; cuando el verdugo se acerca, todos los asesinos lamentan lo que hicieron. Pero el pecador tiene que arrepentirse, no solo por temor al castigo que lleva el pecado, sino porque su pecado está en contra de un Dios perdonador, contra un Salvador que derramó su sangre, contra una ley santa, contra un tierno evangelio. El verdadero penitente se arrepiente de su pecado contra Dios, y lo haría aunque no hubiera un castigo.

Debemos hablar de la fuente del arrepentimiento, que es el Señor Jesucristo otorgando el arrepentimiento y la remisión de pecados. El arrepentimiento es una planta que nunca crecerá en el desperdicio de la naturaleza: tiene que ocurrir un cambio en la naturaleza, el Espíritu Santo es quien implanta el arrepentimiento, de lo contrario, nunca florecería en nuestros corazones. Si no lo predicamos como un fruto del Espíritu Santo, cometemos un gran error.

A través de la Biblia en un año: Proverbios 25–27

Inténtalo

La palabra del Señor vino a mí: «Antes de formarte en el vientre, ya te había elegido; antes de que nacieras, ya te había apartado; te había nombrado profeta para las naciones». Yo le respondí: «¡Ah, Señor mi Dios! ¡Soy muy joven, y no sé hablar!» Pero el Señor me dijo: «No digas: Soy muy joven, porque vas a ir adondequiera que yo te envíe, y vas a decir todo lo que yo te ordene».

JEREMÍAS 1:4-7

Si tenemos una aversión especial hacia un determinado tipo de trabajo cristiano, en vez de tomar esa aversión como una señal de que no hemos sido llamados a ello, debemos considerarlo como una señal de que debemos, al menos, intentarlo. El diablo te conoce mejor de lo que tú mismo te conoces. Como sabes, él ha estado en este mundo mucho más tiempo que tú y conoce mucho más acerca de la naturaleza humana que tú; así que viene a ti y te mide con gran exactitud y dice: «Este hermano sería muy útil en tal esfera de la obra, por lo tanto, debemos apartarlo de ella». Así que le dice al hermano que él no ha sido llamado para eso, que ese no es el tipo de cosas que debe hacer, y cosas por el estilo; y luego se dice a sí mismo: «Me he librado de un enemigo que dañaría mi causa».

Por allí hay una buena hermana. Oh, cuánto pudiera hacer ella por Cristo, pero Satanás la tiene entretenida con un trabajo en el que nunca brillará, mientras que el trabajo santo que pudiera hacer tan bien no le llama la atención. Perdemos muchas oportunidades, estoy convencido de que así es. Nunca hemos pensado en muchas formas en las que podríamos hacer el bien, pero debemos pensar en ellas y cuando las descubrimos, debemos ponerlas en práctica.

A través de la Biblia en un año: Proverbios 28–29

Una oposición gloriosa

Por último, hermanos, oren por nosotros para que el mensaje del Señor se difunda rápidamente y se le reciba con honor, tal como sucedió entre ustedes. Oren además para que seamos librados de personas perversas y malvadas, porque no todos tienen fe. Pero el Señor es fiel, y él los fortalecerá y los protegerá del maligno.
2 TESALONICENSES 3:1-3

Nada es tan bueno para el evangelio como la oposición. Cierto hombre entra al tabernáculo esta noche y, al marcharse, dice: «Sí, me siento complacido y satisfecho». En el caso de dicho hombre, yo he fallado. Pero otro hombre está mordiéndose la lengua porque no puede soportar la predicación. Está muy molesto, hay algo en la doctrina que no le gusta y expresa: «No entraré de nuevo a este lugar mientras viva». En ese hombre hay esperanza. Él está comenzando a pensar. El anzuelo lo ha atrapado. Con un poco de tiempo, ese pez será nuestro. No es una mala señal cuando un hombre se molesta al escuchar el evangelio. No es bueno, pero es mucho mejor que el horrible letargo en que se sumen los hombres cuando no piensan. Ten esperanza de un hombre que no deja que le hables, a ese te debes acercar en otra ocasión. Y cuando por fin te permita que le hables, si parece como si te fuera a escupir el rostro, siéntete agradecido por ello porque está sintiendo tus palabras. Estás tocando en un lugar donde le duele. Lo ganarás para Cristo. Cuando jura que no cree una palabra de lo que le estás diciendo, no creas una palabra de lo que él te dice, porque con frecuencia el hombre que abiertamente rechaza, cree en su interior. Como los niños silban cuando atraviesan el pasillo de la iglesia para mantener su valentía, así el blasfemo se muestra profano para tratar de silenciar su conciencia.

A través de la Biblia en un año: Proverbios 30–31

Trabaja para Cristo

Precisamente por esto los judíos perseguían a Jesús, pues hacía tales cosas en sábado. Pero Jesús les respondía: «Mi Padre aun hoy está trabajando, y yo también trabajo».

JUAN 5:16-17

Pienso que una iglesia fuerte es una institución muy valiosa, pero siempre he rechazado la idea de que todo lo que tienes que hacer es sentarte en un banco domingo tras domingo y escucharme, y a algunos de ustedes les he hablado con el propósito de no verlos con tanta frecuencia. No quiero verlos, porque sé que están sirviendo al Maestro en otra parte. Hay algunos de nuestros hermanos que solo vienen a la iglesia para la Santa Cena, ¿por qué? Porque están sirviendo en otros lugares de una u otra forma. Son los mejores miembros que tenemos y no tachamos sus nombres de la lista porque no asistan con frecuencia. Están trabajando en alguna misión, o tratando de abrir un nuevo lugar de predicación, o haciendo alguna otra cosa para el Maestro. ¡Dios los bendiga! Esta es la mayor bendición que puedes tener, en el momento que encuentras la luz y te das cuenta que el mundo está en oscuridad, corre y pásale a otro la antorcha. Si vas a otra persona y le dices: «No tendré menos luz por darte un poco a ti», Dios, el Espíritu Santo, derramará sobre ti nuevos haces de luz y brillarás cada vez más hasta que el día sea perfecto.

A través de la Biblia en un año: 1 Pedro 1–2

El León de Judá

¡Qué hermosos son, sobre los montes, los pies del que trae buenas nuevas; del que proclama la paz, del que anuncia buenas noticias, del que proclama la salvación, del que dice a Sión: «Tu Dios reina»!

ISAÍAS 52:7

Creo que la mejor forma de defender el evangelio es esparcirlo. Muchos eruditos defienden el evangelio; no hay duda de que esto es algo muy loable y correcto, pero siempre he notado que cuántos más libros hay de ese tipo, menos se predica el evangelio en sí mismo. Imagínate que un grupo de personas creyera que tiene que defender a un león, ¡al rey de la selva! Allí está en su jaula, y aquí vienen todos los soldados del ejército a pelear por él. Bueno, yo les sugeriría, si no tienen objeción ni piensan que los estoy humillando, que lo que deben hacer es abrir la jaula y apartarse ¡para que salga el león! Creo que esa sería la mejor forma de defenderlo, porque él cuidará de sí mismo. La mejor «defensa» del evangelio es dejarlo libre. No te preocupes por defender Deuteronomio o todo el Pentateuco. Predica a Jesucristo y a este crucificado. Deja que el León salga, y verás quién se atreve a acercarse a él. El León de la tribu de Judá pronto vencerá a todos sus adversarios.

A través de la Biblia en un año: 1 Pedro 3–5

El Dios de la diversidad

¿Tienes idea de cuán ancha es la tierra? Si de veras sabes todo esto, ¡dalo a conocer!

JOB 38:18

Si es cierto que «el orden es la primera ley en el cielo», pienso que de la misma forma es cierto que la Variedad es la segunda. La línea de la belleza no es una línea recta, sino que tiene curvas. De la misma forma Dios no actúa en uniformidad sino en diversidad. Compruebas esto cuando echas un vistazo a la creación que nos rodea. Dios no ha hecho todas las criaturas de una misma especie, sino que ha creado animales salvajes, aves, peces, insectos, reptiles. En cualquiera de los reinos de la naturaleza, ya sea en el animal, en el vegetal o el mineral, encontrarás muchas subdivisiones, las cuales se estudian a lo largo de muchos años para aprender a clasificarlas, y una vida entera no sería suficiente para comprenderlas todas.

Esta observación es cierta en la obra de la providencia. ¡De cuántas extrañas y diversas maneras ha tratado Dios con su iglesia! Todo pecador tiene que conocer el mismo camino a la vida, la obediencia al mismo evangelio, el lavamiento en la misma sangre, el vestirse de la misma justicia, la plenitud de la misma energía divina, en algún momento todos irán al mismo cielo y, sin embargo, no encuentras dos pecadores cuyas conversiones hayan sido idénticas. Desde el primer amanecer de la vida divina hasta que se consuma en el atardecer de la perfecta santificación en el cielo, encontrarás que Dios trabaja de muchas formas diferentes, y emplea este método y ese y aquel otro, porque Dios es y será el Dios de la diversidad.

A través de la Biblia en un año: Eclesiastés 1–4

Busca la causa

Cuando Jesús entró en casa, sus discípulos le preguntaron en privado: «¿Por qué nosotros no pudimos expulsarlo?»
MARCOS 9:28

Si estamos desconcertados, tiene que haber una causa, y es bueno que la busquemos. Debemos ir al Maestro y preguntarle: «¿Por qué nosotros no pudimos expulsarlo?»

Esta pregunta, si buscáramos la respuesta correcta, es una pregunta muy sabia, porque cada hombre necesita saber lo más que pueda de sí mismo. Si tengo éxito, ¿por qué lo tengo? Déjame saber el secreto, para colocar la corona en la cabeza que lo merezca. Si no tengo éxito, tengo que averiguar por qué no lo tengo, para tratar de eliminar cualquier impedimento, no vaya a ser que yo mismo esté obstaculizando mi camino. Si no soy un vaso apto para que el Maestro me use, tengo que averiguar por qué no me puede usar para que, en todo lo que de mí dependa, me prepare para servir de la mejor manera al Maestro. Sé que si soy apto para que él me use, así lo hará; y si no lo hace, debe ser porque hay algo en mí que no está bien.

Cualquiera que sea la razón de tu fracaso, debe tener cura. Con toda certeza no debe ser algo grave, que constituya una dificultad insuperable para el Maestro. Por la gracia de Dios él quitará de ti ese impedimento para que nunca más te prive de tu poder. Busca entonces esa razón, mira con ambos ojos y busca con la ayuda de la luz más brillante que puedas encontrar, para que encuentres lo que está estorbando al Espíritu de Dios y restrinjas tu propia utilidad.

A través de la Biblia en un año: Eclesiastés 5–8

La preparación

«Mi hijo Salomón, pensaba David, es muy joven e inexperto, y el templo que hay que construir para el Señor debe ser el más grande y famoso de toda la tierra; por eso le dejaré todo listo». Así que antes de morir David dejó todo listo.

1 CRÓNICAS 22:5

En los inicios de la historia cristiana, hubo una preparación previa de la iglesia antes de que se expandiera. Observa los obedientes discípulos sentados en el Aposento Alto, esperando ansiosos. Cada corazón presente había sufrido la muerte del Señor, y cada uno de ellos esperaba recibir el poder del Espíritu prometido. Allí, con un corazón y una mente, esperaban y velaban en oración, hasta que vino el Consolador, y con él fueron añadidas tres mil almas.

Un hombre que no muestra sensibilidad ni compasión por otras almas puede ser usado en alguna ocasión para ganar un alma. La buena palabra que predica no dejará de ser buena porque el proclamador no tenga el derecho de declarar los estatutos de Dios. Pero como regla general, los que traen las almas a Cristo son aquellos que primero han sentido una agonía y un deseo ferviente de que las almas se salven. En esto reflejamos el carácter de nuestro Maestro. Él es el gran Salvador de los hombres, pero antes de que pudiera salvar a otros, aprendió en su carne a solidarizarse con ellos. Lloró sobre Jerusalén, sudó gotas de sangre en Getsemaní, fue y es un Gran Sacerdote que sufrió nuestros dolores. Como Capitán de nuestra salvación, al traer muchos hijos a la gloria, los sufrimientos lo perfeccionaron. Ni siquiera Jesús fue a predicar sin antes haber pasado noches enteras orando e intercediendo y derramando lágrimas por la salvación de sus oyentes.

A través de la Biblia en un año: Eclesiastés 9–12

Incluso unos pocos

Así que Jonatán le dijo a su escudero: «Vamos a cruzar hacia la guarnición de esos paganos. Espero que el Señor nos ayude, pues para él no es difícil salvarnos, ya sea con muchos o con pocos».

1 SAMUEL 14:6

En general, cuando Dios tiene el propósito de bendecir una iglesia, comienza de esta forma: dos o tres personas en ella están preocupadas por la situación actual y hasta se angustian por ello. Quizá no se comunican entre ellos ni conocen de su dolor común, pero comienzan a orar con un deseo ferviente y una insistencia incansable. Los motiva la pasión por ver un avivamiento en la iglesia. Piensan en esto cuando se van a dormir, sueñan con eso, meditan en esto cuando van caminando por la calle. Esa sola cosa los consume. Se preocupan y angustian por las almas que se están perdiendo, sufren dolores de parto por las almas. Cuando sale el sol, las cimas de las montañas son las primeras en recibir su luz, y aquellos que viven siempre cerca de Dios serán los primeros en sentir la influencia de la frescura que vendrá. Si el Señor me diera una docena de hombres de oración perseverantes, apasionados por las almas, por su gracia sacudiríamos Londres de punta a cabo. El trabajo continuaría sin la mayoría de ustedes, cristianos, quizá algunos solo estorban la marcha del ejército. Pero denme doce hombres que sean como el león y como el cordero, que sientan un ferviente amor por Cristo y por las almas, y nada será imposible para su fe.

A través de la Biblia en un año: 2 Pedro 1–3

A través de la iglesia

Y mandó a la gente que se sentara sobre la hierba. Tomó los cinco panes y los dos pescados y, mirando al cielo, los bendijo. Luego partió los panes y se los dio a los discípulos, quienes los repartieron a la gente. Todos comieron hasta quedar satisfechos, y los discípulos recogieron doce canastas llenas de pedazos que sobraron. Los que comieron fueron unos cinco mil hombres, sin contar a las mujeres y a los niños.

MATEO 14:19-21

El mundo perece por falta de conocimiento. ¿Alguno de nosotros pensó alguna vez en la China? Tu imaginación no puede concebir tal cantidad de población en ese poderoso imperio, sin Dios, sin Cristo, extraños a la heredad de Israel. Pero China no es el único país en esta situación, existen otras grandes naciones que viven en la oscuridad; la gran serpiente se ha enrollado alrededor del mundo y, ¿quién lo librará de ella? Reflexiona en esta ciudad y sus millones de habitantes. ¡Cuánto pecado debe ver la luna desde allá arriba! ¡Cuánto pecado debe ver el Día del Señor! Porque son muchas las transgresiones de esta malvada ciudad. Babilonia no pudo haber sido más corrupta que Londres, ni más culpable, porque no tenía la luz que Londres recibió un día. Hermanos, mientras que la iglesia continúe adormecida en su letargo no hay esperanza para la China, no hay esperanza para el mundo, no hay esperanza para nuestra ciudad. Es a través de la iglesia que viene la bendición. Cristo multiplica el pan y lo da a los discípulos, la multitud solo puede adquirirlo a través de los discípulos. ¡Ay, es tiempo de que las iglesias se despierten a favor de los millones que están muriendo!

A través de la Biblia en un año: Cantar de los Cantares 1-4

Más importante que el aliento

Si mi pueblo, que lleva mi nombre, se humilla y ora, y me busca y abandona su mala conducta, yo lo escucharé desde el cielo, perdonaré su pecado y restauraré su tierra. Mantendré abiertos mis ojos, y atentos mis oídos a las oraciones que se eleven en este lugar.

2 Crónicas 7:14-15

Nunca desmayes en la oración. Cuando no tienes deseos de orar, es una alerta de que debes orar más. Ningún hombre tiene tanta necesidad de orar como aquel a quien no le interesa hacerlo. Si puedes orar por largo rato, entonces no representa ningún sacrificio para ti, pero si no puedes y no deseas orar, entonces tienes que orar o el malvado se aprovechará de tu situación. Él está listo para arruinar a aquel que se olvida del trono de la misericordia. Cuando el corazón se muestra apático ante la oración, el hombre está padeciendo una peligrosa enfermedad. ¿Cómo puede cansarse de orar? Esto es esencial para la vida. Si alguien se cansa de respirar, de seguro está a punto de morir; si alguien se cansa de orar, tenemos que orar mucho por él, porque está corriendo un gran riesgo.

A través de la Biblia en un año: Cantar de los Cantares 5–8

Nuestro más sagrado llamado

¡Alabado sea Dios, Padre de nuestro Señor Jesucristo! Por su gran misericordia, nos ha hecho nacer de nuevo mediante la resurrección de Jesucristo, para que tengamos una esperanza viva y recibamos una herencia indestructible, incontaminada e inmarchitable. Tal herencia está reservada en el cielo para ustedes, a quienes el poder de Dios protege mediante la fe hasta que llegue la salvación que se ha de revelar en los últimos tiempos.

1 PEDRO 1:3-5

En la actualidad, tal parece que la opinión de muchos es que el papel de la iglesia es educar a las personas. Te aseguro que la educación es algo muy valiosa, tan valiosa que estoy convencido de que todas las iglesias cristianas se regocijan de tener un sistema nacional de educación que, al encausarse de forma correcta, capacita a los niños de esta nación y coloca las llaves del conocimiento en sus manos. Pero si la iglesia de Dios piensa que está en el mundo solo para capacitar las facultades mentales, ha cometido un grave error porque el objetivo del cristianismo no es educar a los hombres para las ocupaciones seculares, o educarlos en las más finas artes o en las profesiones elegantes, o capacitarlos para disfrutar la belleza de la naturaleza o los encantos de la poesía. Jesucristo no vino al mundo para ninguna de estas cosas, sino que vino a buscar y salvar lo que se había perdido, y ha dado a su iglesia la misma encomienda, y traicionaría al Maestro que la envió si al contemplar la belleza del arte y la naturaleza se olvidara de que predicar a Cristo y a este crucificado es el único objetivo para el cual existe entre los hijos de los hombres. El negocio de la iglesia es la salvación.

A través de la Biblia en un año: 1 Juan 1–5

Todo para todos

Aunque soy libre respecto a todos, de todos me he hecho esclavo para ganar a tantos como sea posible.
1 CORINTIOS 9:19

Pablo siempre hizo su trabajo con una profunda simpatía por aquellos que lo rodeaban, simpatía que lo hizo adaptarse a cada caso en particular. Si hablaba con un judío, no comenzaba proclamando que él era el apóstol enviado a los gentiles, sino que decía que era judío, porque de hecho lo era. No preguntaba acerca de nacionalidades ni ceremonias. Su deseo era hablarle al judío de aquel de quién Isaías había dicho: «Despreciado y rechazado por los hombres, varón de dolores, hecho para el sufrimiento» (Isaías 53:3), de modo que pudiera creer en Jesús y ser salvo. Si se encontraba con un gentil, el apóstol de los gentiles no mostraba ningún escrúpulo hacia ellos, como era de esperar de alguien que fue educado en los preceptos del judaísmo. Comía lo que comían los gentiles y bebía lo que ellos bebían, se sentaba y se relacionaba con ellos; se comportaba como otro gentil más entre ellos, nunca preguntaba nada acerca de la circuncisión o la incircuncisión, sino que su único deseo era hablarles de Cristo, quien vino al mundo para salvar tanto a judíos como a gentiles y hacerlos un solo pueblo. Si se encontraba con un griego, hablaba con él como lo hizo en el Areópago, con un lenguaje apropiado para dirigirse a los cultos atenienses. Se hizo todo para todos, a fin de salvar a algunos por todos los medios posibles. Así que tú, cristiano, tu negocio en esta vida es llevar a los hombres al conocimiento de Cristo por medio del poder del Espíritu Santo, y todo lo demás debe tributar a ese objetivo. Si logras salvarlos, todó lo demás vendrá a su debido tiempo.

A través de la Biblia en un año: Isaías 1–4

Semejantes a Dios

Entre los débiles me hice débil, a fin de ganar a los débiles. Me hice todo para todos, a fin de salvar a algunos por todos los medios posibles. Todo esto lo hago por causa del evangelio, para participar de sus frutos.
1 CORINTIOS 9:22-23

Anhelar la salvación de otros nos hace semejantes a Dios. ¿Deseamos el bienestar de los hombres? Dios lo desea. ¿Anhelamos librarlos del infierno? Día tras día Dios lleva a cabo esa obra de gracia. ¿Podemos decir que no nos complacemos con la muerte de aquellos que mueren? Jehová ha declarado eso mismo en uno de sus juramentos. ¿Lloramos por los pecadores? ¿Acaso no lloró también por ellos el Hijo de Dios? ¿Trabajamos para que se conviertan? ¿No murió él para que ellos pudieran vivir? Eres semejante a Dios si en tu espíritu arde esta pasión.

Esta es una expresión de tu amor a Dios, así como de tu amor a los hombres. Al amar al Creador sentimos misericordia por sus criaturas caídas y un amor benévolo hacia las obras de sus manos. Si amamos a Dios, sentimos lo que él siente, y al considerar los misterios del juicio, no podemos permitir que aquellos que él ha creado se pierdan para siempre.

Cuando amamos a Dios, lamentamos que el resto de los hombres no lo ame también. Nos inquieta ver que el mundo entero está bajo el maligno, enemistado con su Creador, peleado con aquel que es el único que puede bendecirlos.

Si amamos a otros debemos, así como Pablo, ser sabios para atraerlos, sabios para persuadirlos, sabios para convencerlos, sabios para animarlos; tenemos que aprender a utilizar los medios a nuestro alcance y descubrir en nosotros los talentos que de otro modo habrían quedado enterrados, si el deseo ferviente de salvar a los hombres no hubiera removido el suelo.

A través de la Biblia en un año: Isaías 5–8

Quita los ídolos

No se vuelvan a los ídolos inútiles, ni se hagan dioses de metal fundido. Yo soy el Señor su Dios.

LEVÍTICO 19:4

En todas las épocas, desde la caída del hombre, ha existido la tendencia en el corazón humano de olvidarse de Dios y huir de su presencia. La idolatría ha sido el pecado de todas las naciones, incluyendo el pueblo escogido por Dios, los judíos, e incluyendo ciertas personas que se llaman cristianas pero se construyen ídolos de cruces e imágenes. Este principio impuro de no tomar en cuenta a Dios y poner algo en nuestras mentes entre nosotros y nuestro Creador, se presenta en todo lugar, en cualquier tipo de pensamiento.

Cuando el hombre estudia la obra de Dios en la naturaleza, con frecuencia coloca un velo para tapar al Creador. Ya que Dios actúa de una manera determinada, llaman a esa forma de actuar ley, y luego hablan de esas leyes como si fueran fuerzas o poderes de ellos y sobre ellos, y así echan a Dios de su propio universo permitiendo que los ídolos del mundo científico llamados «leyes naturales» ocupen su lugar.

En el campo de la providencia encontrarás personas que, en vez de buscar la mano de Dios en todas las cosas, buscan causas secundarias, buscan causas de prosperidad y se sienten desanimados si no las encuentran, o ven los motivos de aflicción y se enojan contra ellos, en vez de inclinarse ante el Dios que los ha usado para corregirlos. Es fácil crear ídolos de causas secundarias y olvidar al Dios que está presente en todas partes, causando que todas las cosas ayuden a bien. Es muy triste que este principio malvado se introduzca en la iglesia; sin embargo, es bien difícil de eliminar. Puedes cerrar todas las puertas tan rápido como quieras, pero los fabricantes de ídolos entrarán con sus instrumentos.

A través de la Biblia en un año: Isaías 9–12

Trabaja en equipo

¿Quién eres tú para juzgar al siervo de otro? Que se mantenga en pie, o que caiga, es asunto de su propio señor. Y se mantendrá en pie, porque el Señor tiene poder para sostenerlo.

ROMANOS 14:4

Si todos estamos bajo la autoridad del mismo Maestro, entonces no discutamos. Es penoso que los ministros se critiquen unos a otros y que los maestros de Escuelas Dominicales hagan lo mismo. Es una actitud miserable no poder soportar ver el bien que han hecho otras denominaciones diferentes a la nuestra que tienen otro estilo de trabajo. Si un nuevo labrador llega al campo y usa una chaqueta de un corte diferente y un pico con una forma distinta, ¿debo convertirme en su enemigo? Si hace su trabajo mejor de lo que yo hago el mío, ¿debo sentirme celoso?

Hermano, si el gran Señor te empleó, no tienes por qué cuestionar lo que hace. Quizá no me guste cómo te ves y no sé cómo podré trabajar contigo, pero si el Señor te empleó, no tengo derecho a juzgarte, porque me atrevería a afirmar que te parezco tan raro como tú a mí. Si se inventan nuevos métodos de predicar el evangelio, deja que los hermanos los usen; y si no los podemos imitar, sintamos al menos que todavía somos uno solo, porque «uno es nuestro Maestro, Jesucristo».

A través de la Biblia en un año: Isaías 13–16

Ten fe en Dios

Ahora bien, la fe es la garantía de lo que se espera, la certeza de lo que no se ve. Gracias a ella fueron aprobados los antiguos.
HEBREOS 11:1-2

Siempre que Dios ha hecho una obra poderosa, la ha hecho mediante el uso de un instrumento insignificante. Para derrotar a Goliat utilizó al pequeño David, cuando no era más que un jovencito. Cuando Dios mató a Sísara, fue mediante una mujer que usó un martillo y un clavo. Dios ha llevado a cabo sus más grandes obras utilizando los instrumentos más insignificantes: este es un hecho que se repite en todas las obras de Dios. Pedro, un pescador que estuvo presente en Pentecostés. Lutero, un humilde monje que protagonizó el movimiento de la Reforma. Whitefield, un mesero de una taberna en Gloucester en los tiempos del avivamiento del siglo diecinueve, y así será hasta el final de los tiempos. Dios no utiliza las carrozas y los caballos de Faraón sino que trabaja por medio de la vara de Moisés; no muestra sus maravillas en el torbellino y la tempestad, sino que lo hace mediante el silbido apacible, para que toda la gloria y el honor sean suyos.

¿No nos anima eso a ti y a mí? ¿Por qué no puede Dios emplearnos para llevar a cabo su obra poderosa en este lugar? Además, en todas estas historias de las obras poderosas de Dios en los tiempos pasados hemos notado que siempre que Dios hizo algo grande, fue por medio de alguien que tenía una gran fe. Los hombres que tienen una fe grande hacen grandes cosas. Fue la fe de Elías la que derrotó a los profetas de Baal. Lo mismo sucedió con Whitefield; él creyó y esperó que Dios hiciera grandes cosas. Cuando se dirigió al púlpito, creyó que Dios iba a bendecir a su pueblo, y Dios lo hizo. Una fe pequeña puede hacer pequeñas cosas, pero una fe grande recibirá gran honor.

A través de la Biblia en un año: Isaías 17–20

Pasado, presente y futuro

«Vienen días» afirma el Señor, «en los cuales el que ara alcanzará al segador y el que pisa las uvas, al sembrador».

AMÓS 9:13

Cuando las personas escuchan lo que Dios hizo en el pasado, una de las cosas que dicen es: «Ah, pero eso fue hace mucho tiempo». Piensan que los tiempos han cambiado desde entonces. Otros entre ustedes dicen: «Bueno, considero esas cosas grandes prodigios, milagros. No podemos esperar que sucedan todos los días». Esa es la razón por la cual no las vemos en la actualidad. Si hubiéramos aprendido a esperarlas, sin duda las obtendríamos, pero las colocaríamos en un estante, como si fueran cosas fuera de nuestro estilo de religión moderado, como curiosidades de la historia de las Escrituras. Creemos que esas cosas, aunque ciertas, son prodigios de la Providencia, no podemos imaginarlas como parte del trabajo ordinario de su poder maravilloso. Les ruego, hermanos, que desechen esa idea, que la saquen de su mente. Todo lo que Dios ha hecho en su propósito de convertir a los pecadores debe considerarse como un precedente, porque «La mano del Señor no es corta para salvar, ni es sordo su oído para oír» (Isaías 59:1). ¿Ha cambiado Dios? ¿Acaso no es él un Dios inmutable, el mismo ayer, hoy y siempre? ¿No es eso un argumento más que suficiente para pensar que lo que Dios hizo en algún momento lo puede volver a hacer? Incluso, creo que debo ir un poco más allá y decir que lo que una vez hizo es una profecía de lo que hará otra vez, que se repetirán las poderosas obras que ha llevado a cabo en los tiempos pasados, y otra vez se cantará en Sión la canción del Señor, y una vez más será glorificado.

A través de la Biblia en un año: Isaías 21–24

Odia tu pecado

Y ahora, queridos hijos, permanezcamos en él para que, cuando se manifieste, podamos presentarnos ante él confiadamente, seguros de no ser avergonzados en su venida.

1 JUAN 2:28

Cuando la ley de Dios nos dice: «No harás», está colocando una señal de peligro que nos advierte acerca de los lugares peligrosos. Y cuando dice: «Esto harás», está señalándonos el camino mejor y más seguro. No hay nada en la ley de Dios que te prive de la felicidad; solo te prohíbe lo que te causará dolor. Sabemos que es así y por eso nos detenemos e inclinamos nuestro rostro y lamentamos haber sido tan tontos como para cometer esa transgresión, tan malvados en nuestra obstinación suicida como para hacer aquello que Dios odia y que tanto nos daña.

Recuerden que les estoy hablando a aquellos de ustedes que son salvos, a aquellos cuyos pecados han sido perdonados. En lo profundo de mi corazón puedo escuchar al resto decir: «¿No nos dejarás unirnos contigo en el arrepentimiento para también ser perdonados?» Bendito seas, sí, sí, Dios te ayudará a unirte a nosotros y si lo haces, también encontrarás el perdón porque ¡el perdón viene por el arrepentimiento!

Amados, mientras más amen a su Señor, más odiarán el pecado. Si con frecuencia te sientas a su mesa y metes tu mano en su plato, si reclinas tu cabeza en su pecho así como Juan, si eres favorecido con la hermandad del Bien Amado, sé que a menudo encontrarás lugares de reposo donde podrás derramar tus lágrimas de amargo arrepentimiento por haber pecado contra un Salvador como Jesús.

A través de la Biblia en un año: Isaías 25–28

Nosotros estuvimos allí

Por eso, de la manera que recibieron a Cristo Jesús como Señor, vivan ahora en él, arraigados y edificados en él, confirmados en la fe como se les enseñó, y llenos de gratitud.

COLOSENSES 2:6-7

El delito más grande que se ha cometido contra el cielo fue el de asesinar la deidad, cuando los hombres clavaron en la cruz al Hijo de Dios y lo mataron como si fuera un criminal. ¿Dónde están los miserables que cometieron tan horrible hecho? Aquí están, no voy a decir que están delante de nosotros porque cada uno de nosotros lleva uno adentro. ¿Cómo puedo entonces hablarle yo a ustedes? Bueno, quizá es mejor así porque entonces, desde lo más profundo de mi corazón, les puedo rogar que permanezcamos al pie de la cruz y contemos las gotas de sangre y digamos: «Estas gotas han lavado mi pecado, sin embargo, yo ayudé a derramarlas. Esas manos, esos pies, me salvaron, sin embargo, yo los clavé allí. Ese costado abierto es el refugio de mi espíritu culpable, sin embargo, mi pecado provocó ese horrible hueco. Fue mi pecado el que mató a mi Salvador». ¡Oh, pecado, tres veces maldito, fuera de aquí! ¡Fuera de aquí! Vengamos con gozo solemne, con dolor bendito, y sentémonos debajo de la cruz para ver lo que ha hecho el pecado y, sin embargo, notemos también cómo aquel que murió en la cruz del Calvario borró ese mismo pecado.

A través de la Biblia en un año: Isaías 29–32

Nuestro más querido amigo

Pero cuando se manifestaron la bondad y el amor de Dios nuestro Salvador, él nos salvó, no por nuestras propias obras de justicia sino por su misericordia. Nos salvó mediante el lavamiento de la regeneración y de la renovación por el Espíritu Santo, el cual fue derramado abundantemente sobre nosotros por medio de Jesucristo nuestro Salvador. Así lo hizo para que, justificados por su gracia, llegáramos a ser herederos que abrigan la esperanza de recibir la vida eterna.

Tito 3:4-7

¡Oh, cuánto le debemos al Espíritu Santo! Hablo con ustedes que lo conocen. Fue el Espíritu Santo el que te despertó de tu letargo, el que te convenció de pecado, el que te consoló y ¡en qué dulce forma todavía te consuela el Divino Consolador! Sin embargo, lo resistimos y lo entristecimos. ¿No recuerdas, en tu juventud, cómo traicionaste tus convicciones, cómo acallaste tu conciencia para que no te reprendiera? Ese Espíritu bendito, a quien disgustamos y rechazamos, pudiera haberse ido y habernos abandonado para no luchar más con nosotros; pero nos amó tanto que vino e hizo su morada en nosotros, y ahora habita en nosotros. Se rebajó dentro de la pequeña celda de nuestro pobre corazón para encontrar un templo y hacerlo su habitación para siempre. Ay, alma mía, ¿cómo pudiste entristecerlo alguna vez? ¿Cómo pudiste haber resistido al mejor y más tierno de los amigos?

A través de la Biblia en un año: Isaías 33–36

Protección divina

¿No son todos los ángeles espíritus dedicados al servicio divino, enviados para ayudar a los que han de heredar la salvación?
HEBREOS 1:14

¡Cuán seguros y felices nos deberíamos sentir al saber que Dios ha encargado a los ángeles para que nos cuiden! Mi querida hermana, no te pongas tan nerviosa la próxima vez que haya una pequeña tormenta, o incluso una gran tormenta. No tengas miedo, mi querido amigo, cuando la enfermedad visite tu hogar.

¡Cuán santos debiéramos ser al tener seres tan santos velando por nosotros! Si los ángeles están siempre a tu alrededor, ten en cuenta cómo te comportas. ¿Habrías hablado como lo hiciste cuando entraste por esa puerta si hubieras visto un ángel de pie a tu lado, escuchando lo que decías? Oh, no, actúas con mucho decoro cuando hay alguien cerca a quien respetas. ¡Con cuánta frecuencia controlas tu lengua afilada cuando te puede escuchar un cristiano o una cristiana a quien estimas mucho! ¡Cuántas cosas haces que no harías delante de alguien a quien amas! Ya sea que estemos solos o acompañados, evitemos pecar, porque los ángeles siempre nos están mirando, y el ángel del Señor también nos mira. Que por su gracia nos mantenga en su santo camino y, si permanecemos en él, nos libraremos de toda maldad mientras estemos aquí, y al final veremos su rostro con gran alegría y viviremos con él para siempre.

A través de la Biblia en un año: Isaías 37–40

No es lo que parece

Cuando traté de comprender todo esto, me resultó una carga insoportable, hasta que entré en el santuario de Dios; allí comprendí cuál será el destino de los malvados.

SALMO 73:16-17

Hay tiempos cuando parece que los malvados logran todo lo que se proponen. Esta tierra no es el reino de la justicia final, todavía no estamos compareciendo ante el trono del juicio de Dios. Dios permite que por el momento algunas cosas estén confusas. Aquellos que más lo estiman con frecuencia son los menos estimados por los hombres, y aquellos que no lo tienen en cuenta parecen acaparar todos los tesoros del mundo hasta que se le saltan los ojos de gordura y tienen más de lo que cualquier corazón pudiera desear. Que ningún hijo de Dios se asombre de esto.

También es cierto que los malvados triunfan y los servidores de la iniquidad se deleitan en los mejores lugares de esta tierra. Los justos no tienen que asombrarse de estar sufriendo ahora pues este ha sido el destino del pueblo de Dios en todas las épocas, y ha habido tiempos en la historia de la humanidad cuando parece que Dios está sordo ante los lamentos de su pueblo que sufre. En dichos tiempos también se ha comprobado el poder de la Palabra de Dios. Cuando tu barca atraviesa un mar en calma, la Palabra de Dios puede llegar a convertirse en letra muerta para ti, pero cuando las olas son enormes y amenazan con ahogarte, y te hundes cada vez más y temes que las profundidades te traguen, entonces comienzas a poner a prueba las promesas de Dios y a comprobar el poder de la Palabra de Dios. Cuando su dulzura inexplicable cautiva tu corazón, entonces puedes reconocer que la Palabra de Dios te ha enseñado. Te das cuenta que «dichoso es aquel a quien tú, Señor, corriges; aquel a quien instruyes en tu ley» (Salmo 94:12).

A través de la Biblia en un año: Isaías 41–44

El amor y la disciplina

En la lucha que ustedes libran contra el pecado, todavía no han tenido que resistir hasta derramar su sangre. Y ya han olvidado por completo las palabras de aliento que como a hijos se les dirige: «Hijo mío, no tomes a la ligera la disciplina del Señor ni te desanimes cuando te reprenda, porque el Señor disciplina a los que ama, y azota a todo el que recibe como hijo. Lo que soportan es para su disciplina, pues Dios los está tratando como a hijos. ¿Qué hijo hay a quien el padre no disciplina?»

HEBREOS 12:4-7

El amor y la misericordia de Dios hacia sus hijos es constante; cuando estos se desvían, él lamenta toda su culpa y su pecado. Entonces toma la vara en su mano y, a veces, los hace llorar con amargura debido al dolor que el castigo provoca. Aplica la vara a sus mismas almas y el hierro a sus espíritus, los hace llorar y gemir y suspirar, pero todo lo que hace es en su misericordia, porque está decidido a salvarlos. No permitirá que vayan sin castigo, porque tiene misericordia de su necedad y su pecado. Y nota también que el propio castigo es un acto de misericordia, no hay un latigazo más de los que deben ser, ni un golpe más de los que están determinados, ni una gota de amargura más allá de las que son, y dicha gota nunca es demasiado amarga; la aflicción tiene su medida y es balanceada y sopesada, todo ocurre como debe ser, nunca más de lo que es necesario.

A través de la Biblia en un año: Isaías 45–48

Una fragancia santa

Sin embargo, gracias a Dios que en Cristo siempre nos lleva triunfantes y, por medio de nosotros, esparce por todas partes la fragancia de su conocimiento. Porque para Dios nosotros somos el aroma de Cristo entre los que se salvan y entre los que se pierden. Para éstos somos olor de muerte que los lleva a la muerte; para aquellos olor de vida que los lleva a la vida.

2 CORINTIOS 2:14-16

El Señor Jesús mantiene una íntima comunión con aquellos que lo conocen y ejerce una poderosa influencia sobre ellos. Él es bendito, y produce bendición. Para quienes lo aman, Jesucristo se convierte en el sabor de vida que los lleva a la vida. Para aquellos que son rebeldes y lo desprecian una y otra vez, se convierte en sabor de muerte que los lleva a la muerte. Nuestro Salvador, entonces, ejerce una influencia sobre todos aquellos que entran en comunión e intimidad con él. Si comparo dicha naturaleza humana con el barro, la tengo que comparar con el barro perfumado, que esparce su perfume por todas partes. No puedes escuchar hablar de Jesús sin recibir o rechazar una bendición. Repito, él se convierte en una bendición para todos aquellos que lo rodean o, por el contrario, si se rechaza esa bendición, ocasiona un sentimiento de culpa en aquellos que lo rechazan. Él puede ser, o bien la roca sobre la que fundamos nuestra esperanza y nuestra fe, o la piedra de tropiezo que hace caer a los que tropiezan en su Palabra, al ser desobedientes.

A través de la Biblia en un año: Isaías 49–52

¿Un siervo leal o un enemigo?

Luego miré, y oí la voz de muchos ángeles que estaban alrededor del trono, de los seres vivientes y de los ancianos. El número de ellos era millares de millares y millones de millones. Cantaban con todas sus fuerzas: «¡Digno es el Cordero, que ha sido sacrificado, de recibir el poder, la riqueza y la sabiduría, la fortaleza y la honra, la gloria y la alabanza!»

APOCALIPSIS 5:11-12

De nada sirve que un hombre diga, refiriéndose a un monarca: «Siento un gran respeto por el monarca en cuanto a su carácter en particular. No haría nada para dañarlo, hasta podría tenerle respeto. Pero como rey nunca le rendiré homenaje, nunca lo obedeceré. De hecho, haré todo lo que pueda para quitar la corona de su cabeza». ¿Pudiera el rey considerar a esa persona como otra cosa que no fuera su enemigo? Sería en vano que el hombre dijera: «En privado puedo ser tu amigo». El rey diría: «Oh, pero yo estimo mi corona tanto como mi vida». Así mismo el Señor Jesús no puede separar su derecho a la corona de su deidad. Él, «siendo por naturaleza Dios, no consideró el ser igual a Dios como algo a qué aferrarse» (Filipenses 2:6), y es llamado «Dios sobre todas las cosas. ¡Alabado sea por siempre!» (Romanos 9:5). Aquel que caminó sobre las olas del mar de Galilea, cuya voz hizo a la muerte soltar su presa, aquel que abrió las puertas del paraíso para que entrara el ladrón moribundo, dice ser igual al Padre Eterno, y así como él es «Dios sobre todas las cosas»; por tanto, es en vano que digas que respetas su carácter como hombre si no lo aceptas en su deidad. A menos que lo aceptes en su carácter oficial como Salvador de los pecadores, serás contado entre sus enemigos.

A través de la Biblia en un año: Isaías 53–56

Un pariente cercano

«¡Que el Señor lo bendiga!» exclamó Noemí delante de su nuera. «El Señor no ha dejado de mostrar su fiel amor hacia los vivos y los muertos. Ese hombre es nuestro pariente cercano; es uno de los parientes que nos pueden redimir».

RUT 2:20

Tenemos la tentación de considerar la humanidad de nuestro Señor como algo muy diferente a nuestra propia humanidad; estamos prestos a espiritualizarla y no pensar en él como hueso de mis huesos y carne de mi carne. Todo esto es un grave error, podemos pensar que estamos honrando a Cristo al tener tal concepción, pero Cristo nunca se siente honrado con algo que no sea verdad. Él fue un hombre, un verdadero hombre, un hombre de nuestra misma raza, el Hijo del Hombre. Es cierto que fue un hombre representativo, el segundo Adán: «Ya que ellos son de carne y hueso, él también compartió esa naturaleza» (Hebreos 2:14).

Ahora bien, esa participación en nuestra naturaleza lo acerca a nosotros. En su naturaleza como hombre, aunque también era Dios, fue, de acuerdo a la ley hebrea, nuestro pariente, nuestro pariente cercano. Ahora, según la ley, si se perdía una herencia, el pariente más cercano tenía derecho a redimirla. Nuestro Señor Jesucristo ejerció su derecho legal y, al vernos vendidos como esclavos y privados de nuestra herencia, vino para redimirnos, tanto a nosotros como a todas nuestras posesiones perdidas. Es una gran bendición tener un pariente como ese. La circunstancia de mayor gracia en la vida de Rut fue dirigirse a los campos de Booz y descubrir que él era su pariente cercano. Y nosotros que hemos espigado en los campos de la misericordia alabamos al Señor porque su Hijo único es nuestro pariente cercano, nuestro hermano, nacido para la adversidad.

A través de la Biblia en un año: Isaías 57–60

Una elección redentora

Pablo, siervo de Dios y apóstol de Jesucristo, llamado para que, mediante la fe, los elegidos de Dios lleguen a conocer la verdadera religión.

TITO 1:1

En las Escrituras hay una doctrina que proviene del Padre en particular. Es la doctrina de la elección. El Padre nos ha elegido para que seamos su pueblo. En las Escrituras, por todas partes, esto se señala como la obra de la primera persona de la bendita Trinidad: elegir para sí mismo un pueblo que viva para alabar su gloria. Ahora bien, hay muchos que quieren entender esta doctrina. He conocido a muchos inconversos que quieren entenderla. Con frecuencia recibo cartas de personas que no la comprenden. Dicen que sentirían paz si lograran entender esa doctrina. Pero si esta noche hay algunos de ellos aquí, les hablaré. Tú no puedes entender la elección, no puedes llegar al Padre por un camino recto desde donde estás. Solo lee la señal: «Nadie llega al Padre sino por mí (Jesús)» (Juan 14:6). Entonces, si quieres entender la elección, comienza con la redención. Nunca entenderás la elección eterna si no comienzas en la cruz. Empieza con esto: «en Cristo, Dios estaba reconciliando al mundo consigo mismo, no tomándole en cuenta sus pecados» (2 Corintios 5:19).

Sería algo raro que nuestros hijos insistieran en ir a la universidad antes de ir al colegio. Sería algo extraño si un hombre tomara su Biblia y comenzara a leerla de atrás hacia delante y leyera primero el Apocalipsis, y si todos los hombres pronunciaran la oración del Señor comenzando por el «Amén» y así siguieran hasta llegar al «Padre Nuestro». Sin embargo, algunos insisten en esto. Les fascina el misterio de la soberanía y la elección y se sienten obligados a comenzar por ello. No existe otro camino a la elección que no sea la redención.

A través de la Biblia en un año: Isaías 61–63

Comienza y termina con Cristo

En lo que atañe a la ley, ésta intervino para que aumentara la transgresión. Pero allí donde abundó el pecado, sobreabundó la gracia, a fin de que, así como reinó el pecado en la muerte, reine también la gracia que nos trae justificación y vida eterna por medio de Jesucristo nuestro Señor.

ROMANOS 5:20-21

Cada día me doy cuenta que lo más saludable para mi alma es tratar de caminar siempre en santidad, pero para hacer esto, primero tengo que venir a Jesucristo como un pecador. Voy a tratar de ser perfecto, voy a luchar por tener todas las virtudes y abandonar todas las falsedades pero, al permanecer ante Dios, mi mayor felicidad es sentarme en aquel lugar donde conocí a Jesús por primera vez, en la roca de su salvación, que no tiene nada que ver con mi propia justicia, sino con la suya. Depende de esto: la manera más feliz de vivir es hacerlo como un pobre pecador que es nada en sí mismo y tiene a Jesucristo como el todo en todo. Puedes alcanzar un alto grado en la santificación, hacer progresos extraordinarios en la gracia, desarrollar todas las virtudes que quieras; pero ruego con fervor que nunca pongas esto en el lugar que solo Cristo debe ocupar. Si has comenzado en Cristo, termina en él. Si has comenzado en la carne y continúas en la carne, sabemos cuáles serán los nefastos resultados. Pero si has empezado con Cristo como tu Alfa, deja que él sea tu Omega. Mi oración es que cuando alcances ciertas virtudes, nunca pienses que estás en un lugar más elevado, porque no es así, sino que te están encaminando a tu propia ruina.

A través de la Biblia en un año: Isaías 64–66

La piedad práctica

Al partir para Macedonia, te encargué que permanecieras en Éfeso y les ordenaras a algunos supuestos maestros que dejen de enseñar doctrinas falsas y de prestar atención a leyendas y genealogías interminables. Esas cosas provocan controversias en vez de llevar adelante la obra de Dios que es por la fe. Debes hacerlo así para que el amor brote de un corazón limpio, de una buena conciencia y de una fe sincera. Algunos se han desviado de esa línea de conducta y se han enredado en discusiones inútiles.

1 TIMOTEO 1:3-6

Algunos cristianos son muy curiosos pero no son obedientes. Descuidan preceptos claros y, sin embargo, tratan de resolver problemas difíciles. Recuerdo uno de ellos que parecía estar siempre ocupado en las trompetas, los sellos y el resto de los símbolos apocalípticos. Sabía mucho acerca de ese tema pero tenía una familia de siete hijos y nunca celebraban un tiempo de oración familiar. Si hubiera dejado un poco las trompetas y los sellos para ocuparse de sus hijos, habría sido mucho mejor. He conocido hombres que saben mucho de Daniel y de Ezequiel y, sin embargo, con frecuencia se olvidan de Éxodo 20 y no están muy claros acerca de Romanos 8. No critico a tales hombres por estudiar a Daniel o a Ezequiel, todo lo contrario, pero hubiera querido que fueran más celosos en la búsqueda de la conversión de los pecadores de su vecindario y más cuidadosos para ayudar a los santos en necesidad. Reconozco el valor de estudiar el significado de los pies de la imagen en la visión de Nabucodonosor y la importancia de conocer los reinos que representan cada uno de los diez dedos, pero no estoy de acuerdo con que estos asuntos ocupen el lugar de practicar la piedad. Si dicho hombre dedicara el tiempo que emplea en el estudio de complicados asuntos teológicos a llevar a cabo una obra de evangelismo en los alrededores de su casa, sus semejantes recibirían mayor beneficio y Dios, mayor gloria.

A través de la Biblia en un año: 2 Juan, 3 Juan, Judas

Procura depender de la oración

¿Está afligido alguno entre ustedes? Que ore. ¿Está alguno de buen ánimo? Que cante alabanzas.
SANTIAGO 5:13

Los problemas alejan a los hombres carnales de la religión que dicen que profesan pero unen al verdadero rebaño, tal y como cuando las ovejas se asustan y se alarman, buscan al Buen Pastor. Mientras más dolor sentimos, más gracia necesitamos y más cerca de nuestro Consolador venimos. «¡Más cerca de Dios!» es el clamor del santo cuando está en problemas. El consuelo de un hijo de Dios en la oscuridad es la oración. La adversidad, que es una bendición del Espíritu Santo, nos hace recordar las promesas. Las promesas alimentan nuestra fe y la fe nos conduce a la oración, Dios oye y responde nuestra petición. Esta es la cadena de acontecimientos que experimenta un alma atribulada. Cuando pasemos por la tribulación, ya que conocemos las promesas, ejercitemos nuestra fe y vayamos a Dios en oración; porque nunca se ha vuelto un hombre a Dios de todo su corazón sin que Dios no se vuelva a él. Si decidimos orar, podemos confiar en que Dios decidirá bendecirnos. Las bendiciones se encuentran en el camino al cielo; su sombra está siempre sobre nosotros. «Días y años nos has afligido, nos has hecho sufrir; ¡devuélvenos ahora ese tiempo en alegría!» (Salmo 90:15).

A través de la Biblia en un año: Jeremías 1–4

Prisioneros espirituales

Pero la Escritura declara que todo el mundo es prisionero del pecado, para que mediante la fe en Jesucristo lo prometido se conceda a los que creen. Antes de venir esta fe, la ley nos tenía presos, encerrados hasta que la fe se revelara.

GÁLATAS 3:22-23

¿Alguna vez has visitado una celda de un prisionero condenado a muerte? Asomarte a ella y ver a dicho hombre allí es suficiente para hacerte desmayar. ¡Imagina que fuera tu hijo! ¡Imagina que fuera tu esposo! ¡Imagina que fuera tu hermano! Pero escucha: «El que no cree ya está condenado» (Juan 3:18). Perdónennos, ustedes nuestros familiares inconversos, por decirles que corren un tremendo peligro al estar sentados en la celda de los condenados a muerte y serán ejecutados en breve, a no ser que la infinita misericordia les conceda el perdón gratuito. Qué horribles escenas debe ver una persona en un campo de batalla. Cuando veo un hombre que sangra porque se ha cortado me siento el corazón en la boca, no puedo resistir la escena; ¡cuánto más al ver hombres desmembrados, desentrañados, retorciéndose en sus últimos minutos de vida! ¡Qué horroroso es caminar entre un montón de cadáveres y tropezar a cada instante con alguno de ellos! Sin embargo, ¿qué es la muerte física comparada con la muerte espiritual? Qué horroroso es vivir bajo el mismo techo con familiares que están muertos en vida, muertos para Dios. El pensamiento está lleno de angustia. Si Dios contendiera con nuestros parientes que están muertos desde el punto de vista espiritual, si le diera vida a aquel que ha sido «puesto aparte, entre los muertos; parece un cadáver que yace entre los muertos» (Salmo 88:5), ¡qué gran consuelo recibiríamos nosotros!

A través de la Biblia en un año: Jeremías 5–8

El bálsamo del servicio

Alabado sea el Dios y Padre de nuestro Señor Jesucristo, Padre misericordioso y Dios de toda consolación, quien nos consuela en todas nuestras tribulaciones para que con el mismo consuelo que de Dios hemos recibido, también nosotros podamos consolar a todos los que sufren.

2 CORINTIOS 1:3-4

Con frecuencia nuestro trabajo es una gran fuente de consuelo. En el campo de batalla de Gettysburgo hubo una horrible confrontación y entre los heridos se encontraba un cierto capellán llamado Eastman cuyo caballo le había dañado la espalda al caer sobre él. La noche llegó con su densa y temible oscuridad y aquel hombre, incapaz de ponerse en pie, yacía allí en su profundo dolor, pero en eso escuchó alguien que exclamaba con una débil voz: «¡Oh, Dios!» Al escucharlo, se sintió motivado y se arrastró por los charcos de sangre entre los muertos hasta llegar al lado de aquel moribundo y le habló de Jesús y de la salvación gratuita que le ofrecía. El hombre murió lleno de esperanza y precisamente entonces vinieron dos soldados y le dijeron a Eastman que no muy lejos de allí se estaba muriendo el capitán y debían llevarlo hasta allí. De modo que, a pesar de su intenso dolor, se dispuso a llevar a cabo su obra de misericordia, y mientras aún era de noche, habló de Jesús a muchos hombres moribundos. ¿Podía acaso haber tenido un alivio mayor para su dolor? Pienso que no. ¿Por qué? Porque creo que el haber permanecido allí sobre su espalda sin otra cosa que hacer que no fuera gemir y llorar habría sido horrible, sin embargo, el hecho de ser llevado a otros, a pesar de su angustia y dolor, para proclamar el mensaje de misericordia, ¡hizo soportable el dolor de su espalda! Así mismo cuando extrañas a un amigo, o has perdido alguna posesión, o tu espíritu está cargado, encontrarás tu consuelo más seguro al servir a Dios con todas tus fuerzas.

A través de la Biblia en un año: Jeremías 9–12

La más preciosa labor

Por eso les dije: «Ustedes son testigos de nuestra desgracia. Jerusalén está en ruinas, y sus puertas han sido consumidas por el fuego. ¡Vamos, anímense! Reconstruyamos la muralla de Jerusalén para que ya nadie se burle de nosotros!» Entonces les conté cómo la bondadosa mano de Dios había estado conmigo y les relaté lo que el rey me había dicho. Al oír esto, exclamaron: «¡Manos a la obra!» Y unieron la acción a la palabra.

NEHEMÍAS 2:17-18

Pienso que el mejor trabajo que se hace para Dios, con frecuencia se lleva a cabo de una manera irregular. Cada vez más me siento como aquel viejo soldado de Waterloo cuando le preguntaron acerca del mejor uniforme que debía usar un soldado. El duque de Wellington le dijo: «Si tuviera que combatir otra vez en Waterloo, ¿cómo le gustaría ir vestido?» La respuesta fue: «Por favor, señor, me gustaría ir solo con mi camisa», creo que eso es lo mejor. Libérate de todas las cosas superfluas y enfrenta lo que sea. Allí están las multitudes, yéndose directo al infierno, y nosotros estamos considerando este modo de obrar o aquel otro, y calculando las mejores formas de no hacerlo, y creando comités para considerar y debatir, para decidir fechas y posponer, y dejar la obra suspendida por el momento. La mejor forma es levantarse y llevar a cabo el trabajo, y luego reunir al comité y debatir. Dios nos asegura que lo podemos hacer. Hijo mío, ve a trabajar hoy. Haz algo práctico, real, con resultados.

Y al referirnos a un buen trabajo, queda implícita la idea de que necesitarás esfuerzos, dedicación, seriedad, negación de uno mismo, quizá algo que exigirá perseverancia. Con toda responsabilidad tendrás que aferrarte a ello. Tendrás que entregarte a la tarea de todo corazón y dejar muchas otras cosas que estorben tu labor.

A través de la Biblia en un año: Jeremías 13–16

Vale la pena hacerlo bien

Recordarán, hermanos, nuestros esfuerzos y fatigas para proclamarles el evangelio de Dios, y cómo trabajamos día y noche para no serles una carga.
1 TESALONICENSES 2:9

Oh, hombres y mujeres cristianos, no glorificarán mucho a Dios a menos que dediquen todas sus fuerzas y consagren todo su cuerpo, alma y espíritu —todo su ser— a la obra del Señor Jesucristo. Para hacer esto no necesitan abandonar a sus familias, ni sus negocios ni sus ocupaciones seculares. Pueden servir a Dios en estas cosas. Con frecuencia constituirán oportunidades para ti, pero tienes que lanzarte a estas. Un hombre es incapaz de ganar almas para Cristo cuando él mismo está medio dormido. Tenemos que estar bien despiertos y llenos del Espíritu de Dios para librar la batalla en nombre del Señor Jesucristo. Hijo mío, ve a trabajar hoy. No vayas a jugar a ser el maestro de la Escuela Dominical. No vayas a jugar a ser el predicador. No vayas a jugar a ser el que exhorta a las personas en las calles o el que reparte los tratados. Hijo mío, ve a trabajar. Involucra tu alma en ello. Si vale la pena hacerlo, vale la pena hacerlo bien; y si vale la pena hacerlo bien, vale la pena hacerlo mejor que nunca antes; e incluso entonces, valdrá la pena hacerlo aún mejor. Porque cuando lo hayas hecho lo mejor que puedas, todavía tendrás que extenderte a algo mejor, ya que lo mejor de lo mejor es muy poco para un Dios como el nuestro y un servicio como el suyo. Hijo mío, ve a trabajar.

A través de la Biblia en un año: Jeremías 17–20

Tú eliges

Ningún sirviente puede servir a dos patrones.
LUCAS 16:13

Ay, hombre inmundo, ¿cómo puedes soñar con la salvación cuando estás lleno de suciedad? ¿Qué? ¡Tú y tu ramera, miembros de Cristo! Ay, no conoces a mi puro y santo Salvador. Él recibe a los pecadores, pero rechaza a los que se deleitan en sus iniquidades. Para ser limpio de la culpa del pecado tienes que dejar de ser indulgente ante él. No puedes continuar en tus transgresiones y mantener tu salvación, esta es una presuposición licenciosa. Cristo vino para salvarnos de nuestros pecados, no para que estemos seguros mientras hacemos lo malo. La sangre que lava nuestras manchas también trae como consecuencia odio hacia aquellas cosas que provocaron esas manchas. Si no rechazamos el pecado, no recibiremos la salvación.

Ahora hablo con mucha franqueza sobre este tema, pero aquí hay algunos de corazón puro que no saben bien cuán claro debemos hablar para despertar ciertas conciencias, pues siento vergüenza al ver que año tras año algunos se deleitan en un pecado oculto y, no obstante, asisten con frecuencia a la casa de Dios. Tú pensarías al verlos allí que están convertidos o que pronto lo estarán pero, si los siguieras hasta su casa, te asombrarías de lo que verías. Ay, amantes del pecado, no se engañen a sí mismos pues, con toda seguridad, cosecharán lo que siembren. ¿Cómo puede reinar la gracia en ustedes si son esclavos de sus propias pasiones? ¿Cómo es posible, mientras estén anclados a un pecado oculto, que sean renacidos mediante la gracia a un estado de seguridad? Si no abandonas tu pecado, puedes abandonar toda esperanza de ir al cielo; si insistes en tu pecado, el infierno te atrapará para siempre. Quiera Dios librarnos a todos del amor al pecado, porque tal liberación es la salvación.

A través de la Biblia en un año: Jeremías 21–24

Salvos de verdad

Porque así dice el Señor omnipotente, el Santo de Israel: «En el arrepentimiento y la calma está su salvación, en la serenidad y la confianza está su fuerza, ¡pero ustedes no lo quieren reconocer!»
Isaías 30:15

Muchas personas cometen un gran error en cuanto a la salvación, confunden el significado del término, y para ellas la salvación significa ser libradas del infierno. Ahora bien, el significado correcto de la salvación es la purificación de la maldad. En realidad, un hombre no tiene muchos deseos de ser salvo si todo lo que quiere es escapar del castigo que sus ofensas merecen. ¿Acaso ha existido algún asesino que no deseara librarse de la horca? Cuando un hombre comete un hecho de brutal violencia, y prepara su espalda para recibir los azotes, puedes estar seguro que se arrepiente de haber hecho lo que hizo, es decir, se arrepiente porque tiene que sufrir por ello, pero eso es todo, y es un todo bastante pobre. No lamenta el daño que causó a su víctima inocente, el haberla perjudicado de por vida. ¿Cuál es el valor de tal arrepentimiento?

¿Deseas tener un corazón nuevo? ¿Deseas ser como Dios quisiera que fueras: justo, amoroso, amable, casto, según el ejemplo del gran Redentor? De ser así, entonces tu deseo proviene de Dios, pero si todo lo que quieres es morir sin temor a despertar en el otro mundo en medio de un horrible lugar de tormento, y eso es todo, no hay nada de gracia en ello, y no te sorprendas si te digo que no sabes lo que significa la salvación. Busca la salvación como el reino de Dios dentro de ti, búscala de esa forma y hazlo ahora, y Dios no te la negará.

A través de la Biblia en un año: Jeremías 25–29

Todos somos responsables

Está escrito: «Tan cierto como que yo vivo» dice el Señor, «ante mí se doblará toda rodilla y toda lengua confesará a Dios». Así que cada uno de nosotros tendrá que dar cuentas de sí a Dios.

ROMANOS 14:11-12

«Rinde cuentas de tu administración» bien puede ser una orden para los impíos (Lucas 16:2). Ellos son responsables ante Dios de todo lo que tienen, o lo que alguna vez tuvieron, o lo que tendrán. La ley del Señor no es menos severa ante su pecado; son responsables ante Dios, a pesar de que intentan evadir el yugo del Todopoderoso. Como criaturas formadas por la mano divina y sustentadas por su poder, tienen el deber de servir a Dios, y si no lo hacen, Dios les reclamará: «Rinde cuentas de tu administración».

Este texto también se aplica a los hijos de Dios, los hombres temerosos de Dios, pero en un sentido diferente. En primer lugar, los hombres temerosos de Dios son hijos de Dios y permanecen en Cristo. No son solo criaturas de Dios, ya que Jesucristo pagó todo lo que debían en su condición de pecadores, y se convirtió en su Sustituto y Salvador. Por tanto, están en un lugar diferente al resto de los hombres pues, luego de haber sido adoptados en la familia de Dios y salvos por gracia, Dios les confió talentos que deben usar para su honra y gloria. Al ser salvos y llegar a ser hijos de Dios, se convierten en sus siervos y, como tales, son responsables ante él y tendrán que rendir cuentas de su mayordomía.

A través de la Biblia en un año: Jeremías 30-32

Valor infinito

¿Qué les parece? Si un hombre tiene cien ovejas y se le extravía una de ellas, ¿no dejará las noventa y nueve en las colinas para ir en busca de la extraviada?
MATEO 18:12

En estos tiempos modernos existe la tendencia de pensar poco en la conversión de los individuos y considerar la obra del Espíritu Santo en cada individuo por separado como un negocio que va demasiado lento para esta época tan progresiva. No temo afirmar que si rechazamos el método de la conversión individual llegaremos a tener un ministerio poco saludable y nos estrellaremos contra las rocas de la hipocresía. Incluso en esos tiempos gloriosos cuando el evangelio ha tenido su mayor auge y se ha expandido más rápido y ha recibido mayor gloria, su progreso ha sido según el mismo orden de la convicción de pecado, la conversión y la santificación de los individuos, quienes deben cada uno creer y ser bautizados de acuerdo a la Palabra del Señor.

Espero que ninguno de ustedes tienda a despreciar aquella oveja extraviada debido a los proliferantes métodos filosóficos que tanto se anuncian en la actualidad. Si queremos que los extraviados vengan a Cristo como grandes multitudes, como oro que suceda, debemos traerlos uno por uno. Pretender una regeneración nacional sin una regeneración personal es soñar con construir una casa sin el uso de ladrillos separados. Convéncete de que no puedes hacer nada mejor que obedecer el ejemplo de nuestro Señor Jesucristo e ir en busca de la oveja extraviada.

A través de la Biblia en un año: Jeremías 33–36

La oveja extraviada

Y si llega a encontrarla, les aseguro que se pondrá más feliz por esa sola oveja que por las noventa y nueve que no se extraviaron. Así también, el Padre de ustedes que está en el cielo no quiere que se pierda ninguno de estos pequeños.

MATEO 18:13-14

Las ovejas requieren de muchos cuidados: pueden sufrir diversas enfermedades, dolencias y tener muchas necesidades, pero cuando conoces a tu rebaño y lo quieres, al cuidarlo te sientes como en casa. Así mismo se describe el Gran Pastor cuando deja las noventa y nueve, su rebaño escogido, las ovejas que tienen comunión con él y, a su vez, con las que él tiene comunión. Sí, deja a aquellas en las que se regocija para buscar a la que le causa dolor. No voy a insistir en el hecho de que él dejó el paraíso y toda la gloria de la casa de su Padre para venir a este mundo de miseria, pero espero que recuerdes que así lo hizo. Fue un descenso maravilloso cuando él vino desde más allá de las estrellas para morar en este planeta rodeado de nubes y redimir a los hijos de los hombres. Pero recuerda, él todavía viene por medio de su Espíritu. Su obra de misericordia es permanente. El Espíritu de Dios guía a sus ministros, que son los representantes de Cristo, para que se priven del alimento de su rebaño y busquen, por medio de sus predicaciones, la salvación de las extraviadas, en cuyo carácter y conducta no hay nada que nos pueda agradar. No quiere que su iglesia dedique todos sus cuidados al rebaño que está en los pastos verdes, sino que anhela que vaya a los campos y busque a aquellas ovejas que todavía no forman parte de su bendito rebaño.

A través de la Biblia en un año: Jeremías 37–40

Consumido en el servicio

Aunque soy libre respecto a todos, de todos me he hecho esclavo para ganar a tantos como sea posible.
1 CORINTIOS 9:19

Si este es nuestro tiempo para hacer el bien, hagámoslo mientras podamos. A veces escucho a algunas personas decir: «El Sr. X trabaja mucho, trabaja demasiado». Ah, pero ninguno de nosotros hace ni la mitad de lo que debía hacer. Nunca digas que alguien hace demasiado por el Señor Jesucristo. Eso es imposible. ¿Debo yo seguir durmiendo mientras las almas perecen? ¿Debe esta carne débil mantenerme inactivo mientras los hombres mueren y el infierno se llena? Dejemos la tibieza. Si Dios nos ha hecho luz del mundo, consumámonos tal como lo hace una vela, que se consume al brindarnos su luz. Como aquella pobre niña que solo tenía una vela y trabajaba con presteza y desesperación porque pronto se consumiría, así mismo instemos nosotros a tiempo y fuera de tiempo, velando, orando, trabajando por la salvación de las almas. Si tan solo pudiéramos ver las almas perdidas y comprender su angustia indecible, nos sacudiríamos el polvo del camino y continuaríamos trabajando mientras aún se dice hoy.

A través de la Biblia en un año: Jeremías 41–44

Su ejemplo

Muy de madrugada, cuando todavía estaba oscuro, Jesús se levantó, salió de la casa y se fue a un lugar solitario, donde se puso a orar.
MARCOS 1:35

Recuerda que *nuestro* Señor no solo insistió en la necesidad de orar sino que él mismo nos dejó un gran ejemplo de lo que es una vida de oración. Las enseñanzas de un profesor se refuerzan cuando él constituye un ejemplo vivo de lo que enseña, al poner en práctica sus propias instrucciones. Jesús fue un maestro poderoso tanto en obra como en palabra, de él leemos: «Jesús comenzó a hacer y enseñar» (Hechos 1:1). En el ejercicio de la oración, «el frío de la medianoche» pudo atestiguar que él fue un gran practicante de lo que enseñaba. Cuando exhortó a sus discípulos a que perseveraran en la oración y «oraran sin cesar», solo les estaba pidiendo que siguieran sus pisadas. Si alguno de los miembros del cuerpo místico no hubiera tenido necesidad de orar, de seguro habría sido nuestra Cabeza del Pacto, pero si nuestra Cabeza tuvo una vida de oración, mucho más nosotros, los miembros inferiores. Él nunca cometió los pecados que a nosotros nos afectan y debilitan desde el punto de vista espiritual. No tenía deseos lujuriosos contra los cuales luchar, pero si aquel que tuvo toda la pureza y la perfección se acercó a Dios con tanta frecuencia, ¡cuánto más debemos nosotros perseverar en nuestras súplicas! ¡Sigamos el ejemplo de quien fue tan poderoso, tan grande y, a la vez, tan consagrado en la oración!

A través de la Biblia en un año: Jeremías 45–48

Una alabanza consagrada

Alaben al Señor, ustedes sus ángeles, paladines que ejecutan su palabra y obedecen su mandato. Alaben al Señor, todos sus ejércitos, siervos suyos que cumplen su voluntad. Alaben al Señor, todas sus obras en todos los ámbitos de su dominio. ¡Alaba, alma mía, al Señor!

SALMOS 103:20-22

El cristiano debe llevar una vida de completa devoción a Dios. Alabar a Dios con nuestras voces y nuestras acciones por las misericordias recibidas, y luego orar a Dios por las misericordias que necesitamos, reconociendo con devoción que provienen de él, son los dos ejercicios que de una u otra forma deben conformar toda la existencia de un ser humano. El salmo de nuestra vida debe alternar versos de oración con versos de alabanza, hasta que lleguemos al otro mundo, donde cesará la oración y la alabanza se ocupará de toda nuestra inmortalidad. «Pero», dice alguien, «tenemos nuestras ocupaciones cotidianas que debemos atender». Sé que es así, pero existe una forma de hacer de las ocupaciones diarias parte de nuestra vida de alabanza y oración. Dices: «Danos nuestro pan diario», esa es una oración que haces antes de irte a trabajar, pero mientras trabajas, si lo haces con un espíritu consagrado, estás activamente orando la misma oración mediante tu legítima labor. Alabas a Dios por las misericordias recibidas mediante un himno que elevas en la mañana, y cuando te dedicas a llevar a cabo los deberes de la vida y haces allí aquellas cosas que honran el nombre de Dios, estás elevando tu alabanza más sublime. Recuerda que, para los cristianos, trabajar es orar, como diría aquel verso de Coleridge: «El que más ora es aquel que más ama».

A través de la Biblia en un año: Jeremías 49–52

Persevera en la oración

Cada uno tenía un arpa y copas de oro llenas de incienso, que son las oraciones del pueblo de Dios.
APOCALIPSIS 5:8

Los hombres «deben orar siempre, sin desanimarse» (Lucas 18:1). Semana tras semana, mes tras mes, año tras año, la conversión de aquel hijo amado debe ser el motivo de ruego constante del padre. Traer a los pies de Cristo a ese esposo inconverso tiene que ser la constante súplica del corazón de la esposa, día y noche hasta que lo logre; el hecho de haber estado orando sin éxito aparente durante diez o veinte años no se debe tomar como una razón para dejar de orar; ella no tiene autoridad alguna para decirle a Dios cuál es el tiempo ni el momento adecuado, sino que mientras tenga vida y viva también el objeto de su constante oración, tiene que continuar insistiendo ante el poderoso Dios de Jacob.

El pastor no debe buscar una bendición ocasional para su pueblo, y al recibir un poco de ella dejar de interceder, sino que debe continuar con vehemencia, sin detenerse, sin disminuir sus energías, con sus ruegos y súplicas, hasta que vea las ventanas de los cielos abiertas de par en par derramando una bendición demasiado grande como para albergarla. Sin embargo, ¡cuántas veces pedimos a Dios y no recibimos porque no esperamos lo suficiente delante de su puerta! Oh, que por gracia aprendamos a esperar junto al ángel de Dios y nunca, nunca, nunca relajar nuestras fuerzas, al comprender que no debemos desmayar hasta obtener aquello por lo cual oramos, porque las almas dependen de ello, la gloria de Dios está involucrada en esto y el estado de nuestros semejantes está en peligro. No podemos cesar de orar por nuestras almas ni por las de nuestros seres más queridos, ni por las almas del resto de los hombres. Tenemos que orar una y otra vez hasta que obtengamos la respuesta.

A través de la Biblia en un año: Apocalipsis 1–2

Sacrificio divino

Él fue entregado a la muerte por nuestros pecados, y resucitó para nuestra justificación.
ROMANOS 4:25

El propio nombre de Jesús nos recuerda que él salvará a su pueblo de los pecados. Me gustaría agregar que, ya que la salvación de Dios es tan grande, tiene que haber sido motivada por grandes pecados. ¿Hubiera Cristo derramado la sangre de su corazón por algunos pecados insignificantes, veniales, que nuestras lágrimas pudieran lavar? ¿Piensas que tu Dios habría ofrecido a su Hijo para que muriera por una simple superficialidad? Si el pecado hubiera sido un asunto de poca envergadura, un pequeño sacrificio habría sido suficiente. ¿Acaso piensas que aquel sacrificio divino fue llevado a cabo solo por unas pequeñas ofensas? ¿Se sacrificó Jesús por los pecados pequeños y no por los grandes? No, el Señor Dios midió el tamaño de nuestro pecado y lo halló tan alto como el cielo, tan profundo como el infierno, tan ancho como el infinito, y por eso nos concedió un Salvador tan grande. Dio a su Hijo único, un sacrificio infinito, un sacrificio que no se puede medir. Con dolores y terrores de muerte que nunca se podrán describir con toda exactitud, el Señor Jesús derramó su alma en un sufrimiento indecible, para proveer una gran salvación al más grande de los pecadores. Mira a Jesús en la cruz y entiende que todo tipo de pecado y blasfemia se le perdonará a los hombres. La salvación, eso es para mí, pues yo estoy perdido. Una gran salvación, eso es para mí, pues yo soy el más grande de los pecadores. ¡Oh, escucha mi palabra en este día! Es una palabra de amor de parte de Dios, y repica como una campana de plata. Lloro por ti y, sin embargo, me siento como si cantara todo el tiempo, porque he sido enviado a proclamar la salvación del Señor para los peores de ustedes.

A través de la Biblia en un año: Apocalipsis 3–5

Nuestra recompensa futura

Que el Señor le pague a cada uno según su rectitud y lealtad.
1 SAMUEL 26:23

Durante el día trabajamos y en la tarde recibimos el pago por nuestro trabajo. De esa misma forma es que muchos cristianos buscan la recompensa inmediata por su labor, y si la reciben, empiezan a regocijarse en ella como si hubieran recibido su verdadera recompensa. Igual que los discípulos que regresaron y le dijeron a Jesús: «Señor, hasta los demonios se nos someten en tu nombre» (Lucas 10:17), se regocijaron solo en la prosperidad presente. Sin embargo, el Maestro los amonestó para que no consideraran el éxito como su recompensa por hacer milagros, ya que no sería siempre así. «Sin embargo», les dijo, «no se alegren de que puedan someter a los espíritus, sino alégrense de que sus nombres están escritos en el cielo» (Lucas 10:20). El éxito en el ministerio no es la verdadera recompensa del ministro cristiano: es un pago inicial, pero todavía se aguarda la recompensa. No debes considerar la aprobación de tus semejantes como la recompensa a la excelencia pues, con frecuencia, tendrás el resultado contrario; verás tus mejores acciones distorsionadas y tus motivos malinterpretados.

Ser desechado y rechazado por los hombres es el destino del cristiano. Ni siquiera gozará siempre de buena reputación entre sus semejantes cristianos. No todo lo que recibimos de los santos es absoluta bondad y puro amor. Te advierto que si buscas tu recompensa en la misma novia de Cristo, no la obtendrás. «Cuando el Rey venga en su gloria», entonces será el tiempo de recibir la recompensa; pero no hoy, ni mañana, ni en algún otro tiempo mientras estemos en este mundo.

A través de la Biblia en un año: Apocalipsis 6–8

Nuestro Divino carpintero

En el hogar de mi Padre hay muchas viviendas; si no fuera así, ya se lo habría dicho a ustedes. Voy a prepararles un lugar.
JUAN 14:2

El gran Dios ha preparado un reino para su pueblo. Él pensó: «Eso les agradará y los bendecirá, mientras esto otro les proporcionará una felicidad pasajera». Él preparó el reino hasta hacerlo perfecto y entonces, como si no fuera suficiente, el Hombre glorioso, Cristo Jesús, ascendió de la tierra al cielo; y tú sabes lo que dijo en el momento de su partida: «Voy a prepararles un lugar». Sabemos que el Dios infinito puede preparar un lugar ideal para una criatura finita, pero sonreímos al darnos cuenta que el propio Jesús, quien también es Hombre y, por lo tanto, conoce los deseos de nuestros corazones, ha participado en la construcción de ese lugar, en su preparación. Es un reino preparado para ti, en el que Dios pensó desde antes de la fundación del mundo, para hacerlo un lugar excelente. Ha preparado un lugar para *ti*. Aquí la elección personal juega un papel importante. Él dijo que cada uno de los suyos estará donde él está. «Preparado desde la fundación del mundo». Aquí vemos la elección eterna, incluso antes de que los hombres fueran creados, preparando coronas para las cabezas antes de que estas existieran. Por lo tanto, nuestra porción está preparada desde la eternidad para nosotros de acuerdo a la elección de la gracia de Dios, una porción que satisfará al carácter más exigente, que estará muy cerca de Cristo, en comunión con Dios, y en un lugar de eterna dignidad y felicidad.

A través de la Biblia en un año: Apocalipsis 9–10

Yo soy

Pero él habló en seguida con ellos y les dijo:
«¡Cálmense! Soy yo. No tengan miedo».
MARCOS 6:50

Jesús dijo estas palabras a los hombres atemorizados por la tempestad, y necesitamos recordarlas cuando nos sentimos deprimidos por los acontecimientos de estos tiempos convulsos. En épocas de depresión económica, abundantes enfermedades, terribles guerras y desastres públicos, es un bálsamo para nuestro espíritu el saber que Jesús todavía es el mismo. Puede que el pecado abunde cada vez más, que la luz del evangelio esté debilitada y que el príncipe de las tinieblas extienda su soberanía destructora, sin embargo, esta verdad permanece firme, Jesús todavía dice: «Yo soy». En algunas épocas la influencia diabólica parece enorme, es como si las riendas de las naciones estuvieran en las manos del Gran Gobernante, pero no es así. Observa a través de la oscuridad y verás a tu Señor en medio del huracán, caminando sobre las aguas de la política, liderando los conflictos entre las naciones, gobernando, ordenando, arreglándolo todo, haciendo incluso que la ira de Dios lo alabe, y restringiéndola de acuerdo a su sabiduría. Más allá del rugido de la tormenta, escucho su voz decir: «Soy yo». Cuando los corazones de los hombres se hunden en el temor y sienten que se esfuerzan en vano sus remos al punto de quebrarlos, escucho aquella palabra que es el alma misma de la música: «Soy yo. No tengan miedo. Yo dirijo todas las cosas. Vengo a rescatar la barca, mi iglesia; ella flotará una vez más en aguas mansas y alcanzará el puerto deseado».

A través de la Biblia en un año: Apocalipsis 11–13

Él todavía hace milagros

Los que son de Cristo Jesús han crucificado la naturaleza pecaminosa, con sus pasiones y deseos.

GÁLATAS 5:24

El pecado pierde su poder en aquel hombre que acude a Jesús para que lo libre de él. Incluso algunos pecados que se han convertido en hábitos desaparecen en un momento cuando Jesucristo mira con amor a un hombre. Conozco varios ejemplos de hombres que, durante muchos años, no podían hablar sin jurar o maldecir en su conversación, pero que luego de convertirse eliminaron todo este tipo de lenguaje y nunca más se sintieron tentados a utilizarlo. He conocido a otros que cambiaron de forma tan radical que aquello que más los tentaba pasó a ser lo que menos les molestaba luego de su conversión. Sufrieron tal transformación mental que, mientras otros pecados los acosaron durante años y tuvieron que luchar para mantenerse firme ante ellos, aquel pecado dominante y favorito nunca más ejerció la menor influencia sobre ellos, excepto para provocarles un sentimiento de horror y un profundo arrepentimiento. ¡Ah, si tuvieras la fe suficiente para creer que Jesús es capaz de echar de ti los pecados que más te dominan! Cree en el brazo conquistador del Señor Jesús, y él lo hará. La conversión es el mayor milagro de la iglesia. Cuando es genuina, es una prueba infalible del poder divino que acompaña al evangelio, como lo fue la expulsión de los demonios o como lo será la resurrección de los muertos en el día del Señor.

A través de la Biblia en un año: Apocalipsis 14–16

Hijos obedientes

Su madre dijo a los sirvientes: «Hagan lo que él les ordene».

JUAN 2:5

Si la gracia de Dios te ha salvado, tu salvación te obliga a hacer lo que Jesús te ordena. ¿Has sido redimido? Entonces no te perteneces, fuiste comprado por precio. ¿Has sido adoptado en la familia de Dios? Entonces se deduce que, al ser hijo, debes obedecer las leyes de la familia. ¿Acaso no es este un aspecto esencial que es inherente al hecho de ser hijo, el reverenciar al gran Padre de familia? El Señor se complació en quitar tu pecado y ahora estás perdonado. ¿Pero no incluye el perdón una transformación? ¿Haríamos bien en volver a nuestros pecados pasados de los que fuimos limpiados? ¿Debemos regresar a practicar las iniquidades de las que fuimos lavados por la sangre de nuestro Señor Jesús?

Como le dijo María a los sirvientes de la boda en Caná de Galilea, así les digo yo a ustedes: «Todo lo que él les diga, háganlo». ¿Te dice que ores? Entonces ora sin cesar. ¿Te ordena velar, además de orar? Entonces vigila cada acto, cada palabra y cada pensamiento. ¿Te ordena amar a tus semejantes? Entonces ámalos con un corazón puro y ferviente. ¿Te ordena servirlos y humillarte por amor a ellos? Entonces hazlo y conviértete en el siervo de todos. ¿Te dijo él: «Sean ustedes santos, porque yo, el Señor, soy santo»? Entonces procura esto mediante su Espíritu Santo. ¿Te dijo él: «Sé perfecto, así como tu Padre en los cielos es perfecto»? Entonces esfuérzate por alcanzar la perfección, porque aquel que te hizo completo tiene el derecho de dirigir tu camino y, a su vez, encontrarás tu felicidad y tu seguridad al someterte a sus mandamientos.

A través de la Biblia en un año: Apocalipsis 17–19

Frutos santos

Este evangelio está dando fruto y creciendo en todo el mundo, como también ha sucedido entre ustedes desde el día en que supieron de la gracia de Dios y la comprendieron plenamente.

COLOSENSES 1:6

En la actualidad, la iglesia de Dios desea con gran fervor llevar el mensaje del evangelio a todo el mundo. Por amor a Cristo, deseamos que las personas reconozcan las verdades que predicamos y obedezcan los preceptos que Dios ha establecido. Pero hay que tener en cuenta que ninguna iglesia tendrá poder sobre las multitudes de uno u otro lugar, a no ser en la medida que les haga bien. Ahora, si una iglesia puede demostrar que está contribuyendo a hacer a los hombres honestos, templados, puros, morales, santos; que está buscando a los ignorantes para instruirlos; que está convirtiendo los desiertos morales en jardines, tomando la mala hierba y la maleza de la selva para transformarlas en preciosos árboles frutales, entonces el mundo estará listo para escuchar lo que tiene que decir y pensar en ello.

Si tienes una iglesia que es devota, que es santa, que vive para Dios, que hace buenas obras en su vecindario, que a través de la vida de sus miembros esparce la santidad y la justicia; en una palabra, si tienes una iglesia que en verdad está haciendo al mundo mejor en el nombre de Jesús, a la larga te darás cuenta que incluso los más carnales y superficiales dirán: «La iglesia que está haciendo todo este bien merece ser respetada; por tanto, escuchemos lo que tiene que decir». Una iglesia santa se dirige al mundo con autoridad en el nombre de Jesucristo su Señor y el Espíritu Santo usa esta fuerza para someter a los corazones humanos a la verdad.

A través de la Biblia en un año: Apocalipsis 20-22

Dios ordena las circunstancias

Por causa del fuerte viento que soplaba, el lago estaba picado.

JUAN 6:18

No pienses que las circunstancias adversas son una prueba de que te has desviado del camino, pues ellas pueden ser incluso una evidencia de que estás en la buena senda antigua, ya que el camino de los creyentes casi siempre está lleno de pruebas. Hiciste bien en zarpar y alejarte de la orilla, pero recuerda, aunque nuestro Señor ha asegurado tu barca y te ha garantizado que llegarás al puerto deseado, no ha prometido qúe navegarás en un mar de cristal; por el contrario, te ha dicho que «en este mundo afrontarán aflicciones» (Juan 16:33), e incluso puedes aumentar tu fe en él cuando encuentras que su advertencia es cierta.

El Señor les había ordenado a los discípulos que pasaran al otro lado y, por lo tanto, ellos se esforzaban lo más que podían y remaban toda la noche, pero no progresaban porque tenían el viento en su contra. Seguro has oído decir que si un cristiano no marcha hacia adelante, entonces va para atrás; eso nò siempre es cierto, pues hay tiempos de pruebas espirituales cuando, si un hombre no va para atrás, realmente está avanzando. Puede que un cristiano no progrese mucho en su camino, sin embargo, puede que no sea su culpa, pues quizá el viento le sea contrario. Nuestro buen Señor tendrá en cuenta las buenas intenciones y reconocerá nuestros progresos, no por nuestro avance aparente, sino por la intensidad con que nos esforcemos con los remos.

A través de la Biblia en un año: Lamentaciones 1–2

La influencia limpiadora de Dios

Lo único que sé es que yo era ciego y ahora veo.
JUAN 9:25

Todos los hombres son ciegos. Nuestro padre Adán se encargó de extirparnos los ojos. Somos incapaces de ver las cosas espirituales. No tenemos una óptica espiritual, esta ha desaparecido para siempre. Cristo viene al mundo y los hombres tienen en muy baja estima su evangelio, lo desprecian e incluso escupen al escuchar acerca de él; el pensar en ello disgusta a la mayoría de los hombres. Él presenta el evangelio ante los ojos de los ciegos, un evangelio que como el barro, parece que hiciera a los hombres incluso más ciegos que antes, pero es por medio de «la locura del evangelio» que Cristo salva a aquellos que creen. El Espíritu Santo es como la fuente de Siloé. Vamos a él, o más bien, él viene a nosotros; la influencia limpiadora del Divino Consolador lava la convicción de pecado que el evangelio produce; y he aquí, nosotros que éramos tan ciegos que no podíamos ver la belleza de la divinidad ni la excelencia de las joyas que adornan la corona de Dios, comenzamos a ver las cosas a la clara luz celestial y nos regocijamos con todo nuestro corazón delante del Señor.

A través de la Biblia en un año: Lamentaciones 3–5

Un testimonio personal

Lo único que sé.
JUAN 9:25

En algunas ocasiones los hombres escépticos te abrumarán con sus conocimientos. Conversa con ellos, pero hazlo con la seguridad de que tu conocimiento es mejor que el de ellos. No intentes enfrentarte a ellos en su propio terreno, enfréntalos con este conocimiento. «Bueno», pudieras decir, «sé que tienes más conocimiento que yo; soy un pobre cristiano ignorante, pero tengo algo aquí que responde a todos tus argumentos, cualesquiera que estos puedan ser. No sé lo que dice la geología; quizá no sepa mucho de historia, tal vez no comprenda todas las cosas extrañas que se ven en la actualidad, pero una cosa sé —y es algo de lo que estoy convencido— que yo una vez fui ciego y ahora puedo ver». Luego explica la diferencia que obró en ti el evangelio, diles que en un tiempo pasado cuando leías la Biblia, la considerabas un libro tonto e inservible, que cuando pensabas en la oración, la veías como algo inútil. Diles que ahora la Biblia es para ti como un panal repleto de miel y que la oración es tu aliento de vida. Diles que una vez intentaste huir de Dios y no podías ver la excelencia del carácter divino, pero ahora estás luchando y esforzándote por acercarte cada vez más a Dios. Diles que una vez despreciaste la cruz de Cristo y pensaste que era por gusto acudir a ella, pero que ahora la amas y sacrificarías todo lo que tienes y hasta tu propia vida por ella. Y este cambio radical en tu conciencia, esta obra sobrenatural que se ha llevado a cabo en lo más profundo de tu espíritu, te capacitará para rebatir cualquier argumento de la ciencia. Tu único argumento vencerá los miles de ellos, si puedes decir: «Era ciego y ahora veo».

A través de la Biblia en un año: Ezequiel 1-4

Alabanza y gratitud

«¿Acaso no quedaron limpios los diez?» preguntó Jesús «¿Dónde están los otros nueve? ¿No hubo ninguno que regresara a dar gloria a Dios, excepto este extranjero?» «Levántate y vete» le dijo al hombre; «tu fe te ha sanado».

LUCAS 17:17-19

Si buscas en el mundo que te rodea, entre todas las finas especias, te costará trabajo descubrir el incienso de la gratitud. No alabamos al Señor como debiéramos, en toda la proporción y con toda la intensidad que merece. Recibimos un continente de misericordias y solo le devolvemos una isla de alabanza. Cada mañana y cada noche él nos llena de nuevas y frescas bendiciones; grande es su fidelidad. Y, a pesar de eso, dejamos pasar años y casi nunca dedicamos un día completo a la alabanza. ¡Es triste ver toda la bondad de Dios y toda la ingratitud del hombre!

Lo voy a decir de otra forma para ustedes que son el pueblo de Dios, la mayoría de nosotros oramos más de lo que alabamos. Temo que ores bastante poco, pero la alabanza, ¿dónde está? En nuestros altares familiares solemos orar pero casi nunca alabamos. En nuestra habitación privada oramos con frecuencia pero, ¿alabamos con frecuencia? La oración no es un ejercicio tan divino como lo es la alabanza; la oración es durante un tiempo, pero la alabanza será durante toda la eternidad: Por lo tanto, la alabanza merece el primero y más alto lugar, ¿no crees? Empecemos a dedicarnos a la actividad de los seres celestiales. Un vagabundo puede orar pero será un pobre vagabundo desdichado a menos que exprese su alabanza una vez que reciba la limosna. La alabanza debe seguir de forma natural a la oración e incluso, por la gracia divina, debe ir antes que ella.

A través de la Biblia en un año: Ezequiel 5–8

Nuestro verdadero poder

Tengan fe en Dios —respondió Jesús—. Les aseguro que si alguno le dice a este monte: «Quítate de ahí y tírate al mar», creyendo, sin abrigar la menor duda de que lo que dice sucederá, lo obtendrá. Por eso les digo: Crean que ya han recibido todo lo que estén pidiendo en oración, y lo obtendrán.

MARCOS 11:22-24

Ya sea que vivamos o que muramos, tengamos fe en Dios. Siempre que predicamos o enseñamos el evangelio, tengamos fe, porque sin fe trabajaremos en vano. Siempre que distribuyas libros cristianos o visites a los enfermos, hazlo con fe, porque la fe es la sangre que da vida a nuestro servicio. Si solo por la fe pudo aquel Jacob moribundo bendecir a sus descendientes, entonces es solo por la fe que nosotros podemos bendecir a los hijos de los hombres. Ten fe en Dios y las enseñanzas que impartas serán edificantes, las oraciones que eleves traerán como consecuencia lluvias de misericordia y los esfuerzos que hagas por tus hijos e hijas prosperarán. Dios bendecirá lo que se haga con fe, pero si no creemos, nuestras obras no se afirmarán. La fe es la columna vertebral y la médula espinal del poder del cristiano que lo capacita para hacer el bien. Somos tan débiles como el agua hasta que no entramos en unión con Dios por medio de la fe, y entonces somos omnipotentes. No obtendremos resultado alguno al intentar motivar a nuestros semejantes en las cosas espirituales y eternas si caminamos por vista, pero cuando confiamos en el poder de Dios y nos aferramos a sus promesas con una confianza que lo arriesga todo, entonces es cuando obtenemos el poder para bendecir.

A través de la Biblia en un año: Ezequiel 9–12

Una comunicación preciosa

Alégrense en la esperanza, muestren paciencia en el sufrimiento, perseveren en la oración.
ROMANOS 12:12

Establecer tiempos para dedicarse a la oración es el privilegio y el deber de cada cristiano. No creo que un hombre pueda mantener la vitalidad de la santidad si no se retira a orar con regularidad, por lo menos cada mañana y cada noche. Daniel oraba tres veces al día, y David dice: «Siete veces al día te alabo» (Salmo 119:164). Es bueno para tu corazón, bueno para tu mente, bueno para tu constancia moral, que dediques ciertos espacios de tiempo y digas: «Estos le pertenecen a Dios. Haré negocios con Dios en este y este otro tiempo y trataré de ser tan puntual con él como lo sería si me fuera a reunir con un amigo íntimo».

Cuando Sir Thomas Abney era el Señor Alcalde en Londres, los banquetes lo perturbaban un poco, porque a esa hora Sir Thomas siempre tenía un tiempo de oración con su familia. Lo difícil era cómo retirarse del banquete para mantener las meditaciones familiares, pero eso era tan importante para él que dejaba su puesto en el banquete y se retiraba, diciéndole a cualquier persona que estuviera cerca que debía ausentarse pues tenía una cita especial con un querido amigo y no podía faltar. Y entonces se iba, pero luego regresaba a su puesto, y excedía a todos en sabiduría, y era el mejor de todos por cumplir con su cita con Dios.

A través de la Biblia en un año: Ezequiel 13–16

Una vida de oración

Por eso los fieles te invocan en momentos de angustia; caudalosas aguas podrán desbordarse, pero a ellos no los alcanzarán. Tú eres mi refugio; tú me protegerás del peligro y me rodearás con cánticos de liberación.

SALMO 32:6-7

Me he dado cuenta que predico mejor cuando oro mientras predico. Y la mente es impresionante en sus actividades. La mente puede orar mientras está estudiando, puede volverse a Dios mientras está hablando con un hombre, y puede extender su mano para recibir las provisiones de parte de Dios mientras la otra mano está extendida ofreciendo algo de aquello que ha recibido. Ora mientras tengas vida. Ora cuando estés sufriendo un gran dolor, mientras más agudo sea el dolor, más y más debes perseverar en tu ruego ante Dios. Y cuando te rodeen sombras de muerte y sientas cosas extrañas que te hagan sobrecogerte y que te adviertan que estás a punto de llegar al final de tu viaje, entonces haz oraciones cortas como esta: «No escondas tu rostro de mí, oh, Dios», o esta: «No te alejes de mí, oh, Dios», sin duda te confortarán. «Señor Jesús, recibe mi espíritu», fueron las emotivas palabras de Esteban al momento de morir; y «Padre, en tus manos encomiendo mi espíritu», fueron las palabras que tu propio Maestro pronunció antes de inclinar su cabeza y entregar su espíritu. Puede que tú sufras algún dolor similar y, entonces, deberás imitarlo.

A través de la Biblia en un año: Ezequiel 17–20

La mayoría invisible

Por la fe Noé, advertido sobre cosas que aún no se veían, con temor reverente construyó un arca para salvar a su familia. Por esa fe condenó al mundo y llegó a ser heredero de la justicia que viene por la fe.

HEBREOS 11:7

Noé era muy diferente del resto de los hombres de su época. *Ellos* se olvidaron de Dios, mientras él le temía, ellos vivían para las cosas que se ven y que son temporales, mientras que él vivía a la vista de lo invisible. Cuando estaba construyendo su arca, formaba parte de una minoría miserable, e incluso luego de ciento veinte años de ministerio, cuando terminó de construir el arca y su familia entró en ella, eran ocho contra muchos millones, una cantidad insignificante, como dirían los hombres, una secta digna de lástima comparada con toda una humanidad. ¿Quién habría pensado que los ocho estaban en lo cierto y los demás eran los que estaban equivocados? Donde está Dios, allí está la mayoría. Pero es evidente que había una distinción muy marcada entre Noé y su familia, y el resto de la humanidad.

Hermanos, en la actualidad la iglesia de Dios se encuentra en un mundo muy parecido al de Noé y su familia. Esto nos hace ser la familia escogida de Dios que estará segura cuando el mundo se consuma en el fuego final. Pero el tiempo llegará —llegará a cada hombre en el día de su muerte y llegará a todos los impíos cuando el Señor Jesús descienda del cielo a la final trompeta— cuando la puerta se cierre, entonces se escuchará la voz que dirá: «Hay un gran abismo entre nosotros y ustedes, de modo que los que quieren pasar de aquí para allá no pueden, ni tampoco pueden los de allá para acá» (Lucas 16:26). El carácter no cambiará, los impíos todavía seguirán actuando con impiedad y los inmundos seguirán siendo inmundos.

A través de la Biblia en un año: Ezequiel 21-24

Rendirse al llamado divino

Por la fe Abraham, cuando fue llamado para ir a un lugar que más tarde recibiría como herencia, obedeció y salió sin saber a dónde iba.
HEBREOS 11:8

Abraham fue llamado y obedeció. No hay sombra de duda, debate ni demora; cuando él fue llamado a salir, él salió. La queja del Señor es: «Como ustedes no me atendieron cuando los llamé» (Proverbios 1:24). Tales llamados vienen a muchos en repetidas ocasiones, pero les prestan oído sordo. Solo son oyentes de la Palabra, no hacedores. Incluso entre los oyentes más atentos, ¿cuántos hay a quienes la Palabra les llega sin casi ningún resultado práctico de obediencia verdadera? Qué tonto es añadir un pecado tras otro, aumentando la dureza del corazón, aumentando la distancia entre el alma y Cristo y al mismo tiempo, soñando tiernamente con un momento encantado en el que sea más fácil ceder al llamado divino y romper con el pecado.

Abraham tuvo una oportunidad y tuvo la gracia de captarla y hasta el día de hoy no hay en nuestra raza un nombre más insigne que el de «el padre de la fe». Él fue un hombre imperial, muy superior a sus semejantes. Su corazón estaba en el cielo, la luz de Dios bañaba su frente y su alma estaba llena de la influencia divina, de manera que él vio el día del Señor Jesús y se alegró. Él fue bendecido por el Señor que hizo el cielo y la tierra e hizo de él una bendición para todas las naciones. Algunos de ustedes nunca obtendrán semejante honor, vivirán y morirán innobles porque juegan con los llamamientos supremos. Y, sin embargo, creíste en Dios, y si viviste por fe, tendrás delante de ti un camino de honor inmortal que te llevará a la gloria eterna.

A través de la Biblia en un año: Ezequiel 25–28

Lleva la imagen

El Señor estaba con José y las cosas le salían muy bien.
GÉNESIS 39:2

El hombre mira la apariencia exterior, pero el Señor mira el corazón; y por lo tanto las descripciones bíblicas de los hombres no son solo de su vida visible sino de su vida espiritual. Aquí tenemos a José como Dios lo veía, el verdadero José. Exteriormente no siempre parecía que Dios estuviera con él, porque él no siempre tuvo la apariencia de un hombre próspero; pero si uno mira al alma más íntima de este siervo de Dios, ve su verdadera imagen: él vivía en comunión con el Altísimo, y Dios lo bendecía: «El Señor estaba con José y las cosas le salían muy bien» (Génesis 39:2).

Esta notable imagen de José nos recuerda mucho a nuestro Señor y Maestro, un José superior, que es Señor de todo el mundo por el bien de Israel. Pedro, en su sermón a la familia de Cornelio, dijo de nuestro Señor que él «anduvo haciendo el bien y sanando a todos los que estaban oprimidos por el diablo, porque Dios *estaba con él*» (Hechos 10:38, énfasis del autor), exactamente lo mismo que se había dicho de José. Es maravilloso que las mismas palabras describan tanto a Jesús, el perfecto Salvador, como a José, el imperfecto patriarca. Cuando tú y yo somos perfeccionados en gracia, debemos llevar la imagen de Cristo, y aquello que describa a Cristo también debe describirnos a nosotros. Aquellos que viven con Jesús serán transformados mediante su comunión hasta que sean semejantes a él.

A través de la Biblia en un año: Ezequiel 29–32

Conciencia de Dios

En esta casa no hay nadie más importante que yo. Mi patrón no me ha negado nada, excepto meterme con usted, que es su esposa. ¿Cómo podría yo cometer tal maldad y pecar así contra Dios?

GÉNESIS 39:9

Ah, si tú y yo siempre sintiéramos que Dios está cerca, mirándonos fijamente, no nos atreveríamos a pecar. La presencia de un superior a menudo frena a un hombre de hacer cualquier cosa en la cual él pudiera haberse aventurado, y la presencia de Dios, si nos percatáramos de ella, sería una barrera perpetua contra la tentación y nos mantendría firmes en la santidad. Después de esto, cuando José hablaba de Dios en cualquier ocasión, cuando Dios lo ayudó no solo a soportar la tentación sino a hacer cualquier servicio, te darás cuenta de cómo él siempre se lo atribuía a Dios. Él no interpretó el sueño del faraón sin antes decirle: «No soy yo, Dios le ha mostrado al faraón lo que va a hacer». Él estaba tan consciente de la presencia de Dios cuando se paró frente al gran monarca como cuando rechazó a aquella mujer pecadora.

Temo que no siempre hablamos de esta manera pero José sí lo hacía. Sin el menor remilgo, él decía lo que había en su corazón debido a una sensación de la presencia y la obra divina. ¡Cómo se parece él en esto a nuestro divino Señor! La presencia de Dios era todo para Cristo, así como lo era para José. Ahora bien, si tú y yo siempre ponemos al Señor delante de nosotros, si nuestras almas moran en Dios, ten por seguro que Dios está con nosotros. No hay ningún error en eso.

A través de la Biblia en un año: Ezequiel 33–36

Instrumentos en las manos de Dios

Ustedes han visto todo lo que el Señor su Dios ha hecho con todas aquellas naciones a favor de ustedes, pues él peleó las batallas por ustedes. Yo repartí por sorteo, como herencia de sus tribus, tanto las tierras de las naciones que aún quedan como las de aquellas que ya han sido conquistadas, entre el río Jordán y el mar Mediterráneo.

JOSUÉ 23:3-4

Se cometen muchos errores con respecto a las promesas de Dios. Algunos piensan que si Dios está con ellos, no tendrán que hacer nada. Pero para Josué no fue así. Él y sus tropas tuvieron que matar a todo amorreo, hitita y heveo que cayó en la batalla. Él tuvo que luchar y usar su espada tanto como si no hubiera habido ningún Dios.

Lo mejor y lo más sabio que se puede hacer en el mundo es trabajar como si todo dependiera de uno y luego confiar en Dios, sabiendo que todo depende él. Él no nos fallará, pero no por eso vamos a cruzarnos de brazos y quedarnos sentados. Él no nos abandonará, pero no por eso vamos a subir a acostarnos y esperar que nuestro pan diario nos caiga en la boca. Dios no consiente nuestra haraganería y cualquier hombre que espere salir adelante en este mundo con cualquier cosa buena sin trabajo, es un tonto. Lanza toda tu alma al servicio de Dios y luego recibirás la bendición de Dios si estás descansando en él. Oliver Cromwell tenía una perspectiva con sentido común acerca de esta verdad. «Confía en Dios», decía él mientras iban a la batalla, «pero prepárate para la lucha». Y lo mismo debemos hacer nosotros.

A través de la Biblia en un año: Ezequiel 37–40

A favor de otros

Así que recomiendo, ante todo, que se hagan plegarias, oraciones, súplicas y acciones de gracias por todos.
1 TIMOTEO 2:1

Es un gran privilegio que se nos permita orar por nuestros semejantes. En cada caso es necesario que la oración comience con peticiones personales ya que hasta que Dios no acepte al hombre, este no puede actuar como intercesor por otros y aquí yace parte de la excelencia de la oración intercesora, porque esta es, para quien la ejercita, una marca correcta de gracia interior y una señal de bien de parte del Señor. Puedes estar seguro que tu Rey te ama si te permite pronunciar palabras a favor de tu amigo. Aquel que en respuesta a su intercesión ha visto a otros bendecidos y salvados, puede tomarlo como una garantía del amor divino y regocijarse en la condescendiente gracia de Dios. Una oración así sube más alto que cualquier petición por nosotros mismos, porque solo aquel que tiene el favor del Señor puede aventurarse a suplicar por otros.

La oración intercesora es un acto de comunión con Cristo, porque Jesús suplica por los hijos de los hombres. Es parte de su función sacerdotal interceder por su pueblo. Él ha subido a lo alto para esto y continuamente ejerce esta función en el lugar sagrado. Cuando oramos por los pecadores, estamos de acuerdo con nuestro divino Salvador quien hace intercesión por todos los transgresores.

A través de la Biblia en un año: Ezequiel 41–44

Aprender de Dios

El fruto del justo es árbol de vida; Y el que gana almas es sabio.
PROVERBIOS 11:30 (RVR 1960)

Si yo deseo la salvación de alguien, debo decirle como mejor pueda cuál es su condición, cuál es el camino de la salvación y cómo puede encontrar descanso. Todos los hombres son accesibles en un determinado momento o de alguna manera. Es muy imprudente abalanzarse sobre la gente en cuanto uno se encuentra con ellos, sin pensar en la prudencia ordinaria porque puede que causes disgusto en aquellos a quienes quieres ganar. Pero aquellos que con ahínco suplican por otros y se mueven para buscarlos, por lo general han aprendido de Dios y por tanto son sabios en cuanto al tiempo, la forma y el tema. Un hombre que desea cazar aves, después de un tiempo se convierte en un experto de este deporte porque le dedica tiempo. Así mismo el que anhela ganar almas y le dedica su corazón, le encuentra las mañas de alguna manera y el Señor le da el éxito. Yo no podría enseñártelo, tú tienes que practicarlo para descubrirlo. Pero te diré esto: ningún hombre está limpio de la sangre de su semejante sencillamente por haber orado que así sea.

Escuché de alguien en Nueva York que oró por varias familias muy pobres que había visitado. Su hijo pequeño dijo: «Padre, si yo fuera Dios, te diría que respondieras tu propia oración porque tú tienes dinero suficiente». Así mismo podría decirnos el Señor cuando hemos estado intercediendo: «Ve y responde tu propia oración al hablarle a tus amigos de mi Hijo». Hay poder en tus dones, hay poder en tu hablar, usa estos poderes. Ve y enseña lo bueno y lo correcto y tus oraciones serán escuchadas.

A través de la Biblia en un año: Ezequiel 45–48

Cuenta con eso

Además de todo esto, tomen el escudo de la fe, con el cual pueden apagar todas las flechas encendidas del maligno.

EFESIOS 6:16

La fe es un escudo que puedes usar para guardarte de todo tipo de flechas, sí, hasta de los dardos llameantes del gran enemigo, porque ni las jabalinas de fuego pueden penetrar este escudo. No puedes caer en una condición en la que la fe no te ayude. Hay una promesa de Dios adecuada para cada situación y Dios tiene sabiduría, habilidad, amor y fidelidad para librarte de cada posible peligro; y por lo tanto, solo tienes que confiar en Dios y de seguro vendrá la liberación.

Hasta si el problema que tienes es culpa tuya, la fe sigue estando disponible. Cuando tu aflicción es evidentemente un castigo por una transgresión dolorosa, a pesar de todo confía en el Señor. El Señor Jesús oró por el falible Pedro para que su fe no fallara; su esperanza de recuperación estaba ahí. Cuando te has hecho a un lado y por fin el Padre celestial te azotó un poco con su vara, para que te entregues a él, entonces necesitas la fe. Sigue confiando en la misericordia del Señor aunque en este mismo momento quizá alguno de ustedes esté en gran aflicción y esté consciente de merecer sin duda alguna todos sus problemas debido a su desatino. No dudes del Señor, tu salvador, porque él invita a sus hijos descarriados a regresar a él.

A través de la Biblia en un año: Daniel 1–3

Fe cotidiana

¿No fue declarado justo nuestro padre Abraham por lo que hizo cuando ofreció sobre el altar a su hijo Isaac? Ya lo ves: Su fe y sus obras actuaban conjuntamente, y su fe llegó a la perfección por las obras que hizo.

SANTIAGO 2:21-22

Confía en el Señor tu Dios. Cree también en Jesús, su hijo. Despójate de la fe falsa y cree realmente. Despójate de la fe profesional y confía en el Señor en todo tiempo para todas las cosas. «¿Qué, confiar en él en cuanto a libras, chelines y peniques?» Sin duda alguna. Yo le temo a la fe que no puede confiar en Dios en cuanto al pan y la ropa, es una fe que miente. Ten por seguro que esa no es la fe sólida y práctica de Abraham, quien confiaba en Dios para su tienda, su ganado, su esposa y su hijo. La fe que hizo que David confiara en Dios en cuanto a los hijos, las hijas y el botín, es el tipo de fe que tú y yo debemos tener. Si no se puede confiar en Dios para panes y peces, ¿cómo confiar en él para las cosas de la eternidad y las glorias que todavía no se han revelado? Permanece en Dios con una fe cotidiana. La fe en Dios es el ejercicio del sentido común santificado. La razón más pura aprueba la confianza en Dios. El final declarará la sabiduría de creer en Dios. Al final, cuando nosotros junto con todos los creyentes elevemos el gran aleluya al Señor, Dios de Israel que reina sobre todas las cosas por su pueblo, todos sabrán que la fe es honorable y la incredulidad despreciable.

A través de la Biblia en un año: Daniel 4–6

Siervos firmes

¡Pues Daniel respondieron ellos, que es uno de los exiliados de Judá, no toma en cuenta a Su Majestad ni al decreto que ha promulgado! ¡Todavía sigue orando a su Dios tres veces al día!

DANIEL 6:13

Daniel había alcanzado gran prosperidad en el mundo, pero su alma también había prosperado. A menudo los avances externos significan un deterioro interno. El éxito ha envenenado a miles de miles. Aunque al comenzar la carrera de la vida prometieron ganar el premio, fueron tentados a desviarse para recoger las manzanas doradas y, por consecuencia, se perdieron la corona. No fue así con Daniel, él era tan perfecto delante de Dios cuando estaba en la cumbre como cuando estaba en baja condición, y esto se explica con el hecho de que él sostuvo la energía de su profesión exterior mediante una comunión secreta constante con Dios. Se nos dice que él era un hombre de espíritu excelente y un hombre de mucha oración; por lo tanto, su cabeza no estaba perturbada con su eminencia sino que el Señor cumplió en él la promesa: «da a mis pies la ligereza del venado, y me mantiene firme en las alturas». No obstante, aunque Daniel preservó su integridad, no encontró que una posición de grandeza fuera una de descanso.

Hoy yo presento el ejemplo de Daniel para tu consideración porque creo que estos son tiempos en los cuales necesitamos ser tan firmes y resueltos como él, y porque de cualquier modo a cada uno de nosotros a veces nos llegarán situaciones antes de que ganemos nuestra corona en la cual necesitaremos poner nuestros pies en el suelo y ser firmes y decididos por el Señor y su verdad.

A través de la Biblia en un año: Daniel 7–9

Con la fuerza de Dios

Por eso concluyeron: «Nunca encontraremos nada de qué acusar a Daniel, a no ser algo relacionado con la ley de su Dios».

DANIEL 6:5

Recuerda que Daniel es un tipo de nuestro Señor Jesucristo. Jesús tuvo enemigos que buscaban destruirlo; no podían encontrar nada en su contra excepto «tocando a su Dios». Lo acusaron de blasfemia y luego, como hicieron en contra de Daniel, presentaron un cargo de sedición. Lo lanzaron en el foso, en la tumba: su alma estuvo entre los leones. Sellaron la tumba con su sello, no fuera a ser que alguien se lo robara durante la noche, pero él se levantó al igual que Daniel, vivo e ileso y sus enemigos resultaron destruidos. Ahora, si Daniel es un tipo de Cristo, y el Señor Jesús es el gran Hombre simbólico de todos los que están en él, tú, creyente, debes esperar que aparezcan aquellos que te atacarán, que arremeterán contra ti especialmente en cuanto a tu religión. También debes esperar que estos prevalezcan por un tiempo para que tú seas echado al foso, que buscarán encerrarte como si estuvieras destruido para siempre, pero habrá una resurrección no solo del cuerpo sino de las reputaciones y tú te levantarás.

Oh, ¡ser un seguidor de Jesús como el gran Daniel! ¡Seguir sus pasos adondequiera que vaya! ¡Estar mucho con él, ya sea en público o en privado! Esto es algo que debe desearse y aunque te exhorto a hacerlo, no espero que lo logres con tus propias fuerzas, pero te señalo al Espíritu Santo, quien puede hacer esto en ti y hacer que seas muy amado como lo fue este profeta de antaño.

A través de la Biblia en un año: Daniel 10–12

Sombra celestial

Nuestro querido hermano Tíquico, fiel servidor y colaborador en el Señor, les contará en detalle cómo me va.

COLOSENSES 4:7

Conozco a algunos santos de Dios que viven muy cerca de él y son evidentemente un árbol de vida porque su misma sombra consuela y refresca a muchas almas cansadas. He sabido que los jóvenes, los probados y los abatidos, van a ellos, se sientan bajo su sombra y cuentan la historia de sus problemas y después sienten una rica bendición al recibir su simpatía cuando se les habla de la fidelidad del Señor y se les ha guiado en el camino de la sabiduría. Hay unos pocos hombres buenos en este mundo a quienes conocer es hacerse rico. Su carácter es un árbol vivo y verdadero, no es un simple poste de la madera muerta de la doctrina que lleva una inscripción y que se está pudriendo, sino que es vital, organizado, produce fruto, una planta que el Señor ha plantado con su mano derecha.

Algunos santos no solo dan consuelo a otros sino que además les entregan alimento espiritual. Los cristianos bien preparados se convierten en padres y madres de lactancia, fortalecen a los débiles y vendan las heridas de los desconsolados. Así también las obras fuertes, valientes y generosas de los cristianos generosos son un gran servicio para sus compañeros cristianos y tienden a elevarlos a un nivel superior. Uno se siente refrescado al ver cómo actúan, su paciencia en el sufrimiento y su valor en el peligro, su santa fe en Dios, sus rostros felices durante la prueba, todas estas cosas te dan ánimo en tus propios conflictos. El ejemplo del creyente santificado actúa de mil maneras para sanar y consolar a sus hermanos y ayuda a elevarlos por encima de la ansiedad y la incredulidad.

A través de la Biblia en un año: Oseas 1–4

Desde la juventud

Instruye al niño en el camino correcto, y aun en su vejez no lo abandonará.
PROVERBIOS 22:6

Está bien reclamar al pródigo, pero es mejor aún salvarlo de que alguna vez se convierta en pródigo. Es algo digno de alabanza el recuperar al ladrón y al borracho, pero es mucho mejor actuar para que el niño nunca se convierta en un ladrón o en un borracho; por tanto, la instrucción de la Escuela Dominical ocupa un lugar prominente en la lista de las empresas filantrópicas y los cristianos deben ser muy vehementes en esta. Aquel que convierta a un niño del error de su camino evita y también cubre una multitud de pecados.

Y, además, le da a la iglesia la esperanza de estar amueblada con los mejores hombres y mujeres. Los Samuel y Salomón de la iglesia se hacen sabios en su juventud; los David y los Josías tenían buen corazón en sus años jóvenes. Lee las vidas de los ministros más eminentes y por lo general descubrirás que su historia cristiana comenzó temprano. Aunque no es absolutamente necesario, no obstante, es altamente propicio para el crecimiento de un carácter cristiano bien desarrollado que su cimiento esté puesto sobre la base de una piedad juvenil. No espero ver que aquellos que han vivido una vida de pecado edifiquen de manera ordinaria las iglesias de Jesucristo sino que sean hombres y mujeres jóvenes, criados en medio de esta, en el temor y la exhortación del Señor, que se conviertan en los pilares de la casa de nuestro Dios. Si queremos cristianos fuertes, debemos mirar a aquellos que fueron cristianos en su juventud.

A través de la Biblia en un año: Oseas 5–8

Nuestro mayor gozo

Hacia ti dirijo la mirada, hacia ti, cuyo trono está en el cielo.
SALMOS 123:1

Es muy triste que la gente entre en casa de cualquier hombre y vean todo menos al hombre mismo. Admiran sus alfombras, se regocijan por la regularidad con que se sirven las comidas, ven que hay ciertas leyes que hacen provisiones para el desayuno y la cena de toda la familia; aprueban las «leyes» que mantienen limpia la casa y las «leyes» que la han decorado y las «leyes» que gobiernan todo. Pero, ¿dónde está el amo que hace todas esas leyes? Por desgracia, ¡no quieren verlo! Les gusta ver lo que él ha provisto, les gusta sentarse con sus piernas bajo sus mesas de caoba, pero no quieren ver al amo de la casa. Sin duda, eso debe surgir de una falta de comprensión. Cuando me quedo con un amigo, me complacen sus atenciones pero quiero pasar tanto tiempo como sea posible con *él*. Es el anfitrión, y no su comida, lo que constituye el verdadero gozo de la visita; y en el mundo es el mismo Dios, y no sus leyes, ni los productos de estas, lo que nos proporciona el mayor gozo. Al igual que sería insensato el que hace una visita y se olvida comunicarse con su amigo y solo se fija en su casa y en los terrenos, así es más que insensato el que, en este mundo inigualable, lo ve todo excepto a aquel que está en todas partes y que lo hizo todo. Esto es ciertamente una necedad.

A través de la Biblia en un año: Oseas 9–11

La enemistad de Dios

Yo estuve a punto de caer, y poco me faltó para que resbalara. Sentí envidia de los arrogantes, al ver la prosperidad de esos malvados.
SALMOS 73:2-3

Cuando Dios se convierte en el enemigo de un hombre y lucha contra él, este está en un gran aprieto. Con otros enemigos podemos luchar con alguna esperanza de tener éxito, pero no con el Omnipotente. Enemistarse con otros es aflicción, pero enemistarse con Dios es destrucción. Si él resulta ser nuestro enemigo, entonces todo se vuelve en nuestra contra. «Si Dios está de nuestra parte, ¿quién puede estar en contra nuestra?» (Romanos 8:31). Pero, si Dios está en contra de nosotros, ¿quién puede estar de nuestra parte?

Los hombres pudieran intentar persuadirse de que a Dios no le importa, que no tiene importancia para él cómo actúen los hombres, ya sea que guarden o quebranten sus leyes. Los hombres pudieran alegar que él «es bondadoso con los ingratos y malvados» (Lucas 6:35), y que lo mismo les sucede tanto a los justos como a los malvados; y por el momento así parece en verdad. La limitación de nuestra vista hasta puede asegurarnos que los impíos prosperan y se llevan la mejor parte, pero esto es solo debido a nuestra ceguera.

Dios detesta el pecado ahora y siempre. No sería Dios si no fuera así. Dios siente una justa indignación contra toda clase de mal: esto motiva la ira en su Espíritu. Algunos creen en un Dios impasible pero no hay duda alguna de que al Dios de la Biblia nunca se le describe así. Las Santas Escrituras lo presentan a la manera de los hombres. Si lo presentaran a la manera de Dios, ni tú ni yo podríamos entender nada de esa descripción; pero según se nos presenta en las Escrituras, el Señor advierte el pecado, lo siente, se enoja con él, el pecado lo irrita y su Espíritu Santo se exaspera ante la rebelión de los hombres.

A través de la Biblia en un año: Oseas 12–14

El peso del pecado

*Que abandone el malvado su *camino, y el perverso sus pensamientos. Que se vuelva al Señor, a nuestro Dios, que es generoso para perdonar, y de él recibirá misericordia. «Porque mis pensamientos no son los de ustedes, ni sus caminos son los míos afirma el Señor».*

ISAÍAS 55:7-8

Al principio los hombres tienen ideas muy bajas del pecado. Es algo insignificante, un simple error, un fallo al juzgar, un pequeño extravío, pero cuando el Espíritu Santo empieza a tratar con ellos, el pecado llega a ser una carga intolerable, algo aterrador, lleno de horror y consternación. Mientras más los hombres conocen del mal del pecado, más atónitos se quedan al pensar que alguna vez hayan encontrado algún placer en este o que puedan haberlo justificado de alguna manera. Ahora bien, es bueno que los hombres comiencen a ver la verdad acerca de sí mismos, porque incluso si esa verdad los hace pedazos, es bueno que se liberen del domino de la falsedad.

El pecado es grande, y por esa razón el pecador piensa que no puede ser perdonado, como si midiera al Señor por su pecado e imaginara que su pecado es mayor que la misericordia de Dios. De ahí que nuestra dificultad con los hombres que están realmente despiertos sea elevar sus pensamientos acerca de la misericordia de Dios en proporción con la idea elevada que tienen de la grandeza del pecado. Mientras no sienten su pecado, dicen que Dios es misericordioso y hablan con mucha ligereza de este, como si el perdón fuera algo trivial. Pero cuando sienten el peso del pecado, entonces creen que es imposible que este se pueda perdonar. En nuestro texto Dios muestra condescendencia para ayudar al pecador a creer en el perdón elevándole su idea acerca de Dios. Debido a que Dios es infinitamente superior al hombre, él puede perdonar abundantemente.

A través de la Biblia en un año: Joel 1–3

Más allá de la comprensión

Oh Señor, ¡cuán imponentes son tus obras, y
cuán profundos tus pensamientos!
SALMOS 92:5

Es muy cierto que los mejores pensamientos: los más lógicos, los más originales, los más correctos que hayas tenido jamás, no son dignos de comparase con los pensamientos de Dios. Mira a la naturaleza. Las cosas que ves en la naturaleza fueron, primero, un pensamiento en la mente de Dios y él los plasmó. ¿Alguna vez tuviste pensamientos como los que tuvo Dios en la creación? Miras a las estrellas y en tus pensamientos estas son como meros puntos de luz. Sus pensamientos no son tus pensamientos porque cuando miras por el telescopio descubres que estas son orbes majestuosas y apenas puedes entender en tu cabeza la gran idea que Dios tiene del cielo.

Lo mismo sucede en tu mente con respecto al futuro. Lee las profecías y mira lo que todavía está por ocurrir. Los pensamientos de Dios acerca de un cielo nuevo y de una tierra nueva ¡cuán por encima de los nuestros! Todavía no podemos entender el libro de Apocalipsis, que nos da parte del pensamiento de Dios acerca del futuro. Tenemos que esperar hasta que los hechos lo expliquen porque los pensamientos de Dios están por encima de lo nuestros. ¡Vaya!, toma un asunto sencillo como la resurrección de los muertos. Enterramos a los que parten y sus cuerpos se disuelven. El pensamiento de Dios es que estos se levantarán de nuevo. La semilla se convertirá en flor. Los pensamientos de Dios están mucho más allá de cualquier pensamiento que pueda surgir en tu alma.

A través de la Biblia en un año: Amós 1–3

La tumba de la esperanza legal

Ahora bien, sabemos que todo lo que dice la ley, lo dice a quienes están sujetos a ella, para que todo el mundo se calle la boca y quede convicto delante de Dios. Por tanto, nadie será justificado en presencia de Dios por hacer las obras que exige la ley; más bien, mediante la ley cobramos conciencia del pecado.

ROMANOS 3:19-20

Si un hombre no hace nada malo, no obstante, no hace lo bueno, es culpable. La omisión es un verdadero defecto, así como lo es la perpetración. Si has omitido, en cualquier momento, amar al Señor tu Dios con toda la fuerza e intensidad de tu naturaleza, si haz omitido en cualquier grado el amar a tu prójimo como a ti mismo, has cometido una infracción de la ley. No obedecer es desobedecer. ¿Quién puede alegar inocencia si esto es así? ¡Cuán hiriente es la oración: «Maldito el que no *practica fielmente* todo lo que está escrito en el libro de la ley!» (Gálatas 3:10, énfasis del autor). Es un pasaje terrible. Me parece a mí que cierra la puerta de las esperanzas mediante las obras, sí, la cierra con clavos. Yo bendigo a Dios porque cierra la puerta de manera eficaz, porque si hubiera una media oportunidad de pasar por ella, todavía veríamos a los hombres luchando por entrar. La salvación por medio de uno mismo es la esperanza querida del hombre: la salvación mediante las obras, los sentimientos o alguna otra cosa propia es la falsa ilusión favorita de los pecadores. Podemos bendecir a Dios porque ha puesto una piedra enorme en la entrada de la tumba de la esperanza legal. Él ha quebrado como con vara de hierro el vaso terrenal que contenía los tesoros de nuestra jactancia. «Nadie será justificado en presencia de Dios por hacer las obras que exige la ley» (Romanos 3:20).

A través de la Biblia en un año: Amós 4–6

Reconciliación perfecta

Por eso Cristo es mediador de un nuevo pacto, para que los llamados reciban la herencia eterna prometida, ahora que él ha muerto para liberarlos de los pecados cometidos bajo el primer pacto.

HEBREOS 9:15

La reconciliación que vino mediante Cristo es absolutamente perfecta. Quiere decir vida eterna. Si ahora Jesús te reconcilia con Dios, nunca más pelearás con Dios ni Dios contigo. Si el Mediador quita el motivo de la contienda, tu pecado y tu maldad, lo quitará para siempre. Él echará tus iniquidades en las profundidades del mar, haciendo desaparecer tus pecados como una nube y como una nube densa tus transgresiones. Traerá tal paz entre Dios y tú que él te amará para siempre y tú lo amarás para siempre, y nada te separará del amor de Dios que es en Cristo nuestro Señor. He escuchado de ciertos remiendos que vuelven a pegar las piezas de los platos rotos de tal manera que se dice que estos son más fuertes de lo que eran antes de romperse. No sé cómo podrá ser eso. Pero esto sé: la unión entre Dios y el pecador, reconciliados mediante la sangre de Cristo, es más cercana y más fuerte que la unión entre Dios y el Adán de antes de su caída. Aquella se rompió de un solo golpe, pero si Cristo te une al Padre mediante su preciosa sangre, él te mantendrá allí con el fluir de su gracia en tu alma; porque, ¿quién nos separará del amor de Dios que es en Cristo Jesús nuestro Señor? Aférrate a Cristo como mediador, confiemos en él y que él traiga la paz entre Dios y nosotros. ¡Y a su nombre sea la gloria por siempre y siempre!

A través de la Biblia en un año: Amós 7–9

El que nos rescata

Dios es nuestro amparo y nuestra fortaleza, nuestra ayuda segura en momentos de angustia.
SALMOS 46:1

Ahora, amados amigos, si alguno de ustedes está pasando por grandes dificultades y problemas, tentado a hacer el mal, e incluso más, presionado a hacerlo, y si hace lo correcto, pareciera como si fuera un gran perdedor y tremenda víctima, crean esto: Dios te puede liberar. Él puede impedir que sufras lo que supones que debes sufrir, y si no lo impide, puede ayudarte a soportarlo y en un breve tiempo puede convertir todas tus pérdidas en ganancias, todos tus sufrimientos en felicidad. Él puede hacer que lo peor que te suceda se convierta en lo mejor que te haya sucedido jamás. Si estás sirviendo a Dios, estás sirviendo a un Ser omnipotente y ese Ser omnipotente no te abandonará en tiempos de dificultad, sino que vendrá a rescatarte. Muchos de nosotros podemos decir con Pablo: «Pero eso sucedió para que no confiáramos en nosotros mismos sino en Dios, que resucita a los muertos. Él nos libró y nos librará de tal peligro de muerte. En él tenemos puesta nuestra esperanza, y él seguirá librándonos» (2 Corintios 1:9-10). El Señor nos ha ayudado en el pasado, nos está ayudando en el presente y creemos que nos ayudará hasta el final. Él también te ayudará si tan solo sigues su Palabra y mediante una fe sencilla haces lo correcto. Creo que tenemos razones para esperar interposiciones de la providencia para ayudarnos cuando se nos llama a sufrir por amor a Cristo.

A través de la Biblia en un año: Abdías

Belleza de las cenizas

Hermanos míos, considérense muy dichosos cuando tengan que enfrentarse con diversas pruebas, pues ya saben que la prueba de su fe produce constancia. Y la constancia debe llevar a feliz término la obra, para que sean perfectos e íntegros, sin que les falte nada.
SANTIAGO 1:2-4

¿Sabes que Dios tiene bellezas en todas partes del mundo y que tienes bellezas para cada experiencia? Hay vistas desde la cima de los Alpes que no pueden verse desde ningún otro lugar. Sí, pero hay bellezas que pueden verse en las profanidades del valle que nunca verías desde las cimas de las montañas; hay glorias que se ven en Pisgá, espectáculos maravillosos que se contemplan cuando por fe nos paramos en Tabor, pero también hay bellezas que se ven en nuestros Getsemaní y algunas flores maravillosamente atractivas hay que recogerlas en el borde de la guarida de los leopardos. Los hombres nunca se volverán grandes en divinidad hasta que se hayan vuelto grandes en el sufrimiento. «Ah», dijo Lutero, «la aflicción es el mejor libro de mi biblioteca». Y déjame añadir que la mejor hoja del libro de la aflicción es la más negra de todas las hojas, la hoja llamada depresión, cuando el espíritu se hunde dentro de nosotros y no podemos soportar como quisiéramos.

Los que han estado en la recámara de la aflicción saben cómo consolar a los que están allí. No creas que cualquier hombre se convertirá en médico a menos que camine los hospitales y estoy seguro de que nadie se convertirá en eclesiástico o en consolador a menos que yazga en el hospital así como que camine por él y tenga que sufrir él mismo.

A través de la Biblia en un año: Jonás 1–4

Bendito advenimiento

Hoy les ha nacido en la ciudad de David un Salvador, que es Cristo el Señor. Esto les servirá de señal: Encontrarán a un niño envuelto en pañales y acostado en un pesebre.

LUCAS 2:11-12

Mira la gloria de nuestro Señor Jesucristo, ¡incluso en su estado de humillación! Nació de padres humildes que lo acostaron en un pesebre y lo envolvieron en pañales y, sin embargo, se conmocionaron los principados y los poderes de los lugares celestiales. Primero, un ángel desciende a proclamar el advenimiento del recién nacido Rey y de pronto se le une una multitud de seres celestiales que cantan y dan gloria a Dios. La conmoción no se limitó a los espíritus de arriba, porque en los cielos que cuelgan por encima de esta tierra hay agitación. Se selecciona a una estrella en nombre de todas las estrellas. A la estrella se le da la misión de esperar en el Señor, de ser su heraldo para hombres que venían de lejos, su guía para llevarlos a su presencia y su guardaespaldas para velar su cuna.

La tierra también está conmovida. Los pastores han venido a dar el homenaje de los sencillos; con todo amor y gozo se inclinan delante del niño misterioso y después de ellos, desde lejos viene la flor y nata de su generación, las mentes más estudiosas de la época. Llegan por fin, luego de un viaje largo y difícil, los representantes de los gentiles. Mira, los reyes de Seba y Sabá ofrecen regalos: oro, incienso y mirra. Hombres sabios, los líderes de sus pueblos, se inclinan delante de él y rinden homenaje al Hijo de Dios.

A través de la Biblia en un año: Miqueas 1–3

Inclínate delante de él

Después que Jesús nació en Belén de Judea en tiempos del rey Herodes, llegaron a Jerusalén unos sabios procedentes del Oriente. —¿Dónde está el que ha nacido rey de los judíos? —preguntaron—. Vimos levantarse su estrella y hemos venido a adorarlo.

MATEO 2: 1-2

Mi profundo deseo es que todos rindamos homenaje a aquel de quien cantamos: «Un niño nos es nacido, hijo nos ha sido dado». Que aquellos de nosotros que han adorado durante mucho tiempo adoren con una reverencia nueva y más humilde y con amor más intenso. Y quiera Dios, ay, sí, ¡que lo quiera!, que algunos que están lejos de él espiritualmente, así como lo estaban los magos de manera física, puedan venir hoy y preguntar: «¿Dónde está el que ha nacido rey de los judíos? Hemos venido a adorarlo». Que los pies que se han acostumbrado a las sendas anchas pero que no están acostumbrados al camino estrecho busquen en este día ver a Jesús e inclinarse delante de él con todo su corazón y encuentren en él salvación. Estos hombres sabios vinieron naturalmente, atravesando el desierto; vengamos espiritualmente, dejando nuestros pecados. Estos fueron guiados por una estrella, que la fe en el divino Espíritu nos guíe a nosotros, mediante la enseñanza de su Palabra y todas esas luces benditas que el Señor utiliza para llevar a los hombres a sí. Solo que vayamos a Jesús. Fue bueno ir donde el bebé Jesús, guiados por los débiles rayos de una estrella; descubrirás que es incluso más bienaventurado venir a él ahora que está exaltado en los cielos y mediante su propia luz revela su perfecta gloria. No te demores porque hoy él clama: «Vengan a mí todos ustedes que están cansados y agobiados, y yo les daré descanso» (Mateo 11:28).

A través de la Biblia en un año: Miqueas 4–7

Una misión santa

Porque el Hijo del hombre vino a buscar y a salvar lo que se había perdido.
LUCAS 19:10

A Jesús no se le conocía originalmente como «el hijo del hombre» sino como «el Hijo de Dios». Antes de todos los mundos, él moraba en el seno del Padre y «no consideró el ser igual a Dios como algo a qué aferrarse» (Filipenses 2:6). Sino que para redimir a los hombres, el hijo del Altísimo se convirtió en el «Hijo del Hombre». Nació de una virgen y con el nacimiento él heredó las dolencias inocentes de nuestra naturaleza y llevó los sufrimientos que conllevan a esas dolencias. Además llevó sobre sí nuestro pecado y su penalidad y por tanto murió en la cruz. En todos los aspectos fue hecho igual a sus hermanos. Él no podía ser el pastor de los hombres sin hacerse igual a ellos, y por lo tanto el Verbo consintió en hacerse carne. ¡Mira el estupendo milagro de la encarnación! Nada puede exceder a este milagro: ¡Emanuel, Dios con nosotros! «Y al manifestarse como hombre, se humilló a sí mismo y se hizo obediente hasta la muerte, ¡y muerte de cruz!» (Filipenses 2:8). Oh, perdido, tú que estás consciente de tu pérdida, anímate hoy cuando el nombre de Jesús se prenuncie en tu presencia: él es Dios, pero es hombre y como Dios-y-hombre él salva a su pueblo de sus pecados.

A través de la Biblia en un año: Nahúm 1–3

Él vino

Así como el Hijo del hombre no vino para que le sirvan, sino para servir y para dar su vida en rescate por muchos.
MATEO 20:28

El Hijo del Hombre vino. Una diligencia extraña y única así como la persona bendita que la realizó. De manera que para venir él se rebajó del trono más alto en gloria hasta el pesebre en Belén y lo hizo de manera voluntaria. Para nosotros es como si nos hubieran lanzado a un escenario de acción, no es por nuestra voluntad que hemos venido a vivir en esta tierra. Pero Jesús no tenía necesidad de nacer de la virgen. Fue su propio consentimiento, su elección, su fuerte deseo, lo que lo hizo asumir nuestra naturaleza, de la simiente de Abraham. Él vino voluntariamente en una misión de misericordia para con los hijos de los hombres. Piensa en esto durante un momento y deja que penetre en tu mente: aquel que era Rey de Reyes y Señor de Señores, el Dios Poderoso, el Padre Eterno, el Príncipe de Paz, voluntaria y alegremente descendió a morar entre los hijos de los hombres, compartir sus penas, llevar sus pecados y darse a sí mismo en sacrificio por ellos, la víctima inocente de la intolerable culpa de los hombres.

A través de la Biblia en un año: Habacuc 1–3

Dios con nosotros

Por eso, el Señor mismo les dará una señal: La joven concebirá y dará a luz un hijo, y lo llamará Emanuel.
Isaías 7:14

«Dios con nosotros»: él no ha perdido ese nombre. Jesús tuvo ese nombre en la tierra y lo tiene ahora en el cielo. Él es ahora «Dios con nosotros». Creyente, él es Dios contigo, para protegerte; tú no estás solo porque el Salvador está contigo. Colócame en el desierto donde no crece la vegetación y todavía puedo decir: «Dios con nosotros». Colócame en el océano tempestuoso y deja que mi barco baile perdidamente en las olas y todavía diré: «Emanuel, Dios con nosotros». Súbeme en un rayo de sol y déjame volar más allá del mar occidental y todavía diré: «Dios con nosotros». Deja que mi cuerpo se zambulla en las profundidades del océano y déjame esconderme en sus cavernas y no obstante, como hijo de Dios, yo podría decir: «Dios con nosotros». Sí, y en la tumba, durmiendo allí en corrupción, todavía puedo ver las huellas de Jesús, él anduvo por el camino de todo su pueblo y todavía su nombre es «Dios con nosotros».

Pero para conocer este nombre más dulcemente, debes conocerlo mediante la enseñanza del Espíritu Santo. ¿Ha estado Dios con nosotros esta mañana? ¿De qué vale venir a la capilla si Dios no está aquí? Lo mismo sería quedarnos en casa si no tenemos visitas de Jesucristo, y sin dudas podemos venir, y venir y venir con regularidad cada vez que esa puerta gira sobre sus bisagras. Es inútil a menos que esté «Dios con nosotros» mediante la influencia del Espíritu Santo. A menos que el Espíritu Santo tome las cosas de Cristo y las aplique a nuestro corazón, no será «Dios con nosotros».

A través de la Biblia en un año: Sofonías 1–3

Tómala y crece

Más bien, crezcan en la gracia y en el conocimiento de nuestro Señor y Salvador Jesucristo. ¡A él sea la gloria ahora y para siempre! Amén.
2 Pedro 3:18

¿Cómo se obtiene la vida eterna? Bueno, se aferra mediante la fe en Jesucristo. Confiar en el Señor Jesucristo es algo muy sencillo y no obstante, es la única manera de obtener la vida eterna. Jesús dice: «Yo soy la resurrección y la vida. El que cree en mí vivirá, aunque muera; y todo el que vive y cree en mí no morirá jamás. ¿Crees esto?» (Juan 11:25-26). Mediante la fe acabamos con toda la confianza que pueda venir de uno mismo y nos apoyamos por completo en la completa expiación que hizo el Señor Jesús, a quien Dios envió como propiciación: es así que podemos recobrar la vida. La fe y la nueva vida van juntas y nunca se pueden dividir.

Esta vida, una vez que se comienza a vivir, se ejercita con acciones santas. Día en día nos aferramos a la vida eterna al ejercitarnos en la piedad mediante obras de santidad y de bondad. Deja que tu vida sea de oración y alabanza porque estas son el aliento de la nueva vida. Todavía tenemos la vida animal y mental pero estas deben ser solo los atrios exteriores de nuestro ser: nuestra vida más íntima debe ser espiritual y completamente consagrada a Dios. Que de ahora en adelante la devoción sea tu respiración, la fe el latido de tu corazón, la meditación tu alimento, el auto examen tu aseo y la santidad tu andar.

Al aferrarte a esta, recuerda que el crecimiento la aumenta. Con todo fervor obtén más y más de esta. No tengas miedo de tener demasiada vida espiritual. Aférrate a ella porque Cristo no solo vino para que tuviéramos vida sino para que la tuviéramos de manera abundante.

A través de la Biblia en un año: Hageo 1–2

Su obra

En él también ustedes son edificados juntamente
para ser morada de Dios por su Espíritu.
EFESIOS 2:22

Un hijo puede olvidar a su madre, este recibe mucho de ella y no siempre ella obtiene a cambio la gratitud. Pero la madre nunca olvida al hijo a quien tanto le ha dado, lo que ella ha dado es un lazo más fuerte entre ella y su hijo que la gratitud del hijo para con la madre. Ahora bien, ya Dios ha hecho tanto por nosotros que es por eso que sigue amándonos. Jesús recuerda que murió por nosotros, el Espíritu Santo recuerda que él luchó con nosotros, el Gran Padre recuerda cómo nos ha preservado y debido a toda esta bondad en el pasado, él se complace en nosotros.

Además, yo creo que el Señor se complace en nosotros no solo por todo lo que ha hecho sino porque ve en nosotros algo que le agrada, algo que es su propia obra. Un escultor, cuando comienza a trabajar el mármol, solo tiene un bloque escarpado, pero luego de días y semanas de mucho trabajo, comienza a ver algo como la imagen que tiene como objetivo producir. Así que creo que Dios se complace cuando ve en cualquier de nosotros alguna gracia, algún arrepentimiento, alguna fe, algún comienzo de esa santificación que un día será perfecta. Sabes cuánto te agrada cuando tus hijos comienzan a hablar, aunque sea un hablar pobre, ¿verdad? Así mismo se agrada Dios con las lágrimas de penitencia, en la confesión resquebrajada, en las primeras evidencias de la fe, en el temblor de la esperanza porque él ha producido todo esto y se complace con lo que ha hecho, se complace con ver que hasta el momento su obra es exitosa.

A través de la Biblia en un año: Zacarías 1–4

El gemelo de la fe

La tristeza que proviene de Dios produce el arrepentimiento que lleva a la salvación, de la cual no hay que arrepentirse, mientras que la tristeza del mundo produce la muerte.
2 Corintios 7:10

Quizá tienes la noción de que el arrepentimiento es algo que sucede al comienzo de la vida espiritual y hay que pasar por él como cuando uno pasa por cierta operación y ahí termina. Si es así, estás muy equivocado; el arrepentimiento vive tanto como viva la fe. Con respecto a la fe yo le llamaría un hermano siamés. Necesitaremos creer y arrepentirnos mientras que vivamos. Quizá tienes la idea de que el arrepentimiento es algo amargo. A veces es amargo: ellos «llorarán como se llora por hijo unigénito, afligiéndose por él como quien se aflige por el primogénito» (Zacarías 12:10, RVR 1960). Pero ese no es el tipo de arrepentimiento del que estoy hablando ahora. Sin duda esa amargura es cosa del pasado, se acabó hace mucho tiempo. Pero esta es una dulce amargura que acompaña la fe mientras que vivamos y se convierte en la fuente de un tierno gozo.

La felicidad más intensa que he sentido jamás la he sentido cuando he estado alegre y lleno de ánimo sino cuando me he recostado en el pecho de Dios, y me ha resultado tan dulce estar tan abajo que difícilmente pudiera estarlo más y, no obstante, no quería estar más arriba. Quiero que se entreguen al deleite más excepcional de la pena a los pies de Jesús, no es pena por el pecado no perdonado sino pena por el pecado perdonado, pena por aquello que se ha acabado, por aquello que ha sido perdonado, por aquello que nunca más te condenará, porque fue puesto en Cristo hace mucho tiempo y ha sido guardado para siempre.

A través de la Biblia en un año: Zacarías 5–8

Será hecho

Obedezco tus preceptos y tus estatutos, porque conoces todos mis caminos.
SALMOS 119:168

Ojalá todo cristiano fuera del todo y para siempre obediente a las leyes celestiales. Así como el planeta gira sin desviarse de su órbita, porque con la ley que se le impuso hay una fuerza que lo obliga y lo impele, así también debiéramos nosotros seguir nuestro curso del deber porque no solo hemos escuchado el precepto divino sino que hemos sentido la sagrada energía del Espíritu Santo que nos guía por el camino recetado. Hermanos, qué seguros nos sentimos y qué felices en nuestras conciencias si estamos seguros de tener la autoridad del Gran Rey para todas nuestras acciones. El negocio de un cristiano en la tierra no es un asunto independiente, él no actúa por su propia cuenta sino que es un mayordomo de Cristo.

Ahora bien, si nos servimos a nosotros mismos o al mundo, debemos asumir las consecuencias de nuestra infidelidad, pero si servimos al Señor honestamente, todo está claro. Cuando un cristiano puede decir con respecto a cualquier conducta: «Jesucristo, mi Señor, me ha ordenado hacer esto, puedo encontrar el capítulo y el versículo que autorizan mis actos», si puede sentir que está trabajando para Cristo y no para sí mismo, con los ojos puestos en la gloria de Dios y no con objetivos siniestros ni motivos egoístas, entonces él pisa sobre la roca y desafía la censura de sus enemigos. Al referirte a una tarea positiva, tu lenguaje será: «Considero que debo hacer esto porque veo una orden expresa para la misma y por lo tanto se hará; aunque sea difícil, se alcanzará, aunque sea imposible, esperaré en aquel que permite que la fe mueva montañas».

A través de la Biblia en un año: Zacarías 9–11

Un corazón con el de él

Y éste es mi mandamiento: que se amen los unos a los otros, como yo los he amado.

JUAN 15:12

Entre todos aquellos que saben que somos discípulos de Cristo, hay una persona muy importante y esa persona eres tú mismo. Si sientes amor por los discípulos de Cristo, sabrás que eres uno de sus discípulos porque, ¿cómo lo expresa el amado apóstol Juan? «Nosotros sabemos que hemos pasado de la muerte a la vida porque amamos a nuestros hermanos» (1 Juan 3:14). Si eres un verdadero discípulo de Cristo, tendrás una de las evidencias más claras de tu propio corazón cuando te des cuenta de que, por amor a Cristo, amas a la familia redimida de Dios. Mediante esta prueba todos los hombres sabrán que ustedes son sus discípulos.

Mediante esta prueba tus hermanos cristianos también sabrán que tú eres discípulo de Cristo. No sé de nada que recomiende más un cristiano a sus hermanos que un verdadero espíritu de amor. Ningún sermón puede ser tan elocuente para el mundo como una verdadera manifestación del amor de Cristo y cuando Dios restaura en su iglesia un amor cristiano genuino, saludable y sincero —yo confío en que no lo hemos perdido totalmente— pero cuando nos da mucho de este, entonces el evangelio impresionará al mundo más de lo que lo está en este momento.

Si la nuestra no es una iglesia amorosa, he trabajado en vano y he gastado mi fuerza por nada. Si ustedes no se aman unos a otros, sin duda no aman al Salvador, pero si están unidos en amor, entonces nuestro gozo se ha cumplido en ustedes y Cristo también se regocija por ustedes.

A través de la Biblia en un año: Zacarías 12–14

El trabajo del domino

Precisamente por esto los judíos perseguían a Jesús, pues hacía tales cosas en sábado. Pero Jesús les respondía: —Mi Padre aun hoy está trabajando, y yo también trabajo.

JUAN 5:16-17

Déjame animar al pueblo de Dios aquí a hacer esto. Ve y anuncia el evangelio, anuncia el evangelio. Yo creo que en esta congregación he logrado mi deseo en gran medida. Extraño a muchos de nuestros amigos los domingos en la noche y me complace extrañarlos porque no tienen entonces nada que hacer aquí. Están afuera predicando, enseñando, trabajando en las escuelas, en las misiones y en todo tipo de servicio santo. Esto es lo que debes hacer si amas al Señor; ten una buena comida en el día de descanso y luego sal y haz un buen trabajo el resto del domingo. Alaba a Dios con tu boca y lleva en tu mano la espada de dos filos. Una de las mejores maneras de alabar al Altísimo es luchar contra la ignorancia, luchar contra los vicios, luchar contra la borrachera, luchar contra la infidelidad y el pecado de todo tipo. Hasta que el último pecador no se haya salvado, ocúpate de mantener en tu mano la espada de dos filos que es la Palabra de Dios y luego deja que para siempre las alabanzas a Dios estén en tu boca.

A través de la Biblia en un año: Malaquías 1-4

Índice de las Escrituras

Proverbios

Eclesiastés

Cantar de los Cantares

Isaías

Jeremías

Lamentaciones